Recent Progress in

HORMONE RESEARCH

The Proceedings of the Laurentian Hormone Conference

VOLUME 39

RECENT PROGRESS IN
HORMONE RESEARCH

Proceedings of the
1982 Laurentian Hormone Conference

Edited by
ROY O. GREEP

VOLUME 39

PROGRAM COMMITTEE

G. D. Aurbach	E. E. McGarry
J. D. Baxter	A. Means
J. C. Beck	B. W. O'Malley
H. Friesen	J. E. Rall
R. O. Greep	K. Savard
I. A. Kourides	N. B. Schwartz

J. L. Vaitukaitis

1983

ACADEMIC PRESS
A Subsidiary of Harcourt Brace Jovanovich, Publishers

New York   London
Paris   San Diego   San Francisco   São Paulo   Sydney   Tokyo   Toronto

ACADEMIC PRESS, INC.
111 Fifth Avenue, New York, New York 10003

United Kingdom Edition published by
ACADEMIC PRESS, INC. (LONDON) LTD.
24/28 Oval Road, London NW1 7DX

LIBRARY OF CONGRESS CATALOG CARD NUMBER: Med. 47-38
ISBN 0-12-571139-5

PRINTED IN THE UNITED STATES OF AMERICA

83 84 85 86   9 8 7 6 5 4 3 2 1

CONTENTS

LIST OF CONTRIBUTORS AND DISCUSSANTS

S. G. Amara
G. D. Aurbach
K. L. Barker
A-L. Barofsky
F. C. Bartter
J. D. Baxter
J. C. Beck
L. Bilezikjian
N. C. Birnberg
F. Bloom
P. Boyd-Leinen
M. R. Brown
C. P. Channing
B. Chatterjee
L. W. K. Chung
S. L. Cohen
D. V. Cohn
W. F. Crowley
G. R. Cunha
G. B. Cutler
W. F. Demyan
D. E. Dobson
B. M. Dobyns
P. K. Donahoe
R. A. Edgren
J. Elting
R. M. Evans
L. L. Ewing
H. Fujii
J. D. Gardner
J. R. Gill
A. L. Goodman
R. O. Greep
J. R. Grove
C. V. Hall
D. H. Hamer
G. D. Hodgen
R. A. Huseby
J. M. Hutson
L. S. Jacobs
R. T. Jensen
R. Jewelewicz
V. C. Jordan
A. D. Kenny
O. L. Kon

T. Kono
G. Koob
I. A. Kourides
J. Larner
C. Lazier
F. Lee
R. Levine
D. M. Linkie
B. Little
B. A. Littlefield
G. Martin Dani
J-J. Mermod
B. S. Milin
F. Morel
N. M. Motwani
W. Moyle
G. H. Murdoch
T. S. Nath
M. I. New
C. S. Nicoll
M. B. Nikitovitch-Winer
R. Osathanondh
H. Papkoff
G. Pavlakis
E. J. Peck
J. C. Penhos
D. W. Pfaff
S. Plymate
J. E. Rall
B. F. Rice
G. Ringold
C. Rivier
J. Rivier
P. Robel
M. G. Rosenfeld
A. K. Roy
M. Saffran
M. J. Schiop
N. B. Schwartz
R. Seelke
A. Segaloff
J. M. Shannon
H. Shima
L. Sokoloff
T. Spelsberg

PREFACE

As this the thirty-ninth volume of *Recent Progress in Hormone Research,* representing the proceedings of the 1982 Laurentian Hormone Conference, goes to press it seems not amiss, perhaps even edifying, to take a backward glance. The forerunner of this Conference, the Hormone Conference of the American Association for the Advancement of Science, met for the first time in 1943 at Gibson Island. There an unanticipated segregation problem arose. In 1944, through the kindly intercession of the Montreal Physiological Society, the Conference met at Mt. Tremblant Lodge in the Laurentian Mountains some ninety miles northwest of Montreal. This setting for both formal and informal scientific exchange proved to be propitious. At a return meeting in 1945 it was unanimously voted to call the assembly the Laurentian Hormone Conference and to publish the papers and discussions.

In inaugurating this series of annual publications the editor, Gregory Pincus, expressed the hope that "the publication of critical evaluations and work-in-progress by leading authorities will be valuable not only as records of knowledge and accomplishment but as excitements to research. The spirit of inquiry dies without criticism and discussion, and it is largely the purpose of these Conferences to nourish that spirit." What was then a hope became an enduring reality from which there has been no deviation. As with Volume 1, this volume will attest that in the field of hormone research the spirit of inquiry remains very much alive and that the Laurentian Hormone Conference from which this series derives remains, as in Olympia, a gathering where the best is put to test. It has been my good fortune to attend all but four of these Conferences, including the one at Gibson Island, and to edit the last ten volumes of this series. On the basis of that perspective it is clear that hormone research has been keeping pace with the momentous advances in science and technology and continues to offer challenging problems of great intrigue and biomedical importance. To my knowledge the record of progress in hormone research as depicted in these volumes remains unmatched elsewhere. Volume 39 is in keeping with that proud tradition.

Publication of the hour-long discussions following each paper is a valuable feature of *Recent Progress in Hormone Research.* Persons chairing these discussion sessions are carefully chosen for their relevant expertise and nimbleness in the arena of issues and answers. For their services in this capacity we are indebted to Drs. Ernest J. Peck, Alexander D. Kenny, Murray Saffran, Gerald D. Aurbach, John D. Baxter, Iones Kourides, Joseph Larner, and Maria New.

It is again my pleasure to thank our executive secretary, Martha Wright, for efficient and dedicated attention to every aspect of the arrangements for the 1982 Conference and the assemblage of all the copy for this volume. To Lucy Felicissimo and Linda Carsagnini we extend our gratitude for transcribing the tapes with skill and alacrity, and, as always, the expertise and care lavished on the production of this volume by Academic Press is deeply appreciated.

Roy O. Greep

Recent Progress in

HORMONE RESEARCH

The Proceedings of the Laurentian Hormone Conference

VOLUME 39

The Ovarian Triad of the Primate Menstrual Cycle[1]

ARNOLD L. GOODMAN AND GARY D. HODGEN

Department of Physiology and Biophysics, University of Alabama in Birmingham, Birmingham, Alabama, and Pregnancy Research Branch, National Institute of Child Health and Human Development National Institutes of Health, Bethesda, Maryland

I. Introduction

To be offered so coveted a forum to present our findings on the workings of the primate ovary leaves us flattered by the opportunity and awed by the prospect of addressing such a distinguished audience. This good moment derives much from the contributions of co-workers—the energetic efforts of a cohort of imaginative postdoctoral fellows and the unrelenting labors of a talented and devoted technical staff. Speaking for all of them, we are pleased that our efforts will become a part of the legacy of The Gregory Pincus Memorial Lectures.

While not a strict chronicle, this presentation will review our efforts aimed toward an improved understanding of the primate ovarian cycle and the regulation of its endocrine and gametogenic activities, based on studies in rhesus and cynomolgus monkeys. We will concentrate on a few fundamental, unifying issues. These studies, along with the findings of others, have enabled us to decipher and construct a clearer image of the workings of the primate ovary. However, as you will see, what emerges is far from a portrait in vivid color; rather, it is more a sketch in chiaroscuro.

II. The Ovarian Triad

As we began our work in the early 1970s, we were fortunate to have a rather firm foundation on which to design our own studies on the regulation of follicle growth. In particular, we had the advantage of drawing on knowledge of the rhesus monkey menstrual cycle, provided by the classical studies of Hartman, Hisaw, Corner, Allen, van Wagenen, and Knobil, among many others. Detailed characterizations of the human cycle by Ross, Gemzell, Vande Wiele, Lunenfeld, Yen and others were also highly

---

[1] The Gregory Pincus Memorial Lecture.

1

instructive. Without their solid contributions, our opportunities would have been more constrained and our attempts less focused.

Since the fundamental themes of folliculogenesis appear to transcend species differences, we considered them then, and again here, as axiomatic for primates, as well. Unlike adult male mammals, which continuously produce new sperm, female mammals are born with their lifetime supply of eggs, enclosed in primordial follicles. This pool of primordial follicles serves as a nonreplenished, progressively depleted stockpile (or genetic bank) from which growing follicles (and oocytes) are continuously withdrawn. As an adult, each mammalian female ovulates a species-characteristic number of ova (the ovulatory quota) each week, month, season, or year—the frequency again being a species characteristic. Thus, litter size and annual fecundity rate of a species are proximately determined by the physiology of the female through the size of the ovulatory quota, frequency of the ovarian cycle, and the duration of pregnancy and lactation. The process of folliculogenesis may be seen as providing three products essential for successful reproduction: (1) the surge of estradiol secretion to trigger the release of the preovulatory LH surge, (2) the species-characteristic number of fertilizable haploid ova, and (3) the luteal body(ies) and secretion of progesterone necessary to prepare the uterus for implantation and to maintain at least the early stages of pregnancy. Thus, this ovarian triad—the ovulatory *follicle, oocyte,* and *corpus luteum*—must each function properly for successful reproduction; impairment of follicle growth and secretion, oocyte maturation, or luteal function will preclude natural fertility.

III. Regulation of Folliculogenesis

A. SOME QUESTIONS

At first, the questions we posed were not new; indeed, they were much the same as asked by earlier workers (Hisaw, 1947; Young, 1961). Later, as our understanding improved, we began to ask more precise questions. Some we have answered; others, including many important ones, remain unanswered.

We accept as dogma that typically ovulation of a single, fertilizable ovum each menstrual cycle completes a course of oogenesis that began during fetal development. But, how is it that, from among the thousands of follicles present from birth, only a relative few are recruited each cycle to grow, at the same time others remain at rest? How is it that, from the host of follicles maturing in each ovary, (typically) only a single follicle escapes atresia and is selected to ovulate each cycle? Since the vast majority of follicles falls victim to atresia (>99%), we recognized that understanding the selection of the follicle destined to ovulate is fraught with the inherent difficulty of studying the rare exception rather than the predominant rule. As a consequence, we have tried to be assiduous in distinguishing follicle growth that culminates in ovulation (gametogenic follicle growth) from that ending in atresia (see illustrated overview of the life cycle of the primate ovary—Fig. 1a and b).

The latter stages of oogenesis in adults (i.e., folliculogenesis) are known to depend, to a large degree, on a complex interplay of hormones from the hypothalamus, pituitary, and ovary. However, even though much more is understood today of these endocrine relationships (diZerega and

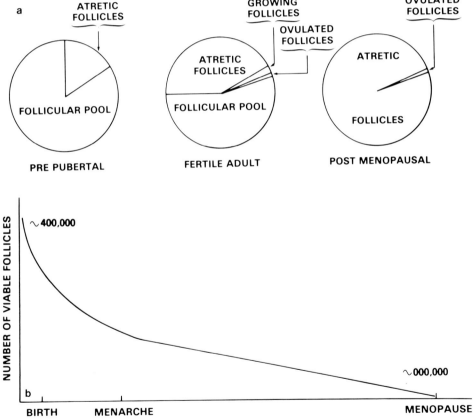

FIG. 1.   (a) Pie chart depicting the fate of follicles as a function of age and as fraction of the total present from birth. (b) Hypothetical curve depicting progressive depletion of viable follicles from the ovary from fetal-life through menopause.

Hodgen, 1981a; Knobil, 1980; Richards, 1979; Jones, 1978), what determines the fate of an individual follicle remains largely unknown. Is it primarily extraovarian factors that regulate follicle growth, or do intraovarian factors play important governing roles, as well (Franchimont and Channing, 1981; Jagiello and Vogel, 1981)? When is the follicle destined to ovulate selected? Is it only events in the current cycle that determine the outcome, or do events in the preceding cycle(s) also influence this process.

This last question leads immediately to another intriguing aspect of folliculogenesis in monotocous primates, including women and macaques: how just a single follicle matures to ovulation on only one ovary each cycle, even though both ovaries are perfused by a common systemic circulation. Since in higher primates both ovaries are functional (i.e., one has not remained rudimentary), the maturation of a single follicle with the potential to ovulate brings with it the obvious concomitant of one active and one quiescent ovary each cycle. Is this ovarian asymmetry and side-to-side partition of ovulation between cycles regulated or random? Do the ovaries communicate, and, if so, how? Which comes first, so to speak, the follicle or the ovary? That is, is one ovary in a given cycle somehow more suited than the other to sponsor follicle development (as a consequence of events in the preceding cycle?), or is ovarian asymmetry merely a consequence of follicle selection?

B. A NASCENT HYPOTHESIS

As we attempt to answer some of these questions, we will also present evidence in support of an emerging hypothesis of the regulation of follicle growth and selection during the primate ovarian cycle. This hypothesis suggests that many remaining answers, and doubtless new questions as well, will be found within the ovary.

We hypothesize (1) that the precise regulation of follicle growth and selection is accomplished primarily by specific ovarian factors that act directly on the ovaries, and (2) that gonadotropins, at tonic levels, are merely permissive to folliculogenesis. We envisage a two-tier ovarian mechanism (Fig. 2). At the first tier, specific ovarian factors govern the progressive winnowing of the cohort of developing follicles down to the size of the species characteristic ovulatory quota each cycle. Some factors may act within the ovary of origin as intraovarian regulators; other ovarian factors may be secreted and circulate to the opposite ovary, to act as extraovarian signals (but of ovarian origin). Together, they regulate the culling-out or inhibit the maturation of supernumerary growing follicles. This first tier of the proposed ovarian mechanism, which precisely regu-

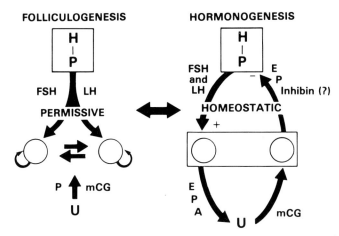

FIG. 2. A two tier mechanism involving both intra- and extraovarian regulation of folliculogenesis is proposed. Ovarian (follicular) factors acting directly on the ovaries, against a background of permissive gonadotropic support, are hypothesized to be the primary regulators of follicle selection and dominance.

lates follicle selection (cohort size), is operative, however, only when circulating gonadotropins are above minimal tonic levels and near the tonic "set-point." At the second tier, ovarian hormones (steroidal and nonsteroidal) inhibit gonadotropin secretion in a negative feedback fashion to constrain circulating gonadotropin levels to an appropriate range around the tonic set-point. If gonadotropin levels are too far below this tonic set-point, then folliculogenesis will be arrested as a result of inadequate stimulation. Contrariwise, if circulating gonadotropin levels are too far above the tonic set-point, then first tier ovarian mechanisms, ordinarily at work to regulate the size of the ovulatory quota, are impaired or inactivated; in such instances superovulation occurs. That is, we propose that the emergence of multiple follicles on both ovaries after administration of exogenous gonadotropins to monkeys or women is not only the result of augmenting the availability of gonadotropins, per se, but is also an indirect result of overriding first tier ovarian mechanisms of follicle selection.

Clearly, as exploited by several well-known bioassays for gonadotropins, both FSH and LH can have graded, dose-dependent effects on the ovary. However, in the physiological setting of the menstrual cycle, we find it more useful to consider that the folliculogenic actions of gonadotropins (principally FSH) are permissive at tonic levels and that the steroidogenic actions of gonadotropins (principally LH) are graded. If FSH at tonic levels is actually permissive to folliculogenesis, then graded effects observed may be attributable to supraphysiological (supratonic) levels. Graded actions of gonadotropins on steroidogenesis [and perhaps on "inhibin" secretion(s) as well, see below] are necessary for the second tier of the ovarian mechanism to constrain circulating gonadotropins near the tonic set-point, so that first tier mechanisms of follicle selection are effective. Evidence that these two activities (tiers) are dissociable, in some circumstances, is presented below. More direct evidence for this hypothesis must come from future studies.

C. TOWARD A MORE CONSISTENT TERMINOLOGY

Before considering how we arrived at this hypothesis, we shall explain some important terms, with the hope of avoiding misunderstandings later on. These terms are not new yet, although in wide use, they have not been employed with uniform precision. While even our definitions remain lacking, they are, nonetheless, useful in drawing important distinctions.

That the ovary performs dual roles as an organ of reproduction and a gland of internal secretion is well known. To distinguish the regulation of these ovarian activities, we shall refer to the gametogenic activity as *folliculogenesis* and to the secretory activity as *hormonogenesis* (Fig. 3). Extra- or intraovarian factors that directly influence the ovary's gametogenic role have a folliculogenic action or elicit a folliculogenic response. While some may balk at the introduction of a term like hormonogenesis, it is used here because we find current nomenclature inadequate. Since, in our scheme, some ovarian secretions may act locally within the ovary in a paracrine (or perhaps even autocrine) manner, they are not, in the strict-

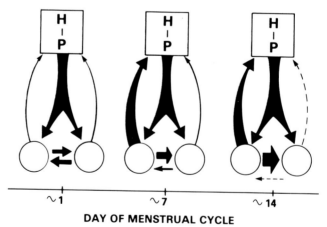

DAY OF MENSTRUAL CYCLE

FIG. 3. Hypothetical scheme depicting the relationships between the regulation of the ovary's gametogenic and secretory activities by extraovarian and intraovarian factors.

est sense, endocrine. In addition, since some ovarian hormones secreted into the circulation may be nonsteroidal (inhibins), steroidogenesis is too restrictive. Consequently, we will use the term hormonogenesis to encompass all nature and manner of such ovarian secretions.

During each cycle primordial follicles depart the resting pool and begin a well-characterized pattern of growth and development (Brambell, 1956; Harrison and Weir, 1977). Groups of (quasi)synchronously growing follicles are called *cohorts*. In the same or some subsequent cycle,[2] a few (or only one) members of one cohort continue to develop and escape atresia,[3] until they become preovulatory Graafian follicles, ultimately providing the species-characteristic ovulatory quota of eggs. Schwartz (1974) has aptly termed this pattern the "trajectory of follicle growth." Extending the trajectory metaphor into our hypothesis outlined above, gonadotropins may be seen as providing the "thrust" and ovarian factors the "guidance" along the trajectory, not unlike some surface launched missle (Fig. 4). Clearly, without continued "thrust" the trajectory will be limited; with "thrust" in excess of the guidance system's design the accuracy and precision of the course are compromised.

We shall use the term *recruitment* to indicate that a follicle has entered on this growth trajectory. Thus, under this definition, recruitment includes the entry of primordial follicles onto the trajectory, without excluding the reentry of more mature follicles which may have been transiently at rest. Pedersen's (1970) studies in mice have generally been interpreted to mean that, once a follicle leaves the resting primordial pool, it must continue to mature or succumb to atresia, i.e., it does not again rest. Whether or not this is true for primates is unknown, hence the broader definition used here. Since follicles at various preantral stages of development were observed in ovaries of hypophysectomized rats and rabbits (Hertz and Hisaw, 1934), recruitment of primordial follicles is not wholly dependent on gonadotropins, but may be only enhanced by these hormones (Lunenfeld *et al.*, 1976). Growing follicles are vulnerable to atresia and may depart the trajectory at any point. Thus, while an obligatory step, recruitment does not guarantee ovulation. That recruitment is a necessary, but not a sufficient, condition for ovulation is particularly

[2] The ovarian cycle and the estrous or menstrual cycle are often equated or at least considered coextensive. With respect to folliculogenesis, the fundamental frequency (or a major harmonic) of the ovarian cycle may actually extend across several estrous cycles, as in the rat, for example (Richards, 1979).

[3] As used here, and by others (Ingram, 1962), atresia is an irreversible process (or set of processes) that eliminates follicles (and oocytes) from the ovary other than by ovulation, i.e., follicle death. Whether atresia is a regulated process or only one of "default" is unknown.

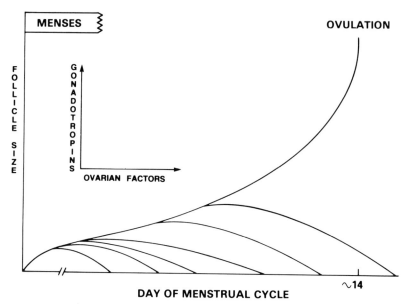

FIG. 4.   Proposed relationship between gonadotropins and ovarian factors in regulating maturation or atresia along the so-called trajectory of follicle growth.

important when interpreting results of experiments employing exogenous gonadotropins to stimulate follicle development, as discussed below.

The term *selection* will be used here to indicate the final winnowing of the cohort (via atresia of "excess" follicles) down to a size equal to the species-characteristic ovulatory quota. That is, when the number of healthy follicles (i.e., with ovulatory potential) in the cohort equals the size of the ovulatory quota, then selection is complete. Implicit in this definition is the notion that the cohort may be the regulated variable rather than the fate of an individual follicle. That is, which follicles, in particular, are culled from the cohort may be due to a random process that continues until cohort size matches the ovulatory quota, in contrast to a deterministic process in which specific follicles are individually chosen according to some unknown criteria. The character (stochastic vs deterministic) of the selection mechanism remains uncertain. What is certain, however, is that the process operates in primates with great precision; a spontaneous multiple ovulation is extremely atypical.[4] Like recruitment,

---

[4] Indeed, the frequency of fraternal twinning may in some cases include the rupture of a single follicle which contained two or more eggs (Kreitmann and Hodgen, 1980; Gougeon, 1981; Koering, 1982).

selection does not guarantee ovulation, but, given its greater temporal proximity to ovulation, selection may, with high probability, be expected to be followed by ovulation in a typical cycle. Evidence will be presented that selection is begun and is completed only during the cycle in which ovulation occurs. In contrast, the time of recruitment, and thus the total length (duration) of the trajectory are unknown. Based on findings discussed below, the duration of the trajectory in macaques and women appears to be not less than about 2 weeks.

Clearly, the ovulatory quota in higher primates is generally unity; hence, although actual cohort size as a function of day-of-cycle is unknown, the possibility of a "cohort of one" even as early as recruitment is not excluded. Even if this were true, cohort remains a meaningful construct, and it is still useful to consider recruitment and selection as distinct processes.

Although anticipating facts not yet in evidence, so to speak, the term *dominance* is introduced here to limit our lexicography to this section. As we shall demonstrate below, the follicle destined to ovulate plays a key role in regulating the size of the ovulatory quota, at least in monkeys. That is, the follicle selected for ovulation is functionally (not merely morphologically) dominant; it inhibits the development of other competing follicles on both ovaries. As a necessary corollary, the dominant follicle (i.e., the sole follicle destined to ovulate) somehow continues to thrive in a milieu it, itself, has made inhospitable for others. Whether this capacity to thrive under these circumstances results from a unique ability of the dominant follicle which is newly *acquired* or from a preexisting ability originally shared by the entire cohort, but which is *retained* only by the dominant follicle, is unclear. That is, does the survival of the dominant follicle depend on a process of acquisition or retention of metabolic properties to resist atresia? Underpinning this issue is how the dominant follicle actually exerts its eminence. How is it spared from the very inhibition it imposes on others? As one mechanism, we hypothesize that the dominant follicle secretes a substance we call "selectron," which acts directly on the ovaries to inhibit the development of potentially competing follicles. The motivation for this hypothesis is developed in more detail below. As we will show, the selected follicle becomes dominant about a week before ovulation. Consequently, it must maintain its dominance during the week before ovulation. Unresolved is whether the mechanism(s) by which the follicle *attains* dominance is the same as the mechanism(s) by which the follicle *maintains* dominance. Unresolved as well is the precise temporal relationship between selection and dominance.

D. SELECTION OF THE DOMINANT FOLLICLE

1. The Role of the Ovary's Cyclic Structures

In one of our first studies (Goodman *et al.*, 1977b) we learned that the ovary's cyclic structures: the follicle destined to ovulate and its successor, the corpus luteum, play important roles in the regulation of gametogenic follicle growth. Since the outcome of our initial experiment provided the rationale for a series of subsequent studies, its key findings are reviewed in detail. If logical flaws exist, they may be traced to this first effort.

After we cauterized the largest visible follicle (days 8–12), the cycle in progress was halted (Fig. 5). Estradiol levels, which had been increasing progressively, fell promptly to early follicular phase values. Surges of LH and FSH did not occur at midcycle; instead, gonadotropins were maintained at tonic levels for an average of ~12.5 days before the next preovulatory gonadotropin surges were observed (i.e., about 6 weeks after surges in the previous cycle). These surges, preceded by typical rises in estradiol levels, were followed, in turn, by typical luteal phase patterns of progesterone secretion. As confirmed at laparotomy, only a single follicle ovulated in each monkey; in almost all monkeys the new corpus luteum was contralateral to the side of cautery. In a control group, cautery of the ovarian surface remote from the largest visible follicle, in contrast, did not deter the progressive rise in estradiol levels, delay the midcycle surges of LH and FSH, or diminish progesterone secretion during the ensuing luteal phase.

In another group of monkeys (Fig. 6), after we excised the corpus luteum and cauterized the resulting crater, the cycle in progress was halted during the midluteal phase (days 16–19). Progesterone levels dropped to follicular phase levels in 1–2 days and the onset of menses was premature, appearing 3–4 days after luteal excision. The midluteal phase rise in estrogens was also terminated. As in the follicle cautery group, gonadotropins were maintained at tonic levels until the next preovulatory surges ~12.5 days after luteectomy, or, equivalently, about 18 days after the preceding surges. These surges of FSH and LH were preceded by a typical progressive increase in circulating estradiol levels and were succeeded, in turn, by a typical luteal phase pattern of progesterone secretion. Again, only a single follicle ovulated, in every instance on the contralateral ovary.

That follicle cautery had *delayed,* and luteectomy had *advanced,* the expected times of the next preovulatory gonadotropin surges was consistent with assignment of a zeitgeber role to the ovary in the monkey men-

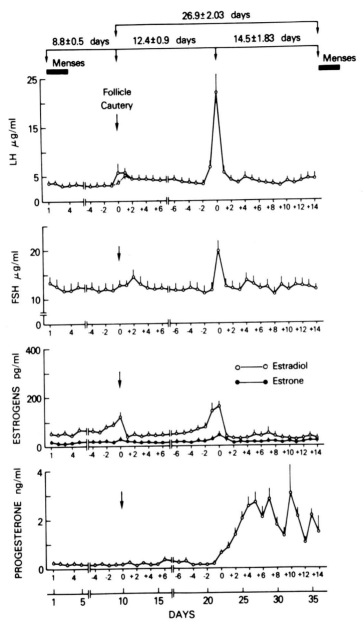

FIG. 5. Hormonal patterns before and after cautery of the largest visible follicle in rhesus monkeys. Important time intervals are marked at top. (From Goodman *et al.*, 1977b, with permission.)

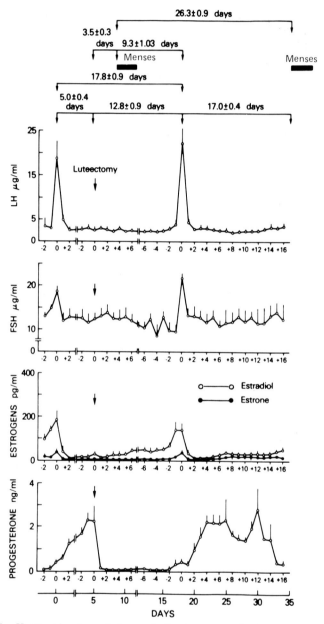

FIG. 6.   Hormonal patterns before and after luteectomy in rhesus monkeys. Important time intervals are shown at top. (From Goodman *et al.*, 1977b, with permission.)

strual cycle (Knobil, 1973, 1974). Thus, the time-keeping function of the primate ovary appeared to be subserved by the activities of the ovary's cyclic structures. More than this, these kinds of findings provided new insights into the regulation of follicle growth and selection in this primate. Not all these inferences are obvious, however, without some explanation.

That cautery of the largest visible follicle halted the cycle in progress, i.e., interrupted the progressive rise in estradiol levels and thereby prevented the expected midcycle surges of LH and FSH, led us to conclude that we had, in fact, destroyed the follicle destined to ovulate that cycle. Moreover, given the lengthy (see below) 2 week delay to the next ovulation, it appeared that no other follicle of the cohort, if any, was competent to serve as a surrogate for the cauterized follicle to achieve a timely, midcycle ovulation. Instead, the next follicle to ovulate was likely derived from another cohort. This, in turn, meant that the selection of the follicle destined to ovulate had already occurred by the time of cautery, i.e., by day 8 of the cycle.

The use of follicle cautery and luteectomy was pioneered by workers studying the ovarian cycle in domestic animals (Dufour et al., 1971). However, the outcome of these kinds of experiments in monkeys versus sheep, swine, or cattle is significantly different. In the domestic species, cautery of the current crop of follicles is rapidly compensated. Removal of the cyclic structures is followed by ovulation within about 2 days in sheep, about 6 days in pigs, and 2 to 3 days in cows, in contrast to the 2-week interval observed in monkeys. In women, too, the interval from ablation of the dominant follicle or corpus luteum to the next ovulation is a fortnight (Nilsson et al., 1982). Thus, since the overall time-course of follicle growth presumably exceeds the brief interval from ablation to ovulation, growth of new follicles in domestic species ordinarily occurs in the presence of the prevailing cyclic structures. In higher primates, in contrast, new *gametogenic* follicle growth appears to be inhibited in the presence of the cyclic structure and proceeds only after its removal. Consequently, in monkeys and women, the follicle destined to ovulate is not merely morphologically dominant, it is functionally dominant, as well.

Thus, we concluded that the dominant follicle, itself, plays a key role in regulating the size of the ovulatory quota in this primate by inhibiting the development of any competing follicles. Inhibition of gametogenic follicle growth is continued by its successor, the corpus luteum. The next round of new gametogenic follicle growth occurs only after the influence of the cyclic structure is removed either artificially by experimental intervention or naturally after the demise of the corpus luteum.

We were also struck by the fact that the interval from either follicle cautery or luteectomy to the next preovulatory LH surge was about 12.5

days (i.e., about the length of a typical follicular phase after adding the 36 to 40 hours for follicular rupture). The similarity of the duration of these intervals was very significant. Based on studies in rats, Schwartz (1974) had hypothesized that the role of the preovulatory FSH elevations was not to ripen the current crop of follicles but rather to recruit new follicles for the next cycle. If this were true in monkeys, then one would predict a priori that the time-course of new gametogenic follicle growth after interuption of the cycle in the follicular phase—before the FSH surge occurred—would differ from the time-course of new gametogenic follicle growth after luteectomy—after the midcycle FSH surge had already occurred. Clearly, this was not the case. Consequently, we concluded that the preovulatory surge of FSH is not necessary for follicle recruitment in monkeys. In addition, since, in this first study at least, gonadotropin levels were apparently maintained after the ablations, follicle recruitment and the subsequent emergence of a single follicle occurred without an attendant increment in circulating gonadotropins. Conversely, then, the inhibition of follicle growth in the presence of the cyclic structure was presumably not due to a decrement or limitation in gonadotropins. Instead, it appeared as if removal of these cyclic structures produced an "unbolting" (Parkes, 1966) or disinhibition of gametogenic follicle growth at the level of the ovaries. Moreover, the steroid milieu (estrogen-dominated vs progesterone-dominated) prevailing at ablation seemed without differential effect, as well. Relationships between *tonic* FSH levels and follicle recruitment and selection are discussed in more detail later on. The key point here, however, is that the midcycle *surge* of FSH is not an important determinant of follicle growth in monkeys.

That gametogenic follicle growth is held in abeyance during the luteal phase in primates was already appreciated by earlier workers, based on morphological findings (Block, 1951; Koering, 1969). The mechanism for this inhibition was unknown. In comparing follicle growth in sheep and primates Baird and co-workers (1975) hypothesized that the reason follicles mature during the luteal phase in sheep, but not in primates, was due to the difference in luteal estradiol secretion. The primate corpus luteum secretes estrogens; the ovine corpus luteum does not. They reasoned that luteal estradiol along with progesterone exerted a stronger negative feedback on gonadotropin secretion and thereby indirectly inhibited follicle growth in the primate luteal phase. However, when we examined this issue in monkeys, we could not confirm their hypothesis.

To learn how gametogenic follicle growth may be inhibited during the primate luteal phase, we (Goodman and Hodgen, 1977) luteectomized monkeys around day 18 of the menstrual cycle and immediately implanted silastic capsules containing crystalline progesterone for 10 days to ap-

proximate the duration of an intact cycle (Fig. 7). These capsules maintained serum progesterone at luteal phase levels (~4 ng/ml) and prevented
the premature onset of menses seen after luteectomy alone. Circulating
estradiol, however, declined to early follicular phase levels ($\leq$50 pg/ml).
Tonic gonadotropin levels appeared to be maintained after luteectomy,
during progesterone treatment, and after capsule removal. Menses began
3 to 4 days after progesterone withdrawal and the next preovulatory go-

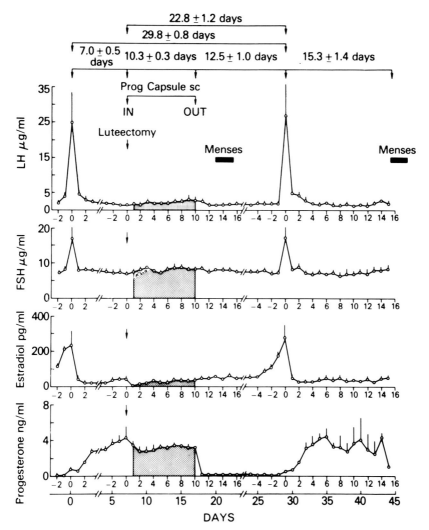

FIG. 7.   Effects of systemic progesterone replacement on time of next ovulation after
luteectomy in rhesus monkeys. (From Goodman and Hodgen, 1977, with permission.)

nadotropin surges occurred, on average, 12.5 days after capsule removal, or, equivalently, ~22.5 days after luteectomy. Thus, replacement with progesterone alone for 10 days was sufficient to delay the next ovulation after luteectomy by 10 days. Consequently, progesterone appears to be the principal luteal hormone inhibiting gametogenic follicle growth in this primate. In a related context, in addition to its well-known ability to block an estradiol-induced LH surge, progesterone has a more profound antifertility action, namely, inhibiting the growth of the follicle that would be the source of the estradiol surge.

Since we observed no changes in gonadotropin levels before and after luteectomy and capsule insertion and withdrawal, we hypothesized that progesterone may exert its inhibition at the level of the ovaries. However, we were unable to inhibit follicle growth by implanting progesterone-impregnated silastic wafers into either ovary after luteectomy. These findings were recently confirmed (Nass *et al.*, 1981). Significantly, however, the side of the next ovulation after systemic progesterone replacement or bilateral ovarian surgery was randomized (see below).

We recently considered the possibility that (exogenous) progesterone's action was mediated by peripheral conversion to 17α-hydroxyprogesterone, which is secreted by both the corpus luteum and dominant follicle in women and monkeys (Goodman and Hodgen, 1982b). This hypothesis appeared attractive for two reasons. First, it might explain the failure of intraovarian implants of progesterone to inhibit follicle growth. Second, it might account for the seemingly similar kind of inhibition of follicle growth exerted by the dominant follicle during the follicular phase when progesterone levels are not elevated. Suffice it to say that whatever may be progesterone's mode of inhibition, it appears not to be mediated by peripheral conversion to 17α-hydroxyprogesterone or, presumably, other steroids along the so-called delta-4 pathway. We shall return to the issue of progesterone's inhibition of gametogenic follicle growth in a later section.

2. The (Un)importance of Previous Ovarian Status

As mentioned above, after surgical removal of the cyclic structure the next ovulation was almost always on the contralateral ovary. Was this merely an experimental artifact or did it indicate a residual inhibitory effect of the ablated cyclic structure? To address this and other issues, we performed the following experiments (Goodman and Hodgen, 1979a,b) whose design is depicted in Figs. 8a and b. Since rhesus monkeys were not available in sufficient supply, in this study we employed cynomolgus monkeys, another macaque (*M. fascicularis*) whose reproductive physiology differs little from the rhesus (Goodman *et al.*, 1977a).

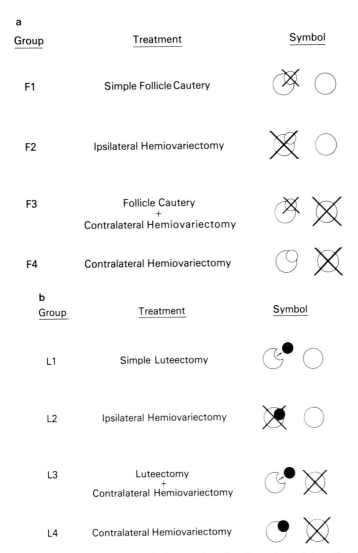

FIG. 8. (a and b) Experimental design employed to investigate interaction between ovaries. (From Goodman and Hodgen, 1979a,b, with permission.)

When the cyclic structure (i.e., dominant follicle or corpus luteum) alone was removed, we observed the same kind of responses described earlier, namely, the current cycle was interrupted and the next ovulation of a single follicle occurred about 2 weeks later on the contralateral ovary (Fig. 9a and b). These same responses were also observed when the entire ovary bearing the structure was removed (Fig. 10a and b). Thus, appar-

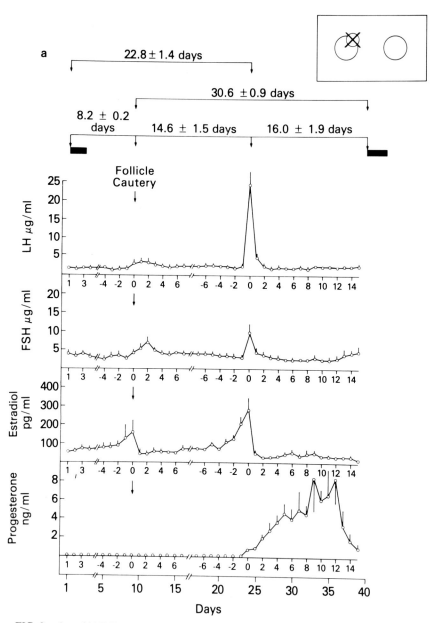

FIG. 9.   (a and b) Effects of ablation of the cyclic structure in the follicular (a) and luteal phase (b) in cynomolgus monkeys. (From Goodman and Hodgen, 1979a,b, with permission.)

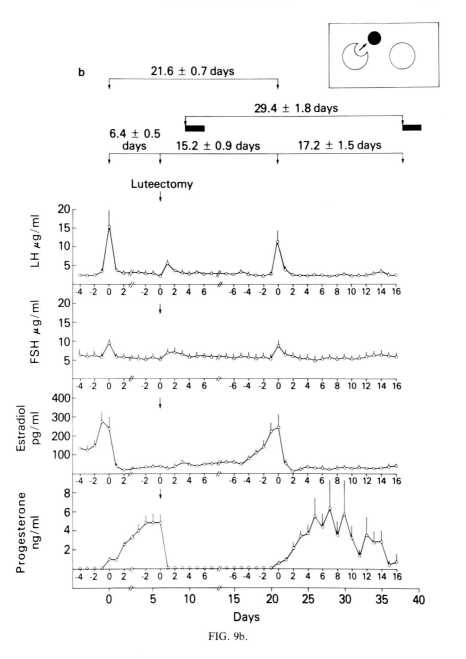

FIG. 9b.

ently, the activity of the ovary bearing the cyclic structure can be accounted for virtually exclusively by the cyclic structure itself. That is, removal of other portions of that ovary was without discernible additive effects. In the third group, we removed the cyclic structure and the entire contralateral ovary in order to force new follicle growth back to the ipsilateral ovary. Despite this maneuver, responses stereotypical of the removal of the cyclic structure alone were observed (Fig. 11a and b).

This last outcome provided two important clues. First, it meant that new gametogenic follicle growth could resume on the operated ovary with the typical time-course to ovulation; thus, any residual inhibitory effects of the cyclic structure, or trauma attending its removal, were not of major significance. More importantly, it suggested that selection of the next dominant follicle did not occur until after the cyclic structure was removed. That is, since a monkey could not have "known" which ovary would be removed, she could not have "queued up" the next one ahead of time. This observation seems inconsistent with the hypothesis that follicles are selected to ovulate in some predetermined fashion (Edwards et al., 1977).

In the fourth group, removal of the ovary contralateral to the cyclic structure during the mid-follicular or mid-luteal phase was without discernible effect (Fig. 12a and b). In each case the cycle continued along its typical course; circulating levels of gonadotropins and ovarian steroids were unaffected. Consequently, the contralateral ovary appeared to be virtually quiescent after the emergence of the dominant follicle and throughout much of the luteal phase. Thus, the influence of the cyclic structure is not limited to its own ovary but extends to the other, as well, to inhibit its gametogenic and endocrine activities. Discounting trauma attending ablation, the previous status of the ovary did not, by itself, seem to influence subsequent gametogenic follicle growth.

This last inference was tested in another but related experiment, namely, in chronically hemiovariectomized rhesus monkeys in which gametogenic follicle growth is repetitively constrained to a single ovary. Such monkeys display seemingly normal ovulatory menstrual cycles (Goodman and Hodgen, 1979c). When we (Goodman et al., 1979) luteectomized chronically hemiovariectomized monkeys, we observed the same, stereotypical folliculogenic response described for two-ovary monkeys—a single follicle ovulated about 2 weeks later (Fig. 13). The same kind of folliculogenic response was observed in monkeys with two ovaries even though the contralateral ovary also underwent wedge-resection as a surgical control (Fig. 14). In this luteectomized wedge-resected group, however, about half of the new ovulations occurred back on the luteectomized ovary. That is, bilateral trauma of the ovaries led to a randomization of the side of the next ovulation as observed previously (Goodman *et al.*, 1979), without affecting the time-course of follicle growth.

The hormonal response to luteectomy in one-ovary monkeys, however, was not stereotypical; after luteectomy, FSH levels increased 2- to 4-fold and did not return to baseline before about 7 days. Consequently, timely new gametogenic follicle growth proceeded, with the maintenance of the ovulatory quota at unity, even though FSH levels were markedly elevated; this indicated that the ability of the remaining ovary to inhibit FSH secretion was somehow temporarily impaired (about 1 week). That is, new follicle growth and feedback inhibition were temporally dissociated. In monkeys with two ovaries, in contrast, luteectomy was followed by either no change in FSH levels or only a comparatively small (<50%), highly transient increase. Thus, the contralateral ovary makes a major contribution to the negative feedback regulation of FSH immediately after luteectomy. However, as indicated above, when the contralateral ovary was subjected to wedge-resection, only about half of the new ovulations occurred contralateral to luteectomy. Curiously, then, we are forced to conclude that, even though the contralateral ovary contributes to the negative feedback of FSH secretion, this activity is not sufficient to ensure that it is the site of the next ovulation. That is, in this circumstance, gametogenic follicle growth and negative feedback on FSH secretion were spatially dissociated in half the luteectomized wedge-resected monkeys.

From these kinds of results we concluded that, during the cycle, previous ovarian status, by itself, does not appear to be an important determinant of the side of the next ovulation. This same conclusion was reached by Clark *et al.* (1978) based on serial laparoscopic observations of rhesus monkeys across several cycles. The frequency of a new corpus luteum on the left or right ovary from cycle to cycle occurred as a binomial distribution with $L = R = 0.5$. Thus, the left-to-right alternation of ovulation in consecutive cycles seems as random as heads-after-tails at the flip of an honest coin.

In other physiological conditions, however, previous ovarian status may influence follicle growth. Ovulation was delayed after luteectomy-induced abortion in fertile cycles (Goodman and Hodgen, 1979d). This delay may be due to an extraluteal antifolliculogenic effect of chorionic gonadotropin (Goodman and Hodgen, 1982a) and may be mediated by differences in intraovarian progesterone levels (diZerega *et al.*, 1982a).

3. Ovarian Asymmetry

Having considered the importance of previous ovarian status, we return now to the question: When is the dominant follicle selected? From

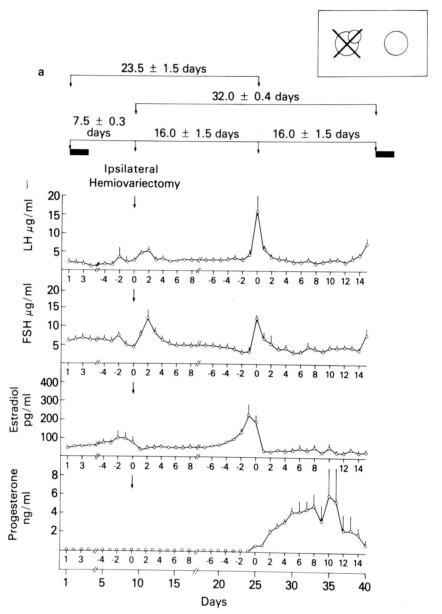

FIG. 10. (a and b) Effects of ablating the entire ovary bearing the cyclic structure in the follicular (a) and luteal phase (b) in cynomolgus monkeys. (From Goodman and Hodgen, 1979a,b, with permission.)

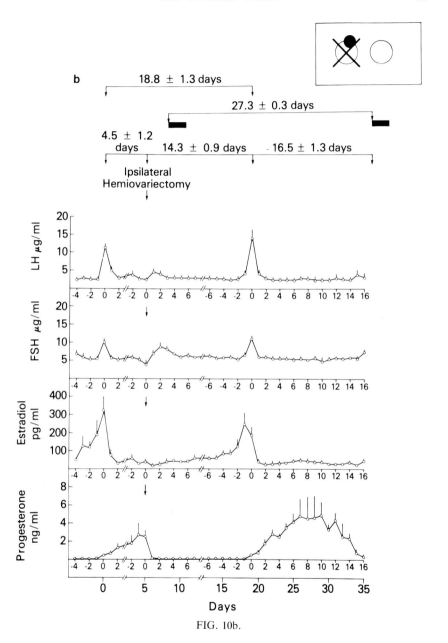

FIG. 10b.

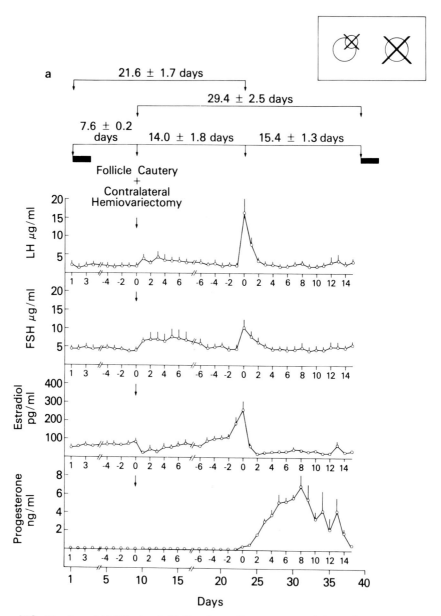

FIG. 11. (a and b) Effects of ablating the cyclic structure and the entire contralateral ovary in the follicular (a) and luteal phase (b) to constrain new follicle growth to the ipsilateral ovary. (From Goodman and Hodgen, 1979a,b, with permission.)

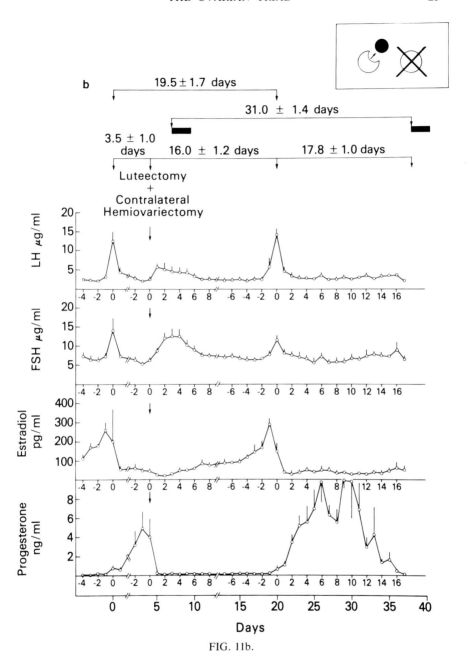

FIG. 11b.

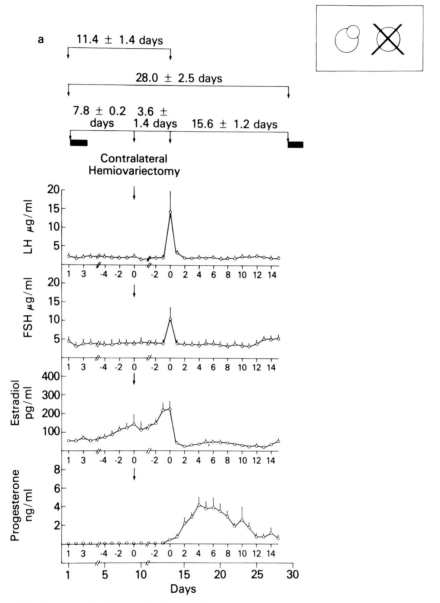

FIG. 12.   (a and b) Effects of ablating only the contralateral ovary during the follicular (a) or luteal phase (b) in cynomolgus monkeys. (From Goodman and Hodgen, 1979a,b, with permission.)

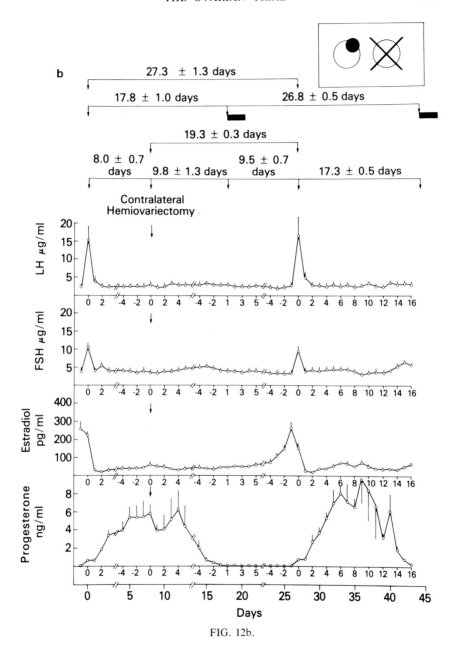

FIG. 12b.

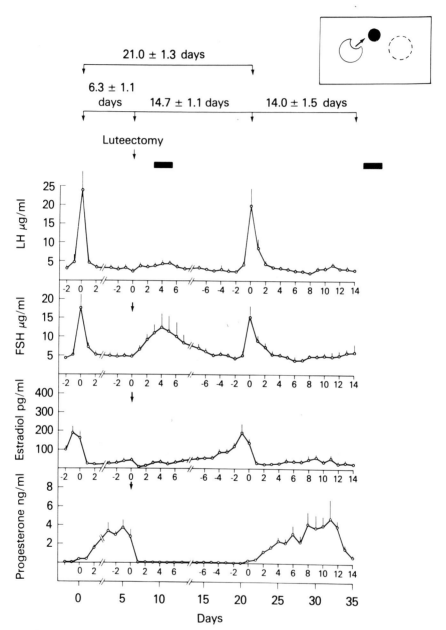

FIG. 13. Effects of luteectomy on FSH secretion and follicle growth in chronically hemiovariectomized rhesus monkeys. (From Goodman et al., 1979, with permission.)

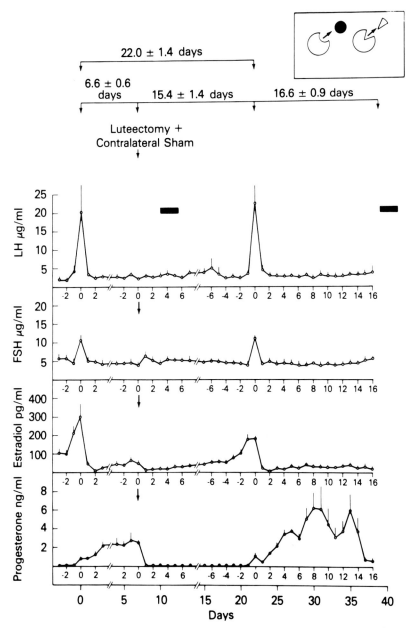

FIG. 14.   Effects of luteectomy and concurrent wedge-resection of contralateral ovary.
(From Goodman *et al.*, 1979, with permission.)

the findings discussed so far we can answer with the interval estimate: after the demise of the corpus luteum in the preceding cycle and before day 8 of the cycle in which ovulation occurs. That is, the onset of ovarian asymmetry appears to be the result of events in the current cycle rather than a reflection of events in the preceding cycle. Do the times of follicle selection and onset of ovarian asymmetry coincide? In this section we bring together evidence that provides a narrower estimate of the time of follicle selection, the attainment of dominance, and the onset of ovarian asymmetry.

a. Follicular Aspects. As described above, when the ovary bearing the dominant follicle was removed, the cycle was interrupted and ovulation was delayed for about 2 weeks; ablation of the entire contralateral ovary, in contrast, had no apparent effect. Thus, when the dominant follicle is clearly recognizable *in situ,* the ovaries are functionally asymmetrical, as well. Conversely, then, we reasoned that if ovarian asymmetry were demonstrable shortly after luteectomy or luteolysis, before the dominant follicle was visible, such asymmetry would signal a latent dominant follicle and thereby refine estimates of when the dominant follicle is selected (Goodman *et al.,* 1982).

To obtain a more precise estimate of the time of follicle selection it was important to employ a procedure that (1) provided a clear starting time-point and (2) synchronized subsequent follicle growth within each experimental group. Luteectomy is such a procedure. To recapitulate, luteectomy in rhesus monkeys is typically followed by the next LH surge in about 12.5 days. Only a single follicle ovulates after luteectomy, as in intact cycles, and this is almost always (>90%) on the opposite ovary. While the last outcome is likely an experimental artifact, since trauma of the opposite ovary randomized the side of the next ovulation (Goodman *et al.,* 1979), it was purposely exploited for its advantage in localizing (predicting) the next side of ovulation. Moreover, in addition to synchronizing subsequent follicle growth among monkeys, luteectomy necessarily ensures that the preceding cycle was ovulatory. Thus, based on these considerations, the time and place of the next ovulation were highly predictable; ovulation would occur about 2 weeks after luteectomy, most likely on the opposite ovary. Accordingly, the procedures of luteectomy and hemiovariectomy were combined into a single study to detect the onset of ovarian asymmetry and thereby reveal a latent dominant follicle.

In the first part of the study, intact rhesus monkeys were luteectomized (day 16–19) and assigned at random to one of two groups. In one group the contralateral ovary was removed 4 days after luteectomy, in the other group the luteectomized (ipsilateral) ovary was removed instead. Since the next ovulation almost always occurs on the contralateral ovary after luteectomy alone, we predicted that removal of this ovary 4 days later—if the next dominant follicle were already selected—would delay the next LH surge by about 4 days over the common reference interval of 12.5 days. [The choice of 4 days was influenced by the variance around the mean interval from luteectomy to the next LH surge (SEM $\cong$ 1); we reckoned that 4 days was the shortest span which would produce a detectable delay of statistical significance.] Alternatively, no delay was expected if gametogenic follicle growth had yet to resume and/or the next follicle destined to ovulate had yet to be selected. The former prediction was seemingly borne out. The interval from luteectomy to the next LH surge was extended to 17.0 ± 1.5 days ($p < 0.01$), which corresponds to an interval of 13.0 ± 1.5 days from contralateral hemiovariectomy to the LH surge.

Since the next ovulation after luteectomy seldom (frequency $<10\%$) occurs on the ipsilateral ovary, we predicted that removing this ovary 4 days after luteectomy would have no effect. Curiously, however, this intervention, like its preceding counterpart, also delayed the next LH surge by about 4 days. The interval from luteectomy to the next LH surge was 12.7 ± 1.6 days, thereby extending the luteectomy–LH surge interval to nearly 17 days ($p < 0.01$).

An overt vesicular follicle was not discernible at hemiovariectomy on day 4 in either group and removal of either ovary at this time produced comparable delays in the next LH surge without differentially affecting tonic gonadotropins levels. Thus, morphological symmetry was reflected in functional symmetry. However, since removal of either ovary engendered a 4-day delay in ovulation, gametogenic follicle growth had apparently resumed promptly after luteal ablation, otherwise, intervention on day 4 presumably would not have delayed ovulation by 4 days.

What was unexpected in these findings was not functional symmetry, per se, but rather that ablation of the ipsilateral ovary had any effect, at all. As discussed above, removal of the entire ovary containing the corpus luteum produced no effect different from luteectomy alone, suggesting that the ipsilateral ovary remained quiescent (vis-à-vis folliculogenesis) after luteal ablation. As mentioned below, laparotomy and collection of ovarian venous blood around this time do not delay the next LH surge (diZerega et al., 1981a). Consequently, the ipsilateral ovary appears to participate in the ovarian cycle for some time after luteectomy in some, as yet inexplicable, fashion. Since this outcome was at variance with our original predictions, we extended the study in an effort to clarify the issue.

In the second portion of the study, hemiovariectomy was performed 8 days after luteectomy—a time when previous evidence indicated that the next dominant follicle was already selected. As expected, ablation of the ipsilateral ovary on day 8 did not significantly delay the next LH surge beyond the 12.5 day reference interval after luteectomy alone; the next LH surge occurred about 5 days after ipsilateral hemiovariectomy or, equivalently, ~13 days after luteectomy. In contrast, removal of the contralateral ovary 8 days after luteal ablation significantly prolonged the luteectomy–LH surge interval to nearly 27 days, roughly twice the interval after luteectomy alone. (The protracted 19-day interval from contralateral hemiovariectomy to the next LH surge was an unexpected departure from the 12.5-day reference interval. The extension may represent combined effects of luteectomy and the subsequent inhibition of follicles on the ipsilateral ovary by the ablated-with-the-contralateral-ovary, new dominant follicle.) We do not consider the protracted difference of significance with respect to the typical cycle. The key finding is that removal of the contralateral ovary, which contained a morphologically distinct dominant follicle, significantly delayed the next ovulation.

Thus, when a dominant follicle is clearly discernible, functional ovarian asymmetry can be demonstrated. Since hemiovariectomy on day 4 (before a dominant follicle was discernible) delayed the next ovulation, the next follicle destined to ovulate had apparently begun to develop, but it had yet to attain dominance over the opposite ovary. Consequently, we cannot be sure whether or not selection was completed by day 4. By day 8, however, unambiguous dominance had been attained and selection could be verified.

In other words, when follicle dominance is demonstrable morphologically or functionally, selection of the follicle destined to ovulate is already a *fait accompli*. Selection, then, appears not to be an instantaneous event, but rather may be a progressive process whose culmination is signaled by the attainment of dominance by a single follicle. If selection is a progressive process, rather than a discrete event, one may never be able to describe its occurrence more precisely than by an interval (rather than a point) estimate.

What emerges from all this is that selection and dominance are conceptually distinct, but physiologically intertwined activities. Attainment of functional dominance is an integral component of the selection process; the detection of dominance is a sufficient condition for adducing selection (if dominance, then selection). Whether the attainment of dominance is a necessary condition for selection is as yet unresolved (if not dominance, then not selection?). That is, the precise temporal relationship between selection and dominance is unclear. Which comes first, dominance or selection? Does one follicle ''select itself'' by first (somehow) attaining dominance over other potential competitors; alternatively, is a single follicle first selected by some other mechanism and afterward ensures its destiny by exerting dominance as some kind of a safety mechanism against multiple ovulations? In either case, the selected follicle, which has attained dominance, must thereafter maintain dominance until ovulation is triggered about a week later. Possible mechanisms of dominance are considered in a later section.

Relating these findings to the menstrual cycle, we conclude (1) that the attainment of unambiguous functional and morphological dominance signals the completion of a follicle selection process that begins (or is perhaps, held in abeyance until) promptly after luteolysis, and (2) that the follicle destined to ovulate attains dominance 4–8 days after the demise of the corpus luteum. Since menses begins 2–4 days after luteolysis, dominance is attained, and hence, selection completed, between the second and sixth day of the cycle.

That a new dominant follicle has not yet emerged by day 4 after luteectomy is supported by our histological data from these ovaries (Koering *et al.*, 1982). However, even though the ipsilateral and contralateral ovaries appeared functionally symmetrical on day 4, morphological asymmetry was already present as divergent follicle distributions. Day 4 contralateral ovaries contained significantly more healthy follicles 0.5–1.0 mm in diameter than did ipsilateral ovaries, even though no obvious dominant follicle was detectable in either group. Moreover, the ipsilateral ovary appears to assume its quiescent status soon after day 4, since the distribution of follicles in day 8 ipsilateral ovaries was not different from day 4, whereas in day 8 contralateral ovaries a presumptive dominant follicle was almost always identifiable.

Other evidence that the dominant follicle is emerging during this interval (i.e., day 2–6 of the cycle) comes from studies of follicle labeling using biologically active fluorescein-tagged hCG (Fig. 15). On days 9 and 11 of the cycle, only the largest follicle among those present on both ovaries displayed a unique pattern of thecal fluorescence. On day 7 this pattern was observed circumscribing only one follicle, even though this follicle was otherwise indistinguishable by size from other follicles in either ovary (diZerega and Hodgen, 1980). Before day 7 no unique pattern of fluorescence was discernible around any single follicle. Autoradiography has also been used to detect specific uptake of radiolabeled hCG by the dominant follicle (Zeleznik *et al.*, 1981).

Using a specially designed laparoscope, which permitted transillumination of the ovary in rhesus monkeys, Clark *et al.* (1978) were able to distinguish one follicle during the first week of the cycle. However, frequently its identity as the dominant follicle required retrospective confirmation.

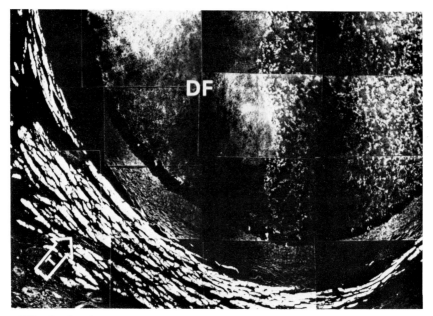

FIG. 15.   Ovarian uptake of biologically active fluorescein-tagged hCG on day 7 of the menstrual cycle in rhesus monkeys. DF, Dominant follicle. (From diZerega and Hodgen, 1980, with permission.)

b. Hormonal Aspects.   Clearly, the gametogenic and hormonal activities of the ovary are closely linked. As described above, ablation of the ovary containing the cyclic structure had profound effects not only on the time-course of the cycle but on circulating ovarian hormone levels as well (Fig. 10a and b). In contrast, removal of the contralateral (quiescent) ovary was without discernible effects (Fig. 12a and b).

How early in the cycle does ovarian endocrine activity become asymmetrical, as indicated by steroid hormone levels in ovarian venous blood? Will differences in hormone secretion between ovaries reliably anticipate the side of the next dominant follicle or merely reflect its presence after it is already discernible by other means? To answer these questions, ovarian venous blood was drawn from monkeys at various times after the onset of menses (diZerega *et al.,* 1980) or after luteectomy (diZerega *et al.,* 1981a). Levels of estradiol in ovarian venous serum were significantly different between ovaries as early as days 5 to 7 of the cycle and by 5 days after luteectomy (diZerega and Hodgen, 1981a). Not surprisingly, the degree of asymmetry increased with progression to ovulation (Fig. 16). Without exception, the ovary secreting more estradiol early on was later

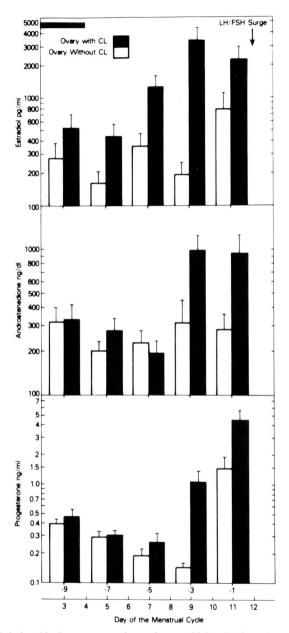

FIG. 16. Relationship between ovarian vein steroid levels throughout the follicular phase and side of current ovulation (ovary with CL). (From diZerega *et al.*, 1980, with permission.)

found to contain a fresh corpus luteum. Only in monkeys in which the cycle proved to be anovulatory was no difference observed. Clearcut differences in androstenedione and progesterone levels developed only in the last 3 days before the LH surge in intact monkeys. In luteectomized monkeys, however, progesterone levels were initially higher in the blood draining the luteectomized ovary, but this difference disappeared within 3 to 5 days. The potential significance of early differences in progesterone secretion is considered in a later section. The important point here is that divergence of estrogen secretion between ovaries provides the earliest hormonal index we have so far in revealing the emergence of the dominant follicle. Indeed, the onset of this asymmetry by days 5 to 7 of the cycle corresponds well with follicular indices of ovarian asymmetry and follicle selection. That the dominant follicle is the source of the differential estradiol secretion at this early stage is uncertain. Later in the cycle, the dominant follicle is doubtless the preponderant source of circulating estradiol.

E. REGULATION OF FOLLICLE RECRUITMENT, SELECTION, AND DOMINANCE

1. Extraovarian Factors

Although much has been learned about the nature of folliculogenesis, the physiological mechanisms regulating it remain imperfectly understood. While earlier workers recognized that extraovarian factors from the pituitary and placenta play major roles in regulating ovarian activities, today's researchers are providing more and more evidence of the importance of intraovarian regulators, as well. Despite these efforts, no unifying scheme has emerged.

Clearly, the pituitary gonadotropins, FSH and LH, are obligatory for normal ovarian function in adults, but their regulatory roles may actually begin antenatally. Ablation of the pituitary in fetal rhesus monkeys in mid-gestation, afterward delivered normally at term, produced marked deficits in gonadal development (Gulyas et al., 1977a, b), including increased atresia of oocytes and follicles (Fig. 17a and b). Yet, we know that the hypothalamic–pituitary–ovarian axis is not continuously operative from birth through menarche. Both the tonic and surge modes of gonadotropin secretion undergo some kind of maturation (Fig. 18). After age 6 months, but before 2 years, castration is not followed by a prompt rise in tonic gonadotropin secretion, indicating an absence of negative feedback regulation (Williams and Hodgen, 1982). Similarly, before menarche, estradiol challenges do not reliably induce surges of LH and FSH

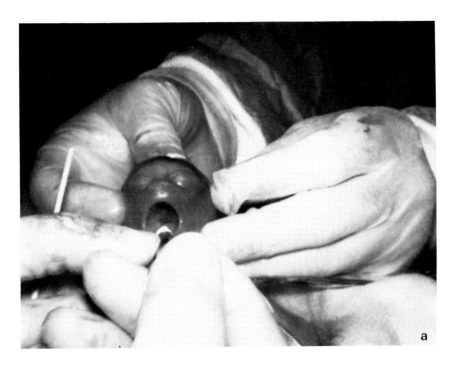

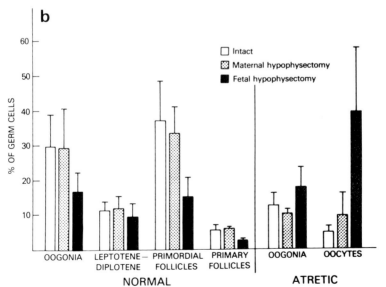

FIG. 17. Effects of fetal hypophysectomy (a) on oocyte and follicle development (b) in newborn rhesus monkeys. (From Gulyas *et al.*, 1977a, with permission.)

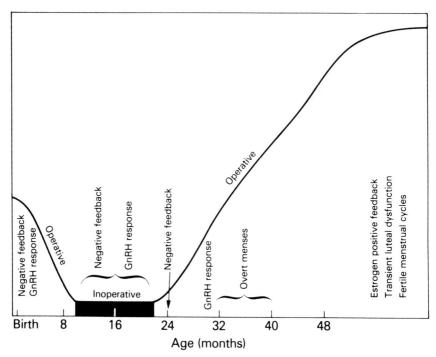

FIG. 18.   Ontogeny of hypothalamic–pituitary–ovarian function in primates.

secretion (Dierschke *et al.*, 1974); also, the responsiveness of the pituitary to a GnRH bolus is attennated until well after menarche (Fig. 19) (Williams *et al.*, 1982).

As discussed above, midcycle surges of FSH and LH do not appear to be necessary to instigate new follicle growth in a subsequent cycle. Consequently, the pattern of tonic gonadotropin secretion is the important component of pituitary control of ovarian function. Yet, understanding this extraovarian mechanism is still not adequate to account for such precise regulation of the maturation of a single follicle on only one ovary observed cycle after cycle. So, in addition to extraovarian signals, intraovarian factors may also be expected to play important regulating roles, as well. In this section, then, we will consider, in turn, extraovarian and intraovarian signals governing folliculogenesis.

2. Extraovarian Signals

Inhibin(s)—Is It an Important Regulator of Folliculogenesis?   Deriving in large measure from the elegant studies of Knobil (1973, 1980) and his colleagues, estradiol appears to be the principal regulator of the tonic secretion of LH. While circulating estradiol no doubt plays an important role in regulating tonic secretion of FSH, it is less certain that this steroid acts alone. Before considering this issue further, it is important to point out at this juncture that so much of our understanding of the regulation of gonadotropin secretion derives from estimates of circulating hormone levels provided by radioimmunoassay (RIA). Patterns of immunoreactive hormone may not tell the whole story, so to speak. As an example, Knobil (1980) and others, using RIA, have detected circhoral, pulsatile secretion of LH in castrates, but observed no pulsations at tonic levels in intact monkeys. In contrast, using a mouse testicular mince in a bioassay (Van Damme *et al.*, 1974) for LH, coupled with a vest and mobile tether assembly permitting frequent blood drawing via chronic cannulation during normal ovulatory menstrual cycles (Figs. 20 and 21), we have detected pulsatile secretion of LH in intact monkeys (Fig. 22). This circhoral release of LH was not apparent from RIA measurements of the same samples (Marut *et al.*, 1981). Thus, it is important to introduce a caveat at this point that some RIA measurements alone may give an incomplete, if not misleading, impression of actual tonic gonadotropin secretion. What follows should be assessed with this warning in mind.

New observations bring relevance and meaning to some long-standing

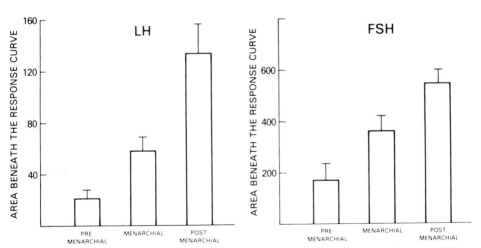

FIG. 19.   Evaluation of pituitary responsiveness to a GnRH bolus (50 mg). Hypophysial receptivity to GnRH stimulation was assessed by calculating the area beneath the 0 to 80 minute response curves for LH and FSH. Responses were evaluated with respect to physiological status at the time of treatment (premenarchial, menarchial, and postmenarchial). The postmenarchial LH and FSH responses to the GnRH treatment were significantly greater ($p < 0.05$) than the response during other intervals. (From Williams *et al.*, 1982, with permission.)

FIG. 20.   Illustration of the sleeveless nylon-net primate vest fastened to a swivel-tether assembly, permitting chronic femoral to vena caval cannulation. (From Sopelak *et al.*, 1983, with permission.)

concerns about nonsteroidal ovarian inhibin(s) and its putative role in the normal physiologic characteristics of the hypothalamic–pituitary–ovarian axis (Hodgen, 1982). We have noted that administration of human menopausal gonadotropins (hMG), either an FSH/LH combination (Fig. 23) (Kreitmann et al., 1981) or "pure" FSH (Fig. 24) (Schenken and Hodgen, 1983), can produce familiar bilateral ovarian hyperstimulation with attendant supraphysiologic elevations of circulating estradiol. However, these monkeys failed to manifest timely gonadotropin responses to estrogen-positive feedback; that is, these normal, intact, cycling primates did not have expected midcycle-like LH surges, despite escalating levels of serum estradiol that sometimes exceeded 600 pg/ml during 12 days of FSH therapy. Previously, we had observed failure of spontaneous LH surges when hMG induced ovarian hyperstimulation occurred in postpartum monkeys (Fig. 25) (Goodman and Hodgen, 1978), followed by transient hyperprolactinemia. Elevated serum prolactins probably result from an estrogen–progesterone synergy (Williams et al., 1981). These observations fit with a frequent clinical finding (G. S. Jones, personal communication): when endocrinologically normal patients are given hMG to increase the number of follicles/ova available for in vitro fertilization and embryo transfer therapy, hCG is usually required for the final maturation of these follicles. Seldom do these women have spontaneous LH/FSH surges, even though circulating estradiol exceeds 300 pg/ml for several days.

Why are these several preovulatory follicles not ovulated spontaneously? Perhaps excessive secretion of one or more inhibitors of ovarian origin is driven uncontrollably by unrelenting (exogenous) FSH stimulation, therein blocking the expected FSH/LH surges otherwise induced by estrogen-positive feedback upon the hypothalamic–pituitary unit. Indeed, we have reported (Hodgen et al., 1980) that pretreating monkeys with charcoal-extracted porcine follicular fluid blocks both the FSH and LH surges after a conventional estrogen challenge in the follicular phase (Fig. 26). Similarly, it was shown that acute GnRH-induced release of FSH and LH was blunted when castrate monkeys were pretreated with a porcine follicular fluid extract (Rettori et al., 1982).

Next, we asked whether the ovaries, in a state of hyperstimulation, were obligatory for this blockade of the spontaneous LH surge versus a "short loop" FSH feedback. Indeed, hFSH administration (12 days) to long-term ovariectomized monkeys did not inhibit responses to an estradiol benzoate challenge; that is, typical midcycle-like gonadotropin surges were observed. Accordingly, the occurrence of estrogen-induced FSH/LH surges in FSH-treated castrated monkeys demonstrates that among intact monkeys the ovaries (hyperstimulated) surely participate in the blockade of estrogen-positive feedback during exogenous gonadotropin

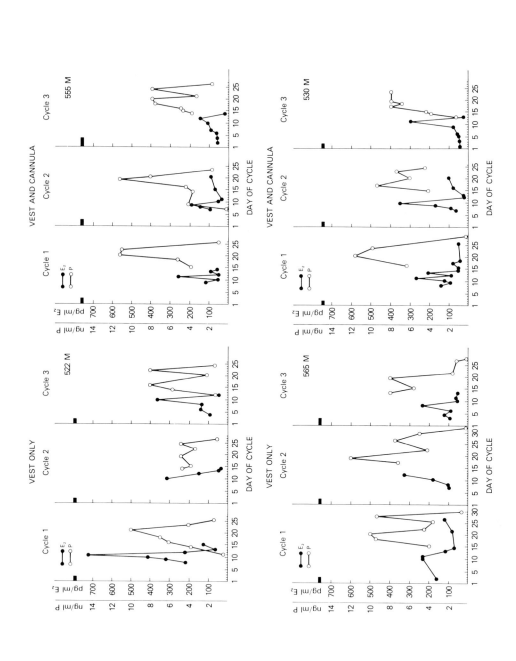

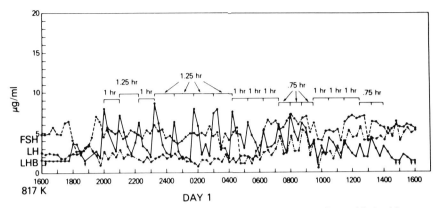

FIG. 22. Circhoral pulsatile pattern of tonic LH secretion was detectable by bioassay, but not radioimmunoassay, in intact female rhesus monkeys. (From Marut *et al.*, 1981, with permission.)

therapy. Further, within hMG medications, blockade of the LH surge probably derives from the actions of its FSH component (Schenken and Hodgen, 1983).

Let us now consider what all this may mean in the context of the normal ovarian cycle, without exogenous hormonal treatment. One hypothesis develops as follows: While a cohort of follicles is being recruited in the early follicular phase, enhanced secretion of inhibin(s) may suppress pituitary FSH release; in turn, lower circulating levels of FSH reduce follicular stimulation, granulosa cells being the primary source of ovarian inhibin activity (Erickson and Hsueh, 1978). Could this mechanism play a central role in selection of the *single* dominant follicle (the normal ovulatory quota in women and monkeys) by regulating FSH release in the early follicular phase, before the dominant follicle overtly manifests its presence through elevation of estradiol in the circulation? As discussed further below, although such a mechanism may not be sufficient by itself to account for the restriction of gametogenic follicle growth to just one ovary, this scheme is well suited to explaining our earlier findings comparing responses (differential) to luteectomy in hemiovariectomized (Goodman *et al.*, 1979) versus intact monkeys (Goodman and Hodgen, 1979a). That is, even the gametogenically quiescent ovary (contralateral to the excised dominant follicle or corpus luteum) participates in regulating FSH

FIG. 21. Serum patterns of estradiol-17β (E$_2$) and progesterone (P) in cynomolgus monkeys wearing a vest and mobile tether assembly with/without an indwelling femoral to vena caval cannula. Timely menses (■) and hormonal indices of normal follicular development and luteal function occurred in 12 of 12 cycles. (From Sopelak *et al.*, 1983, with permission.)

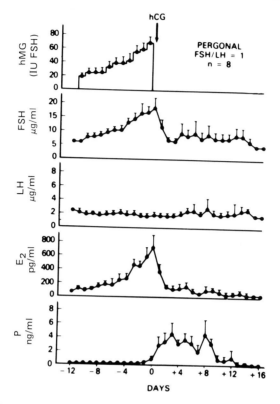

FIG. 23. Hormonal patterns in serum when normal cycling rhesus and cynomolgus monkeys were given 37.5 IU/day of hMG for 12 days, followed by 1000 IU of hCG. Note that the top panel depicts hFSH (exogenous only) levels in monkey serum, whereas the next lower panel illustrates the combined hFSH and mFSH (endogenous) concentrations in a different RIA. Also, the LH RIA used did not crossreact with hLH, so that only endogenous mLH was measured. It is clear that the expected spontaneous LH surge did not occur, despite sustained elevations of serum estradiol. (From Kreitmann *et al.*, 1981, with permission.)

secretion in the early follicular phase (diZerega and Hodgen, 1981a). In the luteal phase, secretions from the ovary bearing the active corpus luteum have the full capacity (alone) to regulate tonic FSH release (Goodman and Hodgen, 1979a). Accordingly, circulating FSH levels may be comodulated, first by inhibin(s) and later by estrogen, emanating principally from the dominant follicle (diZerega *et al.*, 1980). In this novel scenario, the dynamic titrations of inhibin(s) versus FSH may ensure an adequate milieu for timely recruitment and selection of the single dominant follicle while preventing ovarian hyperstimulation and hypothalamic–pituitary refractoriness to estrogen-positive feedback; soon, estro-

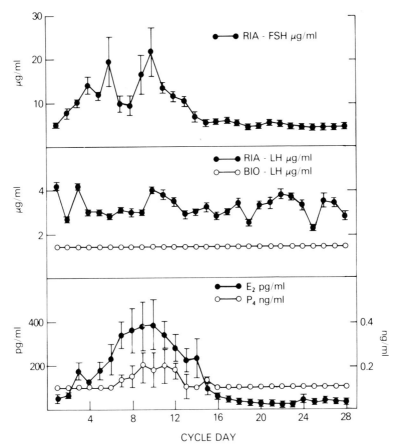

FIG. 24. FSH-induced ovarian hyperstimulations in monkeys blocked the LH surge despite elevations of serum estradiol. ("Pure" FSH, Urofollitropin, Serono Laboratories, Inc., Rome.) Doses were 25 or 50 IU daily (im) from the onset of menses until day 12 of the cycle. (From Schenken and Hodgen, 1983, with permission.)

gen from the newly selected (dominant) follicle sustains and expands that follicle's preeminence (maintenance of dominance), while conditioning the pituitary for timely preovulatory gonadotropin surges and ovulation (Hodgen, 1982).

Owing to the seminal contributions from many laboratories, our interest in understanding ovarian inhibin activity(ies) has been invigorated over the past decade (Schwartz and Channing, 1977; Williams *et al.*, 1979a; Chappel *et al.*, 1979). Conventionally, *inhibin* refers to selective regulation of FSH secretion by a nonsteroidal testicular or ovarian factor (Ward, 1981). In keeping with many new findings, the foregoing strict

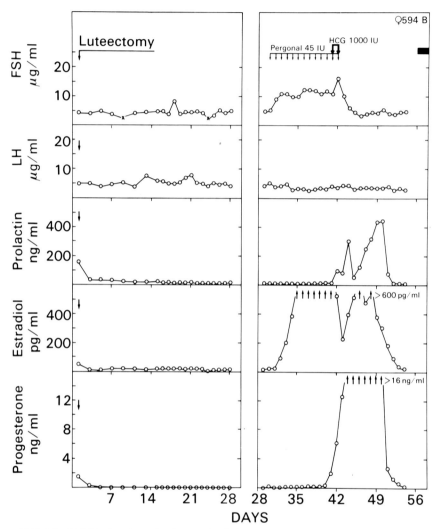

FIG. 25. hMG induced ovarian hyperstimulation in a postpartum, nonnursing monkey. Note absence of an endogenous LH surge and the induction of hyperprolactinemia. (From Goodman and Hodgen, 1978, with permission.)

definitions may change; that is, there may be one or more nonsteroidal inhibitors (inhibins) of ovarian origin. As purported here, the term is broadened to describe the physiologic role of ovarian inhibin(s) in the selection of the dominant follicle, as well as a potential capacity (in excess) to block the estrogen-induced surge of LH during ovarian hyperstimulation (Goodman and Hodgen, 1978; Kreitmann et al., 1981; Schenken

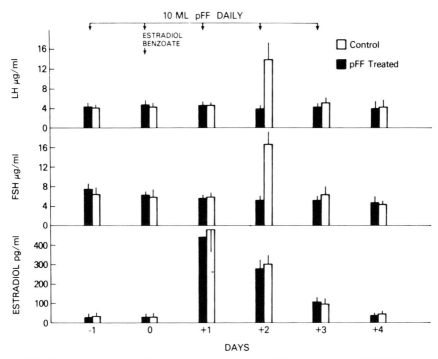

FIG. 26. Pretreatment with porcine follicular fluid (pFF) extract blocks LH/FSH surge responsive to an estradiol challenge. Intact cycling monkeys received the first injection on cycle day 2. (From Hodgen et al., 1980, with permission.)

and Hodgen, 1983; G. S. Jones, personal communication). It follows that ovarian inhibin(s) may contribute to the regulation of the ovulatory quota through precise titration of FSH levels in blood. Accordingly, the number of follicles selected is species-specific and to a large degree a function of the FSH stimulation (strength and duration) provided, although estrogens and LH surely participate synergistically. This proposed mechanism of control upon FSH secretion may permit the selection of the single dominant follicle (typically) in women and these monkeys by other (intra)ovarian factors. Rats and pigs, which are polyovular, may have a different setpoint for inhibin/FSH titrations and therefore do not exhibit follicle selection and follicle dominance as it occurs in monovular primates. These events may be superimposed on the actions of steroids in positive and negative feedback on gonadotropin release. This kind of scheme is consonant with most current dogma of normal folliculogenesis (diZerega and Hodgen, 1981a) and empirical observations (Schenken and Hodgen, 1983; G. S. Jones, personal communication), when ovarian hyperstimulation violates (exceeds) the normal ovulatory quota following exogenous gonadotropin therapy. That is, ovarian inhibin(s) may be an early nonsteroidal signal for constraining FSH secretion, so that circulating FSH levels fall to a tonic set-point. Whereas the evidence reviewed here may be highly persuasive for a central role of one or more nonsteroidal inhibitors of ovarian origin in follicle selection, it is not yet compelling.

3. Intraovarian Factors

a. Antifolliculogenic Actions of Progesterone. That intraovarian progesterone may be a local regulator of folliculogenesis during recruitment and selection of the dominant follicle in the menstrual cycle is inferred from several kinds of findings. Here, we have assimilated a series of experiments that support an antifolliculogenic action of progesterone at the ovarian level.

As discussed above, we previously demonstrated that systemic progesterone replacement after luteectomy was sufficient to mimic the corpus luteum. That is, the resumption of new follicle growth and ovulation after excision of luteal tissue was forestalled for the interval of progesterone elevation. Was this antifolliculogenic action of progesterone exerted at the hypothalamic–pituitary or ovarian level, or both? We had noted that the ovary secreting more progesterone seemed relatively disadvantaged for recruitment and selection of the coming dominant follicle (diZerega *et al.*, 1981a). Was this effect caused solely by surgical trauma of luteectomy? Although elevated circulating progesterone levels were associated with a transient interruption (delay) of cyclic ovarian function, it was not established whether residual intraovarian progesterone played a role apart from, but not exclusive of, the functional corpus luteum in the regulation of folliculogenesis. To answer these questions, we studied the temporal relationship of ovarian venous progesterone concentrations after luteectomy, as well as the influence of hCG given 1, 3, or 5 days later, to the timeliness of new follicle growth and the side of the next ovulation relative to the interovarian progesterone gradient (diZerega and Hodgen, 1982).

Figure 27 illustrates the concentrations of progesterone in ovarian venous sera collected after luteectomy and hCG treatment and their relationship to the side and timeliness of the next ovulation. All monkeys that received hCG 1 or 3 days after luteectomy manifested significant delays of new follicle growth along with elevations of progesterone in ovarian venous effluents, especially contralateral to the ovary destined for ovulation 20 to 22 days later (progesterone ng/ml: 48 ± 13.2 vs 21.3 ± 5.4; 12.2 ± 4.1 vs 4.2 ± 0.8, respectively, $p < 0.05$). In every case (10 of 10 monkeys) the next ovulation was contralateral to the higher ovarian vein progesterone

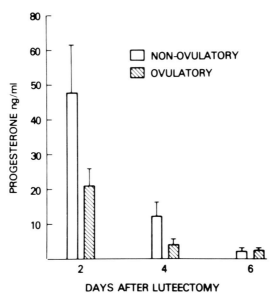

FIG. 27. Ovarian venous progesterone levels on days 2, 4, and 6 after luteectomy ($n =$ 10). Data are presented comparing the progesterone levels in effluents from the subsequent ovulatory ovary to those from the contralateral ovary. The bar represents the mean and SE; 100 IU of hCG was given on day 1, or 3, or, 5. (From diZerega and Hodgen, 1982, with permission.)

concentration, irrespective of the side of luteectomy. That is, it seems that the direction of the progesterone gradient between ovaries was a more important factor than the site of previous luteectomy in determining the side of the next dominant follicle. In contrast, monkeys given hCG 5 days after luteectomy manifested neither asymmetry of ovarian venous progesterone concentrations, nor significantly elevated progesterone levels; there was no delay in the time-course of subsequent ovulations. Clearly, extraluteal ovarian tissue(s) secretion of progesterone was responsive to hCG stimulation at 1 and 3 days after luteectomy, but not by day 5.

That the side of subsequent ovulation following luteectomy and hCG therapy was counter to the higher side of the progesterone gradient suggests that intraovarian progesterone may regulate the side of new follicle growth. Further, when ovarian venous progesterone levels were elevated bilaterally, after hCG on day 1 or 3 after luteectomy, subsequent ovulation was delayed, indicating that intraovarian progesterone can also influence the time-course of new gametogenic follicle growth. As discussed earlier, the dominant follicle may have been selected already when hCG was given 5 days after luteal ablation (Goodman *et al.*, 1977b; diZerega and Hodgen, 1981a); perhaps this accounts for the unique continuance of timely ovulations in this group.

   b. "Selection" and Other Follicular Factors.   During the course of our studies, we were struck over and over again by how robust the regulation of follicle selection and dominance appears to be. Except following the administration of exogenous hormones, we never observed multiple ovulations in any monkey, after any kind of ablation, despite widely differing patterns of circulating FSH. That is, from the one extreme of detecting barely any rise in serum FSH levels after follicle cautery or luteectomy in otherwise intact monkeys (Fig. 9a and b) to the other extreme of finding 2- to 4-fold increases in serum FSH lasting about 1 week after luteectomy in chronically hemiovariectomized monkeys (Fig. 13), only single ovulations supervened. Even if FSH levels rose after every instance of ablation, it would be teleological reasoning to explain the rise as a promoter of resumed follicle growth. Rather, the reason for an FSH rise must, as we understand it now, be due to a decrement in negative feedback inhibition (steroidal and/or nonsteroidal) of FSH secretion.

   The kind of discordance between FSH patterns observed after various ablations and the maintenance of the ovulatory quota at unity raised strong doubts, in our minds, that FSH levels were the exclusive determinant of the selection of a *single* dominant follicle on only *one* ovary. As discussed above, the next dominant follicle appears to be selected by the sixth day of the cycle, i.e., when tonic serum FSH is descending from its highest levels in the typical follicular phase, and presumably has not been limiting. More graphically, selection of a *single* dominant follicle is completed between 4 and 8 days after luteectomy (Goodman *et al.*, 1982; Koering *et al.*, 1982) in chronically hemiovariectomized monkeys, when tonic FSH levels are markedly elevated (Goodman *et al.*, 1979). As discussed below, the late luteal phase rise in FSH levels is not a necessary antecedent for timely recruitment, selection, and ovulation of the next dominant follicle. Consequently, the tonic FSH level—or, indeed, any extraovarian signal—appears inadequate by itself to explain the unilateral emergence of a single dominant follicle with such uncanny precision cycle after cycle, monkey after monkey.

   As one explanation for achieving this kind of consistency and precision, we hypothesize that one follicle may attain dominance over other potentially competing follicles by secreting a substance we call "selectron." This conceptual entity (factor) is imputed to inhibit the development of other follicles, even when FSH levels are not limiting, by acting directly on the ovaries. As the follicular phase progresses, the single follicle that has attained dominance via "selectron," may maintain its dominance by suppressing FSH secretion via inhibin(s) and estradiol. That is, during the early follicular phase one follicle may attain dominance directly by inhibiting others at the ovarian level and, later on, may maintain dominance indirectly by limiting circulatory FSH levels.

At present, there is no direct evidence for the "selectron" hypothesis. However, diZerega and co-workers (1982b) have recently described a nonsteroidal substance(s) present in venous effluent draining the human ovary bearing the dominant follicle (but not the contralateral ovary) which inhibits gonadotropin-stimulated follicle growth in rats. In other studies, they have described a similar protein fraction, from human follicular fluid and spent media from human granulosa cell cultures, which inhibited FSH/LH mediated augmentation of rat ovarian weight and estradiol secretion. Further, this protein(s) suppresses granulosa cell aromatase activity *in vitro* (diZerega *et al.*, 1983a,b). As we have argued above, extraovarian factors alone are difficult to reconcile with unilateral emergence of a single ovulable follicle.

Evidence is accruing that intrafollicular factors may play an important regulatory role, e.g., in oocyte maturation and luteinization (Channing *et al.*, 1982; Hodgen, 1982; Ward, 1982). It seems likely, at this point, that a more complete picture of the regulation of folliculogenesis will emerge as an interplay between extra- and intraovarian (intrafollicular) signals.

IV. Luteal Function as a Sequel to Folliculogenesis

A. AN OVERVIEW

Let us now turn our consideration to the second part of the ovarian triad, the corpus luteum. Among typical menstrual cycles in which pregnancy is not initiated, the life-span of the corpus luteum is limited to 12 to 16 days (diZerega and Hodgen, 1981b; Ross *et al.*, 1970; Wentz, 1979; Jones 1976). Corpus luteum function is established after ovulation, when the newly ruptured follicle completes luteinization. Throughout the luteal phase, progesterone and estradiol are the principal steroidal secretory products of the corpus luteum, although substantial amounts of other steroids are also secreted (Ross *et al.*, 1970; Greenwald, 1973; diZerega and Hodgen, 1981b; Landgren *et al.*, 1980). This transient endocrine activity is followed by spontaneous regression of the corpus luteum, marked by cessation of progesterone secretion, unless maternal recognition of pregnancy has intervened, that is, unless chorionic gonadotropin (CG) induces extension of corpus luteum function in the fertile menstrual cycle. Although the role of luteal progesterone in the support of gestation is incompletely understood, its requirement for nidation and maintenance of early pregnancy is well established (diZerega and Hodgen, 1981b; Thau and Sundaram, 1980; Thau *et al.*, 1979; Horta *et al.*, 1977). Indeed, deficiencies in either the duration of progesterone secretion or the amount secreted during the postovulatory interval of the menstrual cycle have been widely correlated with reproductive failure (Ross *et al.*, 1970; Wentz, 1979; Landgren *et al.*, 1980; Sherman and Korenman, 1974a,b; Moszkowski *et al.*, 1962; Strott *et al.*, 1970; Jones and Madrigal-Castro, 1970; Wilks *et al.*, 1976; diZerega and Hodgen, 1981b).

B. SPONTANEOUS LUTEAL PHASE DEFECTS

Deficiencies in progesterone secretion by the corpus luteum lead to inappropriate endometrial development such that normal nidation is impaired or prevented (Wentz, 1980; Tredway *et al.*, 1973; Rosenfeld and Garcia, 1976). As originally reported (Moszkowski *et al.*, 1962; Sherman and Korenman, 1974a; Jones and Madrigal-Castro, 1970), the short luteal phase defect in women was defined as a duration of 8 days or less from ovulation to menses. Moszkowski *et al.* (1962) and later Sherman and Korenman (1974b) described a second luteal phase abnormality, the inadequate luteal phase, in which the interval from ovulation to menses is normal but progesterone output is lower than expected. Similarly, some rhesus monkeys may manifest either short luteal phase or inadequate luteal phase aberrations, as well (Wilks *et al.*, 1976) (Fig. 28).

Frequently, inappropriate patterns of circulating pituitary gonadotropins lead to (1) abnormalities in the developing dominant follicle, revealed as deficiencies in estrogen secretion during the proliferative phase (Ross *et al.*, 1970; diZerega and Hodgen, 1981a; Sherman and Korenman, 1974a,b; Baird *et al.*, 1975; Williams *et al.*, 1979b; Yoshida *et al.*, 1979; diZerega *et al.*, 1981a; McNatty and Sawers, 1975) and (2) the inability of granulosa cells to luteinize appropriately, evidenced by deficiencies in serum progesterone during the secretory phase of the menstrual cycle (Wilks *et al.*, 1976; McNatty and Sawers, 1975; McNatty, 1979; Stouffer and Hodgen, 1980; diZerega *et al.*, 1981b). Clearly, abnormalities arising during folliculogenesis are likely to limit luteal function and fertility.

C. INTRAOVARIAN FACTORS

Evidence is now compelling that the hormonal milieu of the antecedent follicular phase (either spontaneous or induced) is a major determinant of

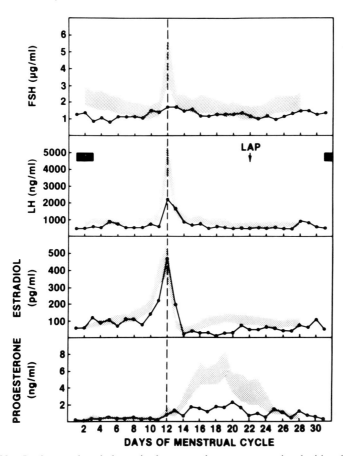

FIG. 28.   Inadequate luteal phases in rhesus monkeys were associated with a decreased FSH : LH ratio in the preceding follicular phase. (From Wilks *et al.*, 1976, with permission.)

luteal phase conditions, both within the corpus luteum and the endometrium. Indeed, corpus luteum function is on a direct continuum of follicle growth and maturation. The first morphologic signs of luteinization begin concurrently with the preovulatory LH surge (diZerega and Hodgen, 1981a,b; Johannson and Wide, 1969; Hoff and Quigley, 1980). Thus, ovulation transforms the dominant structure of the menstrual cycle from primarily an estrogen source (before ovulation) to an equally transient endocrine tissue secreting principally progesterone after ovulation. The main sites of progesterone synthesis and secretion are the granulosa luteal cells, but their metabolic capabilities may be linked with those of the thecal compartment, especially in the preovulatory interval.

McNatty and co-workers (1979), from studies of human follicles and antral fluid, have suggested that at least three criteria need to be fulfilled before the rupturing follicle can be transformed into an appropriately functional corpus luteum: (1) there must be sufficient numbers of granulosa cells in the follicle before ovulation, because thereafter granulosa luteal cells cease proliferation; (2) the follicle must contain granulosa cells with the capacity to secrete sufficient progesterone after ovulation; and (3) the granulosa cells, as well as the theca cells, must be responsive to trophic stimuli (LH/FSH/hCG). In culture, granulosa cells undergo the highest rate of mitosis when they are harvested from follicles that contain elevated levels of FSH in the antral fluid (McNatty *et al.*, 1979; Moon *et al.*, 1978). Indeed, it is reported that a linear correlation exists between the number of granulosa cells in FSH-rich follicles and the concentration of estradiol in follicular fluid (McNatty and Sawers, 1975; McNatty *et al.*, 1979). Conversely, in follicles having lower FSH concentrations, little estradiol was present in the antral fluid regardless of the number of granulosa cells present. Evidence derived *in vitro* suggests that FSH prevents degeneration of granulosa cells. Granulosa cells from antral follicles grown in a culture medium devoid of FSH undergo atresia (McNatty, 1979). In contrast, when FSH is present, the cells remain viable and responsive to tropic stimuli by enhancement of steroidogenesis. Thus, without adequate FSH support, the dominant follicle cannot develop normally as a precursor to the functioning corpus luteum (diZerega and Hodgen, 1981b; Bomsel-Helmreich *et al.*, 1979; McNatty *et al.*, 1975; Sanyal *et al.*, 1974).

Foremost among the characteristics of luteal phase-defective cycles is the frequent inability of the corpus luteum to respond to hCG (Jones *et al.*, 1974), thereby precluding one of the earliest events in maternal recognition of pregnancy. Even among normal corpora lutea, the decline of luteal function in the late luteal phase is associated with a decrease in the responsiveness of the luteal cells to hCG (Stouffer *et al.*, 1977; Halme *et al.*, 1978; Boulton *et al.*, 1980). The progressive inability of the corpus luteum to respond to LH/hCG in the late luteal phase may be associated with the loss of cell surface receptors (diZerega and Hodgen, 1981b). In instances of luteal phase defects, luteal cells are likely to be deficient in LH receptors and/or the intracellular apparatus needed to mediate LH-induced progesterone secretion. FSH, augmented by estrogen, induces expression of LH receptors during folliculogenesis (Richards, 1979; Halme *et al.*, 1978). Necessarily, it follows that gonadotropin secretion in the antecedent follicular phase is the mainstay for subsequent corpus luteum function.

D. FSH DEFICIENCIES IN THE FOLLICULAR PHASE

Frequently, subnormal serum FSH levels during the follicular phase are followed by diminished progesterone circulating during the luteal phase of the menstrual cycle in both women (Ross *et al.*, 1970; Vande Wiele *et al.*, 1970; Gemzell, 1965; Lunenfeld *et al.*, 1976) and monkeys (Wilks *et al.*, 1976; diZerega *et al.*, 1981b). More specifically, a low serum FSH:LH ratio during the follicular phase is indicative of cycles demonstrating luteal dysfunction and resultant infertility. Although these associations (low serum FSH antecedent to aberrant luteal function) were reported more than a decade ago, more direct evidence that an FSH deficiency during follicular growth results in defective corpus luteum function was lacking.

Accordingly, it was of interest to determine the importance of the typical intercycle (end of cycle-start of cycle) FSH elevation during initiation of new follicle growth. This issue was investigated in monkeys by serial cauteries of the largest visible follicle (the putative dominant follicle) during the preovulatory interval in two consecutive cycles (diZerega and Hodgen, 1981a,b). In the third cycle, folliculogenesis was unmolested and the spontaneous ovulation, 13 to 15 days later, was accompanied by normal follicular and luteal phase patterns of peripheral LH, FSH, estradiol, and progesterone, including an increase in late luteal phase FSH levels. These findings indicated that the usual late luteal phase elevation in serum FSH is not obligatory for timely recruitment, selection, and ovulation of the subsequent dominant follicle. That the intercycle FSH elevation is not of major significance to follicle selection must not be construed to imply that low serum FSH levels are inconsequential or even unimportant as a principal determinant of follicular maturation and luteal function. Indeed, even lower circulating FSH levels uniformly give rise to aberrant folliculogenesis and/or corpus luteum dysfunction (Stouffer and Hodgen, 1980), or even prevent ovulation (diZerega and Hodgen, 1981a,b).

When we treated monkeys in the early follicular phase with charcoal-extracted porcine follicular fluid (pFF), which selectively (serum LH unchanged in radioimmunoassay) suppressed serum FSH levels (Fig. 29) (Channing *et al.*, 1979), follicle maturation and ovulation were delayed by higher doses and longer duration of pFF therapy. With smaller doses of pFF for a shorter period, timely ovulations occurred, but were followed by luteal dysfunction—a sequel to mild, transient FSH deficiencies (Fig. 30). In cycles having these pFF-induced luteal phase defects (Stouffer and Hodgen, 1980; diZerega and Hodgen, 1981a), serum progesterone patterns were similar to those characteristic of spontaneously defective luteal phases in monkeys (Wilks *et al.*, 1976) (Fig. 28). Furthermore, in this

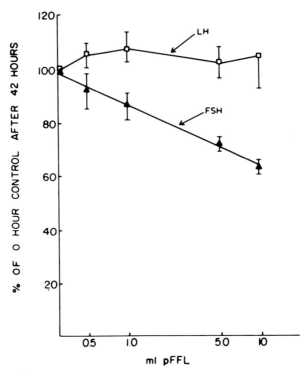

FIG. 29. Selective, dose-dependent inhibition of FSH in castrate rhesus monkeys treated with porcine follicular fluid (pFFL) extract. (From Channing *et al.*, 1981, with permission.)

dysfunctional state, the luteal cells were nearly unresponsive to hCG *in vitro* (Stouffer and Hodgen, 1980). Evidence of diminished basal and go-nadotropin-sensitive progesterone synthetic activity by cultured luteal cells isolated from pFF-treated monkeys (Fig. 31) indicated that an FSH deficiency during the early follicular phase produced the defective corpus luteum, although a direct effect of pFF on the ovary cannot be excluded. The responses observed depended upon the dose and duration of pFF therapy, and the degree of FSH deprivation (diZerega *et al.*, 1981b).

Although the mechanism(s) of pFF-induced luteal defects remains to be determined, the decreased hCG sensitivity of luteal cells from pFF-treated monkeys suggests that hormonal deficiencies during the early fol-licular phase impaired development of LH/hCG receptors or mediation of steroidogenesis. Similarly, Yen and co-workers (Sheehan *et al.*, 1982) have employed brief GnRH agonist treatment in the early follicular phase to induce corpus luteum dysfunction in women as a possible means of con-

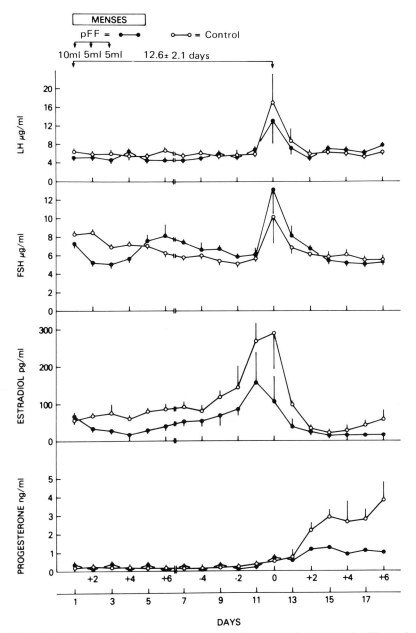

FIG. 30. Diminished luteal progesterone secretion in monkeys treated with porcine follicular fluid (pFF) extract on days 1–3 of the cycle. (From Stouffer and Hodgen, 1980, with permission.)

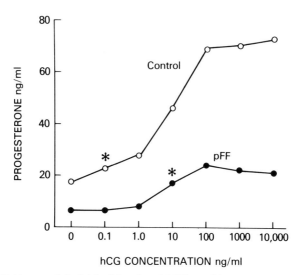

FIG. 31. Evidence of diminished basal and hCG-sensitive progesterone secretion by cultured luteal cells isolated from control and porcine follicular fluid (pFF) treated monkeys. (From Stouffer and Hodgen, 1980, with permission.)

traception. Thus, the early transient reduction of follicular phase FSH concentrations may have irreversibly altered ovarian LH responsivity, which in turn, resulted in defective luteal function (diZerega and Hodgen, 1981b).

In contrast, giving higher doses of pFF for a longer interval produced a hiatus in folliculogenesis, as adjudged by the accompanying marked suppression of serum estradiol levels; that is, serum estradiol deficiencies were associated with delayed ovulation (diZerega et al., 1981a,b). Apparently, the low levels of circulating estradiol may have been a consequence of insufficient gonadotropin-dependent follicular activity, although, again a direct effect of pFF on the ovum cannot be excluded. Collectively, these observations are consistent with the notion that an adequate estrogen level in the early follicular phase is a prerequisite to preovulatory follicular maturation in response to pituitary gonadotropins (Channing, 1975; Richards, 1979). Similarly, these findings suggest that the earliest FSH-mediated events of the follicular phase, in conjunction with prevailing estrogen levels, are important determinants for the normal development and function of the corpus luteum, as proposed by McNatty et al. (1979).

The suppression of serum FSH by pFF on days 9 to 11 of the cycle was followed by either failure (atresia) of the dominant follicle or retardation of its final development (diZerega et al., 1981b). These reports may suggest the dominant follicle's dependence on FSH throughout the preovulatory interval. In fact, when FSH was made deficient by pFF treatment, the steroidogenic function of the preovulatory follicle rapidly declined, as judged by a marked diminution of serum estradiol. Although additional effects from the same or other components of pFF cannot be discounted, the concurrent decline in serum FSH and estradiol, together with cessation and/or delays in follicular maturation, may indicate an "inhibin" effect (diZerega and Hodgen, 1981a; Schwartz and Channing, 1977) on FSH-dependent processes even in the late follicular phase of the primate ovarian cycle.

Although luteolysis is a process of great importance, it was the subject of a recent intensive review (Rothchild, 1981); accordingly, we have not developed this subject here.

E. THE ENDOMETRIUM AND IMPLANTATION

Proliferation of the endometrium in the follicular phase of the menstrual cycle and subsequent development of its secretory capabilities in the luteal phase depend on the synergy of estrogens and progesterone acting sequentially within intracellular compartments (Tseng and Gurpide, 1975; Bayard et al., 1978; Haukkamaa and Lukkainen, 1974; Kreitmann-Gimbal et al., 1979, 1980, 1981). This is a classic end-organ response to a temporal and dose-dependent steroidal milieu. Current evidence indicates (see discussion below) that the availability of receptors for estrogen and progesterone binding regulates genomic expression of endometrial cells after nuclear translocation of these hormones. In this way, biologic effects of circulating ovarian steroids are manifest within the endometrium, in readiness for implantation of the blastocyst (Milgrom et al., 1972; Mester et al., 1974). That steroid receptor concentrations and histologic evaluations of secretory changes in the endometrium depend upon prevailing levels of these principal ovarian steroids in circulation is well known (Wentz, 1980; Rosenfeld and Garcia, 1976). However, the role of intracellular levels of steroid receptors in preparing the endometrium for implantation is not well understood (Kreitmann-Gimbal et al., 1981).

Levels of estradiol and progesterone receptors in endometrial tissue have been evaluated in the normal menstrual cycle (Tseng and Gurpide, 1975; Bayard et al., 1978; Haukkamma and Lukkainen, 1974). These studies indicate that levels of both progesterone and estradiol receptors in endometrial tissue change throughout the menstrual cycle and are primarily responsive to fluctuations in serum steroid levels. Furthermore, there appears to be a requirement for elevated concentrations of endometrial steroid receptors for nidation to occur. Collectively, these observations suggest that development of a "fertile" endometrium, one capable of supporting nidation and early pregnancy, is dependent upon an appropriate orchestration of temporal and sequential steroid-dependent tissue growth, via the dominant ovarian structures.

In summary, we have presented evidence illustrating that luteal dysfunction is a sequel to aberrant folliculogenesis. Such disorders create a cascade of deficiencies in the preovulatory follicle, the corpus luteum, and the endometrium in both the proliferative and secretory phases; the oocyte too may be "at fault" in luteal phase defect infertility. This point brings us to the final member of the ovarian triad, the ovum.

V. The Oocyte and Nature's Genetic Bank

The ovum can be described as a specialized cell that safeguards the female's genetic heritage, linking past and future generations. Among the most remarkable functional properties of the ovary(ies) is its capacity to serve as a repository for ova. In many ways, the generation to generation cycle of the ovary can be likened to the activities within a financial banking system. Indeed, genes are the currency on which all important biologic transactions depend. The deposition of a lifetime supply of female germ cells is accomplished *in utero* during organogenesis of the fetal ovary. As reviewed above (Figs. 1a and b, 17a and b), this reserve of immature egg cells is drawn upon repetitively through adult life, but never replenished after birth. This is in stark contrast to the ever-continuing production of sperms, initiated from the stem cells of the seminiferous epithelium of adult males.

Among long-lived primates, menopause signals the inevitable exhaustion of the reservoir of ovarian germ cells. Typically, this occurs in women after 30 to 40 years of reproductive potential (Ross and Vande Wiele, 1974); in monkeys (Fig. 32) the menopause is manifest after 20–25 years of ovarian function (van Wagenen 1972; Hodgen *et al.,* 1977). Note that probably less than 0.1% of all the germ cells formed in the fetal ovary ever reach ovulation; most are lost by atresia (Fig. 1a and b). Among the few that are ovulated, fewer yet are fertilized and developed; their protracted journey is unique. They alone can restock the "genetic bank" via the next generation.

The means by which the immature egg cell can be preserved over so long an interval, still retaining its developmental potential, is an enigma. Unique among all the cells of the body, these germ cells "rest" in their dictyate condition (Fig. 33), as if held in a "biological deep-freeze"; in some instances this condition is maintained for as long as five or six decades. Of course, germ cells may not be truly languid during this interval. By still mysterious mechanisms, the follicle enclosing a given germ

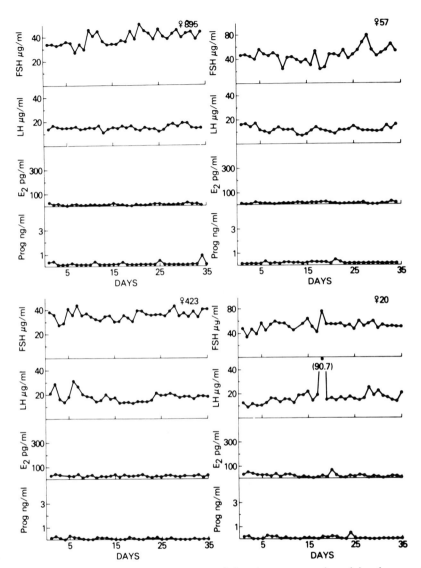

FIG. 32. Concentrations of FSH, LH, estradiol, and progesterone in peripheral serum of four postmenopausal rhesus monkeys. FSH and LH are expressed in terms of rhesus monkey pituitary gonadotropin preparation LER-1909-2. (From Hodgen *et al.*, 1977, with permission.)

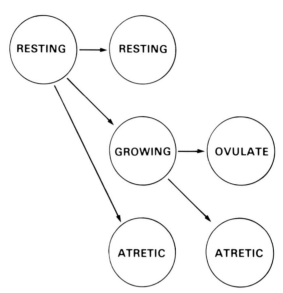

FIG. 33. Ovarian follicles may be found in four basic conditions: at rest, growing, atretic, or ready to ovulate.

cell may become antral and eventually responsive to pituitary gonadotropins, suddenly undergoing maturation in a given ovarian cycle. In this acutely altered antral milieu, the egg undergoes radical nuclear, cytoplasmic, and membranous adaptations in preparation for ovulation and fertilization. Growth of the oocyte is an early event in follicle development; but whether the oocyte actively participates in initiating and directing follicular maturation or accomplishes maturation more passively is not clear.

Surely, our ultimate understanding of oocyte sustenance and maturation will depend on more extensive investigation of the intraovarian/intrafollicular milieu. Interest at these levels is increasing as exemplified by studies on follicular fluid constituents (Channing *et al.,* 1982; Carson *et al.,* 1982; Ward, 1981), including hormonal concentrations, cellular (granulosa and theca) metabolic properties, and the egg itself. Clinically and commercially, these issues are very much a part of improving infertility therapy and animal production, respectively. In the decades now on the horizon, this new knowledge of the egg may eventually allow the ultimate in preventive medicine through "DNA therapy" upon the gamete. Finally, *in vitro* storage and transfer of oocytes or egg nuclei may someday facilitate ovum maturation without completion of gametogenic folliculogenesis *in vivo.* With regard to these scientific opportunities, most of the research is yet to be done; concurrent ethical considerations remain undeveloped.

VI. Summary

To paint an accurate portrait of the primate ovary, the ovarian triad—follicle, oocyte, and corpus luteum—must surely be regarded as a manifold unit whose functions are so integrated as almost to defy meaningful consideration of its parts in isolation. This triad plays a critical role in regulating the primate ovarian cycle in an individual and provides for propagation of the species. In turn, its components are regulated by both extraovarian and intraovarian signals. With respect to follicle selection and dominance, signals in the current cycle appear to be of greatest significance; previous ovarian status, in general, seems unimportant. Luteal function, in contrast, is not only clearly dependent on prevailing signals, but is also, perhaps more importantly, dependent on events in the preceding follicular phase. Most extensive of all, the fate of the oocyte is dependent on processes which occurred during fetal development, extending to events in the follicular and luteal phases of the adult primate ovarian/menstrual cycle.

ACKNOWLEDGMENTS

The investigations described here derive from unexcelled research and training opportunities provided within The National Institute of Child Health and Human Development. I (GDH), as well as my fellows and senior collaborators, remain indebted for the mentorship received at NIH from Drs. William W. Tullner, Roy Hertz, Mortimer B. Lipsett, and Griff T. Ross.

The authors appreciate the secretarial and graphic arts skills of Ms. Linda Baldwin and Ms. Alice Montague, respectively.

REFERENCES

Baird, D. T., Baker, T. G., McKatty, K. P., and Neal, P. (1975). *J. Reprod. Fertil.* **45,** 611.

Bayard, F., Damilano, S., Robel, P., and Baulieu, E. E. (1978). *J. Clin. Endocrinol. Metab.* **46,** 635.

Block, E. (1955). *Acta Endocrinol.* **8,** 33.

Bomsel-Helmreich, O., Gougeon, A., Thebault, A., Saltarelli, D., Milgrom, E., Fryman, R., and Papiernik, E. (1979). *J. Clin. Endocrinol. Metab.* **48,** 686.

Boulton, R. A., Coulam, C. B., and Ryan, R. J. (1980). *Obstet. Gynecol.* **56,** 336.

Brambell, F. W. R. (1956). *In* "Marshall's Physiology of Reproduction" (A. S. Parkes, ed.), Vol. 1, Part 1, p. 397. Longmans, Green, New York.

Carson, R. S., Trounson, A. O., and Findlay, J. K. (1982). *J. Clin. Endocrinol. Metab.* **55,** 798.

Channing, N. P. (1975). *Proc. Soc. Exp. Biol. Med.* **149,** 238.

Channing, N. P., Anderson, L. D., and Hodgen, G. D. (1979). *In* "Ovarian Follicular and Corpus Luteum Function" (C. P. Channing, J. Marsh, and W. Sadler, eds.), p. 407. Plenum, New York.

Channing, N. B., Anderson, L. D., Hoover, D. J., Gagliano, P., and Hodgen, G. D. (1981). *Biol. Reprod.* **25**, 885.

Channing, N. P., Anderson, L. D., Hoover, D. J., Kolena, J., Osteen, K. G., Pomerantz, S. H., and Tanabe, K. (1982). *Recent Prog. Horm. Res.* **38**, 331.

Chappel, S. C., Acott, T., and Spies, H. G. (1979). *In* "Ovarian Follicular and Corpus Luteum Function" (C. P. Channing, J. Marsh, and W. A. Sadler, eds.), p. 361. Plenum, New York.

Clark, J. R., Dierschke, D. J., and Wolf, R. C. (1978). *Biol. Reprod.* **17**, 779.

Dierschke, D. J., Weiss, G., and Knobil, E. (1974). *Endocrinology* **94**, 198.

diZerega, G. S., and Hodgen, G. D. (1980). *J. Clin. Endocrinol. Metab.* **51**, 903.

diZerega, G. S., and Hodgen, G. D. (1981a). *Endocr. Rev.* **2**, 27.

diZerega, G. S., and Hodgen, G. D. (1981b). *Fertil. Steril.* **35**, 489.

diZerega, G. S., and Hodgen, G. D. (1982). *J. Clin. Endocrinol. Metab.* **54**, 495.

diZerega, G. S., Marut, E. L., Turner, C. K., and Hodgen, G. D. (1980). *J. Clin. Endocrinol. Metab.* **51**, 698.

diZerega, G. S., Lynch, A., and Hodgen, G. D. (1981a). *Endocrinology* **108**, 1233.

diZerega, G. S., Stouffer, R. L., and Hodgen, G. D. (1981b). *In* "Intragonadal Regulation of Reproduction" (N. P. Channing and P. Franchimont, eds.), p. 9. Academic Press, New York.

diZerega, G. S., Turner, C. K., Stouffer, R. L., Anderson, L. D., Channing, C. P., and Hodgen, G. D. (1982a). *J. Clin. Endocrinol. Metab.* In press.

diZerega, G. S., Goebelsmann, V., and Nakamura, R. N. (1982b). *J. Clin. Endocrinol. Metab.* **54**, 1091.

diZerega, G. S., Marrs, R. P., Roche, P. C., Campeau, J. D., and Kling, O. R. (1983a). *J. Clin. Endocrinol.* **56**, 35.

diZerega, G. S., Marrs, R. P., Campeau, J. D., and Kling, O. R. (1983b). *J. Clin. Endocrinol. Metab.* **56**, 147.

Dufour, J., Ginther, O. J., and Casida, L. E. (1971). *Proc. Soc. Exp. Biol. Med.* **138**, 475.

Edwards, R. G., Fowler, R. E., Gore-Langton, R. E., Gorden, R. G., Jones, E. C., Readhead, C., and Steptoe, P. C. (1977). *J. Reprod. Fertil.* **51**, 237.

Erickson, G. F., and Hsueh, A. J. W. (1978). *Endocrinology* **103**, 1960.

Franchimont, P., and Channing, C. P., eds. (1981). "Intragonadal Regulation of Reproduction." Academic Press, New York.

Gemzell, C. (1965). *Recent Prog. Horm. Res.* **21**, 179.

Goodman, A. L., and Hodgen, G. D. (1977). *J. Clin. Endocrinol. Metab.* **45**, 837.

Goodman, A. L., and Hodgen, G. D. (1978). *Steroids* **31**, 731.

Goodman, A. L., and Hodgen, G. D. (1979a). *Endocrinology* **104**, 1310.

Goodman, A. L., and Hodgen, G. D. (1979b). *Endocrinology* **104**, 1304.

Goodman, A. L., and Hodgen, G. D. (1979c). *J. Clin. Endocrinol. Metab.* **48**, 345.

Goodman, A. L., and Hodgen, G. D. (1979d). *J. Clin. Endocrinol. Metab.* **49**, 469.

Goodman, A. L., and Hodgen, G. D. (1982a). *Endocrinology* **110**, 1315.

Goodman, A. L., and Hodgen, G. D. (1982b). *Am. J. Physiol.* **243**, E387.

Goodman, A. L., Descalzi, C. C., Johnson, D. K., and Hodgen, G. D. (1977a). *Proc. Soc. Exp. Med.* **155**, 479.

Goodman, A. L., Nixon, W. E., Johnson, D. K., and Hodgen, G. D. (1977b). *Endocrinology* **100**, 155.

Goodman, A. L., Nixon, W. E., and Hodgen, G. D. (1979). *Endocrinology* **104**, 69.

Goodman, A. L., Koering, M. J., Nixon, W. E., Williams, R. F., and Hodgen, G. D. (1982). *Am. J. Physiol.* **243,** E325.

Gougeon, A. (1981). Doctoral thesis, University of Paris.

Greenwald, G. S. (1973). *Handb. Physiol. Sect. 7 Endocrinol.* **2,** 125.

Gulyas, B. J., Hodgen, G. D., Tullner, W. W., and Ross, G. T. (1977a). *Biol. Reprod.* **16,** 216.

Gulyas, B. J., Tullner, W. W., and Hodgen, G. D. (1977b). *Biol. Reprod.* **17,** 650.

Halme, J., Ikonen, M., Rutanen, E. M., and Seppala, M. (1978). *Am. J. Obstet. Gynecol.* **131,** 728.

Harrison, R. J., and Weir, B. J. (1977). *In* "The Ovary" (S. Zuckerman and B. J. Weirm, eds.), 2nd Ed., Vol. 1, p. 113. Academic Press, New York.

Haukkamaa, M., and Lukkainen, T. (1974). *J. Steroid Biochem.* **5,** 447.

Hertz, R., and Hisaw, F. L. (1934). *Am. J. Physiol.* **108,** 1.

Hisaw, F. L. (1947). *Physiol. Rev.* **27,** 95.

Hodgen, G. D. (1982). *Fertil. Steril.* **38,** 281.

Hodgen, G. D., Goodman, A. L., O'Connor, A., and Johnson, D. K. (1977). *Am. J. Obstet. Gynecol.* **127,** 581.

Hodgen, G. D., Channing, C. P., Anderson, L. D., Gagliano, P., Turner, C. K., and Stouffer, R. L. (1980). *Proc. Int. Congr. Endocrinol., 6th* p. 263.

Hoff, J. D., and Quigley, M. E. (1980). *Annu. Meet. Endocr. Soc., 62nd* Abstr. No. 624.

Horta, J. L. H., Fernandez, J. G., DeSoto, L. B., and Cortes-Gallegos, V. (1977). *Obstet. Gynecol.* **49,** 705.

Ingram, D. L. (1962). *In* "The Ovary" (S. Zuckerman, ed.), Vol. 1, p. 247. Academic Press, New York.

Jagiello, G., and Vogel, H. J., eds. (1981). "Bioregulators of Reproduction." Academic Press, New York.

Johannson, E. D. B., and Wide, L. (1969). *Acta Endocrinol. (Copenhagen)* **62,** 82.

Jones, G. S. (1976). *Fertil. Steril.* **27,** 351.

Jones, G. S., and Madrigal-Castro, V. (1970). *Fertil. Steril.* **21,** 1.

Jones, G. S., Askel, S., and Wentz, A. C. (1974). *Obstet. Gynecol.* **44,** 26.

Jones, R. E. (1979). *In* "The Vertebrate Ovary" (R. E. Jones, ed.), p. 763. Plenum, New York.

Knobil, E. (1973). *Biol. Reprod.* **8,** 246.

Knobil, E. (1974). *Recent Prog. Horm. Res.* **30,** 1.

Knobil, E. (1980). *Recent Prog. Horm. Res.* **36,** 53.

Koering, M. J. (1969). *Am. J. Anat.* **126,** 73.

Koering, M. J. (1982). *Am. J. Anat.* In press.

Koering, M. J., Baehler, E. A., Goodman, A. L., and Hodgen, G. D. (1982). *Biol. Reprod.* **27,** 989.

Kreitmann, O., and Hodgen, G. D. (1980). *Fertil. Steril.* **34,** 375.

Kreitmann, O., Lynch, A., Nixon, W. E., and Hodgen, G. D. (1981). *In* "In Vitro Fertilization and Embryo Transfer" (E. S. E. Hafez and K. Semm, eds.), p. 303. MTP Press, Kiel, West Germany.

Kreitmann-Gimbal, B., Goodman, A. L., Bayard, F., and Hodgen, G. D. (1979). *Steroids* **34,** 749.

Kreitmann-Gimbal, B., Bayard, F., Nixon, W. E., and Hodgen, G. D. (1980). *Steroids* **35,** 471.

Kreitmann-Gimbal, B., Bayard, F., and Hodgen, G. D. (1981). *J. Clin. Endocrinol. Metab.* **52,** 133.

Landgren, B. M., Unden, A. L., and Diczfalusy, E. (1980). *Acta Endocrinol.* **94,** 89.

Lunenfeld, B., Kraiem, Z., and Eshkol, A. (1976). *Clin. Obstet. Gynaecol.* **3**, 27.
McNatty, K. P. (1979). *In* "Ovarian Follicular and Corpus Luteum Function" (C. P. Channing, J. M. Marsh, and W. A. Sadler, eds.), p. 465. Plenum, New York.
McNatty, K. P., and Sawers, R. S. (1975). *J. Endocrinol.* **66**, 391.
McKnatty, K. P., Hunter, W. M., McNeilly, A. S., and Sawers, R. S. (1975). *J. Endocrinol.* **64**, 555.
McNatty, K. P., Smith, D. M., Makris, A., Osthnondh, R., and Ryan, K. J. (1979). *J. Clin. Endocrinol. Metab.* **49**, 851.
Marut, E. L., Williams, R. F., Cowan, B. D., Lynch, A., Lerner, S. P., and Hodgen, G. D. (1981). *Endocrinology* **109**, 2270.
Mester, J., Martel, D., Psychoyos, A., and Baulieu, E. (1974). *Nature (London)* **250**, 776.
Milgrom, E., Atger, M., Perrot, M., and Baulieu, E. (1972). *Endocrinology* **90**, 1071.
Moon, Y. S., Tsang, B. K., Simpson, C., and Armstrong, D. T. (1978). *J. Clin. Endocrinol. Metab.* **47**, 263.
Moszkowski, E., Woodruff, J. D., and Jones, G. S. (1982). *Am. J. Obstet. Gynecol.* **83**, 363.
Nass, T. E., Dierschke, D. J., Clark, J. R., and Wolf, R. C. (1981). *In* "Dynamics of Ovarian Function" (N. B. Schwartz and M. Hunziker-Dunn, eds.), p. 135. Raven, New York.
Nilsson, L., Wikland, M., and Hamberger, L. (1982). *Fertil. Steril.* **37**, 30.
Parkes, A. S. (1966). *In* "Marshall's Physiology of Reproduction" (A. S. Parkes, eds.), Vol. 3, p. 1. Little, Brown, Boston.
Pedersen, T. (1970). *Acta Endocrinol.* **64**, 304.
Rettori, V., Siler-Khodr, T. M., Pauerstein, C. J., Smith, C. G., and Asch, R. H. (1982). *J. Clin. Endocrinol. Metab.* **54**, 500.
Richards, J. S. (1978). *In* "The Vertebrate Ovary" (R. E. Jones, ed.), p. 331. Plenum, New York.
Richards, J. S. (1979). *Physiol. Rev.* **60**, 51.
Rosenfeld, D. L., and Garcia, C. (1976). *Fertil. Steril.* **27**, 1256.
Ross, G. T., and Vande Wiele, R. L. (1974). *In* "Textbook of Endocrinology" (R. H. Williams, ed.), Chap. 7, p. 368. Saunders, Philadelphia, Pennsylvania.
Ross, G. T., Cargille, C. M., Lipsett, M. B., Rayford, P. L., Marshall, J. R., Strott, C. A., and Rodbard, D. (1970). *Recent Prog. Horm. Res.* **26**, 1.
Rothchild, I. (1981). *Recent Prog. Horm. Res.* **37**, 183.
Sanyal, M. K., Berger, M. J., Thompson, I. E., Taymor, L., and Horne, H. W. (1974). *J. Clin. Endocrinol. Metab.* **38**, 828.
Schenken, R. S., and Hodgen, G. D. (1983). *J. Clin. Endocrinol. Metab.* In press.
Schwartz, N. B. (1974). *Biol. Reprod.* **10**, 263.
Schwartz, N. B., and Channing, C. P. (1977). *Proc. Natl. Acad. Sci. U.S.A.* **74**, 5721.
Schwartz, N. B., Anderson, C. H., Nequin, L. G., and Ely, C. A. (1974). *In* "Control of the Onset of Puberty" (M. M. Grumbach, G. D. Grave, and F. E. Mayer, eds.), p. 367. Wiley, New York.
Sheehan, K. L., Casper, R. F., and Yen, S. S. C. (1982). *Science* **215**, 170.
Sherman, B. M., and Korenman, S. G. (1974a). *J. Clin. Endocrinol. Metab.* **38**, 89.
Sherman, B. M., and Korenman, S. G. (1974b). *J. Clin. Endocrinol. Metab.* **39**, 145.
Sopelak, V. M., Lynch, A., Williams, R. F., and Hodgen, G. D. (1983). *Biol. Reprod.* In press.
Stouffer, R. L., and Hodgen, G. D. (1980). *J. Clin. Endocrinol. Metab.* **51**, 699.
Stouffer, R. L., Nixon, W. E., Gulyas, B. J., and Hodgen, G. D. (1977). *Endocrinology* **100**, 506.
Strott, C. A., Cargille, C. M., Ross, G. T., and Lipsett, M. B. (1970). *J. Clin. Endocrinol. Metab.* **30**, 246.

Thau, R. B., and Sundarm, K. (1980). *Fertil. Steril.* **33,** 317.

Thau, R. B., Sundaram, S., Thornton, Y. S., and Seidman, L. S. (1979). *Fertil. Steril.* **31,** 200.

Tredway, D. R., Mishell, D. R., and Moyer, D. L. (1973). *Am. J. Obstet. Gynecol.* **117,** 1031.

Tseng, L., and Gurpide, E. (1975). *J. Clin. Endocrinol. Metab.* **41,** 402.

Van Damme, M. P., Robertson, D. M., and Diczfalosy, E. (1974). *Acta Endocrinol.* **77,** 655.

van Wagenen, G. (1972). *J. Med. Primatol.* **1,** 3.

Vande Wiele, R. L., Bogumil J., Dyenfurth, I., Ferin, M., Jewelewicz, R., Warren, M., Rizkallah, T., and Mikhail G. (1970). *Recent Prog. Horm. Res.* **26,** 63.

Ward, D. N. (1981). *In* "Bioregulators of Reproduction" (G. Jagiello and H. J. Vogel, eds.), p. 371. Academic Press, New York.

Ward, D. N. (1982). *In* "Regulation of Ovarian Function" (G. Greenwald and W. Sadler, eds.). Plenum, New York, in press.

Wentz, A. C. (1979). *Clin. Obstet. Gynecol.* **22,** 169.

Wentz, A. C. (1980). *Fertil. Steril.* **33,** 121.

Wilks, J. W., Hodgen, G. D., and Ross, G. T. (1976). *J. Clin. Endocrinol. Metab.* **43,** 1261.

Williams, R. F., and Hodgen, G. D. (1982). *Am. J. Primatol. Suppl.* **1,** 181.

Williams, A. T., Rush, M. E., and Lipner, H. (1979a). *In* "Ovarian Follicular and Corpus Luteum Function" (C. P. Channing, J. Marsh, and W. A. Sadler, eds.), p. 429. Plenum, New York.

Williams, M. T., LeMaire, W. J., Roth, M. S., and Marsh, J. M. (1979b). *Annu. Meet. Study Gynecol., 26th* Abstr. No. 185.

Williams, R. F., Barber, D. L., Cowan, B. D., Lynch, A., Marut, E. L., and Hodgen, G. D. (1981). *Steroids* **38,** 321.

Williams, R. F., Turner, C. K., and Hodgen, G. D. (1982). *J. Clin. Endocrinol. Metab.* **55,** 660.

Yoshida, T., Hattori, Y., Suzuki, H., and Noda, K. (1979). *Tokoku J. Exp. Med.* **129,** 135.

Young, W. C. (1961). *In* "Sex and Internal Secretions" (W. C. Young, ed.), 3rd Ed., p. 449. Williams & Wilkins, Baltimore, Maryland.

Zeleznik, A. J., Schuler, H. M., and Reichert, L. E., Jr. (1981). *Endocrinology* **109,** 356.

DISCUSSION

R. O. Greep: It is a little unorthodox to do this, but there are other concepts about selection of follicles, particularly in the rat, and I would hope that one of the people from Neena Schwartz's or Joanne Richards' laboratory would comment on the mechanism in rats.

N. B. Schwartz: If it is not the preceding LH and FSH surge that starts the ovarian follicular clock, what is it that makes the FSH rise perimenstrually?

G. D. Hodgen: I think the FSH rises because the hormonal negative feedback from the corpus luteum is decreased (progesterone with estrogen). Although it's not a new idea it seems appropriate for our data. There are follicles always becoming available for gonadotropic stimulation, as well as others being removed by atresia. At the time when corpus luteum secretions are taken away spontaneously, or artificially as we have done it by surgical oblation, the follicle or follicles which are at some stage where they're available for stimulation by a gonadotropin milieu above the minimum tonic threshold, these follicles will begin to grow or be recruited. That is perhaps what determines the cohort member. To get back to the question, I think the reason the FSH rises is because the corpus luteum undergoes demise. There is a differential effect such that the FSH : LH ratio increases. Follicles continue to progress because there is sufficient gonadotropin present to make them mature.

N. B. Schwartz: Following the preovulatory LH and FSH surges in the rat, there is a prolongation of serum FSH. If we block that prolonged FSH rise with follicular fluid we can prevent follicular recruitment (Hoak and Schwartz, *Proc. Natl. Acad. Sci. U.S.A.,* 1980). In a short cycle like the rat, the animal has to provide a fail-safe mechanism in case it does not become pregnant. Everytime an ovulation occurs there is provided a group of follicles which has been recruited. If there is a pregnancy they simply become atretic; if there is not a pregnancy those follicles become the follicles ovulating 4 days later. I think the primate does not need that kind of instant fail-safe mechanism.

G. D. Hodgen: Yes! Perhaps this is because the follicular phase of the primate is very long. That was indeed what I was trying to treat conceptually. When we looked at that as one of the hypotheses on how the ovarian cycle in the primate might work, the data did not fit the rat model. As you say the short cycle species may need to reprogram the ovary while it is carrying out the current cycle.

W. F. Crowley: I'd like to offer some evidence in support of what you said regarding the circhoral frequency of gonadotropin pulsations in the follicular phase of the cycle. In our study in the normal menstrual cycle of the human female, we have been looking at the pulsatile release of gonadotropins across the cycle in over 40 women using daily bloods to determine the normalcy of the study cycle but 10 minute sampling during the day that we choose to study their pulsatile release.

G. D. Hodgen: Very ambitious!

W. F. Crowley: It turns out to be extremely interesting and corroborates several things that you have shown. First, the pulsatile release of LH that can be demonstrated is directly dependent on how often you sample. When you sample at 20- or 15-minute intervals in the human, you see an interpulse interval that is quite similar to that reported in the literature, i.e., a range of 90–120 minutes between pulses. However if you start to sample the patients more often you can discern a very clear-cut and very well-defined pulse interval of about 60 minutes which fits very nicely with your data. The second thing that is extremely interesting to us is that while there seems to be no dramatic change in the pulsatile frequency across the follicular phase once the pulsatile program of LH release is "up and running" there is a quite striking slowing of LH pulsatile release very soon after progesterone makes its appearance, which is progressive and gradually slows to no LH pulses by the end of the human menstrual cycle on day 27–28. I noticed that when you showed your one luteal phase 24 hour sampling, that you observed no LH pulses in the face of an appropriate luteal phase progesterone level. What do you then think is supporting the corpus luteum in the absence of LH release?

G. D. Hodgen: The first thing is that it is still a controversy in the literature whether or not the corpus luteum requires continuous support. I think that still has to be held as a controversy. My own opinion is that continuous LH support is probably required, although I do not have the data that would be required to prove it. I think that our assays are insensitive enough that we are not detecting some very important LH that is reaching the corpus luteum. Our bioassay, although its sensitivity is virtually as good as that of radioimmunoassay, is not showing levels that are apparently very important and are being perceived by the corpus luteum.

R. Jewelewicz: As *in vitro* fertilization and embryo transfer is becoming a well-accepted clinical method for treatment of infertility, the question of superovulation is of extreme practical importance and I must say that to induce ovulation on an anovulatory woman is different than to superovulate a normal ovulating subject. Most of the IVF programs are using clomiphene citrate or human menopause gonadotropins to superovulate women undergoing treatment. In listening to your talk, and reading your papers, it seems that we are using the wrong preparations. We use the commercially available human menopausal gonadotropin (Pergonal) which has an LH–FSH ratio of approximately 1 to 1. In looking at your data maybe we should switch to two different preparations. First use a preparation which is dominant in FSH for the first 5 or 6 days to induce follicular growth and development and then switch to the available commercial preparation (Pergonal) until we are ready to give hCG. Maybe we'll be able to induce more successfully superovulation this way.

G. D. Hodgen: Very important commentary! We're not really using this FSH preparation as an adjunct to our models for *in vitro* fertilization therapy, but let me say that I think your remarks are very appropriate. One needs a preparation that has LH also. Perhaps a tapering of the FSH : LH ratio going from a blend that is FSH rich to LH rich. I think this is a philosophy fitting improved results that have been seen. I will only take a moment to tell why we used "pure" FSH. You remember at about the middle of this presentation I was talking about between ovary communication. We had used a study design that I called the phantom ovary model. The monkeys had only one ovary. We were greatly surprised to find that when we oblated the corpus luteum there was a transient elevation of FSH, lasting about a week. But despite that transient FSH elevation, 2- to 3-fold normal, the monkeys still ovulated one follicle on time. Initially, we had misinterpreted these data. Two or three years ago I thought extra FSH, by itself, would not cause more than one follicle to reach the stage of periovulation. So, we gave this "pure" FSH days 1 to 12 of the menstrual cycle to test that notion. We were surprised to find there were many large follicles stimulated. That was really our motive for using it. What this tells us is that if you provide too much FSH all the way through the follicular phase, you'll violate the natural process of selection. However, if you allow the FSH to taper down at the end of the first week, you still get selection of the one dominant follicle. Accordingly, we weren't really so much trying to achieve *in vitro* fertilization modeling here as we were to test this other idea. I think Dr. Jewelewicz's remarks are very appropriate, that you need FSH and LH if we're going to get several mature follicles.

B. F. Rice: I have one question that is more of a general biological question than specifically about the growing follicle. If one looks at the ovary in a more general sense, and looks at the old literature and the current literature, one always seems to find a follicle, a corpus luteum, and a structure in which the follicle sits that's often referred to as the interstitial tissue or the interstitial gland or in the primate as the ovarian stroma. Do you think there is a role for this ovarian stroma in your model or do you conceive of it as some have as just a supportive structure with no particular function?

G. D. Hodgen: If I'm embarrassed at anything, it's how little we have addressed those questions; it's not that I don't think they're important. Having so little data puts me in a very weak position to respond with specifics; but I think your question leads me to expand briefly on several important issues. Among the ovarian stroma are many follicles that are still viable, as well as many follicles that have undergone atresia. Certainly some of the viable population is making some estrogen, not very much maybe by any individual; but there is a residual level of estrogen production that supports an environment in which follicles can respond to FSH. I am referring now to that known synergy between estrogen, FSH, and LH. If you don't have estrogen you're not going to get the response to FSH that leads then to LH receptors. That's one of the things I think is going on in stroma that is very important. Another one may be the angiogenic properties of ovaries. The fluidity with which gonadotropins in circulation reach a given follicle may be a dynamic process. They are or are not available to some follicles resting there in the stroma. We know so little about those early events in follicular recruitment that I don't know how to respond any more specifically. I certainly don't think these are minor issues; indeed, they are very major ones.

C. Channing: I enjoyed your elegant summary combining the concept of a local control of follicular maturation along with the pituitary gonadotropic control. I think we have to continually keep those two regulatory processes in mind. I have some data carried out in collaboration with Drs. Georgianna and Howard Jones in their *in vitro* fertilization program that may explain why women given Pergonal (human menopausal gonadotropin) don't have any endogenous LH–FSH surge. We obtained follicle fluid from women given Pergonal, 2 ampoules a day, starting on day 3 of the normal cycle. This dose amounted to 150 units of LH–FSH (1 : 1 ratio). Patients were given this dose until the follicle(s) was around 14–16 mm in diameter by ultrasound, estrogen exceeded 300 pg/ml. Subsequently these women were then given 10,000 IU of hCG and 36 hours later the largest follicle(s) were aspirated and the egg recovered and cultured with SPRM. The follicular fluid from these patients were subjected to steroid and inhibin measurement. Before inhibin assay the fluid were charcoal treated. For a control group which consisted of patients from Dr. Fortuny's laboratory in Barcelona, Spain, normal preovulatory women were sampled for follicular fluid and the steroids and inhibin levels of the fluid measured as detailed previously (*J. Clin. Endocrinol. Metab.* **52**, 1193, 1981). In the early follicular phase normal medium-sized follicles of untreated women contained around 200 units of inhibin/10 μl follicular fluid. In preovulatory follicles inhibin of normal untreated women decreased down to around 80 units/10 μl using the pituitary cell culture as a bioassay ($n = 15$); progesterone is preovulatory follicular fluid elevated to around 3000 ng/ml. In 10 Pergonal-treated women, interestingly, the follicular fluid, estrogen, and progesterone levels were only around 1000 ng/ml but inhibin levels are around 200. Therefore the inhibin levels were significantly higher than levels in the normal preovulatory follicle. Lahav and his colleagues in Israel observed normal women where there is a drop in follicular fluid inhibin when the human follicle becomes preovulatory (*Int. J. Fertil.,* 1982). It is possible that there may have to be a decrease in inhibin to prolong the preovulatory gonadotropin surge. This does not occur in Pergonal-treated women and may be one of the reasons these women don't have their estrogen-induced surge. Pergonal-treated women have normal estrus, and more than one follicle that can serve as a source of excess inhibin. It will be necessary to have a radioimmunoassay for inhibin to measure it in the peripheral serum in order to find out what its levels are in the blood. One other comment, why do follicles start growing in puberty?

G. D. Hodgen: To answer that question I refer to Dr. Knobil's recent work with his colleagues where the implication is very distinct. If one provides GnRH pulses appropriately the pituitary will begin to secrete appropriate amounts of FSH and LH. What we are showing now is that there may also be important qualitative changes in that pituitary gonadotropin secreted as well. There really are three ways to achieve a greater state of ovarian function; that is, three ways to enhance ovarian function. The first one is for the pituitary to secrete more gonadotropin. The second is for the ovary to be more responsive; the receptors there are greater in number or in availability. The third is for the pituitary, rather than necessarily secreting more gonadotropin, to put out molecules that have more biologic potency, either because they stay in circulation longer or because there is a greater affinity and/or efficiency when they are bound to receptors in the ovary. It seems that during puberty all of those things are happening. Maybe Dr. Knobil's data suggest that the brain matures through processes we don't yet understand—an independent chronologic maturation. This is implied in that pulsatile GnRH treatment hastened the ovarian cycle and menstruation. These induced menstrual cycles were ovulatory even in prepubertal monkeys.

C. Channing: It is interesting that the infant primate ovary can make inhibin and that there is increase in its ability to do so around the time of puberty. We have studies with Dr. Hahn carried out at Ortho, in which we examined ovarian vein levels of inhibin as well as ovarian extract levels of inhibin in monkeys before, during, and after puberty. We found low levels prior to puberty and higher levels after puberty. It would appear that the ovary has to be exposed to FSH and LH in order to start making inhibin. To take this concept one step further we have cultured infant human granulosa cells and find that they make a small amount of inhibin, but if you add LH and FSH to the culture medium, you can increase their ability to make inhibin. Therefore at the time of puberty and later inhibin can play a role in controlling FSH secretion in a feedback situation.

G. D. Hodgen: Yes, that would seem consistent with the data from your laboratory, as well as that of Hsueh and Erickson, showing that FSH stimulates granulosa cells to secrete inhibin in culture.

S. L. Cohen: I have two questions and one comment. The first question is if you remove one ovary premenarche does that interfere in any way with the normal life cycles that occur?

G. D. Hodgen: Unfortunately, we have not done that experiment. I am not aware that anyone has. I have thought about that same experiment too, but have not done it. My only bit of knowledge is that when one ovary has been removed from preadolescent girls, there are a few reported cases in which the life course of the ovarian cycle was not affected. In other words, this is not an experiment, but an empirical observation. I don't know that a definitive experiment in which one ovary was removed from premenarchal females and then the course of their ovarian function was studied has been done.

S. L. Cohen: Do all animals who have ovaries have two ovaries?

G. D. Hodgen: No, at least not in the sense that say avians, a chicken for example. Technically of course it has two ovaries. As you well know, one of them is not functional typically. My knowledge on this is so little comparatively; I need Roger Short to answer such a question. Certainly, the chicken would fit a part of your question in that they function very well with one ovary operative.

S. L. Cohen: My second question concerns ovulation. Why is the ovum released? Most people think it is due to increased intrafollicular pressure and/or a weakened membrane. I think Woolever has done some experiments in which he has measured intrafollicular pressure and finds it does not change, so that means it must be some change in the membrane. Do you have any data on this?

G. D. Hodgen: Well, there are a large number of studies, not the least of which would be by Dr. Beers and his colleagues, Dr. Lemaire and his colleagues, and many others. These indicate that a series of enzymatic properties are gained by the very late follicular phase preovulatory follicle. These changes cause an erosion of the tunica, so that it becomes thinner and weakened. Also, we know that the fluid we find in the cul de sac near ovulation has more steroid hormone than that which occurs concurrently in peripheral blood and less than that which occurs in intrafollicular fluid; this all is occurring just before the follicle ruptures. Such data suggest that as the tunica thins, the constituents of the follicular fluid may leak through the thin wall of the follicle and enter the abdominal space and therefore can be found at an intermediate level of steroid—more than peripheral blood, less than that in the follicle itself. With observations of ovulation actually taking place, I think there is not so much pressure in the preovulatory follicle. Moreover, it is the result of enzymatic digestion of the tunica. So finally an opening is created through which the cumulous mass and the egg can ooze out, rather than explode or pop out.

R. Jewelewicz: I have a comment to make. I don't think the statement which was made by Dr. Channing, that patients treated with gonadotropins do not release or cannot release LH and FSH, is correct. Looking at a larger number of patients where ovulation was induced with gonadotropins, we have occasionally seen patients who ovulated spontaneously before they had a chance to receive hCG. It means they released spontaneously an LH surge which triggered ovulation. In a paper published several years ago, Dr. Carl Gemzel reported several pregnancies in patients who ovulated spontaneously before they had a chance to receive hCG, so it can happen. Particularly, it can happen in normal women where we have tried to superovulate. I cannot give incidences yet, but I have seen it several times in the last year.

R. Osathanondh: In the normal monkeys that were treated with 10 mg of Clomid have you had any chance to look at the ratio of biologically active LH over RIA-LH and would it be any different from that in the normal, uninduced cycle.

G. D. Hodgen: We are looking at that right now. The blood drawing protocols have been done. Some of the assays are done, but I would be premature in giving you any characterization of response. Now we are using 5, 10, 15, 20, and 25 mg daily. Remember that the body weight of these monkeys is about 10 times less than women, so you can figure we are going through the appropriate dose–response range that is used clinically. As I said, we don't have the data yet; I agree that is a very important question. Clomiphine stimulates gonadotropin secretion by deceiving the pituitary into thinking that the estrogen-negative feedback has been taken away. Will that result not only in a quantitative increase in gonadotropin secretion or will it also result in a qualitative enhancement of the biological activity of those gonadotropins. Unfortunately, it is a question that is not quite answered.

N. B. Schwartz: Dr. Crowley pointed out that the perimenopausal FSH rise may be less dependent on GnRH. We have evidence using a GnRH antagonist from Wiley Vale and Jean Rivier, that LH levels are lowered in an ovariectomized rat to about 10% of control values but the FSH remains around 40%. We have also shown that when the FSH is down to this point we can lower it further with follicular fluid. We have concluded that there is a secretion of FSH which is not dependent on GnRH but is dependent on ovarian feedback. Perhaps the singular FSH secretion around the time of menstruation may not be GnRH dependent, because there is no LH rise at the same time.

G. D. Hodgen: Good observation, thank you.

J. Vaitukaitis: In some of the studies presented, you observed a marked increase in the LH B to I ratio for a few days prior to the preovulatory surge of LH and for a few days thereafter; you assumed that the increased B/I ratio was secondary to estrogen because you then went ahead and gave estrogen to postmenopausal monkeys and observed the same marked increase in the LH B to I ratio. If it is simply due to estrogen why didn't you see a persistence of an increase in B to I ratio later on the luteal phase when estrogen levels are at least a third to 50% of those during the preovulatory phase of the cycle?

G. D. Hodgen: It might be because it doesn't take very much progesterone to block estrogen-positive feedback. The presence of the function of the corpus luteum, where the progesterone is elevated at the same time as estrogen may keep estrogen from causing the effect on enhanced biological activity of LH that it does in the near absence of progesterone. Now, if we treat castrate monkeys or early follicular phase monkeys with progesterone and then administer an estradiol challenge, of course we don't get a gonadotropin surge in the face of that progesterone. So that might be an explanation. Remember too, that the B : I ratio was elevated in long-term ovariectomized monkeys, even before estrogen administration.

J. Vaitukaitis: That may be a possible explanation but in studies by other investigators estrogen-induced posttranslational modifications of gonadotropin resulted in greater biological activity. Even though the amount of gonadotropin is decreased in the luteal phase, you should still observe a greater B : I ratio of LH levels even though LH levels are less.

G. D. Hodgen: My failure to answer that is due to the ignorance of our present status. Literally, all we know about explaining this change in B : I ratio is what I've shown you. We don't really know why it happens. We also don't know what an array of comparisons of various RIAs versus the bioassay would show. What if we had 10 different radioimmunoassays and compared each one of them to the bioassay data curves. My guess is the disparity would range from almost none to the very large ones that I have shown here. Such ignorance probably keeps me from really understanding the issue well enough to respond to your question with more specifics.

R. O. Greep: When you flushed the granulosa cells out of the one follicle, and I presume you flushed them out rather thoroughly, this was followed very soon by a rise in estrogen. What was the source of that estrogen?

G. D. Hodgen: Well, I think that for particular follicles we studied here, Dr. Greep, we were trying to take out as few granulosa cells as we could, because this was a modeling experiment for *in vitro* fertilization. However, I can still respond in part to your question. Here, although we were trying to take out as few as we could while we were getting the egg, another study was done by Drs. Marat and Huang with me and presented at the Endocrine Society this year. This series of experiments relates directly to your question. Our objective was to get out as many of the granulosa cells as we could. In that case we still had about 30% of the estrogen production maintained even though we had taken out more than 90% of the granulosa cells. In interpreting the results one could say the residual cells are responsible or alternatively estradiol was coming from theca. I think the data of Dr. Channing and other people bear on that point. Most of the estrogen leaving the dominant follicle, in my opinion, does come from granulosa cells, but certainly not all of it. There's no question that theca also secretes some estrogen independently of the granulosa compartment.

Measurement of Local Glucose Utilization and Its Use in Localization of Functional Activity in the Central Nervous System of Animals and Man

LOUIS SOKOLOFF

Laboratory of Cerebral Metabolism, National Institute of Mental Health, U.S. Public Health Service, Department of Health and Human Services, Bethesda, Maryland

I. Introduction

The brain is a complex, heterogeneous organ composed of many anatomical and functional components with markedly different levels of functional activity that vary independently with time and function. Other tissues are generally far more homogeneous with most of their cells functioning similarly and synchronously in response to a common stimulus or regulatory influence. The central nervous system, however, consists of innumerable subunits, each integrated into its own set of functional pathways and networks and subserving only one or a few of the many activities in which the nervous system participates. Understanding how the nervous system functions requires knowledge not only of the mechanisms of excitation and inhibition but even more so of their precise localization in the nervous system and the relationships of neural subunits to specific functions.

Historically, studies of the central nervous system have concentrated heavily on localization of function and mapping of pathways related to specific functions. These have been carried out neuroanatomically and histologically with staining and degeneration techniques, behaviorally with ablation and stimulation techniques, electrophysiologically with electrical recording and evoked electrical responses, and histochemically with a variety of techniques, including fluorescent and immunofluorescent methods and autoradiography of orthograde and retrograde axoplasmic flow. Many of these conventional methods suffer from a sampling problem. They generally permit examination of only one potential pathway at a time, and only positive results are interpretable. Furthermore, the demonstration of a pathway reveals only a potential for function; it does not reveal its significance in normal function.

Tissues that do physical and/or chemical work, such as heart, kidney, and skeletal muscle, exhibit a close relationship between energy metabolism and the level of functional activity. The existence of a similar relationship in the tissues of the central nervous system has been more difficult to prove, partly because of uncertainty about the nature of the work associated with nervous functional activity, but mainly because of the difficulty in assessing the levels of functional and metabolic activities in the same functional component of the brain at the same time. Much of our present knowledge of cerebral energy metabolism *in vivo* has been obtained by means of the nitrous oxide technique of Kety and Schmidt (1948a) and its modifications (Scheinberg and Stead, 1949; Lassen and Munck, 1955; Eklöf *et al.*, 1973; Gjedde *et al.*, 1975), which measure the average rates of energy metabolism in the brain as a whole. These methods have demonstrated changes in cerebral metabolic rate in association with gross or diffuse alterations of cerebral function and/or structure, as, for example, those that occur during postnatal development, aging, senility, anesthesia, disorders of consciousness, and convulsive states (Kety, 1950, 1957; Lassen, 1959; Sokoloff, 1960, 1976). They have not detected changes in cerebral metabolic rate in a number of conditions with, perhaps, more subtle alterations in cerebral functional activity, for example, deep slow-wave sleep, performance of mental arithmetic, sedation and tranquilization, schizophrenia, and LSD-induced psychosis (Kety, 1950; Lassen, 1959; Sokoloff, 1969). It is possible that there are no changes in cerebral energy metabolism in these conditions. The apparent lack of change could also be explained by either a redistribution of local levels of functional and metabolic activity without significant change in the average of the brain as a whole or the restriction of altered metabolic activity to regions too small to be detected in measurements of the brain as a whole. What has clearly been needed is a method that measures the rates of energy metabolism in specific discrete regions of the brain in normal and altered states of functional activity.

In pursuit of this goal Kety and his associates (Landau *et al.*, 1955; Freygang and Sokoloff, 1958; Kety, 1960; Reivich *et al.*, 1969) developed a quantitative autoradiographic technique to measure the local tissue concentrations of chemically inert, diffusible, radioactive tracers which they used to determine the rates of blood flow simultaneously in all the structural components visible and identifiable in autoradiographs of serial sections of the brain. The application of this quantitative autoradiographic technique to the determination of local cerebral metabolic rate has proved to be more difficult because of the inherently greater complexity of the problem and the unsuitability of the labeled species of the normal substrates of cerebral energy metabolism, oxygen and glucose. The radioisotopes of oxygen have too short a physical half-life. Both oxygen and glucose are too rapidly converted to carbon dioxide, and CO_2 is too rapidly cleared from the cerebral tissues. Sacks (1957), for example, has found in man significant losses of $^{14}CO_2$ from the brain within 2 minutes after the onset of an intravenous infusion of $[^{14}C]$glucose, labeled either uniformly, in the C-1, C-2, or C-6 positions. These limitations of $[^{14}C]$glucose have been avoided by the use of 2-deoxy-D-$[^{14}C]$glucose, a labeled analog of glucose with special properties that make it particularly appropriate for this application (Sokoloff et al., 1977). It is metabolized through part of the pathway of glucose metabolism at a definable rate relative to that of glucose. Unlike glucose, however, its product, $[^{14}C]$deoxyglucose 6-phosphate, is essentially trapped in the tissues, allowing the application of the quantitative autoradiographic technique. The use of radioactive 2-deoxyglucose to trace glucose utilization and the autoradiographic technique to achieve regional localization have recently led to the development of a method that measures the rates of glucose utilization simultaneously in all components of the central nervous system in the normal conscious state and during experimental physiological, pharmacological, and pathological conditions (Sokoloff et al., 1977). Because the procedure is so designed that the concentrations of radioactivity in the tissues during autoradiography are more or less proportional to the rates of glucose utilization, the autoradiographs provide pictorial representations of the relative rates of glucose utilization in all the cerebral structures visualized. Numerous studies with this method have established that there is a close relationship between functional activity and energy metabolism in the central nervous system (Sokoloff, 1977; Plum et al., 1976), and the method has become a potent new tool for mapping functional neural pathways on the basis of evoked metabolic responses.

II. Theory

The method is derived from a model based on the biochemical properties of 2-deoxyglucose (Fig. 1A) (Sokoloff et al., 1977). 2-Deoxyglucose (DG) is transported bi-directionally between blood and brain by the same carrier that transports glucose across the blood–brain barrier (Bidder, 1968; Bachelard, 1971; Oldendorf, 1971). In the cerebral tissues it is phosphorylated by hexokinase to 2-deoxyglucose 6-phosphate (DG-6-P) (Sols and Crane, 1954). Deoxyglucose and glucose are, therefore, competitive substrates for both blood–brain transport and hexokinase-catalyzed phosphorylation. Unlike glucose 6-phosphate (G-6-P), however, which is metabolized further eventually to CO_2 and water and to a lesser degree via the hexosemonophosphate shunt, deoxyglucose 6-phosphate cannot be converted to fructose 6-phosphate and is not a substrate for glucose 6-

A

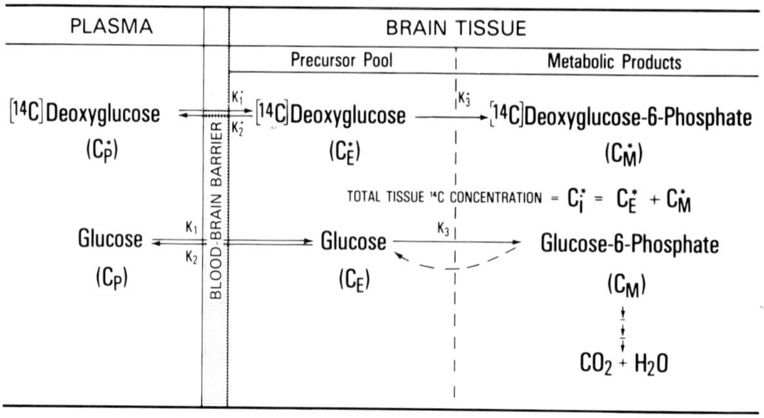

PLASMA	BRAIN TISSUE	
	Precursor Pool	Metabolic Products

$[^{14}C]$ Deoxyglucose
(C_P^*)

$[^{14}C]$ Deoxyglucose
(C_E^*)

$[^{14}C]$ Deoxyglucose-6-Phosphate
(C_M^*)

K_1^*
K_2^*

K_3^*

TOTAL TISSUE ^{14}C CONCENTRATION $= C_i^* = C_E^* + C_M^*$

Glucose
(C_P)

Glucose
(C_E)

Glucose-6-Phosphate
(C_M)

K_1
K_2

K_3

BLOOD-BRAIN BARRIER

$CO_2 + H_2O$

B

Functional Anatomy of the Operational Equation of the $[^{14}C]$ Deoxyglucose Method

General Equation for Measurement of Reaction Rates with Tracers:

$$\text{Rate of Reaction} = \frac{\text{Labeled Product Formed in Interval of Time, O to T}}{\begin{bmatrix} \text{Isotope Effect} \\ \text{Correction Factor} \end{bmatrix} \begin{bmatrix} \text{Integrated Specific Activity} \\ \text{of Precursor} \end{bmatrix}}$$

Operational Equation of $[^{14}C]$ Deoxyglucose Method:

Labeled Product Formed in Interval of Time, O to T

Total ^{14}C in Tissue at Time, T

^{14}C in Precursor Remaining in Tissue at Time, T

$$R_i = \frac{C_i^*(T) - k_i^* e^{-(k_2^*+k_3^*)T} \int_0^T C_p^* e^{(k_2^*+k_3^*)t} dt}{\left[\frac{\lambda \cdot V_m^* \cdot K_m}{\Phi \cdot V_m \cdot K_m^*}\right]\left[\int_0^T \left(\frac{C_p^*}{C_p}\right) dt - e^{-(k_2^*+k_3^*)T} \int_0^T \left(\frac{C_p^*}{C_p}\right) e^{(k_2^*+k_3^*)t} dt\right]}$$

"Isotope Effect" Correction Factor

Integrated Plasma Specific Activity

Correction for Lag in Tissue Equilibration with Plasma

Integrated Precursor Specific Activity in Tissue

phosphate dehydrogenase (Sols and Crane, 1954). There is very little glucose 6-phosphatase activity in brain (Hers, 1957) and even less deoxyglucose 6-phosphatase activity (Sokoloff *et al.*, 1977). Deoxyglucose 6-phosphate, once formed, is, therefore, essentially trapped in the cerebral tissues, at least long enough for the duration of the measurement.

If the interval of time is kept short enough, for example, less than 1 hour, to allow the assumption of negligible loss of [^{14}C]DG-6-P from the tissues, then the quantity of [^{14}C]DG-6-P accumulated in any cerebral tissue at any given time following the introduction of [^{14}C]DG into the circulation is equal to the integral of the rate of [^{14}C]DG phosphorylation by hexokinase in that tissue during that interval of time. This integral is in turn related to the amount of glucose that has been phosphorylated over the same interval, depending on the time courses of the relative concentrations of [^{14}C]DG and glucose in the precursor pools and the Michaelis–Menten kinetic constants for hexokinase with respect to both [^{14}C]DG and glucose. With cerebral glucose consumption in a steady state, the amount of glucose phosphorylated during the interval of time equals the steady-state flux of glucose through the hexokinase-catalyzed step times the duration of the interval, and the net rate of flux of glucose through this step equals the rate of glucose utilization.

These relationships can be mathematically defined and an operational equation derived if the following assumptions are made: (1) a steady state for glucose (i.e., constant plasma glucose concentration and constant rate of glucose consumption) throughout the period of the procedure; (2) homogeneous tissue compartment within which the concentrations of

---

FIG. 1. (A) Diagrammatic representation of the theoretical model. C_i^* represents the total ^{14}C concentration in a single homogeneous tissue of the brain. C_P^* and C_P represent the concentrations of [^{14}C]deoxyglucose and glucose in the arterial plasma, respectively; C_E^* and C_E represent their respective concentrations in the tissue pools that serve as substrates for hexokinase. C_M^* represents the concentration of [^{14}C]deoxyglucose 6-phosphate in the tissue. The constants k_1^*, k_2^*, and k_3^* represent the rate constants for carrier-mediated transport of [^{14}C]deoxyglucose from plasma to tissue, for carrier-mediated transport back from tissue to plasma, and for phosphorylation by hexokinase, respectively. The constants k_1, k_2, and k_3 are the equivalent rate constants for glucose. [^{14}C]Deoxyglucose and glucose share and compete for the carrier that transports both between plasma and tissue and for hexokinase which phosphorylates them to their respective hexose 6-phosphates. The dashed arrow represents the possibility of glucose 6-phosphate hydrolysis by glucose 6-phosphatase activity, if any. (From Sokoloff *et al.*, 1977; Sokoloff, 1978.) (B) Operational equation of radioactive deoxyglucose method and its functional anatomy. T represents the time at the termination of the experimental period; λ equals the ratio of the distribution space of deoxyglucose in the tissue to that of glucose; Φ equals the fraction of glucose which, once phosphorylated, continues down the glycolytic pathway; and K_m^* and V_m^* and K_m and V_m represent the familiar Michaelis–Menten kinetic constants of hexokinase for deoxyglucose and glucose, respectively. The other symbols are the same as those defined in A. (From Sokoloff, 1978.)

[^{14}C]DG and glucose are uniform and exchange directly with the plasma; and (3) tracer concentrations of [^{14}C]DG (i.e., molecular concentrations of free [^{14}C]DG essentially equal to zero). The operational equation which defines R_i, the rate of glucose consumption per unit mass of tissue, i, in terms of measurable variables is presented in Fig. 1B.

The rate constants are determined in a separate group of animals by a nonlinear, iterative process which provides the least-squares best-fit of an equation which defines the time course of total tissue ^{14}C concentration in terms of the time, the history of the plasma concentration, and the rate constants to the experimentally determined time courses of tissue and plasma concentrations of ^{14}C (Sokoloff et al., 1977). The rate constants have thus far been completely determined only in normal conscious albino rats (Table I). Partial analyses indicate that the values are quite similar in the conscious monkey (Kennedy et al., 1978).

The λ, Φ, and the enzyme kinetic constants are grouped together to constitute a single, lumped constant (Fig. 1B). It can be shown mathematically that this lumped constant is equal to the asymptotic value of the product of the ratio of the cerebral extraction ratios of [^{14}C]DG and glucose and the ratio of the arterial blood to plasma specific activities when the arterial plasma [^{14}C]DG concentration is maintained constant (Sokoloff et al., 1977). The lumped constant is also determined in a separate group of animals from arterial and cerebral venous blood samples drawn during a programmed intravenous infusion which produces and maintains a constant arterial plasma [^{14}C]DG concentration (Sokoloff et al., 1977). An example of such a determination in a conscious monkey is illustrated in Fig. 2. Thus far the lumped constant has been determined only in the albino rat, monkey, cat, and dog (Table II). The lumped constant appears to be characteristic of the species and does not appear to change significantly in a wide range of physiological conditions (Table II) (Sokoloff et al., 1977).

Despite its complex appearance, the operational equation is really nothing more than a general statement of the standard relationship by which rates of enzyme-catalyzed reactions are determined from measurements made with radioactive tracers (Fig. 1B). The numerator of the equation represents the amount of radioactive product formed in a given interval of time; it is equal to C_i^*, the combined concentrations of [^{14}C]DG and [^{14}C]DG-6-P in the tissue at time, T, measured by the quantitative autoradiographic technique, less a term that represents the free unmetabolized [^{14}C]DG still remaining in the tissue. The denominator represents the integrated specific activity of the precursor pool times a factor, the lumped constant, which is equivalent to a correction factor for an isotope effect. The term with the exponential factor in the denominator takes into

TABLE I

Values of Rate Constants in the Normal Conscious Albino Rat[a]

Structure	Rate constants (min^{-1})			Distribution volume (ml/g)	Half-life of precursor pool (min)
	k_1^*	k_2^*	k_3^*	$k_1^*/(k_2^* + k_3^*)$	$\mathrm{Log}_e 2/(k_2^* + k_3^*)$
Gray matter					
Visual cortex	0.189 ± 0.048	0.279 ± 0.176	0.063 ± 0.040	0.553	2.03
Auditory cortex	0.226 ± 0.068	0.241 ± 0.198	0.067 ± 0.057	0.734	2.25
Parietal cortex	0.194 ± 0.051	0.257 ± 0.175	0.062 ± 0.045	0.608	2.17
Sensory-motor cortex	0.193 ± 0.037	0.208 ± 0.112	0.049 ± 0.035	0.751	2.70
Thalamus	0.188 ± 0.045	0.218 ± 0.144	0.053 ± 0.043	0.694	2.56
Medial geniculate body	0.219 ± 0.055	0.259 ± 0.164	0.055 ± 0.040	0.697	2.21
Lateral geniculate body	0.172 ± 0.038	0.220 ± 0.134	0.055 ± 0.040	0.625	2.52
Hypothalamus	0.158 ± 0.032	0.226 ± 0.119	0.043 ± 0.032	0.587	2.58
Hippocampus	0.169 ± 0.043	0.260 ± 0.166	0.056 ± 0.040	0.535	2.19
Amygdala	0.149 ± 0.028	0.235 ± 0.109	0.032 ± 0.026	0.558	2.60
Caudate-putamen	0.176 ± 0.041	0.200 ± 0.140	0.061 ± 0.050	0.674	2.66
Superior colliculus	0.198 ± 0.054	0.240 ± 0.166	0.046 ± 0.042	0.692	2.42
Pontine gray matter	0.170 ± 0.040	0.246 ± 0.142	0.037 ± 0.033	0.601	2.45
Cerebellar cortex	0.225 ± 0.066	0.392 ± 0.229	0.059 ± 0.031	0.499	1.54
Cerebellar nucleus	0.207 ± 0.042	0.194 ± 0.111	0.038 ± 0.035	0.892	2.99
Mean ± SEM	0.189 ± 0.012	0.245 ± 0.040	0.052 ± 0.010	0.647 ± 0.073	2.39 ± 0.40
White matter					
Corpus callosum	0.085 ± 0.015	0.135 ± 0.075	0.019 ± 0.033	0.552	4.50
Genu of corpus callosum	0.076 ± 0.013	0.131 ± 0.075	0.019 ± 0.034	0.507	4.62
Internal capsule	0.077 ± 0.015	0.134 ± 0.085	0.023 ± 0.039	0.490	4.41
Mean ± SEM	0.079 ± 0.008	0.133 ± 0.046	0.020 ± 0.020	0.516 ± 0.171	4.51 ± 0.90

[a] From Sokoloff et al. (1977).

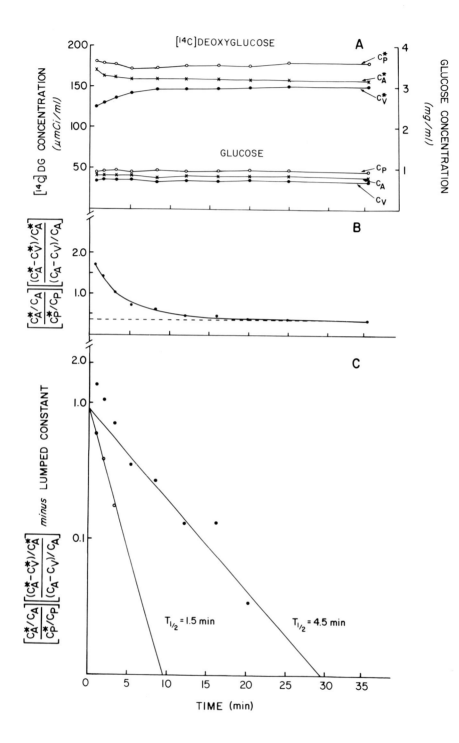

the account the lag in the equilibration of the tissue precursor pool with the plasma.

III. Experimental Procedure for Measurement of Local Cerebral Glucose Utilization

A. THEORETICAL CONSIDERATIONS IN THE DESIGN OF THE PROCEDURE

The operational equation of the method specifies the variables to be measured in order to determine R_i, the local rate of glucose consumption in the brain. The following variables are measured in each experiment: (1) the entire history of the arterial plasma [^{14}C]deoxyglucose concentration, C_P^*, from zero time to the time of killing, T; (2) the steady-state arterial plasma glucose level, C_P, over the same interval; and (3) the local concentration of ^{14}C in the tissue at the time of killing, $C_i^*(T)$. The rate constants, k_1^*, k_2^*, and k_3^*, and the lumped constant, $\lambda V_m^* K_m / \Phi V_m K_m^*$, are not measured in each experiment; the values for these constants that are used are those determined separately in other groups of animals as described above and presented in Tables I and II.

The operational equation is generally applicable with all types of arterial plasma [^{14}C]DG concentration curves. Its configuration, however, suggests that a declining curve approaching zero by the time of killing is the choice to minimize certain potential errors. The quantitative autoradiographic technique measures only total ^{14}C concentration in the tissue

---

FIG. 2.   Data obtained and their use in determination of the lumped constant and the combination of rate constants, $(k_2^* + k_3^*)$, in a representative experiment. (A) Time courses of arterial blood and plasma concentrations of [^{14}C]DG and glucose and cerebral venous blood concentrations of [^{14}C]DG and glucose during programmed intravenous infusion of [^{14}C]DG. (B) Arithemetic plot of the function derived from the variables in A and combined as indicated in the formula on the ordinate against time. This function declines exponentially, with a rate constant equal to $(k_2^* + k_3^*)$, until it reaches an asymptotic value equal to the lumped constant, 0.35, in this experiment (dashed line). (C) Semilogarithmic plot of the curve in B less the lumped constant, i.e., its asymptotic value. Solid circles represent actual values. This curve is analyzed into two components by a standard curve-peeling technique to yield the two straight lines representing the separate components. Open circles are points for the fast component, obtained by subtracting the values for the slow component from the solid circles. The rate constants for these two components represent the values of $(k_2^* + k_3^*)$ for two compartments; the fast and slow compartments are assumed to represent gray and white matter, respectively. In this experiment the values for $(k_2^* + k_3^*)$ were found to equal 0.462 (half-time = 1.5 minutes) and 0.154 (half-time = 4.5 minutes) in gray and white matter, respectively. (From Kennedy *et al.*, 1978.)

TABLE II

Values of the Lumped Constant in the Albino Rat, Rhesus Monkey, Cat, and Dog[a]

Animal	Number of animals	Mean ± SD	SEM
Albino rat			
Conscious	15	0.464 ± 0.099[b]	±0.026
Anesthetized	9	0.512 ± 0.118[b]	±0.039
Conscious (5% CO_2)	2	0.463 ± 0.122[b]	±0.086
Combined	26	0.481 ± 0.119	±0.023
Rhesus monkey			
Conscious	7	0.344 ± 0.095	±0.036
Cat			
Anesthetized	6	0.411 ± 0.013	±0.005
Dog (beagle puppy)			
Conscious	7	0.558 ± 0.082	±0.031

[a] The values were obtained as follows: rat, Sokoloff *et al.* (1977); monkey, Kennedy *et al.* (1978); cat, M. Miyaoka, J. Magnes, C. Kennedy, M. Shinohara, and L. Sokoloff (unpublished data); dog, Duffy *et al.* (1982). (From Sokoloff, 1979.)

[b] No statistically significant difference between normal conscious and anesthetized rats $(0.3 < p < 0.4)$ and conscious rats breathing 5% CO_2 $(p > 0.9)$.

and does not distinguish between [^{14}C]DG-6-P and [^{14}C]DG. It is, however, [^{14}C]DG-6-P concentration that must be known to determine glucose consumption. [^{14}C]DG-6-P concentration is calculated in the numerator of the operational equation, which equals the total tissue ^{14}C content, $C_i^*(T)$, minus the [^{14}C]DG concentration present in the tissue, estimated by the term containing the exponential factor and rate constants. In the denominator of the operational equation there is also a term containing an exponential factor and rate constants. Both these terms have the useful property of approaching zero with increasing time if C_P^* is also allowed to approach zero. The rate constants, k_1^*, k_2^*, and k_3^*, are not measured in the same animals in which local glucose consumption is being measured. It is conceivable that the rate constants in Table I are not equally applicable in all physiological, pharmacological, and pathological states. One possible solution is to determine the rate constants for each condition to be studied. An alternative solution, and the one chosen, is to administer the [^{14}C]DG as a single intravenous pulse at zero time and to allow sufficient time for the clearance of [^{14}C]DG from the plasma and the terms containing the rate constants to fall to levels too low to influence the final result. To wait until these terms reach zero is impractical because of the long time required and the risk of effects of the small but finite rate of loss of [^{14}C]DG-6-P from the tissues. A reasonable time interval is 45 minutes; by this time the plasma level has fallen to very low levels, and, on the basis of the values of $(k_2^* + k_3^*)$ in Table I, the exponential factors have declined through at least 10 half-lives.

B. EXPERIMENTAL PROTOCOL

The animals are prepared for the experiment by the insertion of polyethylene catheters in an artery and vein. Any convenient artery or vein can be used. In the rat the femoral or the tail arteries and veins have been found satisfactory. In the monkey and cat the femoral vessels are probably most convenient. The catheters are inserted under anesthesia, and anesthetic agents without long-lasting aftereffects should be used. Light halothane anesthesia with or without supplementation with nitrous oxide has been found to be quite satisfactory. At least 2 hours are allowed for recovery from the surgery and anesthesia before initiation of the experiment.

The design of the experimental procedure for the measurement of local cerebral glucose utilization was based on the theoretical considerations discussed above. At zero time a pulse of 125 μCi (no more than 2.5 μmoles) of [^{14}C]deoxyglucose per kg of body weight is administered to the animal via the venous catheter. Arterial sampling is initiated with the onset of the pulse, and timed 50–100 μl samples of arterial blood are collected consecutively as rapidly as possible during the early period so as not to miss the peak of the arterial curve. Arterial sampling is continued at less frequent intervals later in the experimental period but at sufficient frequency to define fully the arterial curve. The arterial blood samples are immediately centrifuged to separate the plasma, which is stored on ice until assayed for [^{14}C]DG by liquid scintillation counting and glucose concentrations by standard enzymatic methods. At approximately 45 minutes the animal is decapitated, the brain is removed and frozen in Freon XII or isopentane maintained between -50 and -75°C with liquid nitrogen. When fully frozen, the brain is stored at -70°C until sectioned and autoradiographed. The experimental period may be limited to 30 minutes. This is theoretically permissible and may sometimes be necessary for reasons of experimental expediency, but greater errors due to possible inaccuracies in the rate constants may result.

C. AUTORADIOGRAPHIC MEASUREMENT OF TISSUE ^{14}C CONCENTRATION

The ^{14}C concentrations in localized regions of the brain are measured by a modification of the quantitative autoradiographic technique previously described (Reivich et al., 1969). The frozen brain is coated with chilled embedding medium (Lipshaw Manufacturing Co., Detroit MI) and fixed to object holders appropriate to the microtome to be used.

Brain sections, precisely 20 μm in thickness, are prepared in a cryostat maintained at -21 to $-22°C$. The brain sections are picked up on glass cover slips, dried on a hot plate at 60°C for at least 5 minutes, and placed sequentially in an X-ray cassette. A set of [^{14}C]methyl methacrylate standards (Amersham Corp., Arlington Heights, IL), which include a blank and a series of progressively increasing ^{14}C concentrations, are also placed in the cassette. These standards must previously have been calibrated for their autoradiographic equivalence to the ^{14}C concentrations in brain sections, 20 μm in thickness, prepared as described above. The method of calibration has been previously described (Reivich et al., 1969).

Autoradiographs are prepared from these sections directly in the X-ray cassette with Kodak single-coated, blue-sensitive Medical X-ray Film, Type SB-5 (Eastman Kodak Co., Rochester, NY). The exposure time is generally 5–6 days with the doses used as described above, and the exposed films are developed according to the instructions supplied with the film. The SB-5 X-ray film is rapid but coarse grained. For finer grained autoradiographs and, therefore, better defined images with higher resolution, it is possible to use mammographic films, such as DuPont LoDose or Kodak MR-1 films, or fine grain panchromatic film, such as Kodak Plus-X, but the exposure times are two to three times longer. The autoradiographs provide a pictorial representation of the relative ^{14}C concentrations in the various cerebral structures and the plastic standards. A calibration curve of the relationship between optical density and tissue ^{14}C concentration for each film is obtained by densitometric measurements of the portions of the film representing the various standards. The local tissue concentrations are then determined from the calibration curve and the optical densities of the film in the regions representing the cerebral structures of interest. Local cerebral glucose utilization is calculated from the local tissue concentrations of ^{14}C and the plasma [^{14}C]DG and glucose concentrations according to the operational equation (Fig. 1).

D. COMPUTERIZED COLOR-CODED IMAGE PROCESSING

The autoradiographs provide pictorial representations of only the relative concentrations of the isotope in the various tissues. Because of the use of a pulse followed by a long period before killing, the isotope is contained mainly in deoxyglucose 6-phosphate, which reflects the rate of glucose metabolism. The autoradiographs are, therefore, pictorial representations also of the relative but not the actual rates of glucose utilization in all the structures of the nervous system. Furthermore, the resolution of differences in relative rates is limited by the ability of the human eye to recognize differences in shades of gray. Manual densitometric analysis permits the computation of actual rates of glucose utilization with a fair degree of resolution, but it generates enormous tables of data which fail to convey the tremendous heterogeneity of metabolic rates, even within anatomic structures, or the full information contained within the autoradiographs. Goochee *et al.* (1980) have developed a computerized image-processing system to analyze and transform the autoradiographs into color-coded maps of the distribution of the actual rates of glucose utilization exactly where they are located throughout the central nervous system. The autoradiographs are scanned automatically by a computer-controlled scanning microdensitometer. The optical density of each spot in the autoradiograph, from 25 to 100 μm as selected, is stored in a computer, converted to ^{14}C concentration on the basis of the optical densities of the calibrated ^{14}C plastic standards, and then converted to local rates of glucose utilization by solution of the operational equation of the method. Colors are assigned to narrow ranges of the rates of glucose utilization, and the autoradiographs are then displayed in a color TV monitor in color along with a calibrated color scale for identifying the rate of glucose utilization in each spot of the autoradiograph from its color. These color maps add a third dimension, the rate of glucose utilization on a color scale, to the spatial dimensions already present on the autoradiographs.

IV. Rates of Local Cerebral Glucose Utilization in the Normal Conscious State

Thus far quantitative measurements of local cerebral glucose utilization have been reported only for the albino rat (Sokoloff *et al.*, 1977) and monkey (Kennedy *et al.*, 1978). These values are presented in Table III. The rates of local cerebral glucose utilization in the normal conscious rat vary widely throughout the brain. The values in white structures tend to group together and are always considerably below those of gray structures. The average value in gray matter is approximately three times that of white matter, but the individual values vary from approximately 50 to 200 μmoles of glucose/100 g/minute. The highest values are in the structures involved in auditory functions with the inferior colliculus clearly the most metabolically active structure in the brain.

The rates of local cerebral glucose utilization in the conscious monkey exhibit similar heterogeneity, but they are generally one-third to one-half the values in corresponding structures of the rat brain (Table III). The differences in rates in the rat and monkey brain are consistent with the different cellular packing densities in the brains of these two species.

TABLE III

Representative Values for Local Cerebral Glucose Utilization in the Normal Conscious Albino Rat and Monkey[a] (μmoles/100 g/minute)

Structure	Albino rat[b] (10) (μmoles/100 g/ minute)	Monkey[c] (7) (μmoles/100 g/ minute)
Gray matter		
Visual cortex	107 ± 6	59 ± 2
Auditory cortex	162 ± 5	79 ± 4
Parietal cortex	112 ± 5	47 ± 4
Sensory-motor cortex	120 ± 5	44 ± 3
Thalamus: lateral nucleus	116 ± 5	54 ± 2
Thalamus: ventral nucleus	109 ± 5	43 ± 2
Medial geniculate body	131 ± 5	65 ± 3
Lateral geniculate body	96 ± 5	39 ± 1
Hypothalamus	54 ± 2	25 ± 1
Mamillary body	121 ± 5	57 ± 3
Hippocampus	79 ± 3	39 ± 2
Amygdala	52 ± 2	25 ± 2
Caudate-putamen	110 ± 4	52 ± 3
Nucleus accumbens	82 ± 3	36 ± 2
Globus-pallidus	58 ± 2	26 ± 2
Substantia nigra	58 ± 3	29 ± 2
Vestibular nucleus	128 ± 5	66 ± 3
Cochlear nucleus	113 ± 7	51 ± 3
Superior olivary nucleus	133 ± 7	63 ± 4
Inferior colliculus	197 ± 10	103 ± 6
Superior colliculus	95 ± 5	55 ± 4
Pontine gray matter	62 ± 3	28 ± 1
Cerebellar cortex	57 ± 2	31 ± 2
Cerebellar nuclei	100 ± 4	45 ± 2
White matter		
Corpus callosum	40 ± 2	11 ± 1
Internal capsule	33 ± 2	13 ± 1
Cerebellar white matter	37 ± 2	12 ± 1

[a] The values are the means ± standard errors from measurements made in the number of animals indicated in parentheses.

[b] From Sokoloff *et al.* (1977).

[c] From Kennedy *et al.* (1978).

V. Effects of General Anesthesia

General anesthesia produced by thiopental reduces the rates of glucose utilization in all structures of the rat brain (Table IV) (Sokoloff *et al.*, 1977). The effects are not uniform, however. The greatest reductions occur in the gray structures, particularly those of the primary sensory

TABLE IV

Effects of Thiopental Anesthesia on Local Cerebral Glucose Utilization in the Rat[a,b]

Structure	Local cerebral glucose utilization (μmoles/100 g/minute)		
	Control (6)[c]	Anesthetized (8)[c]	% Effect
Gray matter			
Visual cortex	111 ± 5	64 ± 3	−42
Auditory cortex	157 ± 5	81 ± 3	−48
Parietal cortex	107 ± 3	65 ± 2	−39
Sensory-motor cortex	118 ± 3	67 ± 2	−43
Lateral geniculate body	92 ± 2	53 ± 3	−42
Medial geniculate body	126 ± 6	63 ± 3	−50
Thalamus: lateral nucleus	108 ± 3	58 ± 2	−46
Thalamus: ventral nucleus	98 ± 3	55 ± 1	−44
Hypothalamus	63 ± 3	43 ± 2	−32
Caudate-putamen	111 ± 4	72 ± 3	−35
Hippocampus: Ammon's horn	79 ± 1	56 ± 1	−29
Amygdala	56 ± 4	41 ± 2	−27
Cochlear nucleus	124 ± 7	79 ± 5	−36
Lateral lemniscus	114 ± 7	75 ± 4	−34
Inferior colliculus	198 ± 7	131 ± 8	−34
Superior olivary nucleus	141 ± 5	104 ± 7	−26
Superior colliculus	99 ± 3	59 ± 3	−40
Vestibular nucleus	133 ± 4	81 ± 4	−39
Pontine gray matter	69 ± 3	46 ± 3	−33
Cerebellar cortex	66 ± 2	44 ± 2	−33
Cerebellar nucleus	106 ± 4	75 ± 4	−29
White matter			
Corpus callosum	42 ± 2	30 ± 2	−29
Genu of corpus callosum	35 ± 5	30 ± 2	−14
Internal capsule	35 ± 2	29 ± 2	−17
Cerebellar white matter	38 ± 2	29 ± 2	−24

[a] From Sokoloff *et al.* (1977).

[b] Determined at 30 minutes following pulse of [^{14}C]deoxyglucose.

[c] The values are the means ± standard errors obtained in the number of animals indicated in parentheses. All the differences are statistically significant at the $p < 0.05$ level.

pathways. The effects in white matter, though definitely present, are relatively small compared to those of gray matter. These results are in agreement with those of previous studies in which anesthesia has been found to decrease the cerebral metabolic rate of the brain as a whole (Kety, 1950; Lassen, 1959; Sokoloff, 1976).

VI. Relation between Local Functional Activity and Energy Metabolism

The results of a variety of applications of the method demonstrate a clear relationship between local cerebral functional activity and glucose consumption. The most striking demonstrations of the close coupling between function and energy metabolism are seen with experimentally induced local alterations in functional activity that are restricted to a few specific areas in the brain. The effects on local glucose consumption are then so pronounced that they are not only observed in the quantitative results but can be visualized directly on the autoradiographs which are really pictorial representations of the relative rates of glucose utilization in the various structural components of the brain.

A. EFFECTS OF INCREASED FUNCTIONAL ACTIVITY

1. Effects of Sciatic Nerve Stimulation

Electrical stimulation of one sciatic nerve in the rat under barbiturate anesthesia causes pronounced increases in glucose consumption (i.e., increased optical density in the autoradiographs) in the ipsilateral dorsal horn of the lumbar spinal cord (Kennedy et al., 1975).

2. Effects of Experimental Focal Seizures

The local injection of penicillin into the hand–face area of the motor cortex of the Rhesus monkey has been shown to induce electrical discharges in the adjacent cortex and to result in recurrent focal seizures involving the face, arm, and hand on the contralateral side (Caveness, 1969). Such seizure activity causes selective increases in glucose consumption in areas of motor cortex adjacent to the penicillin locus and in small discrete regions of the putamen, globus pallidus, caudate nucleus, thalamus, and substantia nigra of the same side (Fig. 3) (Kennedy et al., 1975). Similar studies in the rat have led to comparable results and provided evidence on the basis of an evoked metabolic response of a "mirror" focus in the motor cortex contralateral to the penicillin-induced epileptogenic focus (Collins et al., 1976).

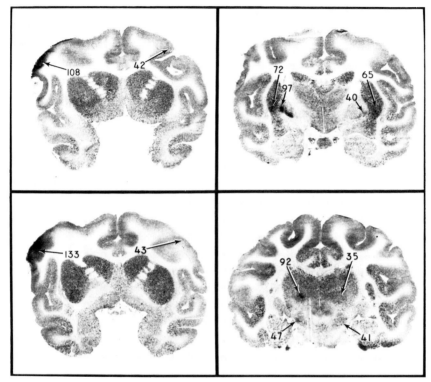

FIG. 3. Effects of focal seizures produced by local application of penicillin to motor cortex on local cerebral glucose utilization in the Rhesus monkey. The penicillin was applied to the hand and face area of the left motor cortex. The left side of the brain is on the left in each of the autoradiographs in the figure. The numbers are the rates of local cerebral glucose utilization in μmoles/100 g tissue/minute. Note the following: upper left, motor cortex in region of penicillin application and corresponding region of contralateral motor cortex; lower left ipsilateral and contralateral motor cortical regions remote from area of penicillin applications; upper right, ipsilateral and contralateral putamen and globus pallidus; lower right, ipsilateral and contralateral thalamic nuclei and substantia nigra. (From Sokoloff, 1977.)

B. EFFECTS OF DECREASED FUNCTIONAL ACTIVITY

Decrements in functional activity result in reduced rates of glucose utilization. These effects are particularly striking in the auditory and visual systems of the rat and the visual system of the monkey.

1. Effects of Auditory Deprivation

In the albino rat some of the highest rates of local cerebral glucose utilization are found in components of the auditory system, i.e., auditory cortex, medial geniculate ganglion, inferior colliculus, lateral lemniscus, superior olive, and cochlear nucleus (Table III). Bilateral auditory deprivation by occlusion of both external auditory canals with wax markedly depresses the metabolic activity in all of these areas (Sokoloff, 1977). The reductions are symmetrical bilaterally and range from 35 to 60%. Unilateral auditory deprivation also depresses the glucose consumption of these structures but to a lesser degree, and some of the structures are asymmetrically affected. For example, the metabolic activity of the ipsilateral cochlear nucleus equals 75% of the activity of the contralateral nucleus. The lateral lemniscus, superior olive, and medial geniculate ganglion are slightly lower on the contralateral side, while the contralateral inferior colliculus is markedly lower in metabolic activity than the ipsilateral structure. These results demonstrate that there is some degree of lateralization and crossing of auditory pathways in the rat.

2. Visual Deprivation in the Rat

In the rat, the visual system is 80 to 85% crossed at the optic chiasma (Lashley, 1934; Montero and Guillery, 1968), and unilateral enucleation removes most of the visual input to the central visual structures of the contralateral side. In the conscious rat studied 2–24 hours after unilateral enucleation, there are marked decrements in glucose utilization in the contralateral superior colliculus, lateral geniculate ganglion, and visual cortex as compared to the ipsilateral side (Kennedy et al., 1975).

3. Visual Deprivation in the Monkey

In animals with binocular visual systems, such as the Rhesus monkey, there is only approximately 50% crossing of the visual pathways, and the structures of the visual system on each side of the brain receive equal inputs from both retinas. Although each retina projects more or less equally to both hemispheres, their projections remain segregated and terminate in six well-defined laminas in the lateral geniculate ganglia, three each for the ipsilateral and contralateral eyes (Hubel and Wiesel, 1968, 1972; Wiesel et al., 1974; Rakic, 1976). This segregation is preserved in the optic radiations which project the monocular representations of the two eyes for any segment of the visual field to adjacent regions of Layer IV of the striate cortex (Hubel and Wiesel, 1968, 1972). The cells responding to the input of each monocular terminal zone are distributed transversely through the thickness of the striate cortex resulting in a mosaic of columns, 0.3–0.5 mm in width, alternately representing the monocular inputs of the two eyes. The nature and distribution of these ocular dominance columns have previously been characterized by electrophysiological techniques (Hubel and Wiesel, 1968), Nauta degeneration methods

(Hubel and Wiesel, 1972), and autoradiographic visualization of axonal and transneuronal transport of [^{3}H]proline- and [^{3}H]fucose-labeled protein and/or glycoprotein (Wiesel *et al.*, 1974; Rakic, 1976). Bilateral or unilateral visual deprivation, either by enucleation or by the insertion of opaque plastic discs, produces consistent changes in the pattern of distribution of the rates of glucose consumption, all clearly visible in the autoradiographs, that coincide closely with the changes in functional activity expected from known physiological and anatomical properties of the binocular visual system (Kennedy *et al.*, 1976).

In animals with intact binocular vision no bilateral asymmetry is seen in the autoradiographs of the structures of the visual system (Figs. 4A and 5A). The lateral geniculate ganglia and oculomotor nuclei appear to be of fairly uniform density and essentially the same on both sides (Fig. 4A). The visual cortex is also the same on both sides (Fig. 5A), but throughout all of Area 17 there is heterogeneous density distributed in a characteristic laminar pattern. These observations indicate that in animals with binocular visual input the rates of glucose consumption in the visual pathways are essentially equal on both sides of the brain and relatively uniform in the oculomotor nuclei and lateral geniculate ganglia, but markedly different in the various layers of the striate cortex.

Autoradiographs from animals with both eyes occluded exhibit generally decreased labeling of all components of the visual system, but the bilateral symmetry is fully retained (Figs. 4B and 5B), and the density within each lateral geniculate body is for the most part fairly uniform (Fig. 4B). In the striate cortex, however, the marked differences in the densities of the various layers seen in the animals with intact bilateral vision (Fig. 5A) are virtually absent so that, except for a faint delineation of a band within Layer IV, the concentration of the label is essentially homogeneous throughout the striate cortex (Fig. 5B).

Autoradiographs from monkeys with only monocular input because of unilateral visual occlusion exhibit markedly different patterns from those described above. Both lateral geniculate bodies exhibit exactly inverse patterns of alternating dark and light bands corresponding to the known laminas representing the regions receiving the different inputs from the retinas of the intact and occluded eyes (Fig. 4C). Bilateral asymmetry is also seen in the oculomotor nuclear complex; a lower density is apparent in the nuclear complex contralateral to the occluded eye (Fig. 4C). In the striate cortex the pattern of distribution of the [^{14}C]DG-6-P appears to be a composite of the patterns seen in the animals with intact and bilaterally occluded visual input. The pattern found in the former regularly alternates with that of the latter in columns oriented perpendicularly to the cortical surface (Fig. 5C). The dimensions, arrangement, and distribution of these

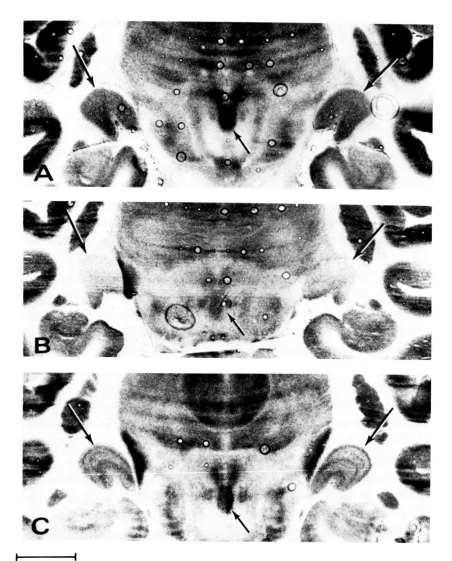

5.0mm

FIG. 4. Autoradiography of coronal brain sections of monkey at the level of the lateral geniculate bodies. Large arrows point to the lateral geniculate bodies; small arrows point to oculomotor nuclear complex. (A) Animal with intact binocular vision. Note the bilateral symmetry and relative homogeneity of the lateral geniculate bodies and oculomotor nuclei. (B) Animal with bilateral visual occlusion. Note the reduced relative densities, the relative homogeneity, and the bilateral symmetry of the lateral geniculate bodies and oculomotor nuclei. (C) Animal with right eye occluded. The left side of the brain is on the left side of the photograph. Note the laminae and the inverse order of the dark and light bands in the two lateral geniculate bodies. Note also the lesser density of the oculomotor nuclear complex on the side contralateral to the occluded eye. (From Kennedy *et al.*, 1976.)

columns are identical to those of the ocular dominance columns described by Hubel and Wiesel (Hubel and Wiesel, 1968, 1972; Wiesel *et al.,* 1974). These columns reflect the interdigitation of the representations of the two retinas in the visual cortex. Each element in the visual fields is represented by a pair of contiguous bands in the visual cortex, one for each of the two retinas or their portions that correspond to the given point in the visual fields. With symmetrical visual input bilaterally, the columns representing the two eyes are equally active and, therefore, not visualized in the autoradiographs (Fig. 5A). When one eye is blocked, however, only those columns representing the blocked eye become metabolically less active, and the autoradiographs then display the alternate bands of normal and depressed activities corresponding to the regions of visual cortical representation of the two eyes (Fig. 5C).

There can be seen in the autoradiographs from the animals with unilateral visual deprivation a pair of regions in the folded calcarine cortex that exhibit bilateral asymmetry (Fig. 5C). The ocular dominance columns are absent on both sides, but on the side contralateral to the occluded eye this region has the appearance of visual cortex from an animal with normal bilateral vision, and on the ipsilateral side this region looks like cortex from an animal with both eyes occluded (Fig. 5). These regions are the loci of the cortical representation of the blind spots of the visual fields and normally have only monocular input (Kennedy *et al.,* 1975, 1976). The area of the optic disc in the nasal half of each retina cannot transmit to this region of the contralateral striate cortex which, therefore, receives its sole input from an area in the temporal half of the ipsilateral retina. Occlusion of one eye deprives this region of the ipsilateral striate cortex of all input while the corresponding region of the contralateral striate cortex retains uninterrupted input from the intact eye. The metabolic reflection of this ipsilateral monocular input is seen in the autoradiograph in Fig. 5C.

The results of these studies with the [14C]deoxyglucose method in the binocular visual system of the monkey represent the most dramatic demonstration of the close relationship between physiological changes in functional activity and the rate of energy metabolism in specific components of the central nervous system.

VII. Applications of the Deoxyglucose Method

The results of studies like those described above on the effects of experimentally induced focal alterations of functional activity on local glucose utilization have demonstrated a close coupling between local functional activity and energy metabolism in the central nervous system. The effects are often so pronounced that they can be visualized directly

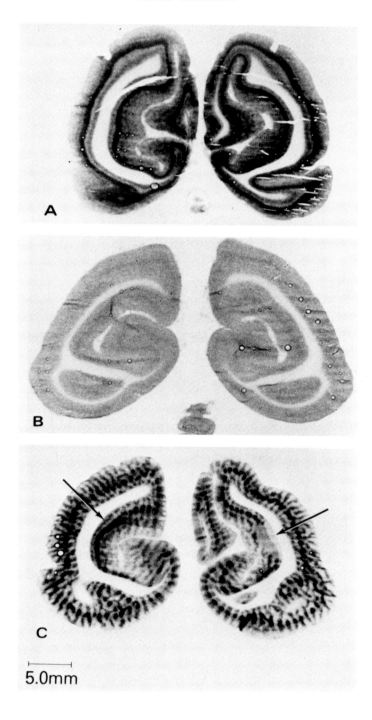

5.0mm

on the autoradiographs, which provide pictorial representations of the relative rates of glucose utilization throughout the brain. This technique of autoradiographic visualization of evoked metabolic responses offers a powerful tool to map functional neural pathways simultaneously in all anatomical components of the central nervous system, and extensive use has been made of it for this purpose (Plum *et al.*, 1976). The results have clearly demonstrated the effectiveness of metabolic responses, either positive or negative, in identifying regions of the central nervous system involved in specific functions.

The method has been used most extensively in qualitative studies in which regions of altered functional activity are identified by the change in their visual appearance relative to other regions in the autoradiographs. Such qualitative studies are effective only when the effects are lateralized to one side or when only a few discrete regions are affected; other regions serve as the controls. Quantitative comparisons cannot, however, be made for equivalent regions between two or more animals. To make quantitative comparisons between animals, the fully quantitative method must be used, which takes into account the various factors, particularly the plasma glucose level, that influence the magnitude of labeling of the tissues. The method must be used quantitatively when the experimental procedure produces systemic effects and alters metabolism in many regions of the brain.

A comprehensive review of the many qualitative and quantitative applications of the method is beyond the scope of this report. Only some of the many neurophysiological, neuroanatomical, pharmacological, and pathophysiological applications of the method will be briefly noted merely to illustrate the broad extent of its potential usefulness.

FIG. 5. Autoradiographs of coronal brain sections from Rhesus monkeys at the level of the striate cortex. (A) Animal with normal binocular vision. Note the laminar distribution of the density; the dark band corresponds to Layer IV. (B) Animal with bilateral visual deprivation. Note the almost uniform and reduced relative density, especially the virtual disappearance of the dark band corresponding to Layer IV. (C) Animal with right eye occluded. The half-brain on the left side of the photograph represents the left hemisphere contralateral to the occluded eye. Note the alternate dark and light striations, each approximately 0.3–0.4 mm in width that represent the ocular dominance columns. These columns are most apparent in the dark band corresponding to Layer IV, but extend through the entire thickness of the cortex. The arrows point to regions of bilateral asymmetry where the ocular dominance columns are absent. These are presumably areas with normally only monocular input. The one on the left, contralateral to the occluded eye, has a continuous dark lamina corresponding to Layer IV which is completely absent on the side ipsilateral to the occluded eye. These regions are believed to be the loci of the cortical representations of the blind spots. (From Kennedy *et al.*, 1976.)

A. NEUROPHYSIOLOGICAL AND NEUROANATOMICAL
APPLICATIONS

Many of the physiological applications of the [14C]deoxyglucose method were in studies designed to test the method and to examine the relationship between local cerebral functional and metabolic activities. These applications have been described above. The most dramatic results have been obtained in the visual systems of the monkey and the rat. The method has, for example, been used to define the nature, conformation, and distribution of the ocular dominance columns in the striate cortex of the monkey (Fig. 5C) (Kennedy *et al.,* 1976). It has been used by Hubel *et al.* (1978) to do the same for the orientation columns in the striate cortex of the monkey. A by-product of the studies of the ocular dominance columns was the identification of the loci of the visual cortical representation of the blind spots of the visual fields (Fig. 5C) (Kennedy *et al.,* (1976). Studies are in progress to map the pathways of higher visual functions beyond the striate cortex; the results thus far demonstrate extensive areas of involvement of the inferior temporal cortex in visual processing (Jarvis *et al.,* 1978). Des Rosiers *et al.* (1978) have used the method to demonstrate functional plasticity in the striate cortex of the infant monkey. The ocular dominance columns are already present on the first day of life, but if one eye is kept patched for 3 months, the columns representing the open eye broaden and completely take over the adjacent regions of cortex containing the columns for the eye that had been patched. Inasmuch as there is no longer any cortical representation for the patched eye, the animal becomes functionally blind in one eye. This phenomenon is almost certainly the basis for the cortical blindness or amblyopia that often occurs in children with uncorrected strabismus.

There have also been extensive studies of the visual system of the rat. This species has little if any binocular vision and, therefore, lacks the ocular dominance columns. Batipps *et al.* (1981) have compared the rates of local cerebral glucose utilization in albino and Norway brown rats during exposure to ambient light. The rates in the two strains were essentially the same throughout the brain except in the components of the primary visual system. The metabolic rates in the superior colliculus, lateral geniculate, and visual cortex of the albino rat were significantly lower than those in the pigmented rat. Miyaoka *et al.* (1979a) have studied the influence of the intensity of retinal stimulation with randomly spaced light flashes on the metabolic rates in the visual systems of the two strains. In dark-adapted animals there is relatively little difference between the two strains. With increasing intensity of light, the rates of glucose utilization first increase in the primary projection areas of the retina, e.g., superficial layer of the superior colliculus and lateral genicu-late body, and the slopes of the increase are steeper in the albino rat (Fig. 6). At 7 lux, however, the metabolic rates peak in the albino rat and then decrease with increasing light intensity. In contrast, the metabolic rates in the pigmented rat rise until they reach a plateau at about 700 lux, approxi-mately the ambient light intensity in the laboratory. At this level, the metabolic rates in the visual structures of the albino rat are consideraby below those of the pigmented rat. These results are consistent with the greater intensity of light reaching the visual cells of the retina in the albino rats because of lack of pigment and the subsequent damage to the rods at higher light intensities. It is of considerable interest that the rates of glucose utilization in these visual structures obey the Weber–Fechner Law, i.e., the metabolic rate is directly proportional to the logarithm of the intensity of stimulation (Miyaoka *et al.*, 1979a). Inasmuch as this law was first developed from behavioral manifestations, these results imply that there is a quantitative relationship between behavioral and metabolic responses.

Although less extensive, there have also been applications of the method to other sensory systems. In studies of the olfactory system Sharp *et al.* (1975) have found that olfactory stimulation with specific odors activates glucose utilization in localized regions of the olfactory bulb. In addition to the experiments in the auditory system described above, there have been studies of tonotopic representation in the auditory system. Webster *et al.* (1978) have obtained clear evidence of selective regions of metabolic activation in the cochlear nucleus, superior olivary complex, nuclei of the lateral lemnisci, and the inferior colliculus in cats in response to different frequencies of auditory stimulation. Similar results have been obtained by Silverman *et al.* (1977) in the rat and guinea pig. Studies of the sensory cortex have demonstrated metabolic activation of the "whisker barrels" by stimulation of the vibrissae in the rat (Durham and Woolsey, 1977; Hand *et al.*, 1978). Each vibrissa is represented in a discrete region of the sensory cortex; their precise location and extent have been ele-gantly mapped by Hand *et al.* (1978) and Hand (1981) by means of the [^{14}C]deoxyglucose method.

Thus far, there has been relatively little application of the method to the physiology of motor functions. Kennedy *et al.* (1980) have studied mon-keys that were conditioned to perform a task with one hand in response to visual cues; in the monkeys which were performing they observed meta-bolic activation throughout the appropriate areas of the motor as well as sensory systems from the cortex to the spinal cord.

An interesting physiological application of the [^{14}C]deoxyglucose method has been to the study of circadian rhythms in the central nervous

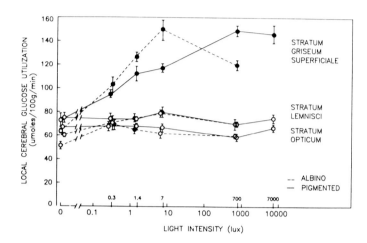

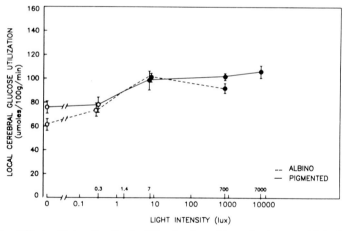

FIG. 6.   Effects of intensity of retinal illumination with randomly spaced light flashes on local cerebral glucose utilization in components of the visual system of the albino and Norway brown rat. Note that the local glucose utilization is proportional to the logarithm of the intensity of illumination, at least at lower levels of intensity, in the primary projection areas of the retina. (From Miyaoka *et al.*, 1979a.)

system. Schwartz and his co-workers (1977, 1980) found that the supra-chiasmatic nucleus in the rat exhibits circadian rhythmicity in metabolic activity, high during the day and low during the night (Fig. 7). None of the other structures in the brain that they examined showed rhythmic activ-

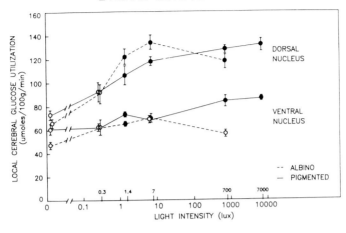

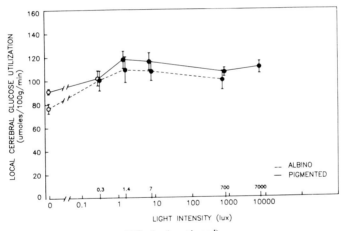

FIG. 6 (*continued*).

ity. The normally low activity present in the nucleus in the dark could be markedly increased by light, but darkness did not reduce the glucose utilization during the day. The rhythm is entrained to light; reversal of the light–dark cycle leads not only to reversal of the rhythm in running activity but also in the cycle of metabolic activity in the suprachiasmatic nucleus. These studies lend support to a role of the suprachiasmatic nucleus in the organization of circadian rhythms in the central nervous system.

    Much of our knowledge of neurophysiology has been derived from

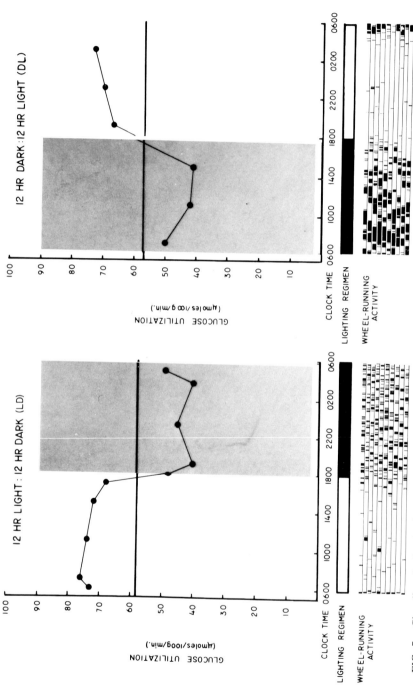

FIG. 7. Circadian rhythm in glucose utilization in suprachiasmatic nucleus in the rat. Left panel, animals entrained to 12 hours of light during day and 12 hours of darkness during night. Right panel, animals entrained to opposite light–dark regimen. (From Schwartz et al., 1980.)

studies of the electrical activity of the nervous system. Indeed, from the heavy emphasis that has been placed on electrophysiology one might gather that the brain is really an electric organ rather than a chemical one that functions mainly by the release of chemical transmitters at synapses. Nevertheless, electrical activity is unquestionably fundamental to the process of conduction, and it is appropriate to inquire how the local metabolic activities revealed by the [^{14}C]deoxyglucose method are related to the electrical activity of the nervous system. This question has been examined by Yarowsky and his co-workers (1979) in the superior cervical ganglion of the rat. The advantage of this structure is that its preganglionic input and postganglionic output can be isolated and electrically stimulated and/or monitored *in vivo*. The results thus far indicate a clear relationship between electrical input to the ganglion and its metabolic activity. Glucose utilization in the superior cervical ganglion is enhanced by electrical stimulation of the afferent nerves. The metabolic activation is frequency dependent in the range of 5 to 15 Hz, increasing in magnitude with increasing frequency of the stimulation. Similar effects of electrical stimulation on the oxygen and glucose consumption of the excised ganglion studied *in vitro* have been observed (Larrabee, 1958; Horowicz and Larrabee, 1958; Friedli, 1978). Recent studies have also shown that antidromic stimulation of the postganglionic efferent pathways from the ganglion has similar effects; stimulation of the external carotid nerve antidromically activates glucose utilization in the region of distribution of the cell bodies of this efferent pathway, indicating that not only the preganglionic axonal terminals are metabolically activated, but the postganglionic cell bodies as well (Yarowsky *et al.*, 1980). As already demonstrated in the neurohypophysis (Mata *et al.*, 1980), the effects of electrical stimulation on energy metabolism in the superior cervical ganglion are also probably due to the ionic currents associated with the spike activity and the consequent activation of the Na^+,K^+-ATPase activity to restore the ionic gradients. Electrical stimulation of the afferents to sympathetic ganglia have been shown to increase extracellular K^+ concentration (Friedli, 1978; Galvan *et al.*, 1979). Each spike is normally associated with a sharp transient rise in extracellular K^+ concentration which then rapidly falls and transiently undershoots before returning to the normal level (Galvan *et al.*, 1979); ouabain slows the decline in K^+ concentration after the spike and eliminates the undershoot. Continuous stimulation at a frequency of 6 Hz produces a sustained increase in cellular K^+ concentration (Galvan *et al.*, 1979). It is likely that the increased extracellular K^+ concentration and, almost certainly, increased intracellular Na^+ concentration activate the Na^+,K^+-ATPase, which in turn leads to the increased glucose utilization.

104 LOUIS SOKOLOFF

B. NEUROENDOCRINOLOGICAL APPLICATIONS

The deoxyglucose method has thus far been applied only sparingly to neuroendocrinology. Several studies have, however, been carried out or are in progress.

1. Hypothalamoneurohypophysial System

Physiological stimulation of the neurohypophysial system by salt loading, which enhances vasopressin secretion, has been found to be associated with increased glucose utilization in the posterior pituitary (Fig. 8) (Schwartz et al., 1979). Surprisingly, there were no detectable effects in the supraoptic and paraventricular nuclei, the loci of the cell bodies which project to the posterior pituitary. Obviously the entire pathway had been activated by the osmotic stimulation. The posterior pituitary is composed (approximately 42%) of axonal terminals of the hypothalamohypophysial tract (Nordmann, 1977), and the discrepancy between the effects on the cell bodies and in the regions of termination of their projections may reflect the greater sensitivity of axonal terminals and/or synaptic elements than that of perikarya to metabolic activation. That the supraoptic and paraventricular nuclei can be metabolically activated is evident from the effects of the α-adrenergic blocking agent, phenoxybenzamine (Fig. 8), or any other condition that produces hypotension (Savaki et al., 1982). In hypotension, however, these nuclei are activated by reflex activity, and it may well be that it is the afferent axonal terminals in these nuclei rather than the cell bodies that exhibit the increased utilization of glucose.

Kadekaro et al. (1982) have applied the deoxyglucose method to studies of the Brattleboro rat, a variant of the Long–Evans strain with a recessive genetic defect in vasopressin synthesis. This rat exhibits the characteristic signs of diabetes insipidus, an abnormally high water intake and a high output of hypoosmolar urine. Despite the deficiency in vasopressin synthesis, glucose utilization was found to be markedly increased in the

FIG. 8. [^{14}C]Deoxyglucose autoradiographs (B, C, D) and stained histological sections (A) of coronal brain sections (left) and pituitary sections (right). The photographs in (A) illustrate the positions of the supraoptic (SON) and paraventricular (PVN) nuclei in the brain section after cresyl violet (Nissl) staining. The positions of the posterior pituitary (PP) and anterior pituitary (AP) are illustrated on the right side in (A) after toluidine blue staining. The autoradiographs in (B) are characteristic of control rats, which were allowed to drink water freely. (C) Autoradiographs of brain and pituitary typical of dehydrated rats, which were given 2% NaCl to drink for 5 days. Note the intense labeling in the posterior pituitary, without comparable change in the SON or PVN. (D) Autoradiographs characteristic of normal rats given an intravenous injection of an α-adrenergic blocker, phenoxybenzamine (20 mg/kg), approximately 45 to 60 minutes before injection of [^{14}C]deoxyglucose. Note the dramatic increase in labeling of the SON, PVN, and PP. (From Schwartz et al., 1979.)

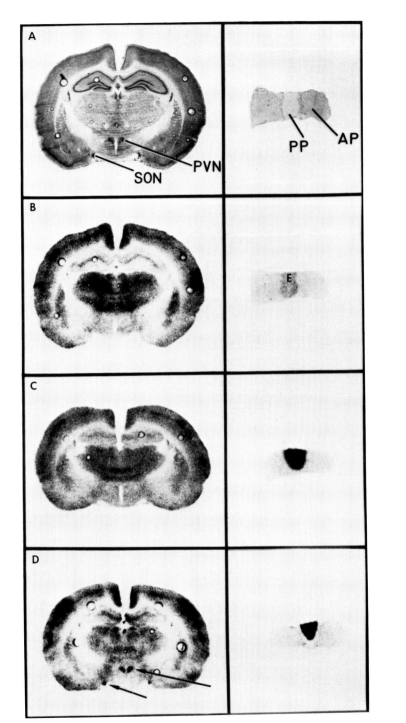

posterior pituitary and also in the subfornical organ, a structure that has been found to mediate drinking behavior in response to high plasma levels of angiotensin II, and angiotensin II is elevated in the Brattleboro rat. As in the normal rat stimulated by salt loading, the supraoptic and paraventricular nuclei were not metabolically more active in the Brattleboro rat. The reason for the high metabolic rate in the posterior pituitary of the Brattleboro rat is still obscure, but it may be related to histological changes that also are present in the gland.

2. Altered Thyroid Function

Hyperthyroidism is known not to alter the average energy metabolism in the mature brain as a whole (Sokoloff et al., 1953). Studies with the deoxyglucose method (D. Dow-Edwards and C. B. Smith, unpublished observations) reveal that there are also no changes in glucose utilization in any anatomical components of the mature brain of the rat. The thyroid hormones are, however, fundamentally involved in the structural and functional maturation of the brain (Eayrs, 1961). Dow-Edwards et al. (1982) have applied the deoxyglucose method to rats radiothyroidectomized at birth but studied at approximately 5 months of age when the brain of normal rats has achieved maturity. Glucose utilization was significantly reduced in all regions of the brain examined. Particularly affected were the cerebral cortical regions and the sensory systems, particularly the auditory system. These metabolic changes are consistent with the histological pattern of impaired brain development in cretinism.

3. Sex Hormones and Sexual Behavior

The deoxyglucose method has been used to demonstrate selective metabolic activation of a number of structures in the female rat brain by vaginocervical stimulation that also elicited lordotic behavior (Allen et al., 1981). The structures so activated were the medial preoptic nucleus, mesencephalic reticular formation, red nucleus of the stria terminalis, dorsal raphe nucleus, and the globus pallidus. Some but not all of these areas had been previously shown by electrical recording, lesioning, and stimulating techniques to participate in the behavioral and physiological responses to coitus. These results provide additional information about the concurrent processing of sensory stimulation in the brain and also indicate that the medial preoptic area is a receptive area for copulatory stimulation.

The female gonadal hormones, estrogen and progesterone, influence sexual behavior and have potent influences on the central nervous system, particularly the hypothalamus. Porrino et al. (1982) have used the deoxyglucose method in an attempt to identify regions of the brain affected by these hormones. In ovariectomized rats estradiol treatment stimulated glucose utilization in anterior, ventromedial, lateral, and posterior areas of the hypothalamus. Progesterone alone had very little effect in these areas. When progesterone was administered to animals which had been implanted previously with estradiol, glucose utilization was reduced in the lateral preoptic, medial preoptic area, and anterior hypothalamus below the levels of the ovariectomized controls. These data suggest an anatomical separation of the effects of gonadal steroids in the hypothalamus; estradiol may facilitate neural activity in the mid and posterior areas of the hypothalamus whereas estrogen in combination with progesterone suppresses activity in the anterior preoptic area. These two patterns in the anterior and posterior hypothalamus may reflect differential involvement in feminine sexual behavior.

C. NEUROPHARMACOLOGICAL APPLICATIONS

The ability of the deoxyglucose method to map the entire brain for localized regions of altered functional activity on the basis of changes in energy metabolism offers a potent tool to identify the neural sites of action of agents with neuropharmacological and psychopharmacological actions. It does not, however, discriminate between the direct and indirect effects of the drug. An entire pathway may be activated even though the direct action of the drug may be exerted only at the origin of the pathway. This is of advantage for relating behavioral effects to central actions, but it is a disadvantage if the goal is to identify the primary site of action of the drug. To discriminate between direct and indirect actions of a drug the [^{14}C]deoxyglucose method must be combined with selectively placed lesions in the CNS that interrupt afferent pathways to the structure in question. If the metabolic effect of the drug then remains, then it is due to direct action; if lost, the effect is likely to be indirect and mediated via the interrupted pathway. Nevertheless, the method has proved to be useful in a number of pharmacological studies.

1. Effects of γ-Butyrolactone

γ-Hydroxybutyrate and γ-butyrolactone, which is hydrolyzed to γ-hydroxybutyrate in plasma, produce trance-like behavioral states associated with marked suppression of electroencephalographic activity (Roth and Giarman, 1966). These effects are reversible, and these drugs have been used clinically as anesthetic adjuvants. There is evidence that these agents lower neuronal activity in the nigrostriatal pathway and may act by inhibition of dopaminergic synapses (Roth, 1976). Studies in rats with the [^{14}C]deoxyglucose technique have demonstrated that γ-butyrolactone produces profound dose-dependent reductions of glucose utilization throughout the brain (Wolfson *et al.*, 1977). At the highest doses studied, 600 mg/kg of body weight, glucose utilization was reduced by approximately 75% in gray matter and 33% in white matter, but there was no obvious further specificity with respect to the local cerebral structures affected. The reversibility of the effects and the magnitude and diffuseness of the depression of cerebral metabolic rate suggest that this drug might be considered as a chemical substitute for hypothermia in conditions in which profound reversible reduction of cerebral metabolism is desired.

2. Effects of D-Lysergic Acid Diethylamide

The effects of the potent psychotomimetic agent, D-lysergic acid diethylamide, have been examined in the rat (Shinohara *et al.*, 1976). In doses of 12.5 to 125 μg/kg, it caused dose-dependent reductions in glucose utilization in a number of cerebral structures. With increasing dosage more structures were affected and to a greater degree. There was no pattern in the distribution of the effects, at least none discernible at the present level of resolution, that might contribute to the understanding of the drug's psychotomimetic actions.

3. Effects of Morphine Addiction and Withdrawal

Acute morphine administration depresses glucose utilization in many areas of the brain, but the specific effects of morphine could not be distinguished from those of the hypercapnia produced by the associated respiratory depression (Sakurada *et al.*, 1976). In contrast, morphine addiction, produced within 24 hours by a single subcutaneous injection of 150 mg/kg of morphine base in an oil emulsion, reduces glucose utilization in a large number of gray structures in the absence of changes in arterial pCO_2. White matter appears to be unaffected. Naloxone (1 mg/kg subcutaneously) reduces glucose utilization in a number of structures when administered to normal rats, but when given to the morphine-addicted animals produces an acute withdrawal syndrome and reverses the reductions of glucose utilization in several structures, most strikingly in the habenula (Sakurada *et al.*, 1976).

4. Pharmacological Studies of Dopaminergic Systems

The most extensive applications of the deoxyglucose method to pharmacology have been in studies of dopaminergic systems. Ascending dopaminergic pathways appear to have a potent influence on glucose utilization in the forebrain of rats. Electrolytic lesions placed unilaterally in the lateral hypothalamus or pars compacta of the substantia nigra caused marked ipsilateral reductions of glucose metabolism in numerous fore-brain structures rostral to the lesion, particularly the frontal cerebral cor-tex, caudate-putamen, and parts of the thalamus (Schwartz et al., 1976; Schwartz, 1978). Similar lesions in the locus coeruleus had no such ef-fects.

Enhancement of dopaminergic synaptic activity by administration of the agonist of dopamine, apomorphine (Brown and Wolfson, 1978), or of amphetamine (Wechsler et al., 1979), which stimulates release of do-pamine at the synapse, produces marked increases in glucose consump-tion in some of the components of the extrapyramidal system known or suspected to contain dopamine-receptive cells. With both drugs, the greatest increases noted were in the zona reticulata of the substantia nigra and the subthalamic nucleus. Surprisingly, none of the components of the dopaminergic mesolimbic system appeared to be affected.

The studies with amphetamine (Wechsler et al., 1979) were carried out with the fully quantitative [^{14}C]deoxyglucose method. The results in Table V illustrate the comprehensiveness with which this method surveys the entire brain for sites of altered activity due to actions of the drug. It also allows for quantitative comparison of the relative potencies of related drugs. For example, in Table V, the comparative effects of d-amphet-amine and the less potent dopaminergic agent, l-amphetamine, are com-pared; the quantitative results clearly reveal that the effects of l-amphet-amine on local cerebral glucose utilization are more limited in distribution and of lesser magnitude than those of d-amphetamine. Indeed, in similar quantitative studies with apomorphine, McCulloch et al. (1979, 1980a) have been able to generate complete dose–response curves for the effects of the drug on the rates of glucose utilization in various components of dopaminergic systems. They have also demonstrated metabolically the development of supersensitivity to apomorphine in rats maintained chron-ically on the dopamine antagonist, haloperidol (J. McCulloch, H. E. Savaki, A Pert, W. Bunney, and L. Sokoloff, unpublished observations). In the course of these studies with apomorphine McCulloch et al. (1980b) obtained evidence of a retinal dopaminergic system that projects specifi-cally to the superficial layer of the superior colliculus in the rat. Apomor-phine administration activated metabolism in the superficial layer of the superior colliculus, as well as in other structures, but the effect in the superficial layer was prevented by prior enucleation (Fig. 9). Miyaoka (unpublished observations) subsequently observed that intraocular ad-ministration of minute amounts of apomorphine caused increased glucose utilization only in the superficial layer of the superior colliculus of the contralateral side.

TABLE V

Effects of d-Amphetamine and l-Amphetamine on Local Cerebral Glucose Utilization in the Conscious Rat[a,b]

Structure	Control	d-Amphetamine	l-Amphetamine
Gray matter			
Visual cortex	102 ± 8	135 ± 11[c]	105 ± 8
Auditory cortex	160 ± 11	162 ± 6	141 ± 6
Parietal cortex	109 ± 9	125 ± 10	116 ± 4
Sensory-motor cortex	118 ± 8	139 ± 9	111 ± 4
Olfactory cortex	100 ± 6	93 ± 5	94 ± 3
Frontal cortex	109 ± 10	130 ± 8	105 ± 4
Prefrontal cortex	146 ± 10	166 ± 7	154 ± 4
Thalamus			
Lateral nucleus	97 ± 5	114 ± 8	117 ± 6
Ventral nucleus	85 ± 7	108 ± 6[c]	96 ± 4
Habenula	118 ± 10	71 ± 5[d]	82 ± 2[d]
Dorsomedial nucleus	92 ± 6	111 ± 8	106 ± 6
Medial geniculate	116 ± 5	119 ± 4	116 ± 4
Lateral geniculate	79 ± 5	88 ± 5	84 ± 4
Hypothalamus	54 ± 5	56 ± 3	52 ± 3
Suprachiasmatic nucleus	94 ± 4	75 ± 4[d]	67 ± 1[d]
Mamillary body	117 ± 8	134 ± 5	142 ± 5[c]
Lateral olfactory nucleus[e]	92 ± 6	95 ± 5	99 ± 6
A$_{13}$	71 ± 4	91 ± 4[d]	81 ± 4
Hippocampus			
Ammon's horn	79 ± 5	73 ± 2	81 ± 6
Dentate gyrus	60 ± 4	55 ± 3	67 ± 7
Amygdala	46 ± 3	46 ± 3	44 ± 2
Septal nucleus	56 ± 3	55 ± 2	54 ± 3
Caudate nucleus	109 ± 5	132 ± 8[c]	127 ± 3[c]
Nucleus accumbens	76 ± 5	80 ± 3	78 ± 3
Globus pallidus	53 ± 3	64 ± 2[c]	65 ± 3[c]
Subthalamic nucleus	89 ± 6	149 ± 10[d]	107 ± 2
Substantia nigra			
Zona reticulata	58 ± 2	105 ± 4[d]	72 ± 4
Zona compacta	65 ± 4	88 ± 6[d]	72 ± 3
Red nucleus	76 ± 5	94 ± 5[c]	86 ± 2
Vestibular nucleus	121 ± 11	137 ± 5	130 ± 4
Cochlear nucleus	139 ± 6	126 ± 1	141 ± 5
Superior olivary nucleus	144 ± 4	143 ± 4	147 ± 6
Lateral lemniscus	107 ± 3	96 ± 5	98 ± 3
Inferior colliculus	193 ± 10	169 ± 5	150 ± 8[d]
Dorsal tegmental nucleus	109 ± 5	112 ± 7	122 ± 6
Superior colliculus	80 ± 5	89 ± 3	91 ± 3
Pontine gray	58 ± 4	65 ± 3	60 ± 1
Cerebellar flocculus	124 ± 10	146 ± 15	153 ± 10
Cerebellar hemispheres	55 ± 3	68 ± 6	64 ± 2
Cerebellar nuclei	102 ± 4	105 ± 8	110 ± 3

TABLE V   (*continued*)

Structure	Control	*d*-Amphetamine	*l*-Amphetamine
White matter			
Corpus callosum	23 ± 3	24 ± 2	23 ± 1
Genu of corpus callosum	29 ± 2	30 ± 2	26 ± 2
Internal capsule	21 ± 1	24 ± 2	19 ± 2
Cerebellar white	28 ± 1	31 ± 2	31 ± 2

[a] From Wechsler *et al.* (1979).

[b] All values are the means ± standard error of the mean for five animals.

[c] Significant difference from the control at the $p < 0.05$ level.

[d] Significant difference from the control at the $p < 0.01$ level.

[e] It was not possible to correlate precisely this area on autoradiographs with a specific structure in the rat brain. It is, however, most likely the lateral olfactory nucleus.

5. *Effects of α- and β-Adrenergic Blocking Agents*

Savaki *et al.* (1978) have studied the effects of the α-adrenergic blocking agent, phentolamine, and the β-adrenergic blocking agent, propranolol. Both drugs produced widespread dose-dependent depressions of glucose utilization throughout the brain, but exhibit particularly striking and opposite effects in the complete auditory pathway from the cochlear nucleus to the auditory cortex. Propranolol markedly depressed and phentolamine markedly enhanced glucose utilization in this pathway. The functional significance of these effects is unknown but they seem to correlate with corresponding effects on the electrophysiological responsiveness of this sensory system. Propranolol depresses and phentolamine enhances the amplitude of all components of evoked auditory responses (T. Furlow and J. Hallenbeck, personal communication).

D. NEUROPATHOPHYSIOLOGICAL APPLICATIONS

The application of the deoxyglucose method to the study of pathological states has been limited because of uncertainties about the values for the lumped and rate constants to be used. There are, however, pathophysiological states in which there is no structural damage to the tissue and the standard values of the constants can be used. Several of these conditions have been and are continuing to be studied by the [^{14}C]deoxyglucose technique, both qualitatively and quantitatively.

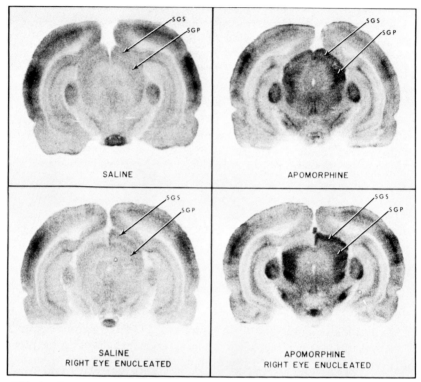

FIG. 9. Representative autoradiographs at the level of superior colliculus in dark-adapted rats studied in the dark. SGS, Stratum griseum superficiale; SGP, stratum griseum profundum. Upper left: Saline, intact visual system. Upper right: Apomorphine (1.5 mg/kg), intact visual system. Note bilaterally increased optical density (that is, elevated glucose utilization) in both superficial and deep laminae of the superior colliculus. Lower left: Saline, right eye enucleated. Asymmetrical optical density with reduction on contralateral side is apparent within the superficial layer, whereas in the deeper layer optical density remains symmetrical. Lower right: Apomorphine (1.5 mg/kg) right eye enucleated. Note increased optical density bilaterally in the deeper layer but only in the right or ipsilateral superficial layer of the superior colliculus. (From McCulloch *et al.*, 1980b.)

1. Convulsive States

The local injection of penicillin into the motor cortex produces focal seizures manifested in specific regions of the body contralaterally. The [^{14}C]deoxyglucose method has been used to map the spread of seizure activity within the brain and to identify the structures with altered functional activity during the seizure. The partial results of one such experiment in the monkey are illustrated in Fig. 3. Discrete regions of markedly increased glucose utilization, sometimes as much as 200%, are observed ipsilaterally in the motor cortex, basal ganglia, particularly the globus pallidus, thalamic nuclei, and contralaterally in the cerebellar cortex (Kennedy *et al.*, 1975). Kato *et al.* (1980), Caveness *et al.* (1980), Hosokawa *et al.* (1980), and Caveness (1980) have carried out the most extensive studies of the propagation of the seizure activity in newborn and pubescent monkeys. The results indicate that the brain of the newborn monkey exhibits similar increases of glucose utilization in specific structures, but the pattern of distribution of the effects is less well defined than in the pubescent monkeys. Collins *et al.* (1976) have carried out similar studies in the rat with similar results but also obtained evidence on the basis of a local stimulation of glucose utilization of a ''mirror focus'' in the motor cortex contralateral to the side with the penicillin-induced epileptogenic focus.

Engel *et al.* (1978) have used the [^{14}C]deoxyglucose method to study seizures kindled in rats by daily electroconvulsive shocks. After a period of such treatment, the animals exhibit spontaneous seizures. Their results show marked increases in the limbic system, particularly the amygdala. The daily administration of the local anesthetic, lidocaine, kindles similar seizures in rats; Post *et al.* (1979) have obtained similar results in such seizures with particularly pronounced increases in glucose utilization in the amygdala, hippocampus, and the enterorhinal cortex.

2. Spreading Cortical Depression

Shinohara *et al.* (1979) studied the effects of local applications of KCl on the dura overlying the parietal cortex of conscious rats or directly on the pial surface of the parietal cortex of anesthetized rats in order to determine if K$^+$ stimulates cerebral energy metabolism *in vivo* as it is well known to do *in vitro*. The results demonstrate a marked increase in cerebral cortical glucose utilization in response to the application of KCl; NaCl has no such effect (Fig. 10). Such application of KCl, however, also produces the phenomenon of spreading cortical depression. This condition is characterized by a spread of transient intense neuronal activity followed by membrane depolarization, electrical depression, and a negative shift in the cortical DC potential in all directions from the site of initiation at a rate of 2–5 mm/minute. The depressed cortex also exhibits a number of chemical changes, including an increase in extracellular K$^+$, lost presumably from the cells. At the same time when the cortical glucose utilization is increased, most subcortical structures that are functionally connected to the depressed cortex exhibit decreased rates of glucose utilization. During recovery from the spreading cortical depression, the glucose utilization in the cortex is still increased, but it is distributed in columns oriented perpendicularly through the cortex. This columnar ar-

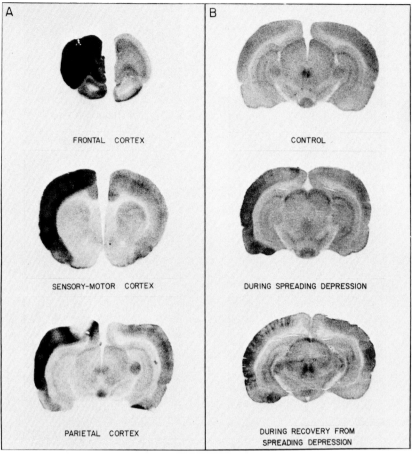

FRONTAL CORTEX

CONTROL

SENSORY-MOTOR CORTEX

DURING SPREADING DEPRESSION

PARIETAL CORTEX

DURING RECOVERY FROM
SPREADING DEPRESSION

FIG. 10.   Autoradiographs of sections of rat brains during spreading cortical depression and during recovery. The autoradiographs are pictorial representations of the relative rates of glucose utilization in various parts of the brain, the greater the density, the greater the rate of glucose utilization. The left sides of the brain are represented by the left hemispheres in the autoradiographs. In all the experiments illustrated, the control hemisphere was treated the same as the experimental side except that equivalent concentrations of NaCl rather than KCl were used. The NaCl did not lead to any detectable differences from hemispheres over which the skull was left intact and no NaCl was applied. (A) Autoradiographs of sections of brain at different levels of cerebral cortex from a conscious rat during spreading cortical depression induced on the left side by application of 5 M KCl to the intact dura overlying the left parietal cortex. The spreading depression was sustained by repeated applications of the KCl at 15- to 20-minute intervals throughout the experimental period. (B) Autoradiographs from sections of brain at the level of the parietal cortex from three animals under barbiturate anesthesia. The top section is from a normal anesthetized animal; the middle section is from an animal during unilateral spreading cortical depression induced and sustained by repeated applications of 80 mM KCl in artificial cerebrospinal fluid directly on the surface of the left parieto-occipital cortex. At the bottom is a comparable section from an animal studied immediately after the return of cortical DC potential to normal after a single wave of spreading depression induced by a single application of 80 mM KCl to the parieto-occipital cortex of the left side. (From Shinohara et al., 1979.)

rangement may reflect the columnar functional and morphological arrangement of the cerebral cortex. It is likely that the increased glucose utilization in the cortex during spreading cortical depression is the consequence of the increased extracellular K^+ and activation of the Na^+,K^+-ATPase.

3. Opening of Blood–Brain Barrier

Unilateral opening of the blood–brain barrier in rats by unilateral carotid injection with a hyperosmotic mannitol solution leads to widely distributed discrete regions of intensely increased glucose utilization in the ipsilateral hemisphere (Pappius et al., 1979). These focal regions of hypermetabolism may reflect local regions of seizure activity. The prior administration of diazepam prevents in most cases the appearance of these areas of increased metabolism (Pappius et al., 1979), and electroencephalographic recordings under similar experimental conditions reveal evidence of seizure activity (C. Fieschi, personal communication).

4. Hypoxemia

Pulsinelli and Duffy (1979) have studied the effects of controlled hypoxemia on local cerebral glucose utilization by means of the qualitative [^{14}C]deoxyglucose method. Hypoxemia was achieved by artificial ventilation of the animals with a mixture of N_2, N_2O, and O_2, adjusted to maintain the arterial pO_2 between 28 and 32 mm Hg. All the animals had had one common carotid artery ligated to limit the increase in cerebral blood flow and the amount of O_2 delivered to the brain. Their autoradiographs provide striking evidence of marked and disparate changes in glucose utilization in the various structural components of the brain. The hemisphere ipsilateral to the carotid ligation was not unexpectedly more severely affected. The most striking effects were markedly higher increases in glucose utilization in white matter than in gray matter, presumably due to the Pasteur effect, and the appearance of transverse cortical columns of high activity alternating with columns of low activity. By studies with black plastic microspheres, they were able to show that the cortical columns were anatomically related to penetrating cortical arteries with the columns of high metabolic activity lying between the arteries.

Miyaoka et al. (1979b) have also studied the effects of moderate hypoxemia in normal, spontaneously breathing conscious rats without carotid ligation. The hypoxemia was produced by lowering the O_2 in the inspired air to approximately 7%. Although this procedure reduced arterial pO_2 to approximately 30 mm Hg, the cerebral hypoxia was probably less than in the studies of Pulsinelli and Duffy (1979) because of the intact cerebral circulation. The animals remained fully conscious under these experimental conditions although they appeared subdued and less active. The quantitative [^{14}C]deoxyglucose method was employed, and rates of glucose utilization were determined. The results revealed many similarities to those of Pulsinelli and Duffy (1979). There was a complete redistribution of the local rates of glucose utilization from the normal pattern. Metabolism in white matter was markedly increased. Many areas showed decreased rates of metabolism. Columns were seen in the cerebral cortex, and the caudate nucleus exhibited a strange lace-like heterogeneity quite distinct from its normal homogeneity. Despite the widespread changes, however, overall average glucose utilization remained unchanged. These results are of relevance to the studies by Kety and Schmidt (1948b), who found in man that the breathing of 10% O_2 produced a wide variety of mental symptoms without altering the average O_2 consumption of the brain as a whole. The mental symptoms were probably the result of metabolic and functional changes in specific regions of the brain detectable only by methods like the deoxyglucose method that measure metabolic rate in the structural components of the brain.

5. Normal Aging

Although, strictly speaking, aging is not a pathophysiological condition, many of its behavioral consequences are directly attributable to decrements in functions of the central nervous system (Birren et al., 1963). Normal human aging has been found to be associated with a decrease in average glucose utilization of the brain as a whole (Sokoloff, 1966). Smith et al. (1980) have employed the quantitative [^{14}C]deoxyglucose method to study normal aging in Sprague–Dawley rats between 5–6 and 36 months of age. Their results show widespread but not homogeneous reductions of local cerebral glucose utilization with age. The sensory systems, particularly auditory and visual, are particularly severely affected. The caudate nucleus is metabolically depressed, and preliminary experiments indicate that it loses responsivity to dopamine agonists, such as apomorphine, with age (C. Smith and J. McCulloch, unpublished observations). A striking effect was the loss of metabolically active neuropil in the cerebral cortex; Layer IV is markedly decreased in metabolic activity and extent. Some of these changes may be related to specific functional disabilities that develop in old age.

VIII. Microscopic Resolution

The resolution of the present [^{14}C]deoxyglucose method is at best approximately 100 μm. The use of [^{3}H]deoxyglucose does not greatly improve the resolution when the standard autoradiographic procedure is used. The limiting factor is the diffusion and migration of the water-soluble labeled compound in the tissue during the freezing of the brain and the cutting of the brain sections. Des Rosiers and Descarries (1978) have been working to extend the resolution of the method to the light and electron microscopic levels. They use [³H]deoxyglucose and dipping emulsion techniques. They have reported that fixation, postfixation, dehydration, and embedding of the brain by perfusion *in situ* result in negligible loss or migration of the label in the tissue. They can localize grain counts over individual cells or portions of them. Although the method is at present only qualitative, it is likely that it can eventually be adopted for quantitative use. An alternative promising approach to microscopic resolution is the use of freeze-substitution techniques (Ornberg *et al.*, 1979; Sejnowski *et al.*, 1980).

IX. The [¹⁸F]Fluorodeoxyglucose Technique

Because the deoxyglucose method requires the measurement of local concentrations of radioactivity in the individual components of the brain, it cannot be applied as originally designed to man. Recent developments in computerized emission tomography, however, have made it possible to measure local concentrations of labeled compounds *in vivo* in man. Emission tomography requires the use of γ-radiation, preferably annihilation γ-rays derived from positron emission. A positron-emitting derivative of deoxyglucose, 2-[¹⁸F]fluoro-2-deoxy-D-glucose, has been synthesized and found to retain the necessary biochemical properties of 2-deoxyglucose (Reivich *et al.*, 1979). The method has, therefore, been adapted for use in man with [¹⁸F]fluorodeoxyglucose and positron-emission tomography (Reivich *et al.*, 1979; Phelps *et al.*, 1979). The resolution of the method is still relatively limited, approximately 1 cm, but it is already proving to be useful in studies of the human visual system (Phelps *et al.*, 1981) and of clinical conditions, such as focal epilepsy (Kuhl *et al.*, 1979, 1980). This technique is of immense potential usefulness for studies of human local cerebral energy metabolism in normal states and in neurological and psychiatric disorders.

X. Summary

The deoxyglucose method provides the means to determine quantitatively the rates of glucose utilization simultaneously in all structural and functional components of the central nervous system and to display them pictorially superimposed on the anatomical structures in which they occur. Because of the close relationship between local functional activity and energy metabolism, the method makes it possible to identify all structures with increased or decreased functional activity in various physiological, pharmacological, and pathophysiological states. The images provided by the method do resemble histological sections of nervous tissue, and the method is, therefore, sometimes misconstrued to be a neuroanatomical method and contrasted with physiological methods, such as electrophysiological recording. This classification obscures the most significant and unique feature of the method. The images are not of structure but of a dynamic biochemical process, glucose utilization, which is as physiological as electrical activity. In most situations changes in functional activity result in changes in energy metabolism, and the images can be used to visualize and identify the sites of altered activity. The images are, therefore, analogous to infrared maps; they record quantitatively the rates of a kinetic process and display them pictorially exactly where they exist. The fact that they depict the anatomical structures is fortuitous; it indicates that the rates of glucose utilization are distributed according to structure, and specific functions in the nervous system are associated with specific anatomical structures. The deoxyglucose method represents, therefore, in a real sense, a new type of encephalography, metabolic encephalography. At the very least, it should serve as a valuable supplement to more conventional types, such as electroencephalography. Because, however, it provides a new means to examine another aspect of function simultaneously in all parts of the brain, it is hoped that it and its derivative, the [18F]fluorodeoxyglucose technique, will open new roads to the understanding of how the brain works in health and disease.

ACKNOWLEDGMENT

The author wishes to express his appreciation to Mrs. Ruth Bower for her excellent editorial and bibliographic assistance.

REFERENCES

Allen, T. O., Adler, N. T., Greenberg, J. H., and Reivich, M. (1981). *Science* **211**, 1070.
Bachelard, H. S. (1971). *J. Neurochem.* **18**, 213.
Batipps, M., Miyaoka, M., Shinohara, M., Sokoloff, L., and Kennedy, C. (1981). *Neurology* **31**, 58.
Bidder, T. G. (1968). *J. Neurochem.* **15**, 867.
Birren, J. E., Butler, R. N., Greenhouse, S. W., Sokoloff, L., and Yarrow, M. R., eds. (1963). "Human Aging: A Biological and Behavioral Study." Public Health Service Publication No. 986, U.S. Gov. Printing Office, Washington, D.C.
Brown, L., and Wolfson, L. (1978). *Brain Res.* **148**, 188.
Caveness, W. F. (1969). *In* "Basic Mechanisms of the Epilepsies" (H. H. Jasper, A. A. Ward, and A. Pope, eds.), pp. 517–534. Little, Brown, Boston, Massachusetts.

Caveness, W. F. (1980). *Ann. Neurol.* **7**, 230.

Caveness, W. F., Kato, M., Malamut, B. L., Hosokawa, S., Wakisaka, S., and O'Neill, R. R. (1980). *Ann. Neurol.* **7**, 213.

Collins, R. C., Kennedy, C., Sokoloff, L., and Plum, F. (1976). *Arch. Neurol.* **33**, 536.

Des Rosiers, M. H., and Descarries, L. (1978). *C.R. Acad. Sci. Paris Ser. D* **287**, 153.

Des Rosiers, M. H., Sakurada, O., Jehle, J., Shinohara, M., Kennedy, C., and Sokoloff, L. (1978). *Science* **200**, 447.

Dow-Edwards, D. L., Crane, A., Kennedy, C., and Sokoloff, L. (1982). *Neurosci. Abstr.* **8**, 872.

Duffy, T. E., Cavazzuti, M., Cruz, N. F., and Sokoloff, L. (1982). *Ann. Neurol.* **11**, 233.

Durham, D., and Woolsey, T. A. (1977). *Brain Res. 137,* 169.

Eayrs, J. (1961). *J. Endocrinol.* **22**, 409.

Eklöf, B., Lassen, N. A., Nilsson, L., Norberg, K., and Siesjö, B. K. (1973). *Acta Physiol. Scand.* **88**, 587.

Engel, J., Jr., Wolfson, L., and Brown, L. (1978). *Ann. Neurol.* **3**, 538.

Freygang, W. H., Jr., and Sokoloff, L. (1958). *Adv. Biol. Med. Phys.* **6**, 263.

Friedli, C. (1978). *Adv. Exp. Med. Biol.* **94**, 747–754.

Galvan, M., Ten Bruggencate, G., and Senekowitsch, R. (1979). *Brain Res.* **160**, 544.

Gjedde, A., Caronna, J. J., Hindfelt, B., and Plum, F. (1975). *Am. J. Physiol.* **229**, 113.

Goochee, C., Rasband, W., and Sokoloff, L. (1980). *Ann. Neurol.* **7**, 359.

Hand, P. J. (1981). *In* "Neuroanatomical Tract Tracing Methods" (L. Heimer and M. J. Robards, eds.), pp. 511–538. Plenum, New York.

Hand, P. J., Greenberg, J. H., Miselis, R. R., Weller, W. L., and Reivich, M. (1978). *Neurosci. Abstr.* **4**, 553.

Hers, H. G. (1957). "Le Métabolisme du Fructose," p. 102. Arscia, Brussels.

Horowicz, P., and Larrabee, M. G. (1958). *J. Neurochem.* **2**, 102.

Hosokawa, S., Iguchi, T., Caveness, W. F., Kato, M., O'Neill, R. R., Wakisaka, S., and Malamut, B. L. (1980). *Ann. Neurol.* **7**, 222.

Hubel, D. H., and Wiesel, T. N. (1968). *J. Physiol. (London)* **195**, 215.

Hubel, D. H., and Wiesel, T. N. (1972). *J. Comp. Neurol.* **146**, 421.

Hubel, D. H., and Wiesel, T. N., and Stryker, M. P. (1978). *J. Comp. Neurol.* **177**, 361.

Jarvis, C. D., Mishkin, M., Shinohara, M., Sakurada, O., Miyaoka, M., and Kennedy, C. (1978). *Neurosci. Abstr.* **4**, 632.

Kadekaro, M., Gross, P. M., Holcomb, H. H., Sokoloff, L., and Saavedra, J. M. (1982). *Neurosci. Abstr.* **8**, 138.

Kato, M., Malamut, B. L., Caveness, W. F., Hosokawa, S., Wakisaka, S., and O'Neill, R. R. (1980). *Ann. Neurol.* **7**, 204.

Kennedy, C., Des Rosiers, M., Jehle, J. W., Reivich, M., Sharp, F., and Sokoloff, L. (1975). *Science* **187**, 850.

Kennedy, C., Des Rosiers, M. H., Sakurada, O., Shinohara, M., Reivich, M., Jehle, J. W., and Sokoloff, L. (1976). *Proc. Natl. Acad. Sci. U.S.A.* **73**, 4230.

Kennedy, C., Sakurada, O., Shinohara, M., Jehle, J., and Sokoloff, L. (1978). *Ann. Neurol.* **4**, 293.

Kennedy, C., Miyaoka, M., Suda, S., Macko, K., Jarvis, C., Mishkin, M., and Sokoloff, L. (1980). *Trans. Am. Neurol. Assoc.* **105**, 13.

Kety, S. S. (1950). *Am. J. Med.* **8**, 205.

Kety, S. S. (1957). *In* "Metabolism of the Nervous System" (D. Richter, ed.), pp. 221–237. Pergamon, Oxford.

Kety, S. S. (1960). *Methods Med. Res.* **8**, 228.

Kety, S. S., and Schmidt, C. F. (1948a). *J. Clin. Invest.* **27**, 476.

Kety, S. S., and Schmidt, C. F. (1948b). *J. Clin. Invest.* **27**, 484.

Kuhl, D., Engel, J., Phelps, M., and Selin, C. (1979). *Acta Neurol. Scand. (Suppl. 72)* **60**, 538.

Kuhl, D. E., Engel, J., Jr., Phelps, M. E., and Selin, C. (1980). *Ann. Neurol.* **8**, 348.

Landau, W. M., Freygang, W. H., Jr., Rowland, L. P., Sokoloff, L., and Kety, S. S. (1955). *Trans. Am. Neurol. Assoc.* **80**, 125.

Larrabee, M. G. (1958). *J. Neurochem.* **2**, 81.

Lashley, K. S. (1934). *J. Comp. Neurol.* **59**, 341.

Lassen, N. A. (1959). *Physiol. Rev.* **39**, 183.

Lassen, N. A., and Munck, O. (1955). *Acta Physiol. Scand.* **33**, 30.

McCulloch, J., Savaki, H. E., McCulloch, M. C., and Sokoloff, L. (1979). *Nature (London)* **282**, 303.

McCulloch, J., Savaki, H. E., and Sokoloff, L. (1980a). *Brain Res.* **194**, 117.

McCulloch, J., Savaki, H. E., McCulloch, M. C., and Sokoloff, L. (1980b). *Science* **207**, 313.

Mata, M., Fink, D. J., Gainer, H., Smith, C. B., Davidsen, L., Savaki, H., Schwartz, W. J., and Sokoloff, L. (1980). *J. Neurochem.* **34**, 213.

Miyaoka, M., Shinohara, M., Batipps, M., Pettigrew, K. D., Kennedy, C., and Sokoloff, L. (1979a). *Acta Neurol. Scand. (Suppl. 72)* **60**, 16.

Miyaoka, M., Shinohara, M., Kennedy, C., and Sokoloff, L. (1979b). *Trans. Am. Neurol. Assoc.* **104**, 151.

Montero, V. M., and Guillery, R. W. (1968). *J. Comp. Neurol.* **134**, 211.

Nordmann, J. J. (1977). *J. Anat.* **123**, 213.

Oldendorf, W. H. (1971). *Am. J. Physiol.* **221**, 1629.

Ornberg, R. L., Neale, E. A., Smith, C. B., Yarowsky, P., and Bowers, L. M. (1979). *J. Cell Biol. Abstr.* **83**, CN142A.

Pappius, H. M., Savaki, H. E., Fieschi, C., Rapoport, S. I., and Sokoloff, L. (1979). *Ann. Neurol.* **5**, 211.

Phelps, M. E., Huang, S. C., Hoffman, E. J., Selin, C., Sokoloff, L., and Kuhl, D. E. (1979). *Ann. Neurol.* **6**, 371.

Phelps, M. E., Kuhl, D. E., and Mazziotta, J. C. (1981). *Science* **211**, 1445.

Plum, F., Gjedde, A., and Samson, F. E. (1976). *Neurosci. Res. Progr. Bull.* **14**, 457.

Porrino, L., Namba, H., Crane, A., Jehle, J., and Sokoloff, L. (1982). *Neurosci. Abstr.* **8**, 69.

Post, R. M., Kennedy, C., Shinohara, M., Squillace, K., Miyaoka, M., Suda, S., Ingvar, D. H., and Sokoloff, L. (1979). *Neurosci. Abstr.* **5**, 196.

Pulsinelli, W. A., and Duffy, T. E. (1979). *Science* **204**, 626.

Rakic, P. (1976). *Nature (London)* **261**, 467.

Reivich, M., Jehle, J., Sokoloff, L., and Kety, S. S. (1969). *J. Appl. Physiol.* **27**, 296.

Reivich, M., Kuhl, D., Wolf, A., Greenberg, J., Phelps, M., Ido, T., Cassella, V., Fowler, J., Hoffman, E., Alavi, A., Som, P., and Sokoloff, L. (1979). *Circ. Res.* **44**, 127.

Roth, R. H. (1976). *Pharmacol. Ther.* **2**, 71.

Roth, R. H., and Giarman, N. J. (1966). *Biochem. Pharmacol.* **15**, 1333.

Sacks, W. (1957). *J. Appl. Physiol.* **10**, 37.

Sakurada, O., Shinohara, M., Klee, W. A., Kennedy, C., and Sokoloff, L. (1976). *Neurosci. Abstr.* **2**, 613.

Savaki, H. E., Kadekaro, M., Jehle, J., and Sokoloff, L. (1978). *Nature (London)* **276**, 521.

Savaki, H. E., McCulloch, J., Kadekaro, M., and Sokoloff, L. (1982). *Brain Res.* **233**, 347.

Scheinberg, P., and Stead, E. A., Jr. (1949). *J. Clin. Invest.* **28**, 1163.

Schwartz, W. J. (1978). *Brain Res.* **158**, 129.

Schwartz, W. J., and Gainer, H. (1977). *Science* **197**, 1089.

Schwartz, W. J., Sharp, F. R., Gunn, R. H., and Evarts, E. V. (1976). *Nature (London)* **261**, 155.

Schwartz, W. J., Smith, C. B., Davidsen, L., Savaki, H., Sokoloff, L., Mata, M., Fink, D. J., and Gainer, H. (1979). *Science* **205**, 723.

Schwartz, W. J., Davidsen, L. C., and Smith, C. B. (1980). *J. Comp. Neurol.* **189**, 157.

Sejnowski, T. J., Reingold, S. C., Kelley, D. B., and Gelperin, A. (1980). *Nature (London)* **287**, 449.

Sharp, F. R., Kauer, J. S., and Shepherd, G. M. (1975). *Brain Res.* **98**, 596.

Shinohara, M., Sakurada, O., Jehle, J., and Sokoloff, L. (1976). *Neurosci. Abstr.* **2**, 615.

Shinohara, M., Dollinger, B., Brown, G., Rapoport, S., and Sokoloff, L. (1979). *Science* **203**, 188.

Silverman, M. S., Hendrickson, A. E., and Clopton, B. M. (1977). *Neurosci. Abstr.* **3**, 11.

Smith, C. B., Goochee, C., Rapoport, S. I., and Sokoloff, L. (1980). *Brain* **103**, 351.

Sokoloff, L. (1960). *Handb. Physiol. Neurophysiol.* **3**, 1843–1864.

Sokoloff, L. (1966). *Res. Publ. Assoc. Nerv. Ment. Dis.* **41**, 237.

Sokoloff, L. (1969). *In* "Psychochemical Research in Man" (A. J. Mandell and M. P. Mandell, eds.), pp. 237–252. Academic Press, New York.

Sokoloff, L. (1976). *In* "Basic Neurochemistry" (G. J. Siegel, R. W. Albers, R. Katzman, and B. W. Agranoff, eds.), 2nd ed., pp. 388–413. Little, Brown, Boston, Massachusetts.

Sokoloff, L. (1977). *J. Neurochem.* **29**, 13.

Sokoloff, L. (1978). *Trends Neurosci.* **1**, 75.

Sokoloff, L. (1979). *Acta Neurol. Scand. (Suppl. 72)* **60**, 640.

Sokoloff, L., Wechsler, R. L., Mangold, R., Balls, K., and Kety, S. S. (1953). *J. Clin. Invest.* **32**, 202.

Sokoloff, L., Reivich, M., Kennedy, C., Des Rosiers, M. H., Patlak, C. S., Pettigrew, K. D., Sakurada, O., and Shinohara, M. (1977). *J. Neurochem.* **28**, 897.

Sols, A., and Crane, R. K. (1954). *J. Biol. Chem.* **210**, 581.

Webster, W. R., Serviere, J., Batini, C., and LaPlante, S. (1978). *Neurosci. Lett.* **10**, 43.

Wechsler, L. R., Savaki, H. E., and Sokoloff, L. (1979). *J. Neurochem.* **32**, 15.

Wiesel, T. N., Hubel, D. H., and Lam, D. M. K. (1974). *Brain Res.* **79**, 273.

Wolfson, L. I., Sakurada, O., and Sokoloff, L. (1977). *J. Neurochem.* **29**, 777.

Yarowsky, P. J., Jehle, J., Ingvar, D. H., and Sokoloff, L. (1979). *Neurosci. Abstr.* **5**, 421.

Yarowsky, P., Crane, A. M., and Sokoloff, L. (1980). *Neurosci. Abstr.* **6**, 340.

DISCUSSION

A-L. Barofsky: We endocrinologists have to thank you, Dr. Sokoloff, for bringing to us a very powerful tool which has tremendous application in our area of interest. We have been utilizing the 2-deoxyglucose procedure which Dr. Sokoloff has very kindly helped us to establish in our laboratory to examine changes in central nervous system metabolic activity associated with the ovulatory release of LH. We've used the ovariectomized rat model of Freeman and co-workers. In this regimen (Table A) animals receive a single injection of estradiol benzoate at 0700 hours on day 0. This induces an LH surge having its onset between 14 and 1600 hours on each subsequent afternoon, shown here for day 1 and day 2 (Table A, top). Our control group animals were ovariectomized and identically treated with estradiol benzoate on day 0, showing the expected LH surge on day 1 (Table A, bottom). However, at 1600 hours on day 1 these animals received 5 mg of progesterone, a procedure

TABLE A

Protocol: CNS Mapping of the Estrogen-Induced LH Surge[a]

Group	Day 0	Day 1	Day 2
OVX			
Estrogen-induced surge	50 μg EB → (0700 hr)	LH surge + oil → (1600 hr)	LH surge ↑ 2-DG (1430 hr)
OVX			
Control	50 μg EB → (0700 hr)	LH surge + 5 mg P → (1600 hr)	No surge ↑ 2-DG (1430 hr)

[a] OVX, Ovariectomized; EB, estradiol benzoate; P, progesterone.

which blocks the surge on the following day, that is day 2. Thus, the nonsurging estrogen plus progesterone group provided the appropriate comparison on day 2 with the estrogen-treated group to examine the pattern of CNS metabolic activity associated with the LH surge. Both groups were implanted with an intracardiac cannula prior to 0900 hours on the morning of day 2, and 2-deoxyglucose at 125 μCi/kg was injected via the cannula at 1430 hours on day 2. Animals were sacrificed by decapitation 45 minutes later and brains were processed for autoradiography according to the procedure of Sokoloff and co-workers.

Table B shows the autoradiographic densities for the preoptic and hypothalamic areas which we have examined so far. The first column of data shows the mean value for white matter expressed as the concentration of ^{14}C in the tissue. The values for white matter are

TABLE B

Metabolic Activity in Preoptic-Hypothalamic Areas of Ovariectomized Female Rats Just Prior to an Estrogen-Induced LH Surge[a,b]

			Autoradiographic densities				
		White matter ± SE (nCi/g brain tissue)	MPO	POP	SC	AH	ARC
Group	N		(nCi/g gray matter/nCi/g white matter)				
Control	4	125	1.34	1.56	2.27	1.27	1.12
(EB-P)		±5	±0.14	±0.09	±0.27	±0.06	±0.07
LH surge	4	121	1.17	1.52	1.86[c]	1.15	1.14
(EB)		±6	±0.02	±0.22	±0.18	±0.10	±0.12

[a] From Barofsky, Stockman, Nero, Harden, and White (unpublished).

[b] MPO, Medial preoptic n; POP, preoptic periventricular n; SC, suprachiasmatic n; AH, anterior hypothalamic n; ARC, arcuate n.

[c] $p = 0.05$.

approximately the same in the two treatment groups. The right-hand columns show the ratio of ^{14}C concentration in gray matter to the concentration in white matter for several preoptic hypothalamic areas. There were no differences between groups in the preoptic periventricular and arcuate nuclei. Contrary to our expectations, however, we observed decreases in metabolic activity in the LH surgers (bottom row). Small decreases in the medial preoptic area and the anterior hypothalamic nuclei were not significant, whereas the suprachiasmatic nuclei showed a significant drop in metabolic activity in the LH surging group. Clearly we need to examine more than a single 45-minute time period on the afternoon of the LH surge to fully understand the significance of these changes. However, we can interpret our data to suggest that superimposed upon the daily photoperiodic changes in metabolic activity in the suprachiasmatic nuclei which Dr. Sokoloff has so elegantly demonstrated, are changes which occur in response to the hormonal environment. Since the normal estrous cycle in the rat is most closely approximated by an estrogen-induced LH surge on proestrus followed by progesterone inhibition of subsequent surges, the role of the suprachiasmatic nuclei in influencing ovulatory LH release must be more than just that of a daily timekeeper. At the very least the suprachiasmatic nuclei must recognize that in one out of four cycle days the hormonal environment is different and respond with a change in metabolic activity. This change may represent a decrease in impulse flow through inhibitory inputs.

L. Sokoloff: I noticed in your data, I think it was in the anterior hypothalamic nucleus and the medial preoptic nucleus, that although the changes were not statistically significant, they were both well on the way to being significantly reduced in your small group of animals with the surge. Maybe in a larger group, these structures would also show a significant change. Is there any reason to suspect that they might be involved? They could be.

A-L. Barofsky: Yes. These are clearly areas that have been implicated in gonadotropin control and, with a larger N, the decrease in these groups may very well be significant. Also, we hope that with the future application of your full quantitative procedure, which may be a little more sensitive to differences, we may be able to demonstrate significant changes in medial preoptic and anterior hypothalamic nuclei.

L. Sokoloff: There is a good reason for using the full quantitative method. With the qualitative method if you get a change in patterns, as for example with the ocular dominance columns, you really don't need quantification to recognize that something dramatically different has happened—so within the same animal you can compare areas for the rates of glucose utilization or changes in them. However, when you go from one animal to another you have a real problem in making comparisons. One critical difference is simply the plasma glucose concentration, and some of the procedures that are used will change the plasma glucose concentration and change the labeling entirely. If you use the full quantitative method, the formula takes all that into account, but just looking at optical densities or just radioactive concentrations in the tissues is not really measuring the rate of the reaction. A lot of other things come into play which the quantitative method takes care of. I, therefore, always recommend the quantitative technique because it isn't that much harder. Just put an arterial catheter in and sample arterial blood, and measure the deoxyglucose and glucose concentrations.

A-L. Barofsky: We appreciate that, and I would like to stress the importance of your comments. I should mention that in fact the differences which we saw were not evident in the autoradiograms visually. We did not pick them up until measuring the autoradiographic densities of the area by microphotometry.

U. Zor: Since this is a hormone conference, I would like to ask what is the effect of hormones in the glucose transport and turnover in the brain, and specifically, what is the effect of insulin which probably produces in the brain at least in low quantity on a glucose transport as well as on glucose metabolism in the brain?

L. Sokoloff: There has not yet been a great deal of work done with hormones in the brain with this technique. Dr. Dow-Edwards in our laboratory has looked at animals that were made cretinous at birth and allowed to grow up for 5 months, and there is a marked diffuse decrease in glucose utilization in most parts of the brain, particularly in the cerebral cortical areas and the auditory system. I don't know whether patients with cretinism have trouble hearing or not, but I might guess that they do. We have work going on in our laboratory by Dr. Kadekaro on the Brattleboro rat. As you know the Brattleboro rat has a deficiency in vasopressin synthesis. She finds, surprisingly, that in spite of the deficiency in vasopressin synthesis, there is a tremendous increase in glucose utilization in the posterior pituitary which is not reduced by vasopressin replacement treatment. Another region that is affected with an increase in glucose utilization in the Brattleboro rat, which by the way has diabetes insipidus, is the subfornical organ. This organ mediates drinking behavior and responds to high levels of angiotensin II. The subfornical organ's change in metabolism is corrected by vasopressin administration, but the posterior pituitary's change in metabolism is not, and so we don't know what is going on. Dr. Porrino in our laboratory is doing some experiments also related to the effects of gonadal hormones on the brain, but it is not at the stage where there is much to say. You asked about insulin. That is a question we have been interested in for a long time. It appears that insulin itself, at least exogenously administered insulin, has no direct effect on brain energy metabolism. The effects that it does have are mediated through its effects on blood glucose concentration. If you produce hypoglycemia with insulin, you decrease cerebral energy metabolism and may produce coma, but if you cover the insulin with glucose, there appears to be no effect whatsoever on the rate of metabolism. However, that is not a very satisfactory answer because there are things that come up every so often that suggest that insulin might do something to the brain. Some work around 1964 by Lowry and his group may, perhaps, give us a lead. What they were doing was to use his technique to study the effects of hypoglycemia on glycolytic flux. They gave insulin and then killed the animals at various times—seconds later—5, 10, 15 seconds after giving the insulin. They found that in the animals killed later, there was a decreased glucose level in the brain tissue, a decreased level in the blood, and decreased glycolytic flux, but earlier before, the blood glucose had fallen, they found a very high level of glucose in the brain, higher than one would have expected from the blood level. One might interpret these results to indicate that insulin is involved in the transport of glucose across the blood–brain barrier. It may stimulate the transport, but since under normal circumstances glucose utilization is not limited by that rate of transport, the metabolism is normally unaffected by insulin. It might be important in cases when blood glucose is limiting. We have some experiments designed and are waiting for an opportunity to schedule them, in which K_1 and K_2, the rate constants in our operational equation, which are related specifically to blood flow and blood–brain barrier transport, will be measured in the presence of insulin but with the blood glucose level maintained normal. These experiments might tell us directly whether insulin affects transport or not.

T. Kono: I would like to point out one thing, that is, the accumulation of 2-deoxy-D-glucose in the tissue and the utilization of glucose are not necessarily synonymous; in the case of muscle cells, the former is stimulated when the utilization of glucose is stimulated, but in the case of adipocytes, the transport and accumulation of 2-deoxy-D-glucose is not stimulated when the glucose utilization is stimulated. However, your data indicate that when the glucose utilization is stimulated, more 2-deoxy-D-glucose is accumulated. This suggests that brain cells have a feedback system, and when the glucose utilization is stimulated, the transport is activated.

L. Sokoloff: You don't have to activate transport in the brain because the transport rate is so fast. Glucose and deoxyglucose are being transported at an excessive rate beyond utilization and in fact the rate constants for transport out are larger than the rate constants for transport in. There is a very large flux of glucose in and out of the brain all the time, and the part that goes to metabolism is just a little trickle tapped off it.

T. Kono: If turnover is very high, the concentration of the sugar inside and outside of cells must be equal. Then, how is the accumulation of the sugar as its 6-phosphate regulated?

L. Sokoloff: The turnover is very high; the glucose half-life in brain tissue is about 1.8 minutes, and the deoxyglucose half-life is about 2.5 minutes.

T. Kono: If the turnover is always very rapid, I fail to understand why a small amount of 2-deoxy-D-glucose is accumulated in the tissue when the glucose metabolism is slow, e.g., when the animal is sleeping.

L. Sokoloff: We are accumulating the product, deoxyglucose 6-phosphate, and that is slowly accumulating over a period of time.

K. Sterling: I thought this was the clearest, most straightforward talk I've heard in a long time. I want to discuss a couple of points and ask Dr. Sokoloff's reaction to some of our own findings. Some years ago, Kety and Schmidt showed that the brain QO_2 does not differ between normal, hyperthyroid, or hypothyroid animals or man. They did it in human subjects with cannulation of the jugular and common carotid arteries, and studied some of the same individuals, as I recall, when hyperthyroid and later when euthyroid after treatment. The subjects had the same cerebral oxygen consumption when hyperthyroid and euthyroid. This agreed with the findings of Barker and Klitgaard that the adult brain, spleen, and testes are not affected by thyroid hormone in so far as QO_2 (oxygen consumption) is concerned. Now along the same lines we found that the mitochondria of these three unresponsive tissues, including brain mitochondria, lack altogether the thyroid hormone receptors which were found in the mitochondria of all other organs including not only liver but striated skeletal muscle and cardiac muscle; however, in the neonatal rat brain, the mitochondrial thyroid hormone receptors are present up to 14 days approximately; after that they're lost, and we find no specific receptors in the brain mitochondria from 17 days to adulthood at various ages of mature rats. The reason I'm dwelling on this is that in the last year or two some other observers including Mary Dratman have been working on the brain synaptosomes and some of the nuclear enthusiasts have been claiming some findings about nuclear concentration of thyroid hormone in adult brain cells and I wonder if I could elicit any reaction from you to all of this about thyroid hormone in the brain?

L. Sokoloff: I myself worked in that field for a while. I think that the evidence is very clear that the brain, once developed and mature, no longer responds to the thyroid hormone, and that would fit with the absence of any receptors for thyroid hormones there which fits with the time course of the disappearance of the receptors in the rat that you described. Your data on receptors also fit very well with the effects on energy metabolism of rat cerebral cortex studied a number of years ago by Fazekas. He found that in the rat cerebral cortex the oxygen consumption is very low at birth, it stays low for about 7 days, then it starts to rise in a typical S-shape pattern and reaches maturity at about 45 days of age. The 45-day-old rat has a cerebral oxygen consumption which is at a normal mature level. Animals treated with thyroxin from birth showed no response in the cerebral oxygen consumption for the first 4 or 5 days; then the oxygen consumption began to rise starting in the upward direction sooner than in the euthyroid rats, rose more steeply and started to taper off somewhere around 20, 25, 30 days or so, and reached the same normal adult level at 35 days of age, about 10 days earlier than the euthyroid rats. These effects indicate that there is something in the brain that allows it to respond to thyroid hormones early during its developmental period, but it disappears sometime before maturation. Also the work of John Eayrs is relevant. He found that if you remove or destroy the thyroid at birth, the brain, of course, will not properly develop morphologically. There will be a deficiency in the synaptic connections being made. Improvement can be achieved by giving thyroid replacement therapy provided it is started early enough. If replacement therapy is begun immediately, the animal's brain will develop normally, but if it is delayed, the degree of maturation is reduced. One can determine the critical period; he reports that it is 24 days. After 24 days of age it is too late for replacement therapy to have any effect on brain development.

J. E. Rall: I think with the increasing availability and sensitivity of PET scanners for humans, many times one might be interested in rather quick responses looking at the change in metabolic rate in the course of a few minutes. Do you have any algorithms set up for computers, so that if you really have good control over the specific activity of the fluoro-deoxyglucose in blood, you can then interpret relatively quick changes in the unsteady state in different areas?

L. Sokoloff: That is a very good question. The equation that I showed applies for any time. In other words, you can use it in 1 minute or 2 minutes or 5 minutes. In fact if you knew the rate constants precisely, you could use it for any time you want. The reason we went to the 45-minute period is because the rate constants are nondeterminable in the same animals at the same time, and we wanted the method to be insensitive to the rate constants. If there was a way to determine in the same animal the rate constants at the same time that glucose utilization is being measured, then you could do it very quickly. As it turns out, with positron emission tomography, you can get a continuous record of the tissue concentrations as a function of time. With these data, you can compute the rate constants for each structure for that individual. What we are awaiting is machines of high enough sensitivity to pick up a reliable number of counts at early times when the tissue uptake occurs. These are coming. In fact Rodney Brooks at NIH is now in the process of trying to determine the rate constants in the same person at the same time when he is measuring glucose utilization.

D. Pfaff: Dr. Sokoloff, what places an upper limit on the resolution of the 2DG technique in animals? In the hypothalamus, for example, using steroid hormone autoradiography, we can see a heavily labeled cell adjacent to an unlabeled cell. With resolution of 50 to 100 micra the 2DG technique would mix the two.

L. Sokoloff: In our case the limit of resolution is probably diffusibility of the water-soluble material. To obtain cellular resolution you really have to do good histology, and when you prepare the sections for histology, you move or wash out your label. However, there is some work going on with freeze-substitution techniques which look very promising. Individual cells have been visualized, and in some cases it is claimed that there was no loss of isotope. We do know that if you do not rupture the cell membrane with ice crystals, the deoxyglucose 6-phosphate will not diffuse out. It is the ice crystals, forming during the freezing or thawing, that ruptures the membrane, and then there is diffusion out. I think that the freeze-substitution technique, which is also sensitive to ice crystals, looks very promising. In fact we have a project going to try to adapt our method for cellular resolution.

F. C. Bartter: In the normal rat, the evidence is I think quite clear that vasopressin is made in the supraoptic and paraventricular nuclei, and proceeds to the posterior pituitary by axon flow. It is then stored in the posterior pituitary. Why then is the posterior pituitary uptake of oxygen higher in the Brattleboro rat, which neither stores vasopressin there nor is "trying" to synthesize it there?

L. Sokoloff: The Brattleboro rat cannot synthesize vasopressin.

F. C. Bartter: My second question concerns the suprachiasmatic area. Does the higher glucose uptake in the "daytime" mean, in your NIH rats, that they sleep by "day" as usual, and are active by "night"? If so, why is glucose uptake in the suprachiasmatic nucleus higher with sleep?

L. Sokoloff: We borrowed a darkroom where the cycle could be controlled. The normal cycle was light during the daytime, dark at night. Six in the morning to 6:00 at night it was light, and 6:00 at night to 6:00 in the morning it was dark. The rats normally sleep during the day and are awake at night. Of course, during the studies they were awake.

Impact of Estrogens on Hypothalamic Nerve Cells: Ultrastructural, Chemical, and Electrical Effects

Donald W. Pfaff

Laboratory of Neurobiology and Behavior, The Rockefeller University, New York, New York

I. Introduction

The modern era of research on cellular effects of estrogens opened with the discovery that tritiated estradiol is specifically retained in target tissues such as rat uterus (Jensen and Jacobson, 1962). Further analyses suggested that transport of estrogens to the cell nucleus would be correlated with their biochemical effects (Gorski *et al.*, 1968). Estradiol could alter transcription in the uterus, because its administration is followed by increases in RNA polymerase activity and increases in the incorporation of tritiated amino acids into protein (Mueller *et al.*, 1972). Thinking about the exact means by which steroids translocated to the cell nucleus might alter transcription has depended on results in the chick oviduct, in which estrogen and progestins increase production of the protein Avidin through specific hormone receptors and subsequent increases in RNA polymerase activity (O'Malley *et al.*, 1969).

Studying hormone action requires understanding the properties of the hormone-dependent system well enough for a meaningful step-by-step analysis of the hormone effects. In some organs this involves the growth or secretion of a single type of cell. For the effects of hormones on neuroendocrine phenomena and behavior, we deal with the complexities of the mammalian central nervous system. Thus, it is best to choose for detailed study a small number of behaviors and neuroendocrine phenomena which are sufficiently simple and specific for reliable experimenting and close reasoning about their properties and neural circuitry.

Among the subjects proven good for study in this way has been lordosis behavior, the primary reproductive behavioral response in female rodents, which allows fertilization by the male. The neural circuitry for this behavior is the best understood of any mammalian behavior pattern (Pfaff, 1980). The effects of estrogen on this behavior also comprise a mechanism of behavioral motivation (Pfaff, 1982).

127

II. Steroid Hormone Binding in the Brains of Vertebrates

A. PROOF OF EXISTENCE AND PROPERTIES AS RECEPTORS

Initial autoradiographic experiments showed that tritiated estradiol is specifically retained by hypothalamic cells in ovariectomized female rats (Pfaff, 1968a,b; Stumpf, 1968). Complete autoradiographic mapping of the rat central nervous system revealed networks of estrogen-concentrating neurons not only in the medial preoptic area and medial hypothalamus, but also in the phylogenetically stable limbic system of the rat forebrain (Pfaff and Keiner, 1973). A very high percentage of estrogen-concentrating cells are at the hypothalamic and forebrain levels of the neuraxis; detailed examination of the spinal cord under autoradiographic conditions favorable for detecting estrogen neurons uncovered very few labeled cells, even in portions of the spinal cord involved in estrogen-dependent lordosis behavior (Morrell et al., 1982).

Steroid hormone binding in the brain is a phenomenon widespread among vertebrates. Autoradiographic work with representatives of all the major classes of vertebrates in our laboratory has led to conclusions about steroid hormone binding which appear to be true of all vertebrate species. Species examined range, for example, from paradise fish (Davis et al., 1977) to rhesus monkeys (Pfaff et al., 1976), and most recently were extended to observations on snakes (Halpern et al., 1982). Specific anatomic findings across this range of species have been reviewed (Morrell and Pfaff, 1978). In general (Table I) estrogen and androgen-concentrating cells can always be found in specific locations with autoradiographic methods in the brain of a vertebrate. These locations always include the medial preoptic area, cell groups in the medial hypothalamus near the

TABLE I

*Autoradiographic Studies of Steroid Sex
Hormone-Binding Cells in the Brains
of Vertebrates*

Features common to all species studied
1. All species have hormone-concentrating nerve cells, in specific locations
2. Hormone-concentrating cells are in medial preoptic area, medial (tuberal) hypothalamus, and limbic forebrain structures
3. Nerve cell groups which bind hormone participate in control of hormone-modulated functions

---

pituitary stalk, and in limbic forebrain structures such as the septum and amygdala or their homologies. Finally, having described the autoradiographic results for their own sake, examination of the neurophysiological, neuroendocrine, and behavioral literature for that species virtually always shows that many of the nerve cell groups that bind a given estrogenic or androgenic hormone participate in the control of reproductive behavior or neuroendocrine phenomena which depend on that hormone. This correlation suggests that the binding of the estrogen or androgen by those nerve cells is part of the causal sequence by which that hormone controls those phenomena.

The series of intracellular steps in estrogen target tissues by which estradiol reaches the nucleus to alter genomic readout has been reviewed (Jensen *et al.*, 1982). Having been taken up by the cell, estradiol binds to a receptor in the cytoplasm, thus activating it to a form which can be translocated to the cell nucleus where, in turn, the estrogen–receptor complex finds an acceptor site. We work on the hypothesis that this series of events is the same for estrogen target cells in the brain. Cell nuclear binding of tritiated estradiol in the hypothalamus and preoptic area (Zigmond and McEwen, 1970) was reminiscent of other target tissues. Where they have been determined, the physicochemical properties of steroid hormone receptors in brain have not differed clearly from those in other target organs (reviewed by McEwen *et al.*, 1982).

Quantitative autoradiographic work has proceeded under conditions which favor the detection of estrogen-concentrating cells: intravenous infusions of high enough levels of tritiated estradiol to match proestrous levels and saturate nuclear receptors for a long enough period that even rhythms of cellular activities would not exclude potential estrogen-concentrating neurons (Krieger *et al.*, 1978; Morrell *et al.*, 1983a). Even with neurons extremely well labeled by tritiated estradiol, in cell groups in the hypothalamus and limbic system which have the highest densities of such estrogen-concentrating cells, it is possible to see unlabeled neurons adjacent to labeled ones (Table II). This proves the cellular heterogeneity with respect to steroid hormone binding that long has been suspected for neural target tissues. Thus, autoradiographic and other histochemical techniques with high cellular resolution are required for the complete analysis of physiological and chemical consequences of hormone action in the brain. Moreover, the quantitated distributions of numbers of grains per cell body are identical across different estrogen-concentrating cell groups: for example, ventromedial nucleus of the hypothalamus, medial preoptic area, arcuate nucleus of the hypothalamus, and medial nucleus of the amygdala (Figs. 1 and 2). This similarity indicates that the different functional consequences of estrogen action on these cells are due to the differ-

TABLE II

*Heterogeneity of Cells with Respect to Estrogen Binding, Even
in Peak Estrogen-Concentrating Cell Groups[a]*

	Number of cells	Estrogen-concentrating cells (%)	Non-estrogen-concentrating cells (%)
Preoptic area (n = 4)	6626	23	77
VL-Ventromedial nucleus (n = 4)	4481	37	63
Arcuate nucleus (n = 4)	3148	28	72
Amygdala (n = 3)	4885	48	52

[a] From Morrell *et al.* (1983a).

ent connectivity of these neurons in circuits rather than to quantitative details of their estrogen-binding properties.

One of the important consequences of estrogen binding by hypothalamic nerve cells in the medial hypothalamus and preoptic area is the induction of progestin receptors (Kato and Onouchi, 1977; Maclusky and McEwen, 1978, 1980). This raised the possibility that estrogen actions on reproductive behavior could be correlated with progestin receptor induction (Moguilevsky and Reynaud, 1979). Indeed, following the time course of the appearance and disappearance of both female reproductive behavior and cytosol progestin receptors at the beginning and end of estradiol treatment in ovariectomized female rats showed marked parallelisms between the two (Parsons *et al.*, 1980). Further, those discontinuous schedules of estrogen treatment sufficient for activating lordosis behavior also were effective for inducing cytosol progestin receptors in the medial basal hypothalamus and preoptic area (Parsons *et al.*, 1982a).

B. PROPERTIES AS NEURONS

Studies of steroid hormone binding cells in the brain have proven their existence and revealed their exact locations and some of their quantitative properties. The more we know about the characteristics of neurons which accumulate a particular hormone, the more we can guess about how that hormone influences a neuron's synthetic processes, electrical activity, and participation in neural circuits. Two broad classifications of cellular

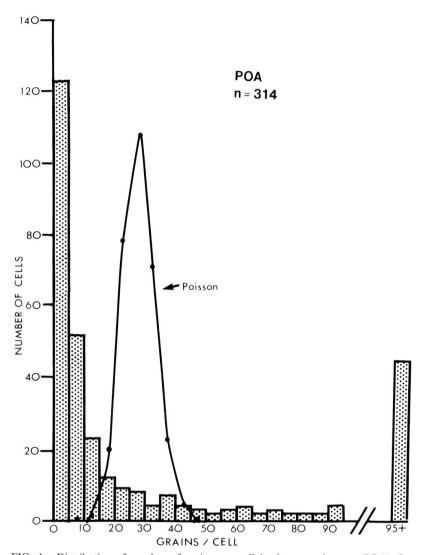

FIG. 1. Distribution of number of grains per cell in the preoptic area (POA), from autoradiograms of female rats administered [³H]estradiol intravenously. Absence of multiple intermediate peaks in the distribution suggests an absence of quantal modes of hormone uptake. Significant deviation of the observed distribution from the Poisson distribution calculated from the same mean and SD shows the estradiol accumulation is not a random process. (Data from Morrell *et al.*, 1983a.)

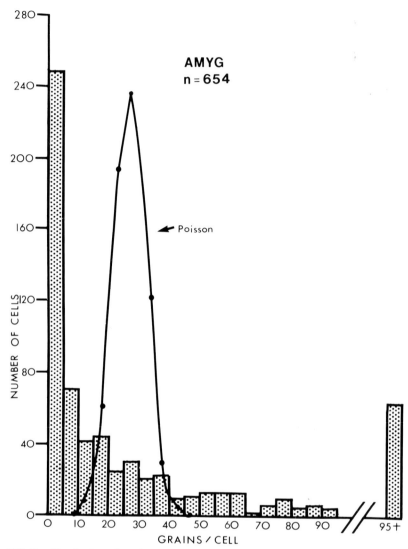

FIG. 2. Distribution of number of grains per cell in the medial amygdala (AMYG), from autoradiograms of female rats administered [³H]estradiol intravenously. Note similarity in the shape of the distribution to that from preoptic area (Fig. 1). (Data from Morrell *et al.*, 1983a.)

properties of neurons are the chemical constituents of any given neuron and the locations to which that neuron sends its axons. We have begun to study both of these types of properties of hormone-binding cells by combining cellular analytic techniques with steroid hormone autoradiography.

Combining immunocytochemistry with steroid hormone autoradiography in the same tissue allows the classification of hormone-binding cells according to the amount of a specific immunologically recognized substance. The neurophysins are carrier proteins for oxytocin and vasopressin. Since estrogen can induce the release of one class of neurophysins, which are contained in cells of the paraventricular nucleus of the hypothalamus as well as the supraoptic nucleus (Rhodes *et al.*, 1981a), and since the paraventricular nucleus has some estrogen-concentrating cells (Pfaff and Keiner, 1973), it became of interest to see if some paraventricular nucleus neurons which accumulate estrogen in their nucleus might have neurophysin in their cytoplasm. Indeed, such double-labeled cells were found, especially in the posterior subnucleus of the paraventricular nucleus of the hypothalamus (Rhodes *et al.*, 1981b). Subsequent work with Brattleboro rats (Fig. 3) indicated that the population of estrogen-addressed neurophysin-containing neurons includes both oxytocin and vasopressin-producing cells (Rhodes *et al.*, 1982). Such cells could mediate the effects of estrogens on neurophysin release as well as effects on oxytocin or vasopressin function.

Similarly, are some of the effects of estrogen on reproductive function mediated by direct accumulation of estrogens in the nucleus of cells that produce luteinizing hormone releasing hormone (LHRH)? To date, having combined LHRH immunocytochemistry with steroid hormone autoradiography, we have not found any cells which both accumulate radioactive estrogen and produce LHRH, even in tissue sections with neurons that have each property individually (Shivers *et al.*, 1983). In contrast, in the arcuate nucleus of the hypothalamus, it is relatively easy to find neurons which accumulate radioactive estrogen and have β-endorphin in their cytoplasm (Morrell *et al.*, 1983b).

The locations to which a hormone-binding cell sends its hormone-influenced information can be determined by discovering where its axons terminate. We have combined retrograde neuroanatomical techniques with steroid hormone autoradiography in the same tissue, to begin this kind of demonstration. The retrograde-transported fluorescent dye Primuline was administered locally to the dorsal midbrain and time allowed for transport back to the cell body (Morrell and Pfaff, 1982). As expected, the number of backfilled cell bodies in specific hypothalamic locations was very large (Morrell *et al.*, 1981). Performing steroid hormone autoradiography, after the administration of tritiated estradiol, on tissue prepared in this manner showed that 25–35% of estrogen-concentrating cells in the ventrolateral portion of the ventromedial nucleus of the hypothalamus send their estrogen-dependent information to the dorsal midbrain (Fig. 4) (Morrell and Pfaff, 1982). In the arcuate nucleus of the hypothalamus, while many estrogen-concentrating cells were detected, hardly any sent axons to the dorsal midbrain.

C. ARE THERE SPECIAL HORMONE-NEURONS?

The typical picture of a "normal" neuron includes the notion of a nerve cell with resting electrical discharge, responding to a large variety of synaptic inputs. Such cells have relatively long axons which conduct electrical action potentials to terminals at some distance, affecting in a punctate fashion individual postsynaptic cells in those locations. The normal neuron responds quickly to synaptic input, through postsynaptic potentials, decremental conduction across the cell body, and eventual conduction of the action potential and, similarly, its effects on other neurons would normally be through postsynaptic potentials of relatively short duration (less than 10 msec). In a wide variety of cases, actions on the postsynaptic cell would be through a classically defined neurotransmitter.

Consider cells in the ventrolateral subdivision of the ventromedial nucleus of the hypothalamus, a cell group important for estrogen effects on reproductive behavior which contains a dense population of estrogen-concentrating cell bodies (Pfaff and Keiner, 1973). Ultrastructurally, cell bodies in this group of neurons appear to be those of normal nerve cells (Cohen and Pfaff, 1981). However, some data gathered with other techniques suggest that these cells addressed by a steroid hormone may differ fundamentally from the typical picture of a normal neuron. Studying antidromically identified ventromedial hypothalamic cells with single unit electrical recording, Sakuma and Pfaff (1982) found that about 70% of those neurons with axons projecting to the central gray of the midbrain had no resting electrical discharge. Indeed, estrogen effects on ventromedial hypothalamic cells appear preferentially in those neurons with very slow discharge rates (Bueno and Pfaff, 1976). Along the same line, comparing the effects on reproductive behavior of sodium channel blocking with local anesthetic as opposed to tetrodotoxin allows the interpretation that those hypothalamic cells especially important for estrogen effects on reproductive behavior are neurons with little or no resting discharge (Section IV, and Harlan et al., 1983).

Many estrogen-concentrating neurons may not have long axons either.

FIG. 3.   Combination of steroid hormone autoradiography and immunocytochemistry in the same tissue. Certain paraventricular hypothalamic neurons accumulate tritiated estradiol in cell nucleus (shown by the silver grains in the autoradiogram) *and* produce neurophysins (brown deposit in cytoplasm, from immunocytochemistry using neurophysin antiserum). (Data from Rhodes et al., 1982.)

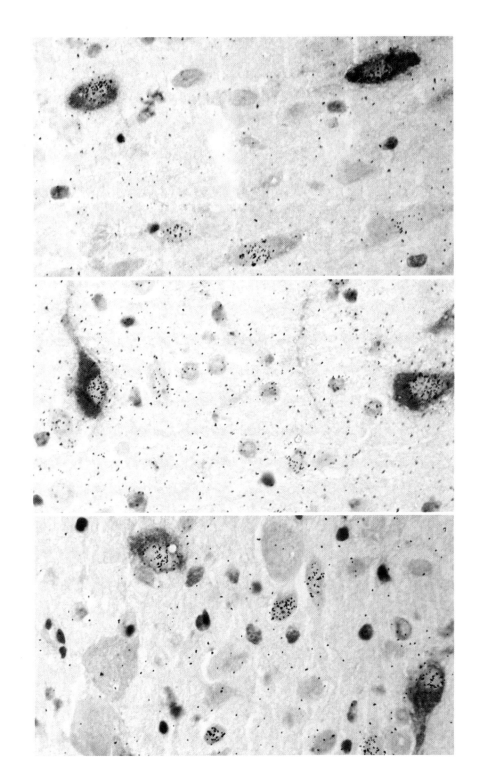

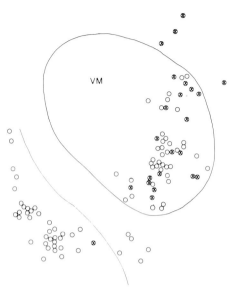

FIG. 4. Combination of steroid hormone autoradiography and retrograde neuroanatomical tracing in the same tissue. Some neurons in the ventromedial nucleus of the hypothalamus (VM) only concentrate estrogen (○), while others accumulate the hormone and send axons to the dorsal midbrain (⊗). In contrast, in the arcuate nucleus of the hypothalamus (lower left) very few estrogen-concentrating neurons can be retrograde identified from the dorsal midbrain. (Data from Morrell and Pfaff, 1982.)

Combinations of retrograde neuroanatomical determinations using the fluorescent dye Primuline, with estrogen autoradiography, have so far left open the possibility that a large percentage of estrogen-concentrating neurons in the medial hypothalamus do not have axons which would have to conduct a spike over long distances (Morrell and Pfaff, 1982). If this is true, such cells would be "local" or "intrinsic" neurons.

Another distinction between medial hypothalamic cells important for reproductive behavior and the typical picture of a neuron is that such hypothalamic cells do not respond rapidly in the classical manner of a reflex control circuit. Instead, a wide variety of evidence suggests that estrogen-dependent hypothalamic neurons provide a tonic output to the midbrain for the control of reproductive behavior (Pfaff, 1980). Basomedial hypothalamic neurons do not respond promptly to cutaneous stimuli (Bueno and Pfaff, 1976). Other key points come from the slow reproductive behavior responses to electrical stimulation of the ventromedial nucleus of the hypothalamus (Pfaff and Sakuma, 1979a) and a correspondingly slow loss of reproductive behavior following hypothalamic lesions (Pfaff and Sakuma, 1979b). In the same manner, the slow time course of the decrement of reproductive behavior following the administration of tetrodotoxin to the medial hypothalamus suggested a different type of mechanism of action for this type of hypothalamic cell than might be expected, for example, from a motor neuron (Harlan *et al.*, 1983).

The substances through which hypothalamic and preoptic neurons act on other neurons are not necessarily restricted to classically defined neurotransmitters. Prominent is the possibility that some of these cells act through the release of LHRH, since LHRH administration to the dorsal midbrain can potentiate female reproductive behavior (Riskind and Moss, 1979; Sakuma and Pfaff, 1980a, 1983). Similarly, administration of prolactin to the central gray of the midbrain facilitates lordosis behavior, probably because of its release from prolactin-containing axons which we have traced immunocytochemically from the hypothalamus (Harlan *et al.*, 1982a). Further work with these systems may give an idea of what "neuromodulation" means in a mammalian central nervous system.

By analogy, Nelson and Prosser (1981), recording from neurons in the fish preoptic area, distinguished two types of cells with responses to thermal input. One type, "pure" thermoreceptors, had regular interspike intervals and little apparent synaptic input, with one form of response to changes in temperature. The other type of preoptic neuron also responded to changes in temperature, but also gave evidence of considerable synaptic input. Likewise, thermosensitivity of rat preoptic neurons (Baldino and Geller, 1982; Kelso *et al.*, 1982) and bursting activity of rat paraventricular neurons (Hatton, 1982) do not depend on synaptic inputs from other brain regions.

In summary, we may find morphological, electrical, and cytochemical techniques all useful in distinguishing the properties of a special group of neurons important for endocrine control: hormone-concentrating neurons with slow temporal electrical properties which sometimes act through local connections and modulate other neurons through the release of peptides.

III. Neural Circuitry for an Estrogen- and Progesterone-Dependent Behavior

Lordosis behavior is a standing response characterized by extreme vertebral dorsiflexion. The most essential part of the reproductive behavior of the female rodent, it permits fertilization by the male. Estrogen is required for lordosis to occur, and if subthreshold doses of estrogen are used, subsequent administration of progesterone greatly facilitates the behavior. While remaining the best analyzed neural circuit among vertebrate behavior patterns, the circuitry for lordosis behavior has been simple enough to support continuing endocrine and neurobiological analyses at the cellular level.

Evidence from long strings of anatomical and physiological experiments not only indicated certain portions of the circuitry for lordosis behavior but, just as important, ruled out alternative hypotheses. Those experiments have been summarized at some length (Pfaff, 1980). Below is just enough description to make the new experiments described in subsequent sections comprehensible.

In brief, to trigger lordosis behavior during mating, the male rat grasps the flanks of the female with his forepaws, and his pelvic thrusting exerts pressure on the skin of her tailbase and perineum. These cutaneous stimuli are necessary and sufficient for the behavior. They cause a barrage of electrical activity in the primary sensory neurons, among which two types, pressure units and Type I units, give the sustained responses required for lordosis.

Electrical activity in the primary sensory units converges to excite a class of interneurons in the intermediate gray of the lumbar spinal cord. The requirements of these pressure-sensitive interneurons closely fit the requirements for lordosis behavior as a whole. However, the passage of electrical excitation from these interneurons to the relevant motor neurons could not be the entire lordosis behavior circuit. Female rats with spinal cord transected at higher levels do not perform lordosis. Therefore, some type of supraspinal facilitation is necessary (Fig. 5). Fibers forming the ascending side of a supraspinal loop relevant for lordosis behavior terminate in the medullary reticular formation, the lateral vestibular nucleus, and in the dorsal midbrain within and nearby the midbrain central gray. Sensory information need not reach the hypothalamus.

In female rats, the sensory information which reaches brainstem neurons in locations that could be relevant for lordosis behavior is not great, either in terms of numbers of cells responding or in terms of its precision in space or time. Thus, lordosis relevant neurons in the midbrain central gray and brainstem reticular formation must be facilitating the behavioral response not primarily by strong and rapid responses to sensory stimulation but instead by carrying the descending hormone-dependent influences originating from the medial hypothalamus.

Neural signals to the brainstem from the hypothalamus and forebrain have a net facilitatory influence on lordosis, since transecting all connections descending to the midbrain abolishes this behavior. The only source of the behavior-facilitating descending signal which has been discovered is the ventromedial nucleus of the hypothalamus. Electrical stimulation of these cells can facilitate lordosis, while abolishing these cells leads to lordosis loss. Nerve cells in the ventromedial nucleus of the hypothala-

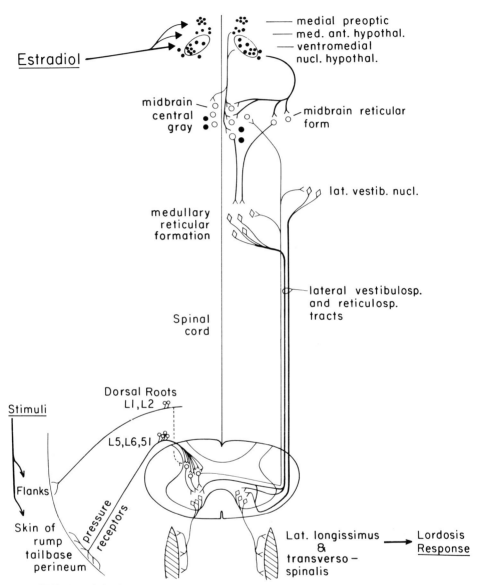

FIG. 5.   Minimal neural circuit for lordosis behavior in the female rat. Neurons which manage behavioral execution from stimulus to response are shown, as well as the hypothalamic nerve cells and connections for carrying the estradiol effect. Stimuli, responses, and hormone effects all are bilateral, and are drawn here on just one side for convenience. (From Pfaff, 1980.)

mus, especially in its ventrolateral aspect, strongly accumulate radioactive estradiol, and local implants of estradiol next to these cells facilitate lordosis behavior. In ovariectomized female rats, estrogen can increase the electrical activity of slowly firing cells in and around the ventromedial nucleus of the hypothalamus and also increases ultrastructural signs of biosynthetic activity in these cells. Through these cellular changes, estrogen can cause a tonically elevated output from the ventromedial hypothalamus to the midbrain, and this output facilitates lordosis behavior.

Axons from nerve cells in and adjacent to the ventromedial nucleus of the hypothalamus descend toward the midbrain in two groups. Some axons circle far laterally and then sweep back to the midbrain, while others go straight back through the periventricular system to reach the midbrain centray gray. Both of these groups of axons contribute to the control of lordosis behavior, but, quantitatively, the lateral running fibers make the more important contribution.

The electrical activity of neurons in the central gray reflects hypothalamic and hormonal influences. Electrical stimulation of the ventromedial hypothalamus and estrogen administration, both of which increase lordosis behavior, raise the electrical excitability of certain central gray neurons. Inputs from the medial preoptic area due to electrical stimulation there, which decreases lordosis, also decreases central gray neuron electrical excitability. In turn, electrical stimulation of the midbrain central gray can facilitate lordosis, while lesions there can disrupt it.

Many neurons in the midbrain central gray have axons which descend in the reticular formation of the brainstem, and some of these axons reach the ventromedial portion of the reticular formation of the medulla. This is a part of the reticular formation with many cell bodies of reticulospinal neurons. Thus, the shortest, quantitatively important linkage from hypothalamus to behavior would be ventromedial hypothalamic neurons to central gray neurons in the midbrain, to medullary reticulospinal cells, to spinal cord motoneurons.

Among all the descending systems through which the brainstem controls the spinal cord only two are necessary for lordosis behavior. Reticulospinal neurons, presumably carrying influences from hormone-dependent hypothalamic cells, participate in lordosis control. The other system, lateral vestibulospinal neurons in Deiters nucleus, contributing axons to the lateral vestibulospinal tract, presumably operates on the muscular apparatus necessary for the behavior to maintain postural tone. Both of these descending pathways control the motor neurons for axial muscles. They branch at different vertebral levels and can act bilaterally. All of these properties of the medullary reticulospinal and lateral vestibulospinal systems are consistent with roles in lordosis behavior.

At the motor neurons relevant for lordosis behavior, the two major driving influences on the behavior converge. Descending signals are one type of influence, with reticulospinal axons carrying hypothalamically originated hormone-dependent information, synergizing with lateral vestibulospinal actions. The second type of influence is the electrical activity triggered by the sensory input from the male rat. The requirement for a combination of these two types of influences gives the necessary specificity to the occurrence of the behavior: that only the female adequately primed endocrinologically and mounted appropriately by a stimulus male will do lordosis behavior.

The motor neurons for lordosis behavior are at the medial and ventromedial borders of the ventral horn in the lumbar spinal cord. They control two epaxial muscle systems: lateral longissimus and transverso-spinalis. These deep back muscles execute the vertebral dorsiflexion of lordosis.

Some of the circuitry for this behavior pattern can be understood in terms of operational "modules," each responsible for a different aspect of the generation of a hormone-dependent behavior. For example, nerve cells in the lumbar spinal cord can be considered a spinal module which handles the sensory and motor mechanisms in the manner of local reflex control. The lower brainstem module includes vestibulospinal and reticulospinal cells which integrate postural adaptations across segmental levels over the entire length of the body axis. The hypothalamic module manages the endocrine dependency of the entire behavior pattern.

Even without the hormone effects to be considered, new anatomical techniques allow us to ask new questions about the logic of the construction of this reproductive behavior circuit. In particular, where do short-axoned cells, called "local neurons," play an essential role? Where they participate, the circuit would have a sequential, ladder-like organization rather than being limited to a single neural connection. At the opposite extreme, sensitive retrograde neuroanatomical techniques, especially those using lectins, are revealing long-axoned trajectories from hypothalamic neurons to previously unsuspected targets (Swanson and Kuypers, 1980). For example, immunocytochemical techniques with wheat germ agglutinin show large numbers of hypothalamic cells projecting all the way to the spinal cord (Schwanzel-Fukuda et al., 1983).

The main purpose of careful neuroanatomical, electrophysiological, and behavioral work in a single well-defined system like lordosis behavior is to set up the possibility of meaningful cell biological studies in a complicated tissue. We can ask ultrastructural, detailed electrophysiological, and certain chemical questions of steroid hormone effects on specific hypothalamic nerve cells with greater confidence that they make behavioral and neurophysiological sense.

IV. Steroids and Hypothalamic Neurons: Electrical Mechanisms

A. ELECTROPHYSIOLOGICAL RECORDING AND STIMULATION

Electrical effects of estrogenic steroids on the hypothalamus have been reviewed (Pfaff, 1980). Recording single unit activity in ovariectomized, urethane anesthetized female rats (Bueno and Pfaff, 1976) we found a significant increase in the number of basomedial hypothalamic cells with very low resting discharge rates in estrogen-treated preparations, without a corresponding decrease in faster firing cells (Fig. 6). The simplest interpretation of this finding was that estrogen allowed the initiation of a resting discharge in silent cells, bringing them into the recording distribution. Just the opposite happened during single unit recording from the medial preoptic area and the bed nucleus of the stria terminalis (Fig. 6). Differences in these effects of long-term systemic estrogen treatment, between medial preoptic neurons and neurons of the basomedial hypothalamus, precisely parallel the differences between these neuronal groups in the control of lordosis behavior. Estrogen facilitates slowly firing cells where those cells promote lordosis, and inhibits them where those cells suppress lordosis behavior.

Overall, many cells in the basomedial hypothalamus have quite low firing rates compared to other brain regions, and this occurred in our experiments with ovariectomized rats (Bueno and Pfaff, 1976) as well as in previous work (Dyer *et al.,* 1972; Lincoln, 1967; Moss and Law, 1971; Yagi and Sawaki, 1973). In fact, in a population of neurons in and around the ventromedial nucleus of the hypothalamus which had been antidromically activated by stimulation of the midbrain central gray (Sakuma and Pfaff, 1981, 1982), about 70% of the cells had no spontaneous electrical activity. In this population of antidromically activated hypothalamic neurons, we detected no estrogen effects. With this number of cells, estrogen-sensitive neurons may have been too small a fraction of the antidromically identified neuron sample to show statistically significant effects of the hormone. But a more interesting interpretation is that previous electrophysiological recording experiments showing estrogen effects were largely due to cells which do not project to the central gray; this is anatomically sensible since combinations of retrograde anatomical techniques with steroid hormone autoradiography have shown that 65–75% of estrogen-concentrating cells in the ventromedial nucleus of the hypothalamus do not send axons to the midbrain central gray (Morrell and Pfaff, 1982). Thus, a great portion of the physiologically significant estrogen effects on electrical activity might be exerted through local, or "intrinsic"

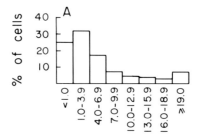

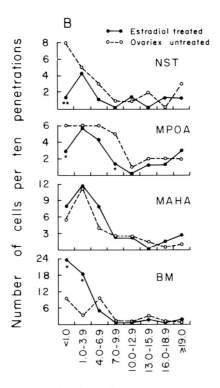

FIG. 6. (A) Distribution of resting discharge rates in medial hypothalamic and preoptic cells which had spontaneous activity. (B) Effect of estradiol on nerve cell resting discharge rate. In the basomedial hypothalamus (BM) estradiol caused the appearance of neurons at slow discharge rates without the disappearance of fast-firing neurons, indicating that estrogen activated silent cells to have a non-zero discharge rate. In the medial preoptic area (MPOA) and bed nucleus of the stria terminalis (NST) exactly the opposite estrogen effect occurred. (From Bueno and Pfaff, 1976.)

neurons, with an important part of the estrogen influence transmitted from hypothalamus to midbrain depending not just on estrogen-altered electrical activity but also on estrogen-altered synthetic and secretory activity.

Electrical stimulation of the ventromedial nucleus of the hypothalamus can facilitate lordosis behavior (Pfaff and Sakuma, 1979a). By the usual standards of electrical stimulation experiments, these behavioral effects were slow. Even under optimal conditions, latencies to lordosis increase could take 25 to 50 minutes and required low frequencies of stimulation (Fig. 7). Apparently, in some respects these ventromedial hypothalamic neurons are similar to sympathetic neurons, which can require low frequencies for their most efficient activation (Zigmond and Chalazonitis, 1979), can actually be blocked by higher frequencies of stimulation (Eccles, 1955), and also fire at very low rates (Bronk *et al.*, 1936; Burnstock and Costa, 1975; Skok, 1973). Similarly, lesions of the ventromedial nucleus of the hypothalamus register their effects on lordosis behavior with an extraordinarily slow time course (Pfaff and Sakuma, 1979b). Even under conditions experimentally arranged to reveal fast lesion effects, animals in which the hypothalamic lesion will severely disrupt lordosis behavior do not reach their lowest behavioral performance until a time as great as 2 days postlesion has passed.

An implication of these findings is that estrogen effects on the basome-

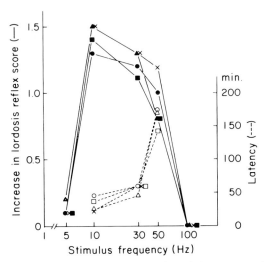

FIG. 7. Low frequencies of electrical stimulation of the ventromedial hypothalamus were required for the largest effects on lordosis behavior. Under optimal conditions, latencies to the behavioral effect were still 25–50 minutes. (From Pfaff and Sakuma, 1979a.)

dial hypothalamus include neurons with slow temporal properties and
neurons which are intrinsic to the medial hypothalamus.

B. IS ELECTRICAL ACTIVITY REQUIRED FOR
ESTROGEN-DRIVEN LORDOSIS BEHAVIOR?

We used intrahypothalamic infusions of the sodium channel blocker
tetrodotoxin to see if electrical activity mediated by voltage-dependent
sodium channels is required for the occurrence of lordosis behavior
(Harlan *et al.*, 1981, 1983). Bilateral applications of tetrodotoxin near the
ventromedial hypothalamus caused a dose-dependent decrease in the
magnitude of lordosis behavior (Fig. 8). The first statistically significant
decrease in lordosis was not reached until 40 minutes after tetrodotoxin
infusion, and lowest lordosis scores occurred 2 to 4 hours after infusion
(Fig. 8). In electrophysiological preparations, the same kind of intrahypothalamic tetrodotoxin infusion suppressed action potentials completely,
within 5 or 6 minutes and lasting for hours. In contrast, intrahypothalamic
infusion of local anesthetics such as Procaine usually depressed electrical
activity only temporarily and incompletely, and had no effect on lordosis

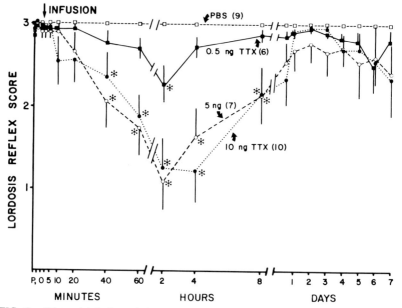

FIG. 8. Bilateral infusion of tetrodotoxin (TTX) into the ventromedial hypothalamus
depressed lordosis behavior in ovariectomized, estrogen-treated female rats compared to
the vehicle control with phosphate-buffered saline (PBS). (From Harlan *et al.*, 1983.)

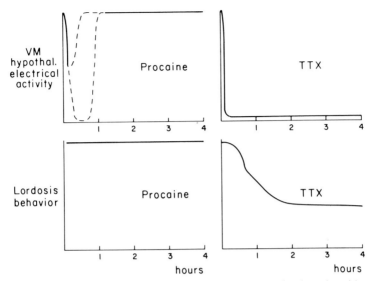

FIG. 9. Schematic summary of electrophysiological and behavioral results with sodium channel blockers. Incomplete or brief disruptions of electrical activity of ventromedial hypothalamic (VM) neurons, as from local anesthetics procaine or marcaine, had no behavioral effect. Profound and prolonged decrease of electrical activity, as from tetrodotoxin (TTX), decreased lordosis behavior.

behavior. Thus, large and prolonged decreases in electrical activity in the basomedial hypothalamus can cause a decline in lordosis behavior (Fig. 9).

Since times as long as 40 minutes after tetrodotoxin was required for a significant decrease in lordosis behavior, even though electrical activity was suppressed within 5 or 6 minutes, it could not be the case that, upon every application of adequate somatosensory stimuli, hypothalamic electrical mechanisms are exerting rapid outputs to facilitate the behavior. Instead, a tonic hypothalamic output must be facilitating the behavior by operating over a much longer time period than an individual mount by the male rat or application of somatosensory input in a reflex test. In the dorsal midbrain, the means by which neuronal electrical activity controls the behavior are much more rapid, as shown by the loss of lordosis behavior within 5 minutes of tetrodotoxin application (Harlan *et al.*, 1982b). This is consistent with rapid responses by neurons in the midbrain central gray to electrical stimulation and other manipulations (references in Section IV,D).

Tetrodotoxin can block a sodium channel whether it is open or closed (Narahashi *et al.*, 1966; Ritchie and Rogart, 1977), while local anesthetics, operating by a different mechanism, act preferentially on open channels

(Courtney *et al.,* 1978) and therefore are poor at suppressing sodium channel activity in slowly firing cells (Tasaki, 1953). The fact that tetrodo-toxin in the medial hypothalamus was much more effective than Procaine for disrupting lordosis behavior is consistent with the notion that the behavior depends upon hypothalamic neurons which electrically are slow or silent. If the behaviorally relevant functions of such cells include a secretory step, the long delay of lordosis decline following the suppression of medial hypothalamic electrical activity is consistent with the idea that substances secreted have a duration of action measured in minutes.

C. HORMONE ACTIONS VERSUS OTHER CELLULAR FUNCTIONS

A general problem in the field of hormone action is to distinguish cellular functions which are on the causal route of the hormone effect from those required for the integrity of the hormone-influenced cell but not directly altered by the hormone itself (Fig. 10). If an experimental manipulation of a hormone-dependent cell decreases the cell's output, was that because the experimental manipulation interfered with a cellular function which is part of the hormone's effect or did it simply disrupt some

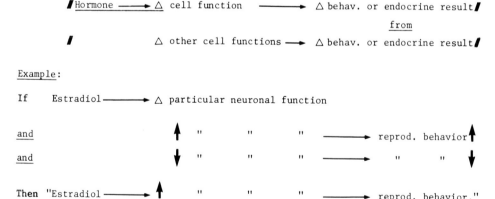

FIG. 10. Top: When an experimental manipulation of a hormone-dependent cell alters a hormone-dependent output, did it do so by intervening in the hormone's mechanism of action or by changing another cell function which has a permissive effect? Bottom: An example, using estrogen and nerve cells, of the pattern of experimental evidence which (in answer to the question above) would allow the conclusion that a particular cellular function is part of the hormone's mechanism of action.

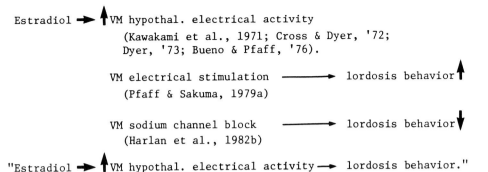

FIG. 11.   The pattern of experimental results called for in Fig. 10 (bottom) is satisfied: One way in which estradiol acts on ventromedial (VM) hypothalamic cells to cause female rat reproductive behavior is to alter their electrical activity. (From Harlan *et al.*, 1982b, read 1983.)

"housekeeping activities" of that cell? Likewise, if stimulation of a particular type of cell causes an increase in that cell's output, is it because that type of stimulation increases cell functions which are also increased by the hormone, or did the experimental stimulation simply exert a permissive effect through other, supportive activities? One way to solve this problem is to understand the chemistry of the hormone-dependent cell so completely that we can make catalog of all important reactions, and then systematically sort them according to hormone dependence, and finally deduce the main causal route of the hormone's effect on cellular output. Clearly, for mammalian cells such a catalog is not available. Alternatively, the strongest empirical approach to this dilemma is to seek a configuration of experimental results as illustrated in the bottom half of Fig. 10. If a hormone causes a change in a particular cellular function, *and* a selective increase in that function causes an increase in the hormone-dependent output, *and* a decrease in that cellular function leads to decrease in the hormone-dependent output, *then* the simplest summary of all these experimental results is to say that the hormone causes the change in the cell's output by operating through that particular cellular function.

Precisely this configuration of experimental results has been achieved for effects of estrogen on lordosis behavior working through the electrical activity of hypothalamic neurons (Fig. 11). Estrogen administration leads to increases in basomedial hypothalamic electrical activity, low frequency electrical stimulation facilitates lordosis behavior, and prolonged and profound decreases in basomedial hypothalamic electrical activity lead to a decline in lordosis behavior. Thus, the simplest summary is that one way in which estradiol acts on hypothalamic neurons to facilitate lordosis behavior is to increase the electrical activity of at least some neurons in and around the ventromedial nucleus of the hypothalamus.

D. DO ELECTRICAL CHANGES EXPLAIN EVERYTHING?

Ventromedial hypothalamic effects on lordosis behavior require axonal connections to the midbrain ending in and around the midbrain central gray (Manogue *et al.*, 1980). Electrical stimulation of central gray neurons can rapidly facilitate female reproductive behavior (Sakuma and Pfaff, 1979a). Blocking sodium channels by tetrodotoxin delivered bilaterally in and around the midbrain central gray leads to lordosis loss (Harlan *et al.*, 1982b). Lesions of midbrain central gray quickly lead to striking decreases in lordosis behavior (Sakuma and Pfaff, 1979b; Pfeifle and Edwards, 1982).

We recorded the electrical activity of midbrain central gray neurons which were antidromically identified from the medullary reticular formation; these neurons would be especially good candidates for carrying hormone-dependent behaviorally relevant information to the lower brainstem (Sakuma and Pfaff, 1980b,c). An important part of each experiment was to measure the effects of hypothalamic or preoptic manipulations on the electrical excitability of these midbrain cells. There were striking parallels between the effects of these hypothalamic and preoptic manipulations on midbrain central gray electrophysiology and their effects on lordosis behavior as a whole (Sakuma and Pfaff, 1980b,c). For example, electrical stimulation of the ventromedial nucleus of the hypothalamus increased central gray neurons' electrical excitability, even as it increases lordosis behavior. Conversely, electrical stimulation of the preoptic area decreases both the electrophysiological and the behavioral measures. Lesions of hypothalamic or preoptic tissue tended to have the effects opposite of electrical stimulation of the same tissue (Table III). This pattern of experimental results is consistent with the notion summarized above that changes in hypothalamic electrical activity are an important part of the means by which estrogen effects on hypothalamic cells alter lordosis behavior.

However, the same electrical recording experiments revealed important differences between estrogen effects on midbrain central gray electrophysiology and the effect of that hormone on lordosis behavior as a whole (Table IV). While the effects of electrical stimulation of the ventromedial hypothalamus on lordosis behavior require subthreshold estrogen priming (Pfaff and Sakuma, 1979a), effects on the electrical activity of central gray neurons could be registered in the absence of circulating

TABLE III

*Parallel Changes in an Electrophysiological and
a Behavioral Measure, following Hypothalamic
or Preoptic Stimulation or Lesion*

Midbrain CG neuron electrical excitation,
lordosis behavior

	Stimulation	Lesion
VM hypothalamus	↑ , ↑	↓ , ↓
Preoptic area	↓ , ↓	↑ , ↑

estrogen (Sakuma and Pfaff, 1980c). In the time domain, ventromedial hypothalamic stimulation could increase central gray neuron electrical excitability almost immediately, while electrical stimulation with the same parameters would require at least 25 to 50 minutes for a full behavioral effect. Therefore, with respect to electrical stimulation of the ventromedial hypothalamus, to go from a well-documented electrical effect in the midbrain to a full behavioral mechanism requires a priming action of estrogen that takes at least 25 to 50 minutes, to be registered.

TABLE IV

*Differences between an Electrophysiological and
a Behavioral Measure following Hypothalamic
Stimulation*

From VM hypothalamic electrical stimulation

	CG neuron electrical excitation	Lordosis behavior
Require estradiol ?	No	Yes
Require ≫ several minutes ?	No	Yes

E. SUMMARY

Electrical effects of estradiol form an obligatory part of the mechanism by which estrogen acts on medial hypothalamic neurons to foster lordosis behavior. Especially important is the participation of slowly firing neurons with little or no resting discharge, some of which may be local, "intrinsic" neurons. The slow registration of the effects of various electrical manipulations on lordosis behavior requires that the mode of action of hypothalamic output be a facilitating background "tonic" action, rather than a rapid gate-closing reflex control that operates on a mount-by-mount basis.

Not all the characteristics of hypothalamic participation in reproductive behavior control can be accounted for by electrophysiological studies. Modes of hormone action in the medial hypothalamus that include synthetic and secretory steps are indicated.

V. Steroids and the Hypothalamus: Protein Synthesis and Secretion

A. ULTRASTRUCTURAL EVIDENCE

One approach to questions about rates of protein synthesis and secretion in neurons is to ask what the nerve cells in question look like. Do any ultrastructural features change following hormone treatment? In particular, one might look at organelles in the cell body whose number, shape, or distribution might reflect aspects of RNA or protein synthesis. In some neurons in the ventrolateral portion of the ventromedial nucleus of the hypothalamus, we noticed protuberances on the surface of the nucleolus (Figs. 12 and 13). Such an altered nucleolar appearance occurred more than twice as often in estrogen-treated compared to control ovariectomized female rats (Cohen and Pfaff, 1982, 1983). The bumps on the nucleolar surface consisted of tightly packed, granular, electron-dense material often separated from the main body of the nucleolus by a fine gap. This material could be newly synthesized and processed RNA. It could also be nucleolus-associated DNA, organized for nuclear RNA synthesis. Experiments with DNA and RNA stains and corresponding experiments with DNase and RNase should distinguish between these alternatives.

The appearance of the cytoplasm, also, in some neurons of the ventrolateral portion of the ventromedial hypothalamus seems highly organized for high rates of protein synthesis and is subject to an estrogen effect (Cohen and Pfaff, 1981). Cells there with large amounts of stacked rough endoplasmic reticulum were seen more than twice as often in estrogen-

TABLE V

Percentage of Nerve Cells with Stacked Rough Endoplasmic
Reticulum (RER) in the Ventrolateral Subdivision of the
Ventromedial Nucleus in Ovariectomized and Ovariectomized
Estrogen-Treated Rats[a,b]

Ovariectomized/estrogen-treated		Ovariectomized/control	
Rat number	%	Rat number	%
1	53	1′	11
2	28	2′	13
3	46	3′	6
4	44	4′	28
5	43	5′	10
6	29	6′	21
Mean	40.5	Mean	16.7

[a] Data from Cohen and Pfaff (1981).

[b] The mean percentage of nerve cells with stacked RER in ovari-ectomized/estrogen-treated rats is 40.5% as opposed to only 16.2% in the control. Experimental vs control = $p < 0.02$.

treated as in ovariectomized control female rats (Table V). Likewise, the number of dense-cored vesicles (which may be prosecretory granules) in the vicinity of the Golgi apparatus was about three times as great in the estrogen-treated compared to the control animals (Table VI). The ultrastructural changes following estrogen treatment could be construed as revealing increased rates of protein synthesis and packaging in the cell bodies of ventromedial hypothalamic neurons. Now we are examining the ending of these neurons in the midbrain.

Thus, in neurons in a part of the ventromedial hypothalamus which has a high density of estrogen-concentrating cells and is important for female reproductive behavior, estrogen treatment is followed by ultrastructural changes in the cell nucleus which may reflect altered RNA synthesis and changes in the cytoplasm which may reflect increased protein synthesis and transport.

B. EVIDENCE FROM INHIBITORS

Administration of the RNA synthesis inhibitor actinomycin-D intracerebrally in a manner which can affect hypothalamic neurons can inhibit the facilitation of female rat reproductive behavior by estrogen (Quadagno *et al.*, 1971; Terkel *et al.*, 1973). As predicted, interruption of

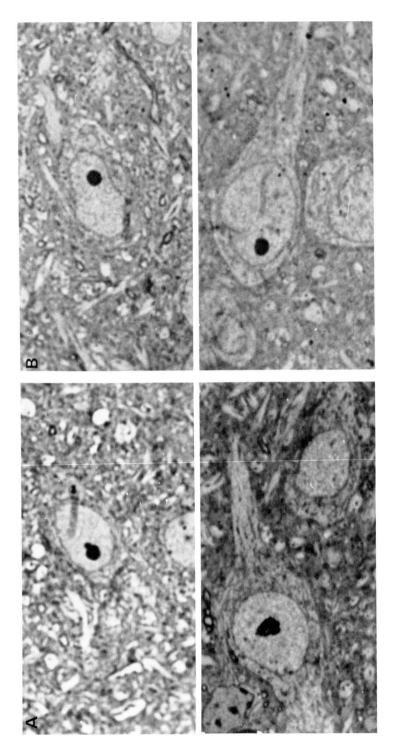

152

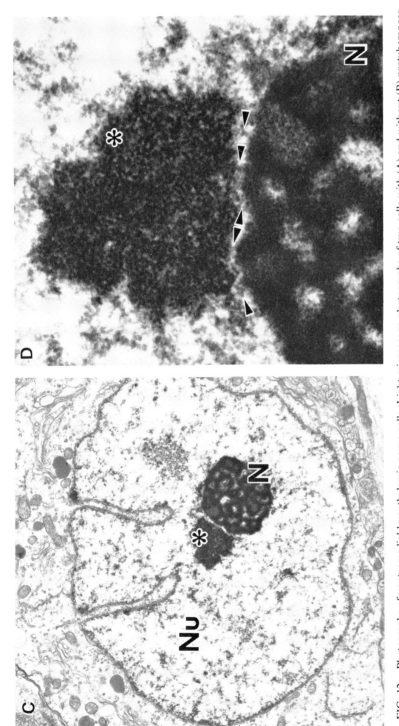

FIG. 12.   Photographs of ventromedial hypothalamic nerve cells. Light microscope photographs of two cells with (A) and without (B) protuberances on the nucleolar surface. (C) Electron micrograph of a cell nucleus (Nu) whose nucleolus (N) has an electron-dense, granular protuberance (*). (D) At higher magnification a small gap separating it from the nucleolar surface is seen, crossed by strands of electron-dense material (arrowheads). (From Cohen and Pfaff, 1982, 1983.)

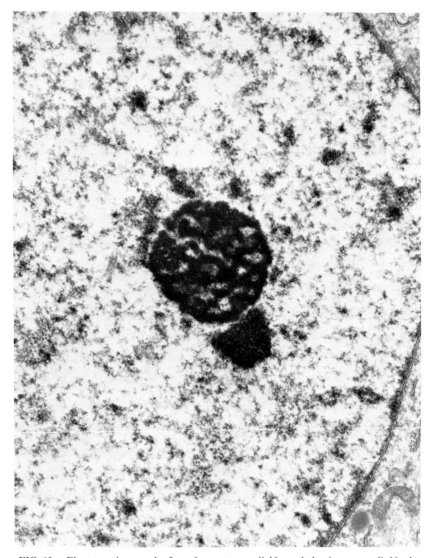

FIG. 13.   Electron micrograph of another ventromedial hypothalamic nerve cell. Nucleolus has a large mass of granular material by its (lower right) surface. (Data from Cohen and Pfaff, 1982, 1983.)

protein synthesis in hypothalamic neurons by cycloheximide (Quadagno and Ho, 1975) or by anisomycin (Rainbow *et al.*, 1982) also reduces the estrogen effect on lordosis. Work in progress in our lab (Meisel and Pfaff, unpublished observations) suggests that the primary anisomycin effect is

TABLE VI

Number of Dense-Cored Vesicles per 10 Nerve Cells Examined in the Ventrolateral Subdivision of the Ventromedial Nucleus in Ovariectomized and Ovariectomized/Estrogen-Treated Rats[a,b]

Ovariectomized/estrogen-treated		Ovariectomized/control ovx	
Rat number	Number of vesicles	Rat number	Number of vesicles
1	21.4	1'	15.0
2	10.0	2'	6.0
3	34.4	3'	1.1
4	15.4	4'	3.3
5	17.2	5'	6.3
6	5.8	6'	5.7
Mean	17.4	Mean	5.7

[a] Data from Cohen and Pfaff (1981).

[b] The mean number in the experimental group is 17.4 compared to the control, 5.7. Experimental vs control = $p < 0.02$.

in the ventromedial hypothalamus as opposed to the preoptic area (Fig. 14). Discontinuous schedules of estrogen treatment usually sufficient for lordosis behavior (Parsons *et al.,* 1982a) can have their behavioral effect interrupted if anisomycin is administered just before an estrogen pulse but not if anisomycin is delayed until more than 2 hours after the termination of sufficient estrogen treatment (Parsons *et al.,* 1982b). This suggests that a large portion of the estrogen-activated protein synthesis essential for the behavior and sensitive to the antibiotic is completed in a small number of hours after the estrogen treatment.

If proteins synthesized in ventromedial hypothalamic neurons under the influence of estrogen are transported down the axon and are important for reproductive behavior, then interruption of axoplasmic transport by colchicine should interfere with the behavior (Harlan *et al.,* 1982c). Indeed, when colchicine was infused bilaterally into the hypothalamus of ovariectomized rats 24 hours before the beginning of estrogen treatment, the onset of lordosis behavior was delayed significantly. In a different endocrine paradigm, ovariectomized rats were implanted subcutaneously with estradiol capsules to ensure high estrogen levels over a long period of time so that control levels of lordosis behavior would be maximal. Under these conditions, colchicine delivered bilaterally to the medial hypothalamus caused a decline in lordotic responsiveness, with a greater effect following a larger dose of colchicine (Fig. 15). In these experiments lordosis scores were significantly lower as quickly as 20 minutes following

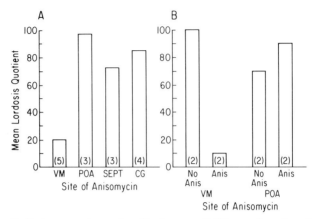

FIG. 14. Preliminary results on the effectiveness of different sites of application of the protein synthesis inhibitor anisomycin (Anis) in blocking lordosis behavior in estrogen-treated ovariectomized female rats. (A) A low dose of estradiol benzoate (2.5 μg) followed by progesterone (500 μg) was given subcutaneously. Bilateral implants of anisomycin (just prior to estrogen injection) in the ventromedial hypothalamus (VM) could reduce lordosis relative to rats with implants in the preoptic area (POA), septum (Sept), or central grey (CG). (B) Anisomycin (Anis) implanted bilaterally in the ventromedial hypothalamus (VM), but not in the preoptic area, was able to block the behavioral facilitation from VM implants of estradiol. In these experiments, Anisomycin was implanted 4 hours before estradiol, and rats were tested 3 days later, 4–6 hours after 500 μg systemic progesterone. (Data from Meisel and Pfaff, 1983.)

colchicine infusion. Then, they tended to recover partially before declining again to levels significantly below control values (Fig. 15). The fastest effect of colchicine is consistent with the possibility of local circuit neurons, important for lordosis behavior, synapsing in or nearby the ventromedial nucleus of the hypothalamus. The longer lasting effects of colchicine could be from actions on short-axoned or long-axoned nerve cells. Further ultrastructural work may clarify the nature of intrinsic neurons in the ventromedial hypothalamus as well as the longer projecting neurons with endings in the midbrain central gray.

C. WHAT IS BEING TRANSPORTED?

One of the best candidates among substances synthesized in the cell bodies of hypothalamic and preoptic neurons, for axoplasmic transport to the midbrain central gray with import for reproductive behavior is luteinizing hormone releasing hormone (LHRH). LHRH given systemically facilitates lordosis behavior in ovariectomized female rats (Moss and Mc-

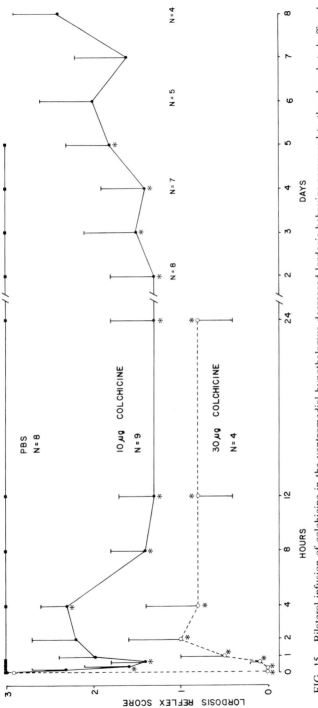

FIG. 15. Bilateral infusion of colchicine in the ventromedial hypothalamus decreased lordosis behavior compared to the phosphate-buffered saline (PBS) control. All experiments in ovariectomized estrogen-treated rats. (From Harlan *et al.*, 1982c.)

Cann, 1973; Pfaff, 1973). Biologically, this effect made sense, since it would tend to synchronize mating behavior with ovulation during the estrous cycle. It was clear that since LHRH was produced by neurons with specific terminal fields, that, physiologically, the most important sites of LHRH action would be in the brain regions where LHRH-bearing axons synapsed. Thus, experiments with rationally chosen central neural sites of LHRH application had to wait for a new generation of hypothalamic neuroanatomy to be completed, which was done largely with the use of tritiated amino acid autoradiography (Pfaff and Conrad, 1978). Such neuroanatomical results, together with the anatomical demonstration of LHRH-containing fibers (Silverman and Krey, 1978) indicated the midbrain central gray as a good site for work with local LHRH application. Further, quantitative use of LHRH immunocytochemistry (Shivers et al., 1981, 1982a) indicated that LHRH might be released from terminals in the midbrain central gray under conditions of estrogen treatment consistent with high levels of lordosis behavior. Thus, we studied reproductive behavior in ovariectomized female rats primed with low doses of estrogen and compared the effects of LHRH microinjected bilaterally in and around the midbrain central gray with the effects of an LHRH antiserum and various control substances (Sakuma and Pfaff, 1980a, 1983). Microinjection of LHRH into the dorsal part of the central gray rapidly facilitated lordosis behavior (Fig. 16). Conversely, delivery of an anti-LHRH globulin to the midbrain could cause a complete loss of lordosis behavior. Pharmacological comparisons of LHRH analogs defined as agonists or antagonists according to their effects on pituitary LH release suggested that the LHRH receptor requirements for triggering behavior through midbrain neurons are different from those for triggering LH release by gonadotrophs (Sakuma and Pfaff, 1983).

Recently, using immunocytochemical techniques for prolactin, we have been able to confirm the existence of prolactin-immunoreactivity in the brain (Shivers et al., 1982b, 1983) which had been reported (Toubeau et al., 1979). Cell bodies with prolactin-like immunoreactivity were found ventrally in the anterior and middle mediobasal hypothalamus and fibers with the immunoreactive substance were traced in the midbrain central gray. Since, in the pituitary, prolactin production can be stimulated strongly by estrogen, we did experiments to see if midbrain applications of prolactin might be related to estrogen-stimulated reproductive behavior (Shivers et al., 1982b; Harlan et al., 1982a). Bilateral microinfusions of prolactin into the dorsal midbrain significantly raised lordosis behavior scores. Control administration of the vehicle and of known contaminants of rat prolactin preparations had no effect. Conversely, administration of a prolactin antiserum to the dorsal midbrain in rats pretreated with estro-

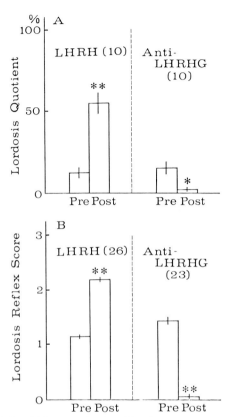

FIG. 16.   LHRH infused bilaterally in the midbrain central grey significantly increased lordosis behavior in ovariectomized estrogen-treated female rats tested (A) with male rats or (B) by artificial cutaneous stimulation. Conversely, antiserum to LHRH (Anti-LHRHG) decreased lordosis. (Data from Sakuma and Pfaff, 1983.)

gen so that they would have strong lordosis behavior actually decreased lordosis scores. Thus, under the influence of estrogen, prolactin may be synthesized by cells in the mediobasal hypothalamus, transported to the central gray, and released there in a manner important for reproductive behavior.

While choosing specific substances of known reproductive importance for immunocytochemical and physiological work is giving promising leads for studying the nature of materials transported from the hypothalamus to other brain regions, it has also made sense to pursue another, more open-minded neurochemical approach. Altogether, what peptides are transported from hypothalamus to midbrain, at what rates are they travelling, and which are affected by estrogen? We are studying this by microinjecting cocktails of tritiated amino acids among the cell bodies of the ventromedial hypothalamus. We systematically vary survival time after administration of these precursors to allow for incorporation and different rates of transport, and then dissect the midbrain central gray (Pfaff *et al.,* unpublished observations). Endings with proteins which were labeled in the hypothalamus and transported are being studied with a variety of centrifugation and chromatographic separation procedures. In one set of experiments, for example, the percentage of counts in the supernatant which would contain synaptic vesicles (following separation from membranes, nuclei, mitochondria, etc.) was almost twice as high following estrogen treatment as in ovariectomized control animals (Fig. 17). Chromatographic separation of the proteins in this fraction according to molecular size should give a further idea of the hormone-sensitive components, and in general, this approach does not limit us to peptides of previously recognized reproductive importance.

At least one protein promoted by estrogen in the mediobasal hypothalamus may not be transported to the midbrain. Cytosol progestin receptors, studied with assays for the binding of ^{3}H-R5020 (Maclusky and McEwen, 1978, 1980) have requirements for estrogen priming similar to those of female reproductive behavior (Moguilevsky and Reynaud, 1979). In particular, those temporal schedules of estrogen treatment sufficient for lordosis also tend to increase cytosol progestin receptor levels by an amount

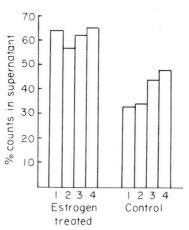

FIG. 17.   Percentage of counts in the supernatant of the third (high-speed) centrifugation, containing vesicles and soluble proteins. A cocktail of tritiated amino acids was delivered bilaterally to the ventromedial hypothalamus and 4 hours allowed for incorporation and fast axoplasmic transport. The dorsal midbrain area containing many hypothalamic endings was then dissected for analysis. Experiments were done with matched pairs of estradiol-treated and control ovariectomized female rats. (Pfaff *et al.,* unpublished observations.)

greater than 25–35% (Parsons *et al.*, 1982a). Presumably, these progestin receptors are partly responsible for mediating subsequent progestin effects on reproductive behavior.

D. SUMMARY

Electron microscopic results and evidence from the use of various synthesis and transport inhibitors fit with the implications from the temporal aspects of previous electrophysiological work: under the influence of estrogen, substances must be transported from hypothalamus to midbrain and released in such a manner as to promote female reproductive behavior. With methods that target specific substances of reproductive importance and with a more open-ended neurochemical approach we are searching for these substances not only to discover their chemical nature but also to study their actions in greater physiological detail.

VI. From Hypothalamus to Midbrain to Reticulospinal Neurons

The shortest established route by which hormone-dependent information from hypothalamic neurons can influence spinal circuits is as follows. Neurons in and around the ventromedial nucleus of the hypothalamus send axons to the central gray of the midbrain, as established with anterograde (Conrad and Pfaff, 1976) and retrograde (Morrell *et al.*, 1981) anatomical techniques, and electrophysiological recording from antidromically identified neurons (Sakuma and Pfaff, 1982). Some central gray cells send axons all the way to the medullary reticular formation, in the ventromedial portion which has many reticulospinal cell bodies. This has been shown by anatomical techniques for degenerating axons (Hamilton and Skultety, 1970), tritiated amino acid autoradiography (Eberhart *et al.*, 1983; Fig. 18) and by single unit recording from antidromically identified neurons in the midbrain (Sakuma and Pfaff, 1980b). Evidence from a variety of physiological techniques show that these connections are involved in lordosis behavior (Pfaff, 1980). Hypothalamic influences must be routed through reticulospinal neurons because the only other tract necessary for lordosis behavior, the lateral vestibulospinal tract, receives inputs neither from the hypothalamus nor from the areas of the midbrain shown to be involved in reproductive behavior.

There are other possible routes for hypothalamic influences. Some neurons in the dorsal midbrain just outside the central gray have anatomical and physiological properties which would serve them for reproductive behavior control. Also, not all behaviorally relevant neurons in the central gray need have long axons which reach the medullary reticular forma-

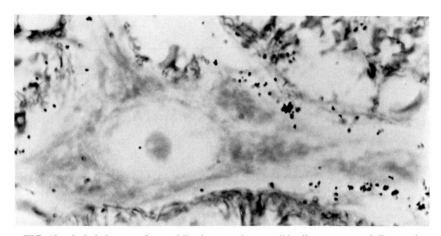

FIG. 18.   Labeled axons, from midbrain central grey cell bodies, near a medullary reticular formation neuron, as shown by silver grains in this autoradiogram. A cocktail of tritiated amino acids was delivered unilaterally to the central grey and 6 days allowed for incorporation and transport. Autoradiograms revealing labeled projections were charted systematically (Eberhart *et al.*, 1982). In this photomicrograph, labeled axons from central grey may be terminating in a region containing medullary reticulospinal cell bodies. (Eberhart *et al.*, 1983.)

tion; some such central gray cells which could not be antidromically identified from a medullary reticulospinal region had electrophysiological properties consistent with a role in lordosis behavior (Sakuma and Pfaff, 1980d).

While the bulk of evidence suggests neural modules for reproductive behavior control—hypothalamic, midbrain, medullary, and spinal cord modules—it is also possible that a small number of neurons with especially long axons can exert behaviorally relevant controls through a smaller number of connections. For example, axons originating from the ventromedial hypothalamus go through the region of the cerebral peduncle and the nucleus of the lateral lemniscus in the midbrain (Conrad and Pfaff, 1976; Saper *et al.*, 1976), where they pass close to and could synapse with neurons which can be retrograde-filled with HRP from the spinal cord (Zemlan *et al.*, 1979). Another possibility is that axons exiting the ventromedial hypothalamus and passing through the zona incerta (Krieger *et al.*, 1979) synapse, *en passant*, on zona incerta neurons which themselves have long descending connections (Basbaum and Fields, 1979). The most direct descending control which has any empirical support could come from the small number of neurons beneath the ventromedial nucleus of the hypothalamus, among fibers of the supraoptic commissure; under special conditions these neurons can be filled with retrograde anatomical techniques by application of the retrograde marker in the spinal cord (Swanson and Kuypers, 1980; Schwanzel-Fukuda *et al.*, 1983).

VII. Reticulospinal Actions

The exact logic by which reticular neurons carry hormone-dependent information to drive a behavior pattern is unknown. In some ways, lateral vestibulospinal and reticulospinal neurons synergize to facilitate lordosis behavior (Modianos and Pfaff, 1976, 1977). Such vesticulospinal–reticulospinal cooperation had been suspected in other physiological experiments (Hassen and Barnes, 1975). Electrical stimulation of reticular neurons (Brink and Pfaff, 1981) can directly trigger electrical activity in motor neurons for muscles involved in lordosis behavior (for example, lateral longissimus), and can also facilitate the responses of such motor neurons to sensory input at the spinal level. Indeed, electrical stimulation of the medullary reticular formation can drive electromyographic activity in the deep back muscles, including lateral longissimus itself (Fig. 19; Femano *et al.*, 1981). The strength of this reticular control over activity in behaviorally relevant back muscle was greater than expected (Fig. 20), with individual reticular pulses associated with bursts of lateral longissimus EMG activity at latencies as short as 4–7 msec (Femano *et al.*, 1982).

The anatomy of the reticulospinal system, as well as the lateral vestibulospinal system, is well suited for lordosis behavior control (Pfaff, 1980). For example, reticulospinal axons branch at different levels of the spinal cord (Peterson *et al.*, 1975), in a manner which makes it easy to understand how these axons could be involved in lordosis, whose vertebral dorsiflexion extends all the way from the tailbase to the head. Lordosis behavior deficits occur only after a very large percentage of the reticulo-

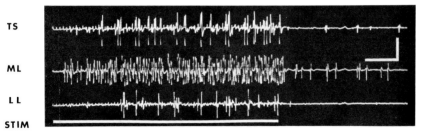

FIG. 19. Electrical stimulation of the nucleus gigantocellularis in the medullary reticular formation activates the EMG of the three main back axial muscle systems: transversospinalis (TS), medial longissimus (ML), and lateral longissimus (LL). Bottom bar (STIM) indicates the duration of a stimulus train at the following parameters: stimulation ipsilateral to recording sites, 200 Hz pulse rate, 25 μA biphasic square wave, leading phase cathodal. Calibrations: 100 μV, 50 msec. (From Femano *et al.*, 1981.)

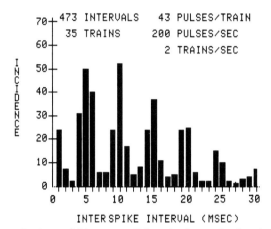

INTER SPIKE INTERVAL (MSEC)

FIG. 20.   Interspike interval histogram of deep back muscle electrical activity during medial medullary reticular formation stimulation with 30 μA at stimulus train parameters indicated on the graph. Peak occurrences of interspike intervals are at multiples of the interpulse interval of the stimulus. This indicates that electromyographic potentials are *not* randomly distributed within the response to a stimulus train, but rather are temporally coupled tightly to individual stimulus pulses. This high efficacy of transmission was seen in each axial muscle group during stimulation of the medial medullary reticular formation. (From Femano *et al.*, 1982a).

spinal system has been removed. This can be deduced from the fact that large lesions of medullary reticulospinal cell bodies (Zemlan *et al.*, 1983) as well as large transections of medullary reticulospinal axons (Kow *et al.*, 1977) were required for significant lordosis loss. To a large extent, therefore, reticulospinal neurons must be able to substitute for each other. This does not suggest a finely organized control system in which each neuron is playing a precisely defined obligatory role. If the reticulospinal behavior-facilitating signal is logically simple, it fits with histochemical evidence on the lordosis-executing muscle lateral longissimus (Section VIII) which suggests that the behavior itself if of a simple ballistic form once it gets started.

These data give the picture of a relatively gross reticulospinal signal (itself dependent on hormones) descending to facilitate lordosis behavior, which is triggered by stimulus input registered primarily at the spinal level.

VIII. Spinal Mechanisms for a Hormone-Dependent Behavior

The precise mechanisms by which behaviorally relevant cutaneous information entering through the dorsal roots and signals descending from the brainstem converge onto behaviorally relevant motor neurons for producing lordosis are unknown. This is because the exact number and functions of spinal interneurons participating in the circuit have been hard to determine. Among the facts that bear on lumbar spinal cord mechanisms for lordosis behavior, some are listed in Table VII. Reasoning from these we can make several points about the properties of the spinal circuit that produces a behavioral response given adequate sensory and descending influences.

Over a large variety of endocrine states, the lordosis response is triggered by cutaneous pressure on the posterior rump, tailbase, or perineum, in the range from 40 to 440 millibars, thus implicating low pressure threshold receptors (Kow et al., 1979). Since adding to the area of cutaneous

TABLE VII
Some Facts Bearing on Lumbar Spinal Cord Mechanisms for Lordosis

Stimulus properties
  Bilateral
  Cutaneous pressure
    (Pfaff et al., 1977; Kow et al., 1979)

Primary sensory neurons
  No spontaneous activity
  Slow-adapting cutaneous mechanoreceptors
    (Kow and Pfaff, 1979)

Interneurons
  Excited by cutaneous pressure
  Deep dorsal horn, intermediate grey
  Deeper units require stronger stimuli
    (Kow et al., 1980; Wall, 1967; Molinari, 1982)

Estrogen
  Few estrogen-concentrating neurons
  No electrophysiological effects yet on individual neurons
    (Morrell et al., 1982; Kow and Pfaff, 1979, 1980)

Ascending fibers
  Through anterolateral columns
  Many reach medulla retic. form
  Few reach midbrain central grey
    (Kow et al., 1977, 1982; Zemlan et al., 1979; Morrell and Pfaff, 1983)

Response properties
  Bilateral
  From tense crouch to vertebral dorsiflexion. Latency 161 msec
    (Pfaff et al., 1971, 1978; Pfaff and Lewis, 1974)

Muscle fibers
  Fast twitch fibers, few spindles
  Correlated with behavior
  Respond to reticulospinal, 4–7 msec latency
    (Schwartz-Giblin et al., 1981, 1983; Femano et al., 1982, 1983b)

Motoneurons
  Small number, in medial ventral horn
  Poor monosynaptic response to dorsal root
    (Brink et al., 1980; Brink and Pfaff, 1981)

Descending systems
  Lateral vestibulospinal and reticulospinal
  Terminate at several levels
  Drive motoneurons and deep back muscles
  Large lesions required for behavior loss
    (Peterson et al., 1975; Modianos and Pfaff, 1976; Zemlan et al., 1983; Brink and Pfaff, 1981; Femano et al., 1981, 1983a,c)

stimulation can increase the strength of the behavioral response, there must be a spinal mechanism for *spatial summation* of sensory input.

The low amounts of pressure needed for triggering lordosis behavior in the female rat well primed with estrogen and the features of those primary sensory neurons whose response properties to various cutaneous stimuli most closely fit those of the reproductive behavior as a whole indicate that we are dealing with pressure receptors named from neurophysiological studies with cats; Type II slowly adapting cutaneous mechanoreceptors (Kow and Pfaff, 1979). These primary sensory neurons have been closely identified with Ruffini endings in the skin. Thus, while stimulation from the male could trigger action potentials in a wide variety of cutaneous receptors, those most closely correlated to the initiation of lordosis behavior would comprise the following train of events: deformation of Ruffini endings leading to action potentials in Type II mechanoreceptors leading to excitatory postsynaptic potentials in a class of interneurons.

Spinal interneurons whose stimulus requirements closely match those for lordosis behavior as a whole were found in the deep layers of the dorsal horn and the intermediate gray during single unit recordings in anesthetized female rats (Kow et al., 1980). A high percentage of these have excitatory responses to cutaneous pressure. Since their receptive fields are just ipsilateral, strong bilateral connections are unlikely, although extensive rostral-caudal branching might be expected. Here, work on interneurons involved in reproductive behavior can take advantage of a wide range of facts collected on spinal interneurons in other types of recording experiments. For example, in the deep layers of the dorsal horn, skin from proximal areas of the body is represented on the lateral side (Brown and Fuchs, 1975; Bryan et al., 1974). That perivaginal regions and skin from the posterior rump could be preferentially represented here is especially interesting, since small numbers of "long distance somatosensory afferents," as might be required for facilitation of lordosis behavior from stimulation of the flanks, also terminate here. Since motor neurons for deep back muscles are found on the medial and ventromedial sides of the ventral horn (Brink et al., 1980), for lordosis behavior the main flow of information must transfer from the lateral side (in the dorsal horn) to the medial side (in the ventral horn). Some evidence suggesting this actually occurs has been seen in recent recording experiments in cats (Molinari, 1982). There is another trend, as one's recording experiments proceed from dorsal horn levels, ventrally through the intermediate gray to the ventral horn. As one encounters neurons with the micropipette more ventrally, cutaneous receptive fields tend to be larger and, especially, more intense cutaneous stimulation is required for a response (Wall, 1967; Kow et al., 1980; Molinari, 1982). Overall, the sizes of the cutaneous receptive fields of lumbar spinal interneurons require the *convergence* of primary sensory neuronal information. Indeed, this is probably the mechanism of the spatial summation required from the behavioral evidence mentioned above.

Compared to the hypothalamus and limbic system there are very few estrogen-concentrating neurons in the lumbar spinal cord, even in the areas which would be predicted from knowledge of spinal mechanisms for lordosis behavior. Those which can be detected are not intensely labeled (Morrell *et al.*, 1982). Recording from single primary sensory neurons and individual lumbar spinal interneurons also has not shown a strong estrogen effect at the spinal level (Kow and Pfaff, 1979; Kow *et al.*, 1980). The facilitation by estrogen of cutaneous input, which has been detected, has been of a statistical nature and has depended on the inherent averaging achieved by recording from the entire pudendal nerve (Komisaruk *et al.*, 1972; Kow and Pfaff, 1973) or the entire dorsal root (Kow and Pfaff, 1979). Therefore, virtually all of the estrogenic facilitation of the spinal circuit executing female reproductive behavior must come through pathways descending from the brainstem and, as indicated above, these must be, primarily, reticulospinal axons.

Fibers ascending to the brainstem, which could be relevant for lordosis, travel through the anterolateral columns and influence neurons in the nucleus gigantocellularis of the medullary reticular formation, as shown by anatomical (Zemlan *et al.*, 1978) and electrophysiological (Kow and Pfaff, 1982; Kevetter and Willis, 1982) techniques. Unless nucleus gigantocellularis relays sensory information to the dorsal midbrain avidly, the dorsal midbrain in the female rat is less dependent on strong, prompt somatosensory information than might have been expected, since only a small number of fibers ascend all the way from the lumbar spinal cord to the midbrain (Morrell and Pfaff, 1983). Indeed, electrophysiological recording in the rat does show neurons in and near the midbrain central gray responding to cutaneous stimulation (Malsbury *et al.*, 1972; Sakuma and Pfaff, 1980d), but the sparse degeneration, using the Fink-Heimer technique, following spinal column section, suggests that this somatosensory information does not follow a direct and strongly protected physiological route (Zemlan *et al.*, 1978). Also, those neurons with the longest descending axons from central gray did *not* respond to cutaneous stimuli (Sakuma and Pfaff, 1980b). Thus, while nerve cells in and nearby the midbrain central gray remain a possible site of sensory-hormonal interactions in governing female reproductive behavior, the possibly indirect and physiologically weak mechanisms by which the cutaneous input reaches the dorsal midbrain suggest that the more powerful role for these midbrain neurons is to transmit descending influences from the hypothalamus. The

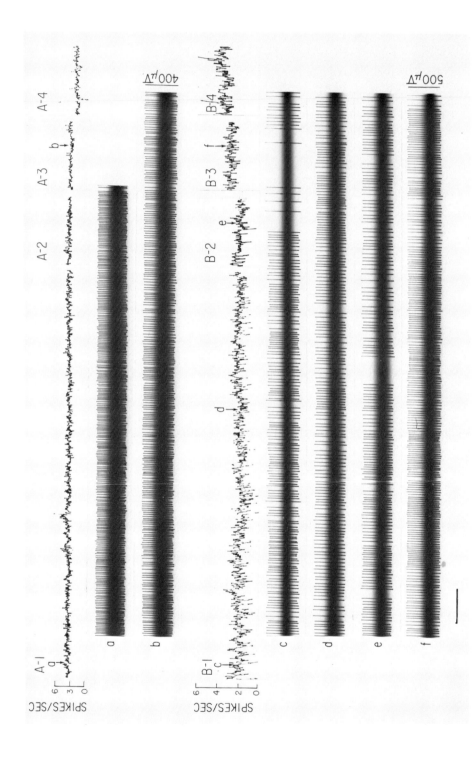

manner in which somatosensory information alters the firing rates of mid-brain neurons known to receive a direct hypothalamic input will be a fruitful subject for new experiments.

Since descending lateral vestibulospinal and reticulospinal axons termi-nate at several levels of the spinal cord and since relatively large lesions of these axons or their cell bodies are required for significant lordosis loss, the contribution of each neuron to spinal behavioral mechanisms could not be extremely specific. On the other hand, these descending influences are very strong. Medullary reticular formation stimulation can drive deep back muscle EMG reliably with latencies as low as 4 to 7 msec (Femano *et al.*, 1982, 1983b). Under a variety of physiological manipulations, the reticulospinal influence on deep back muscle electrical activity does not vary the same way as the influence of stretching these muscles, suggesting independent synaptic inputs to the motor neurons involved. Further stud-ies of the timing of the electromyographic activation of deep back muscles involved in lordosis behavior will allow a more detailed parcellation of the influences on spinal neurons involved in that behavior. Particularly telling will be physiological studies of the influences of neurons on one side of the spinal cord or reticular formation on mechanisms in the other side of the spinal cord, since the stimuli for lordosis behavior are bilateral and the motor response is bilaterally symmetric. Another productive area of study will be the means by which the lateral vestibulospinal tract primes the system (without itself receiving anatomical inputs from the hypotha-lamus or midbrain central gray) for actions by reticulospinal neurons.

Recording from motor neurons which govern deep back muscles in the female rat (Brink and Pfaff, 1981), it is much more difficult to elicit a monosynaptic response by electrical stimulation of a single dorsal root than it would be for a limb muscle motor neuron. Thus, stretch reflexes, which in their strongest form would operate through safe monosynaptic connections, must be relatively weak for these muscles. This means that a relatively greater influence over these motor neurons comes from cutane-

---

FIG. 21. Two examples of long and stable single-unit recordings from hypothalamic tissue slices maintained *in vitro*. A-1 through A-4 and B-1 through B-4 show segments of continuous polygraph recordings of the firing rates of units A and B, respectively. These segments show the firing rates recorded during the first 2 hours (A-1 and B-1), and at 3 (A-2 and B-2), 4.5 (A-3 and B-3), 7 (A-4), and 14 hours (B-4) after the beginning of each recording. Photographs a–f were taken from an oscilloscope to show the details of spike activity at the points indicated by corresponding letters and arrows on polygraph records. Unit A was recorded from the ventromedial nucleus of hypothalamus (VMN) beginning at 22 hours after the rat had been sacrificed, while unit B was from the arcuate nucleus of another rat at 6.5 hours after decapitation. Horizontal calibration: 10 minutes for polygraph records, and 5 seconds for oscilloscope photographs. (From Kow and Pfaff, 1983.)

ous and descending systems. This fits perfectly with what we see in the control of lordosis behavior. Cutaneous pressure promptly drives the reflex. Reticulospinal (Femano *et al.,* 1981, 1983a) and vestibulospinal (Femano *et al.,* 1983c) stimuli reliably drive deep back muscle EMG.

The overall behavioral latency of 161 msec includes time from the first contact of the male's forepaws with the female's flanks to the generation of a visually detectable rump elevation (Pfaff and Lewis, 1974). Minimal times for spinal cord mechanisms are much smaller, since the rump elevation is most closely correlated not with flank stimulation but with pressure on the rump and perineum, and because of the time required from the first motor neuron action potentials to the development of enough muscular force to produce a visible response. Also, it remains to be discovered whether the overall behavioral latency or components thereof are dependent on estrogen and progesterone dose. The first behavioral element in lordosis whose occurrence is clearly estrogen- and progesterone-dependent is rump elevation (Pfaff *et al.,* 1977). Since these first attempts to understand the temporal aspects of the spinal mechanisms for lordosis used numerical estimates from a variety of preparations, further systematic study will be required for a temporal analysis. Among muscle fiber types, fast twitch fibers could develop force 35 to 50 msec following adequate motor nerve stimulation, while slow twitch fibers would require 55 to 70 msec. Histochemistry of the deep back muscle lateral longissimus in the rat shows that it is composed primarily of fast twitch muscle fibers (Schwartz-Giblin *et al.,* 1983). Muscle spindles, serving stretch reflexes, tend to be concentrated in a subdivision of the muscle which has more slow twitch fibers, while the bulk of the muscle, with fast twitch fibers, has few spindles. This suggests that the main force contributed by this muscle toward lordosis behavior must be generated ballistically—a relatively simple trigger working without stretch receptor guided reflex control.

IX. Conclusions and Prospects

Estrogen acts on hypothalamic cells through receptor-mediated processes, which in their neuroanatomical features are similar across a wide variety of vertebrates. Receptor functions are correlated with estrogen effects on reproductive behavior. In female rodents, the neural circuitry for lordosis behavior comprises the best described behavioral mechanism among mammals. This reproductive behavior depends on the action of estrogen on ventromedial hypothalamic neurons. The shortest established route by which these neurons transmit hormone-dependent influences is from hypothalamus to midbrain central gray to medullary reticular forma-

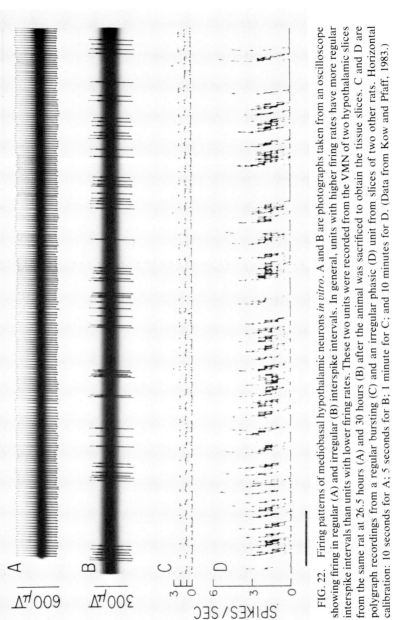

FIG. 22. Firing patterns of mediobasal hypothalamic neurons *in vitro*. A and B are photographs taken from an oscilloscope showing firing in regular (A) and irregular (B) interspike intervals. In general, units with higher firing rates have more regular interspike intervals than units with lower firing rates. These two units were recorded from the VMN of two hypothalamic slices from the same rat at 26.5 hours (A) and 30 hours (B) after the animal was sacrificed to obtain the tissue slices. C and D are polygraph recordings from a regular bursting (C) and an irregular phasic (D) unit from slices of two other rats. Horizontal calibration: 10 seconds for A; 5 seconds for B; 1 minute for C; and 10 minutes for D. (Data from Kow and Pfaff, 1983.)

tion to lumbar spinal cord. There descending reticulospinal and vestibulospinal systems intersect with a powerful cutaneous input to facilitate
activity in behaviorally relevant interneurons and motor neurons.

Estrogenic effects on hypothalamic neurons operate through both electrical and protein-synthetic mechanisms. Substances of proven importance for reproductive behavior are transported at least from the hypothalamus to the midbrain. Among the relevant peptides revealed by
physiological studies are LHRH and prolactin. In a wider ranging set of
neurochemical experiments we are searching for other hormone-dependent peptides arriving at hypothalamic axonal endings, by techniques for
physical separation and analysis of radioactive peptides following delivery of labeled precursors to hypothalamic cell bodies. Another protein
produced in the hypothalamus under the influence of estrogen, but not
transported, is the progesterone receptor in the cytosol, probably responsible for mediating certain progesterone effects.

Ultrastructural effects of estrogen are consistent with the notion of
hormone effects on RNA and protein synthesis. Electron microscopic
work should be pursued to seek correlations between ultrastructure and
function under a wider variety of endocrine conditions.

For hypothalamic neurons, electrical and chemical changes resulting
from steroid hormone treatment will have to be analyzed in parallel. This
suggests that electrophysiological experiments will best be carried out
under precisely determined physicochemical conditions. Recording in hypothalamic tissue slices (Figs. 21 and 22) is proving useful for characterizing hypothalamic cells with the eventual purpose of describing hormone
effects under these conditions. Thus, we may be able to identify particular
electrical, as well as structural or chemical properties, of nerve cells
which participate in endocrine events, to distinguish them from cells classically described elsewhere in the nervous system.

REFERENCES

Baldino, F., Jr., and Geller, H. M. (1982). *J. Physiol. (London)* **327**, 173.
Basbaum, A. I., and Fields, H. L. (1979). *J. Comp. Neurol.* **187**, 513.
Brink, E. E., and Pfaff, D. W. (1981). *Brain Res.* **226**, 43.
Brink, E. E., Morrell, J. I., and Pfaff, D. W. (1979). *Brain Res.* **170**, 23.
Bronk, D. W., Ferguson, L., Margoria, R., and Solandt, D. Y. (1936). *Am. J. Physiol.* **117**,
    237.
Brown, P. B., and Fuchs, J. L. (1975). *J. Neurophysiol.* **38**, 1.
Bryan, R. N., Coulter, J. D., and Willis, W. D. (1974). *Exp. Neurol.* **42**, 574.
Bueno, J., and Pfaff, D. W. (1976). *Brain Res.* **101**, 67.
Burnstock, G., and Costa, M. (1975). "Adrenergic Neurons, Their Organization, Function
    and Development in the Peripheral Nervous System." Chapman & Hall, London.

Cohen, R. S., and Pfaff, D. W. (1981). *Cell Tissue Res.* **217**, 451.
Cohen, R. S., and Pfaff, D. W. (1982). *Soc. Neurosci. Abstr.* **8**, 531.
Cohen, R. S., and Pfaff, D. W. (1983). *Cell Tissue Res.*, in press.
Conrad, L. C. A., and Pfaff, D. W. (1976). *J. Comp. Neurol.* **169**, 221.
Courtney, K. R., Kendig, J., and Cohen, E. (1978). *J. Pharmacol. Exp. Ther.* **207**, 594.
Cross, B. A., and Dyer, R. (1972). *J. Physiol. (London)* **222**, 25P.
Davis, R. E., Morrell, J. I., and Pfaff, D. W. (1977). *Gen. Comp. Endocrinol.* **33**, 496.
Dyer, R. G. (1973). *J. Physiol. (London)* **234**, 421.
Dyer, R., Pritchett, C., and Cross, B. A. (1972). *J. Endocrinol.* **53**, 151.
Eberhart, J., Morrell, J. I., and Pfaff, D. W. (1982). *Soc. Neurosci. Abstr.* **8**, 835.
Eberhart, J. *et al.* (1983). Submitted.
Eccles, R. M. (1955). *J. Physiol. (London)* **130**, 572.
Edwards, D., and Pfeifle, J. (1981). *Physiol. Behav.* **26**, 1061.
Femano, P. A., Schwartz-Giblin, S., and Pfaff, D. W. (1981). *Soc. Neurosci. Abstr.* **7**, 80.
Femano, P. A., Schwartz-Giblin, S., and Pfaff, D. W. (1982). *Fed. Proc. Fed. Am. Soc. Exp. Biol.* **41**, 1758 (Abstr.).
Femano, P. A., Schwartz-Giblin, S., and Pfaff, D. W. (1983a). *Am. J. Physiol.*, submitted.
Femano, P. A., Schwartz-Giblin, S., and Pfaff, D. W. (1983b). *Am. J. Physiol.*, submitted.
Femano, P. A., Schwartz-Giblin, S., and Pfaff, D. W. (1983c). *Fed. Proc. Fed. Am. Soc. Exp. Biol.*, in press (Abstr.).
Gorski, J., Taft, D., Shyamala, G., Smith, D., and Notides, A. (1968). *Recent Prog. Horm. Res.* **24**, 45.
Halpern, M., Morrell, J. I., and Pfaff, D. W. (1982). *Gen. Comp. Endocrinol.* **46**, 211.
Hamilton, B. L., and Skultety, F. M. (1970). *J. Comp. Neurol.* **139**, 105.
Harlan, R. E., Shivers, B. D., and Pfaff, D. W. (1981). *Soc. Neurosci. Abstr.* **7**, 615.
Harlan, R. E., Shivers, B. D., and Pfaff, D. W. (1982a). *Science* **219**, 1451.
Harlan, R. E., Shivers, B. D., and Pfaff, D. W. (1982b). *Soc. Neurosci. Abstr.* **8**, 930.
Harlan, R. E., Shivers, B. D., Kow, L.-M., and Pfaff, D. W. (1982c). *Brain Res.* **238**, 153.
Harlan, R. E., Shivers, B. D., and Pfaff, D. W. (1983). *Brain Res.*, in press.
Hassen, A. H., and Barnes, C. D. (1975). *Brain Res.* **90**, 221.
Hatton, G. I. (1982). *J. Physiol. (London)* **327**, 273.
Jensen, E. V., and Jacobson, H. I. (1962). *Recent Prog. Horm. Res.* **18**, 387.
Jensen, E. V., Greene, G. L., Closs, L. E., DeSombre, E. R., and Nadji, M. (1982). *Recent Prog. Horm. Res.* **38**, 1.
Kato, J., and Onouchi, T. (1977). *Endocrinology* **101**, 920.
Kawakami, M., Terasawa, E., Ibuki, T., and Manaka, M. (1971). *In* "Steroid Hormones and Brain Function" (C. Sawyer and R. Gorski, eds.), p. 79. Univ. of California Press, Los Angeles.
Kelso, S. R., Perlmutter, M. N., and Boulant, J. A. (1982). *Am. J. Physiol.* **242**, R77.
Kevetter, G. A., and Willis, W. D. (1982). *Brain Res.* **238**, 181.
Komisaruk, B. R., Adler, N., and Hutchison, J. (1972). *Science* **178**, 1295.
Kow, L.-M., and Pfaff, D. W. (1973). *Neuroendocrinology* **13**, 299.
Kow, L.-M., and Pfaff, D. W. (1979). *J. Neurophysiol.* **42**, 203.
Kow, L.-M., and Pfaff, D. W. (1982). *Exp. Brain Res.* **47**, 191.
Kow, L.-M., and Pfaff, D. W. (1983). In preparation.
Kow, L.-M., Montgomery, M., and Pfaff, D. W. (1977). *Brain Res.* **123**, 75.
Kow, L.-M., Montgomery, M. O., and Pfaff, D. W. (1979). *J. Neurophysiol.* **42**, 195.
Kow, L.-M., Zemlan, F. P., and Pfaff, D. W. (1980). *J. Neurophysiol.* **43**, 27.
Krieger, M. S., Morrell, J. I., and Pfaff, D. W. (1978). *Soc. Neurosci. Abstr.* **4**, 347.

Krieger, M. S., Conrad, L. C. A., and Pfaff, D. W. (1979). *J. Comp. Neurol.* **183,** 785.
Lincoln, D. (1967). *J. Endocrinol.* **37,** 177.
McEwen, B. S., Biegon, A., Davis, P. G., Krey, L. C., Luine, V. N., McGinnis, M. Y., Paden, C. M., Parsons, B., and Rainbow, T. C. (1982). *Recent Prog. Horm. Res.* **38,** 41.
MacLusky, N. J., and McEwen, B. S. (1978). *Nature (London)* **274,** 276.
MacLusky, N. J., and McEwen, B. S. (1980). *Endocrinology* **106,** 192.
Malsbury, C., Kelley, C. B., and Pfaff, D. W. (1972). *Proc. Int. Congr. Endocrinol., 4th* pp. 205–209.
Manogue, K., Kow, L.-M., and Pfaff, D. W. (1980). *Horm. Behav.* **14,** 277.
Mathews, D., and Edwards, D. (1977). *Physiol. & Behav.* **19,** 319.
Meigel, ., and Pfaff, D. W. (1983). In preparation.
Modianos, D., and Pfaff, D. W. (1976). *Brain Res.* **106,** 47.
Modianos, D. T., and Pfaff, D. W. (1977). *Brain Res.* **134,** 333.
Moguilewsky, M., and Raynaud, J.-P. (1979). *Endocrinology* **105,** 516.
Molinari, H. H. (1982). *Brain Res.* **234,** 165.
Morrell, J. I., and Pfaff, D. W. (1978). *Am. Zool.* **18,** 447.
Morrell, J. I., and Pfaff, D. W. (1982). *Science* **217,** 1273.
Morrell, J. I., and Pfaff, D. W. (1983). *Am. J. Anat.,* in press.
Morrell, J. I., Greenberger, L. M., and Pfaff, D. W. (1981). *J. Comp. Neurol.* **201,** 589.
Morrell, J. I., Wolinsky, T. D., Krieger, M. S., and Pfaff, D. W. (1982). *Exp. Brain Res.* **45,** 144.
Morrell, J. I., Krieger, M. S., and Pfaff, D. W. (1983a). *Endocrinology,* submitted.
Morrell, J. I., McGinty, J., and Pfaff, D. W. (1983b). *Soc. Neurosci. Abstr.,* in press.
Moss, R., and Law, O. T. (1971). *Brain Res.* **30,** 435.
Moss, R., and McCann, S. M. (1973). *Science* **181,** 177.
Mueller, G. C., von der Haar, B., Kim, V. H., and Le Mahiev, M. (1972). *Recent Prog. Horm. Res.* **28,** 1.
Narahashi, T., Anderson, N., and Moore, J. (1966). *Science* **153,** 765.
Nelson, D. O., and Prosser, C. L. (1981). *Science* **213,** 787.
O'Malley, B. W., McGuire, W. L., Kohler, P. O., and Korenman, S. G. (1969). *Recent Prog. Horm. Res.* **25,** 105.
Parsons, B., MacLusky, N. J., Krey, L., Pfaff, D. W., and McEwen, B. S. (1980). *Endocrinology* **107,** 774.
Parsons, B., McEwen, B. S., and Pfaff, D. W. (1982a). *Endocrinology* **110,** 613.
Parsons, B., Rainbow, T. C., Pfaff, D. W., and McEwen, B. S. (1982b). *Endocrinology* **110,** 620.
Peterson, B. W., Filion, M., Felpel, L., and Abzug, C. (1975). *Exp. Brain Res.* **22.** 335.
Pfaff, D. W. (1968a). *Endocrinology* **82,** 1149.
Pfaff, D. W. (1968b). *Science* **161,** 1355.
Pfaff, D. W. (1973). *Science* **182,** 1148.
Pfaff, D. W. (1980). "Estrogens and Brain Function: Neural Analysis of a Hormone-Controlled Mammalian Reproductive Behavior." Springer-Verlag, Berlin and New York.
Pfaff, D. W. (1982). "The Physiological Mechanisms of Motivation." Springer-Verlag, Berlin and New York.
Pfaff, D. W., and Conrad, L. C. A. (1978). *Int. Rev. Cytol.* **54,** 245–265.
Pfaff, D. W., and Keiner, M. (1973). *J. Comp. Neurol.* **151,** 121.
Pfaff, D. W., and Lewis, C. (1974). *Horm. Behav.* **5,** 317.
Pfaff, D. W., and Sakuma, Y. (1979a). *J. Physiol. (London)* **288,** 189.
Pfaff, D. W., and Sakuma, Y. (1979b). *J. Physiol. (London)* **288,** 203.

Pfaff, D. W., Gerlach, J., McEwen, B. S., Ferin, M., Carmel, P., and Zimmerman, E. (1976). *J. Comp. Neurol.* **170,** 279.

Pfaff, D. W., Montgomery, M., and Lewis, C. (1977). *J. Comp. Physiol. Psychol.* **91,** 134.

Pfaff, D. W., Diakow, C., and Montgomery, M. (1978). *J. Comp. Physiol. Psychol.* **92,** 937.

Pfeifle, J., and Edwards, D. (1982). *Conf. Reprod. Behav. Michigan State Univ., June* Abstract.

Quadagno, D., and Ho, G. (1975). *Horm. Behav.* **6,** 19.

Quadagno, D., Shryne, J., and Gorski, R. (1971). *Horm. Behav.* **2,** 1.

Rainbow, T., McGinnis, M., Davis, P., and McEwen, B. S. (1982). *Brain Res.* **233,** 417.

Rhodes, C. H., Morrell, J. I., and Pfaff, D. W. (1981a). *J. Comp. Neurol.* **198,** 45.

Rhodes, C. H., Morrell, J. I., and Pfaff, D. W. (1981b). *Neuroendocrinology* **33,** 18.

Rhodes, C. H., Morrell, J. I., and Pfaff, D. W. (1982). *J. Neurosci.* **12,** 1718.

Riskind, P., and Moss, R. (1979). *Brain Res. Bull.* **4,** 203.

Ritchie, J., and Rogart, R. (1977). *Rev. Physiol. Biochem. Pharmacol.* **79,** 1.

Sakuma, Y., and Pfaff, D. W. (1979a). *Am. J. Physiol.* **237,** R278.

Sakuma, Y., and Pfaff, D. W. (1979b). *Am. J. Physiol.* **237,** R285.

Sakuma, Y., and Pfaff, D. W. (1980a). *Nature (London)* **283,** 566.

Sakuma, Y., and Pfaff, D. W. (1980b). *J. Neurophysiol.* **44,** 1002.

Sakuma, Y., and Pfaff, D. W. (1980c). *J. Neurophysiol.* **44,** 1012.

Sakuma, Y., and Pfaff, D. W. (1980d). *Exp. Neurol.* **70,** 269.

Sakuma, Y., and Pfaff, D. W. (1981). *Brain Res.* **225,** 184.

Sakuma, Y., and Pfaff, D. W. (1982). *Exp. Brain Res.* **46,** 292.

Sakuma, Y., and Pfaff, D. W. (1983). *Neuroendocrinology,* in press.

Saper, C., Swanson, L. W., and Cowan, W. M. (1976). *J. Comp. Neurol.* **169,** 409.

Schwanzel-Fukuda, M., Morrell, J. I., and Pfaff, D. W. (1983). *J. Histochem. Cytochem.,* in press.

Schwartz-Giblin, S., Rosello, L., and Pfaff, D. W. (1983). *Exp. Neurol.* **79,** 497.

Shivers, B. D., Harlan, R. E., Morrell, J. I., and Pfaff, D. W. (1981). *J. Histochem. Cytochem.* **29,** 901 (Abstr.).

Shivers, B. D., Harlan, R. E., Morrell, J. I., and Pfaff, D. W. (1982a). *Neuroendocrinology* **36,** 1.

Shivers, B. D., Harlan, R. E., and Pfaff, D. W. (1982b). *Soc. Neurosci. Abstr.* **8,** 930.

Shivers, B. *et al.* (1983a). *Nature (London),* in press.

Shivers, B. *et al.* (1983b). Submitted.

Silverman, A. J., and Krey, L. C. (1978). *Brain Res.* **157,** 233.

Skok, V. I. (1973). "Physiology of Autonomic Ganglia." Igakushoin, Tokyo.

Stumpf, W. E. (1968). *Science* **162,** 1001.

Swanson, L. W., and Kuypers, H. G. J. M. (1980). *Neurosci. Lett.* **17,** 307.

Tasaki, I. (1953). "Nervous Transmission." Thomas, Springfield, Illinois.

Terkel, A., Shryne, J., and Gorski, R. (1973). *Horm. Behav.* **4,** 377.

Toubeau, G., Desclin, J., Parmentier, M., and Pasteels, J. L. (1979). *J. Endocrinol.* **83,** 261.

Wall, P. D. (1967). *J. Physiol. (London)* **188,** 403.

Yagi, K., and Sawaki, Y. (1973). *In* "Neuroendocrine Control" (K. Yagi and S. Yoshida, eds.), p. 297. Univ. of Tokyo Press, Tokyo.

Zemlan, F. P., Leonard, C. M., Kow, L.-M., and Pfaff, D. W. (1978). *Exp. Neurol.* **62,** 298.

Zemlan, F. P., Kow, L.-M., Morrell, J. I., and Pfaff, D. W. (1979). *J. Anat.* **128,** 489.

Zemlan, F. P., Kow, L.-M., and Pfaff, D. W. (1983). *Exp. Neurol.,* in press.

Zigmond, R. E., and Chalazonitis, A. (1979). *Brain Res.* **164,** 137.

Zigmond, R. E., and McEwen, B. S. (1970). *J. Neurochem.* **17,** 889.

DISCUSSION

N. B. Schwartz: In the intact female rat in which lordosis lasts for 5 to 10 hours, what turns behavior off?

D. W. Pfaff: The biphasic action of progesterone. With progesterone you get a short latency facilitation of the behavior, and the behavior may stay high for 6 to 10 hours. But if you were to try and reinstate it the next day with another administration of progesterone you would get no behavior.

N. B. Schwartz: Are you saying then that in an animal whose ovaries and adrenals are removed late in the afternoon, after the estrogen trigger has been set, but before the progesterone has been released, that the behavior would not turn off?

D. W. Pfaff: If the estrogen support were adequate.

I. A. Kourides: Dr. Pfaff you have shown us very nicely that estrogen is stimulating messenger RNA either through transcription or accumulation of mRNA in brain cells of the hypothalamus. What I would like to know is whether you know anything about the specific proteins that these messenger RNAs are being translated into. Probably the studies are feasible to do. You could look, for example, at cell-free translation of extracted mRNA with analysis of the proteins synthesized by two-dimensional gel electrophoresis. Such studies might be important to tell you on a protein basis what is happening that may be leading to behavioral changes. That would be quite exciting to know about.

D. W. Pfaff: Thank you. It is a very reasonable question, and I would like to hear Dr. Peck's reaction. I'll express the opinion that nerve cells are a poor source for high quantities of a specific message, because they are doing too many things at once. So our approach is to use protein products as a first step.

I. A. Kourides: I agree with what you said. It is likely that there are numerous different messages making many proteins. Indeed that was why I suggested a technique that would give you a crude overview of what proteins might be increased most. You could then use this information as a handle to go backward to effects on specific game expression.

D. W. Pfaff: How technically difficult might the cell-free aspect of that approach be?

E. J. Peck: We have tried to do that and the fact is that the brain is a very heterogeneous target, as you could see from the figures. The number of neurons that have receptors is a small fraction of the total and the amount of message that is estrogen-dependent in a given neuron is a vanishingly small fraction of the total for that cell, so that you have a very large ratio of noise to signal. Thus the signal so far has been buried. I have to agree with Dr. Pfaff. The route that we are taking at this point is to work backward, slightly illogical, but we presume a specific product is under estrogen control, LHRH, the same molecule Dr, Pfaff is studying. Now we are synthesizing probes for presumed message for LHRH. Thus we will have one small signal, but we are looking for *one* selectively. If we just spread out all the proteins being made *in vitro* translation systems we cannot find any changes. If you have a better way to enrich, I would love to know because I think that would be a much faster approach than the one we are taking right now.

L. S. Jacobs: I have two questions. First, I was intrigued by the slow firing rates of the ventromedial hypothalamic neurons. Is there any evidence that such slow firing rates might be correlated with any other distinctive neuronal function, perhaps having to do with peptides? Could you offer enlightenment from the neurophysiologic point of view as to what other nervous system entities share this slow firing rate and whether this property might allow useful inferences regarding other functions. Second, I wonder if you would elaborate a bit on whether or not prolactin affects the functions of either the ventromedial or the midbrain central gray neurons.

D. W. Pfaff: There was a report about 3 years ago (Toubeau *et al.*, 1979) which suggested, immunocytochemically, that there may be prolactin-producing cells in the hypothalamus. We have done a lot of immunocytochemistry to replicate and extend that finding, and have localized the cell bodies and a rich plexus of prolactin-immunoreactive endings in the midbrain central gray (Shivers *et al.*, 1983b). Richard Harlan and Brenda Shivers delivered prolactin to the central gray of the midbrain and have facilitated lordosis behavior (Harlan *et al.*, 1982). We have done the reasonable controls for suspected prolactin contaminants. If you deliver a prolactin antiserum to the midbrain central gray you can decrease lordosis behavior.

L. S. Jacobs: Thank you. Is there any comment you would like to make on the slow firing rates?

D. W. Pfaff: I don't see an obligatory connection between the slow average firing range and the production of a particular kind of neuropeptide. Another way of looking at slowly firing cells, is to record the electrical properties of neurons in the sympathetic ganglia.

D. M. Linkie: I am wondering if and why you have purposely excluded a possible membrane locus for steroid action. Also, whether or not you can integrate some of the data that addresses steroids and steroid derivatives and their effects on membrane potentials.

D. W. Pfaff: We thought about possible membrane mechanisms of action, especially for progesterone, for about 15 years and I would be disappointed if, within the next couple of years, we hadn't at least begun studies with artificial membranes.

K. Sterling: I have a couple of technical questions on the second figure you showed and then a question on the last item that was discussed. Now on the second figure you have shown that you went through all sorts of vertebrates, primates, and carnivores as well as rats; you mentioned at the lower right-hand part of the figure, four hypothalamic nuclei in the rat. I didn't quite get the four, could you repeat it?

D. W. Pfaff: In the hypothalamus that figure included the arcuate nucleus, the ventromedial nucleus, and the ventral premammillary nucleus.

K. Sterling: And what is the fourth?

D. W. Pfaff: The fourth mentioned was the preoptic area, in its medial or suprachiasmatic subdivision.

K. Sterling: I have another question about that. At the middle part of the figure where you are dealing with the caudal projections of the extrapyramidal motor systems, you have projections from the lateral vestibular nuclei, the medullary reticular formation and, of course, the midbrain central gray going caudally. Now some of those are both contralateral and ipsilateral. Could you say a few words as to laterality. I believe the pyramidal tracts are 100% crossed, but I am aware that some of these extrapyramidal motor tracts are both crossed and uncrossed.

D. W. Pfaff: Before talking about the crossing aspect, let me say that the lateral vestibulospinal tract was not mentioned further for the following reason: that it is required for the behavior but that it does not receive input from the hypothalamus or from the parts of the midbrain which receive from the hypothalamus, so the lateral vestibulospinal tract must be having a postural effect on neuromuscular systems such that the behavior can occur, but it is the reticulospinal tract that carries the hormone-dependent signal.

K. Sterling: I might interrupt that the vestibulospinal tract has neurons coming from the cerebellum to a large extent and in all species.

D. W. Pfaff: Yes, but you can remove the entire cerebellum and the animal will do lordosis behavior. About the bilateral aspect of these tracts, the lateral vestibulospinal and the medullary reticulospinal tracts are largely uncrossed.

K. Sterling: Now the last question deals with the interesting topic of sex hormones and behavior. As I understand it, male and female tigers mate for life and the male is very pleasant to the female during the preponderance of time when she is not in heat, which is very interesting, when we see what has been going on in the human race in the last several decades. So my understanding, you can correct me if I am wrong, is that the nearest related great apes, namely the chimpanzee and gorilla, do have definite estrus periods, I think two/ year in the case of the gorilla, and that is the only time they mate, whereas human beings, of course, are supposed to mate all through the year. Now I am curious about the nearest living human relative, so close that it is almost the same in terms of blood proteins, and yet the sexual behavior is so different. Could you comment on the distinction between the gorilla which mates only at estrus versus the human race with constant mating behavior.

D. W. Pfaff: I can't answer your question in factual detail. If you look across a range of hormone behavior and therefore hormone nervous system relationships, they are not always identical when you consider a wide phylogenetic span; strength, direction, and timing tend to reflect the adaptive pressures on each particular species. That is all the more reason for an for an investigator who wants to get down to increasing cellular detail to stick to relatively simple neuroendocrine problems.

E. Peck: I might add to that that you need not compare primates and humans. You can study different strains of rat and find the same thing. There are remarkable differences in response to steroids, both biochemical and behavioral within strains of rats.

M. G. Rosenfeld: Thank you for presenting such a logical approach to attempt an understanding of cortical neuroendocrine regulation. What are the kinetics of the appearance of the perinucleolar estrogen-stimulated body? Would you comment regarding the kinetics of depolarization events, estrogen accumulation events in the cells trying to address in particular the question of whether there are later kinetic effects that might be considered consequential to estrogen action. I would also like you to address the question which, for example, has been raised in the vitamin D mechanism field, suggesting primary membrane effects of the steroid hormone as opposed to those which are mediated secondary to transcriptional events.

D. W. Pfaff: Regarding the nucleolar ultrastructure study and electrophysiological studies, we've not followed estrogen effects systematically as a function of time.

A. Segaloff: Unless I am mistaken, this is the major area for conversion to catechol estrogens of which the 4-hydroxy is the one that is particularly formed in this area. This has both physical and chemical properties that are very different than estradiol itself, and it not only may explain part of the lag, but part of the difference in localization.

D. W. Pfaff: That's a good idea but even in the ventromedial hypothalamus, well over 90% of the isotope recovered after estradiol administration is in the form of estradiol, and physiologically the catechol estrogens are not more effective than estradiol.

S. L. Cohen: I wanted to ask whether you had tried any estrogens other than estradiol?

D. W. Pfaff: We have not. It would be good to start doing that in the experiments where it's easiest.

S. L. Cohen: Because I wondered whether there might be some estrogens which were antiestrogenic, like estriol?

D. W. Pfaff: Many people have blocked neuroendocrine estrogen effects with antiestrogens. In a circumstance which requires a particular level of estrogenic stimulation, adding a weak estrogen, such as estriol, might have an antiestrogenic action. We have not done that experiment with electrophysiological or chemical end points.

E. Peck: Nor have I. I don't know. But I do have a couple of questions. I want to go back to your interesting and provocative demonstration of increases in stacked RER on estrogen treatment. We did a thorough study of endogenous nuclear RNA polymerase activities in hypothalamic nuclei and, while the preparation was not pure estrogen responsive nuclei, it was certainly enriched for the same. We saw a marked increase in RNA polymerase II activity which is involved in the synthesis of messenger RNA but we saw no increase at all or in fact a small decrease in polymerase I activity, that is, the activity responsible for ribosomal RNA synthesis. Does this stacked RER shown by electron microscopy come from preformed ribosomes or do you presume that new ribosomal synthesis must occur? Must you see an increase in ribosomal RNA synthesis to see your increase in stacked reticulum, If so, I must go back and do that study over again.

D. W. Pfaff: On the quantitative aspect of your question, how big was your effect on RNA polymerase II?

E. Peck: On polymerase II, it varies from a 50 to a 70% increase.

D. W. Pfaff: And, given that, do you need an increase in the rate of polymerase I activity to support an increased number of ribosomes?

E. Peck: Well, you do not have to presume an increase in the activity of RNA polymerase I. You could have organization of ribosomes that are synthesized at a constant rate.

D. W. Pfaff: On that quantitative note, remember that we got a significant effect, a factor of about 2½, in the percentage of cells that have stacked RER, but that's going from a low number to a somewhat higher number and, second, remember that even the cells that don't have large amounts of stacked RER have some RER.

E. Peck: So perhaps we have the same signal to noise problem there.

M. B. Nikitovitch-Winer: Among your other comments, I was fascinated with your ultrastructural findings showing the nucleolar changes in neurons stimulated by estrogen treatment. Has any similar change been observed in other neurons under the influence of other stimuli or has anyone described these nucleolar changes in pituitary cells which are stimulated by a variety of stimuli?

D. W. Pfaff: This is the first study of a steroid effect in nerve cells.

R. O. Greep: My mind was running along the same comparative endocrinology channels as Ken Sterling's. With chickens the rooster treads and the hen takes off, but she doesn't run too fast. The boar doesn't have to run at all. He just makes a boar sound and freezes the female in a mating posture. I was wondering about the sensory input in rats. Does the male play some part in triggering lordosis other than by perhaps stroking her tail? Is there any olfactory, visual, or audible input that triggers off lordosis?

D. W. Pfaff: Pheromones among laboratory animals have been best studied in hamsters, where dimethyl disulfide is present in the vaginal secretion, in greatly increased amounts, in the estrous female hamster. The male under the influence of androgen is strongly attracted to this odor. These rodents also emit ultrasounds and that probably has something to do with their attraction to each other. Under the influence of estrogen and progesterone the female has an unusual form of locomotion—she darts, stops, darts again in such a way that seems to attract the male, and if the male is following her when she suddenly stops the male would contact her in a position appropriate for mounting. Signaling systems in a variety of rodents appear to ensure that only reproductively competent conspecifics will get close enough to mate.

RECENT PROGRESS IN HORMONE RESEARCH, VOL. 39

Biosynthesis, Processing, and Secretion of Parathormone and Secretory Protein-I

DAVID V. COHN[1] AND JAMES ELTING

University of Kansas Medical Center, Kansas City, Kansas and
Division of Biomedical Research, Immuno Nuclear Corporation, Stillwater, Minnesota

Calcium serves a variety of key functions in animal physiology (1–3). It is required together with phosphate for physical strength of the bones (the skeleton contains about 99% of the total Ca of vertebrates). It is essential for muscular contraction, for transmission of nervous impulses, for exocytosis, and for maintenance of cell–cell interactions. As the level of ionized Ca in the extracellular fluid drops below the physiological set-point of 1.2 mM (total Ca, 2.5 mM), the animal becomes increasingly hyperexcitable and may undergo tetanic convulsions. If ionized Ca concentration rises much above 1.2 mM, decreased irritability of muscle occurs, and ectopic calcification may ensue.

In view of these and other functions, it is not surprising that a complex homeostatic mechanism for regulation of Ca has developed in higher animals (2,4). This mechanism involves the actions of parathormone (PTH), calcitonin (CT), and 1,25-dihydroxycholecalciferol [1,25(OH)$_2$D$_3$] on bone, kidney, and intestine (Fig. 1). When the level of ionized Ca in the plasma drops below normal, the parathyroid gland increases its secretion of PTH (5). The hormone stimulates osteoclasts (6) to increase transfer of Ca and phosphate from the bone to the blood (3,7), and inhibits osteoblasts (6) so that transfer of those ions into bone is reduced (7). It acts on the kidney to increase Ca retention and phosphate excretion (8–11) and at the same time stimulates hydroxylation of 25-hydroxycholecalciferol [25(OH)D$_3$] to form 1,25(OH)$_2$D$_3$ (12). The latter, the active form of vitamin D, acts on the intestine to increase Ca absorption (13). Each of these actions tends to raise the level of ionized Ca of the extracellular fluid and plasma, which feeds back to diminish PTH secretion. When the ionized Ca concentration moves above normal (for example, after eating) the secretion of CT from the C cells of the thyroid, or in lower animals from the ultimobranchial bodies, increases (2,14). Calcitonin's primary action

---

[1] Present address: 1238 Wyncrest Court, Arden Hills, Minnesota 55112.

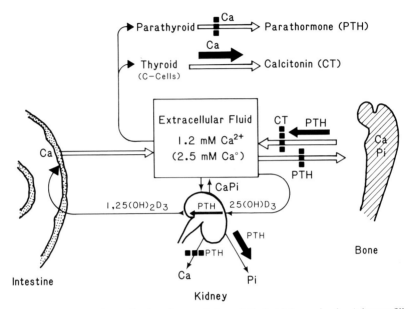

FIG. 1.   Homeostatic mechanism for regulation of Ca in higher animals. A heavy filled arrow denotes stimulation of a pathway. A dashed line indicates inhibition.

seems to be to inhibit bone resorption and hence indirectly causes blood Ca levels to drop (6,14). In this homeostatic scheme most agree that PTH plays the key role in the moment-to-moment modulation of blood Ca levels (4).

This article for the most part restricts itself to PTH, its synthesis, packaging, and secretion. Also presented is new information on another protein of the parathyroid, secretory protein-I (SP-I), that is cosecreted with PTH. Recent data have demonstrated that SP-I is closely related, if not identical, to chromogranin A, a major secretory protein contained within chromaffin granules of the adrenal medulla. This relationship may provide clues to parathyroid function as well as to other secretory tissues.

I. Chemistry and Structure of PTH, ProPTH, and PreproPTH

PTH in man and in those other species studied is comprised of 84 amino acids in a single peptide chain (15–18) (Fig. 2). It contains no carbohydrates or other covalently bound structures (4). The biological activity of the hormone resides in the first third of the molecule (4,19–21) in a mini-

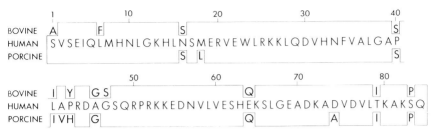

FIG. 2. The amino acid sequences of human (18), bovine (15,16,99), and porcine (17) PTH. The one-letter code for amino acid residues has been used (39). These are A, alanine; D, aspartic acid; E, glutamic acid; F, phenylalanine; G, glycine; H, histidine; I, isoleucine; K, lysine; L, leucine; M, methionine; N, asparagine; P, proline; Q, glutamine; R, arginine; S, serine; V, valine; W, tryptophan; Y, tyrosine. Only those residues in the bovine and porcine sequences that differ from those of the human hormone are shown.

mum structure comprised of residues 1–27 (19). Removal of residues 1 and 2 renders the molecule biologically inert (19).

Although PTH has not been crystallized, some indication of its three-dimensional structure has been derived from hydrodynamic studies (22), dark-field electron microscopy (23), and optical measurements (4,24,25). According to these results, PTH may contain two domains connected by a stalk (Fig. 3). When the amino acid chain is folded into the conformation predicted by the Chou-Fasman rules (26–29) and placed in the visualized two domain representation, the amino-terminal biologically active region of the hormone occupies one domain and the inactive carboxyl-terminal region the other. The placement of the region containing residues 30–40 in the connecting "stalk" was in part to account for the ease with which enzymes cleave PTH in this portion of the hormone (23).

The immediate precursor of PTH is ProPTH (30–32). It differs from the native hormone by containing an amino-terminal highly basic hexapeptide extension (33) (Fig. 4). The function of the pro-extension is obscure. The primary gene product for PTH and the precursor of ProPTH is Prepro-PTH (Fig. 4) (34–36). It differs from ProPTH by containing a 25 amino acid amino-terminal extension (37,38), which, in common with other pre-sequences, is hydrophobic.

Based on analysis of PreproPTH by the technique of Barker and Day-hof (39) for detecting evolutionarily related proteins, it has been proposed that PreproPTH was formed by gene duplication and fusion of a primitive gene containing the *prepro* sequence followed by the first third of the present PTH molecule (40) (Fig. 5). This interpretation is supported by the retention of presumed secondary structure in the portions of the molecule believed to be homologous.

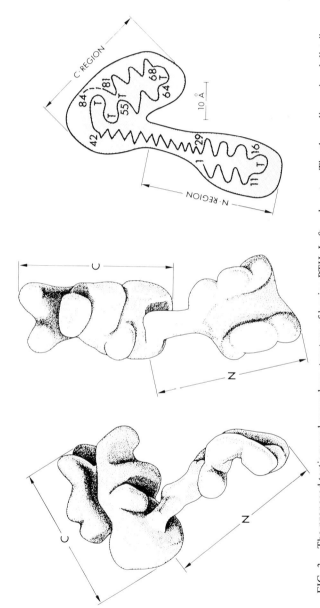

FIG. 3. The proposed tertiary and secondary structure of bovine PTH. Left and center: The three-dimensional distribution of mass as visualized by dark-field electron microscopy. The view of the molecule pictured in the center is rotated 90° clockwise relative to the view at the left. Right: The predicted distribution of α-helix (sine waves), β-sheet (saw-tooth), β-turn (T), and random coil (---) in bovine PTH according to the modified procedures of Fasman and associates (26–29). These structural features were drawn to scale and were arbitrarily positioned to fit into the distribution of masses. Revised from Fiskin et al. (23). Structural predictions illustrated in the view at the right suggest that the region marked N represents the biologically active amino-terminal portion of the molecule and that marked C the inactive carboxyl-terminal region.

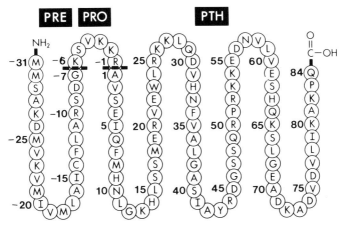

FIG. 4. The amino acid sequence of bovine preproPTH (38). The dashed lines separate the *pre* and *pro* amino acid segments and the native hormone (PTH). The one-letter code for amino acid residues is provided in Fig. 2.

II. Biosynthesis of PTH and Its Precursors

Figure 6 portrays the overall scheme for the formation and secretion of PTH. This diagram is based on a variety of *in vitro* and *in vivo* studies from several laboratories (see 4) and borrows heavily from the pathway described by Palade and associates (41) for exportable proteins. As shown in the figure, PreproPTH is transferred to the cisternal space of the endoplasmic reticulum during translation of mRNA by the ribosomes (42,43). During this transfer the *pre* peptide is removed yielding ProPTH. ProPTH is transported to the Golgi zone (44,45) by an energy-dependent mecha-

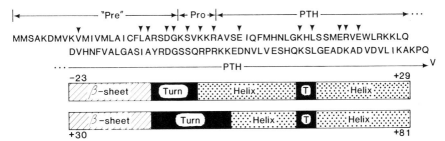

FIG. 5. Alignments of the bovine preproPTH homology regions. Upper: The numbering of residues and the one-letter code for residues are as shown in Fig. 2. An exact match or close substitution is designated by an arrow. Lower: Predicted secondary structural homology as determined by the formulations of Fasman *et al.* (26–29). Redrawn and revised from Cohn *et al.* (40).

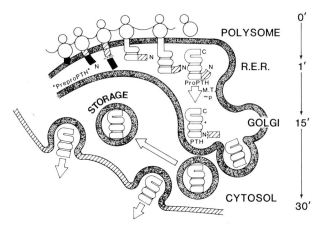

FIG. 6. Biosynthesis and secretion of PTH by the parathyroid cell. See text for details.

nism possibly involving microtubules (46) during a 10–15 minute time span. In the Golgi a membrane-associated "convertase" removes the *pro* extension yielding native PTH (47–49). At this time PTH is released from the Golgi within secretory vesicles (50,51). The newly formed hormone has three fates: immediate secretion, degradation, or transport into a storage pool (4). As will be described later, secretion of the newly formed hormone and secretion of "older" hormone in the storage pool may not be equivalent processes.

III. Control of PTH Secretion

The physiological regulation of PTH secretion has been extensively studied both in the intact animal (52–54) and *in vitro* (31,56–59). The latter systems generally have consisted of incubated gland slices or dispersed parathyroid cells. In all cases Ca and usually Mg inhibit the release of hormone (4) (Fig. 7). In the *in vitro* systems one can readily examine hormone-related products in the medium as well as within the gland. Figure 8A portrays radioactive peptides detected by gel electrophoresis found within the gland after porcine parathyroid cells were incubated with radioactive amino acids for only 2 minutes (60). At this time the cells contained radioactive ProPTH but no radioactive PTH since there was insufficient time for the prohormone to reach its conversion site in the Golgi. There was also formed during this brief period a major amount of SP-I, to be discussed later. Figure 8B portrays the radioactive species in the incubation medium of the same cells after 1 hour of incubation. Radioactive PTH and SP-I were present but not ProPTH. To our knowledge,

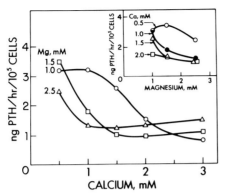

FIG. 7.   The effect of Ca and Mg on parathormone secretion by dispersed porcine parathyroid cells. The cells were incubated for 2 hours at 37°C in Krebs-supplemented medium containing the indicated concentrations of CaCl₂. The inset is a replot of the data at constant Ca and variable Mg concentrations. From Morrissey and Cohn (59).

the prohormone is never secreted. The product–precursor relationship between cellular ProPTH and PTH is presented in Fig. 9.

In contrast to Ca and Mg there is a variety of agents that increase cellular cAMP levels that markedly enhance secretion of PTH (4,61–67). These include cAMP derivatives, isoproterenol and other β-agonists, prostaglandins E₁ and E₂, dopamine, secretin, cholera toxin, and agents that

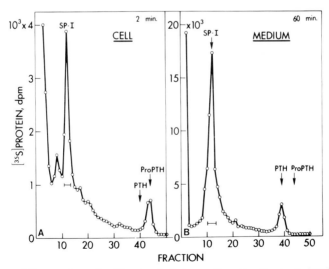

FIG. 8.   Acid/urea polyacrylamide gels of whole parathyroid cell extracts incubated with [³⁵S]methionine for 2 minutes (A) or medium incubated for 60 minutes (B). From Morrissey et al. (60).

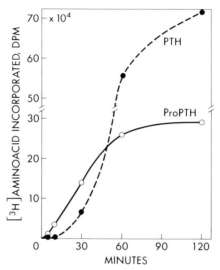

FIG. 9.   Rates of biosynthesis of [³H]PTH and [³H]proPTH by bovine parathyroid slices. From Cohn *et al.* (31).

increase intracellular cAMP levels through inhibition of phosphodiesterase. Although most of these studies were performed *in vitro,* physiological doses of epinephrine given to a cow produced discrete releases of PTH to the blood (68–70). Other substances that lower cAMP levels such as β-adrenergic antagonists, α-adrenergic agonists, prostaglandin F_2, and nitroprusside, inhibit secretion (4,66). There is a linear relationship between intracellular levels of cAMP and hormone release regardless of the agent

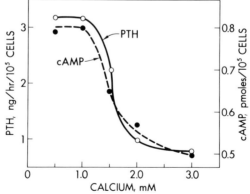

FIG. 10.   PTH secretion and intracellular cAMP as a function of Ca concentration in porcine parathyroid cells in culture (Cohn and Morrissey, unpublished).

that produced the change in cAMP concentration (66). The change in level of cAMP produced by Ca also can be correlated with PTH secretion (Fig. 10). Ca and Mg may affect the intracellular level of cAMP through an indirect action on phosphodiesterase via calmodulin or directly on the cyclase generating system, or both (72,73).

IV. Multiple Intracellular Secretory Pools of Parathormone

In studies with parathyroid gland slices (74) it was noted that newly synthesized PTH and ProPTH were readily extracted by detergents from membrane preparations of the parathyroid, whereas preexisting, that is, nonradioactive, parathormone resisted extraction. Comparison of the specific radioactivity of secreted PTH to intracellular PTH indicated that the bulk of the secreted hormone was derived from newly synthesized rather than from the preexisting PTH. More recently (58), it has been shown with porcine parathyroid cells that Ca at all concentrations tested stimulated the secretion of preexisting and newly synthesized PTH to the same degree. In contrast, dibutyryl-cAMP and isoproterenol enhanced the secretion primarily of preexisting hormone (Fig. 11). In pulse–chase experiments (71) it was determined that at least 60 minutes was required for the newly synthesized PTH to move into the pool that was sensitive to cAMP generators (Fig. 12). Chemical analysis of the hormone of both pools (unpublished observations) has not revealed any chemical differ-

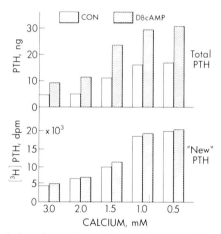

FIG. 11.   The stimulation of secretion by Ca and dibutyryl cAMP (DBcAMP) of total and newly synthesized PTH from dispersed porcine parathyroid cells. The cells were incubated with [³H]amino acids at the indicated Ca concentration with or without DBcAMP for 90 minutes. The medium was analyzed for total PTH by immunoassay and for radioactive hormone after separation of protein species. Data from Morrissey and Cohn (58).

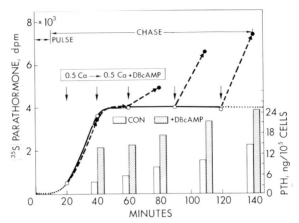

FIG. 12. Stimulated secretion of preexisting (i.e., nonradioactive) PTH by dibutyryl cAMP (DBcAMP). Dispersed porcine cells were pulsed and chased as described in the legend in Fig. 11. At the times indicated by the arrows, 1 mM DMcAMP was added. Radioactive and total (immunoactive) PTH was determined in the medium. The figure shows that DBcAMP did not affect the secretion of newly formed (radioactive) PTH until after 60 minutes but stimulated secretion of total PTH equally at all times. Data of Morrissey and Cohn (71).

ences between the PTH they contain. This must mean that the difference between the older and newly synthesized PTH is accounted for by a difference in the environment in which the hormone exists. Some environmental factors to be considered include an altered composition within the secretory granules involved in the exocytotic process, a difference in the membranes of the secretory vesicle that affects response of the granule to secretagogues, or a difference in location of the granules of the two pools such that some are not available for secretion following a specific type of secretory stimulus.

V. Action of Ca on PTH Production

Under maximum stimulation, glandular stores of PTH would disappear in a few hours were not new hormone generated (52). The initial assumption that the synthesis of PTH increases when Ca is low and secretion is high has proved not to be the case. In studies *in vitro* of stimulated and repressed parathyroids from rats fed diets containing high or low levels of Ca (75) (Fig. 13), or with parathyroid cells examined in different concentrations of Ca (58) (Figs. 14 and 15), it was found that the rates of synthesis and turnover of ProPTH were the same regardless of Ca status. Yet,

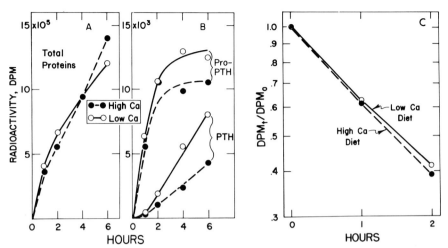

FIG. 13. Rates of formation of protein (A), PTH and ProPTH (B), and turnover of ProPTH (C) in rat parathyroids in culture. The glands were excised from rats receiving either a low or high Ca diet for 13 days.

the rate of formation of PTH was always greater at the lower Ca conditions. A key observation in these studies was that as much as 80–90% of the ProPTH that was synthesized and presumably converted to PTH could not be accounted for as intact PTH in the cell or incubation medium. Presumably the PTH or ProPTH, or both, were proteolytically

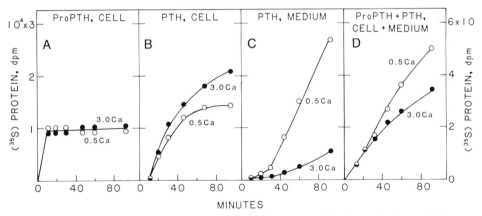

FIG. 14. (A–D) Effect of Ca on the synthesis of ProPTH and the formation, intracellular degradation, and secretion of PTH by dispersed porcine parathyroid cells. The cells were incubated with [^{35}S]methionine. The reaction products in cells and medium were isolated by electrophoresis on acid-urea gels. Redrawn from Cohn and MacGregor (4).

degraded. It could be calculated that there was less degradation of PTH and ProPTH peptide when the Ca load was low and more when it was high (Table I).

These experiments indicate that Ca affects hormone production through control of degradation, not synthesis. At all Ca loads the rate of synthesis of ProPTH is the same and greater than the amount required for secretion as determined by the status of extracellular ionized Ca. Most of that not secreted is degraded. A small amount is put into storage. What happens then, if the need for PTH is greater than can be supplied by the basal synthetic rate? Under this circumstance the gland must increase its synthetic capacity via hypertrophy and hyperplasia, as, in fact, is observed in the intact animal.

The kinetics of PTH formation and degradation and the action of calcium on this process (Fig. 15D) show that the degradation of hormone begins about 20 minutes after the first PreproPTH is synthesized and

TABLE I

*Degradation of PTH in the Parathyroid as a Function of
Calcium Load[a]*

	Ca level	
Ca load altered via	High (dpm $\times$ 10^{-5})	Low (dpm $\times$ 10^{-5})
Diet[b]		
Protein synthesis, total	6500	6500
ProPTH synthesis	10.5	10.5
PTH formed	1.5	3.4
PTH degraded	9.0	7.1
% Degraded	86	68
Incubation medium[c]		
Protein synthesis, total	4880	4880
Pro PTH synthesis	5.3	5.3
PTH formed	1.4	3.2
PTH degraded	3.9	2.1
% Degraded	74	40

[a] Data from Morrissey and Cohn (58) and Chu *et al.* (75).

[b] Rats were fed for 13 days a diet containing either 0.02% (low) or 2.0% (high) Ca. The parathyroids were then excised and studied in incubation medium at 1.3 mM Ca.

[c] Normal porcine parathyroid cells incubated in 0.5 (low) or 3.0 (high) mM Ca.

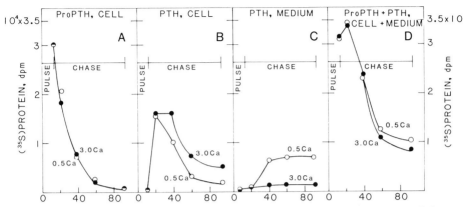

FIG. 15. (A–D) Effect of Ca on the synthesis of ProPTH and the formation, intracellular degradation, and secretion of PTH by dispersed porcine parathyroid cells. The experiment was performed as in Fig. 14, except that the cells were incubated only 10 minutes with [³⁵S]methionine (pulse) and incubated an additional 90 minutes (chase).

initially is not affected by Ca concentration. According to the flowsheet for intracellular translocation (Fig. 6) at 20 minutes newly made PTH has just left the Golgi and is in secretory granules. The effect of Ca on degradation occurs sometime after this (Fig. 15). One interpretation of these

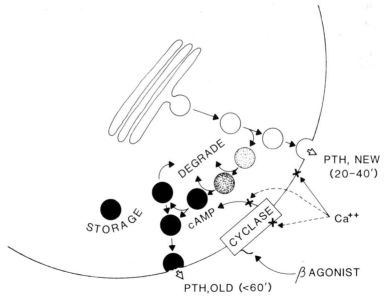

FIG. 16. Processing, secretion, and degradation of PTH in a parathyroid cell. See text for details.

data is that the action of Ca on degradation is indirect. Proteolysis of PTH might proceed independent of Ca concentration but at high Ca concentrations there would be more PTH in the gland available for degradation, and at lower Ca concentrations, less.

A model based on the above considerations to portray processing and secretion of PTH from multiple intracellular pools and the action of Ca and β-agonist on secretion and degradation is provided in Fig. 16. The diagram shows newly formed PTH leaving the Golgi destined either for immediate secretion or for storage and/or subsequent secretion. Degradation is shown commencing as soon as the secretory vesicle enters the storage route. Ca is shown affecting secretion in two ways: directly on the membrane or affecting intracellular cAMP levels. Other slightly different models to account for multiple intracellular pools of PTH are presented by Cohn and MacGregor (4).

VI. The Intracellular Proteolytic Degradation of PTH

There is substantial direct evidence for the generation and secretion of large amounts of carboxyl-terminal PTH fragments by the parathyroid (76–78). Of particular interest, Mayer et al. (54) reported that cow parathyroids in situ released a greater proportion of carboxyl-terminal fragments relative to intact PTH the higher the Ca concentration perfusing the gland. The isolation and characterization of at least two PTH fragments secreted by porcine parathyroid cells have been accomplished (79). Upon gel electrophoresis of incubation medium, a region containing carboxyl-terminal fragments was detected (Fig. 17A). These fragments were isolated by fractional precipitation with trichloroacetic acid (Fig. 17B) and subjected to peptide mapping and sequencing. They proved to be PTH_{34-84} and PTH_{37-84} present in a ratio of 1:2. About 2 moles of these carboxyl-terminal fragments were secreted for each mole of intact PTH, in keeping with the observations cited above that the bulk of newly synthesized PTH is degraded.

Although it is not yet possible to know with certainty what enzymes within the gland are responsible for the degradation of PTH, McGregor et al. (80) isolated and characterized cathepsin B from bovine and porcine parathyroids. This enzyme acted on native PTH in a manner that makes it a prime candidate for at least one of the intracellular PTH degrading proteases (21). It cleaved the hormone into two fragments, PTH_{37-84} and PTH_{1-36}. The former was not further degraded whereas PTH_{1-36} was converted into continually smaller fragments by removal of di- or tripeptides from the carboxyl-terminal end. This type of cleavage if going on in vivo could account for the inability to find substantial amounts of amino-termi-

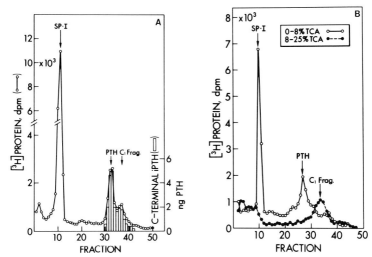

FIG. 17.   (A) Polyacrylamide gel electrophoretic profile of radioactive and immunoactive proteins secreted by porcine parathyroid cells. The cells were incubated with a [³H]amino acid mixture, and the proteins of the medium were precipitated with 25% trichloroacetic acid (TCA) before electrophoresis. C_1-fragment represents the radioactive and immunoactive peak containing carboxyl-terminal fragments of parathormone. (B) Differential precipitation with TCA of the C_1-fragment peak and its separation from SP-I. As in A but at the end of the incubation period, the medium was brought to 8% and then to 25% TCA. The proteins precipitating at 8% and between 8 and 25% were examined by polyacrylamide gel electrophoresis. From Morrissey *et al.* (79).

nal fragments in glandular secretions. A second protease in the parathyroid, cathepsin D, has recently been described by Hamilton (81). He showed that it uniquely cleaved PTH between residue 34 and 35 yielding PTH_{1-34} and PTH_{35-84}. These results together with the characterization of cleavage products above suggest that the intracellular degradation of PTH is accomplished by a mixture of enzymes. Since the cathepsins are considered to be lysosomal enzymes, it is not far fetched to assume that the degradation of PTH is accomplished via a fusion of secretory granules and lysomes, as has been proposed by Judah and Foreman (82) for albumin.

VII. The Similarity of Secretory Protein-I to Adrenal Medulla Chromogranin A

Licata *et al.* (83) originally observed that Ca inhibited the secretion of a glycosylated protein or proteins by rat parathyroids in culture. Kemper *et al.* (84) reported that Ca inhibited the secretion of a major protein of unknown function from parathyroid slices that they named *parathyroid secretory protein,* or PSP. The degree of this inhibition was the same as that for PTH. Morrissey and Cohn (59) subsequently reported that this same protein, referred to by them as Secretory Protein-I (SP-I), was released under Ca control by porcine parathyroid cells and that it was glycosylated (85).

SP-I is comprised of two main cellular and secreted species of about 64,000 and 72,000 D in pig (60) and 70,000 and 72,000 D in cow parathyroids (86,87). About one-third of its residues are acidic resulting in a p*I* of 4.8. Immunocytochemical analysis suggests that SP-I and PTH coexist in the same secretory granules (88). In agreement with this, newly synthesized SP-I, ProPTH, and PTH are all removed from parathyroid membrane preparations in about the same relative proportions by fractional extraction of samples indicating that they exist in similar structures (60) (Fig. 18). It is not surprising, therefore, that the kinetics and secretion of SP-I resemble that of PTH, and that it, like PTH, exists in multiple intracellular pools (71). A role for SP-I has not yet been ascribed.

While the studies on SP-I were progressing, investigators in the field of adrenal gland function were characterizing the chemical and physical nature of the chromaffin granule (for example, see Refs. 89–92). This structure represents the storage vesicle for epinephrine and norepinephrine but contains as well an assortment of other constituents including dopamine β-hydroxylase, met- and leu-enkephalins, ATP, and other nucleotides, Ca, Mg, and other ions, complex carbohydrates, and various proteins termed "chromogranins." Among the latter is chromogranin A comprising 40% of the total soluble protein (89). It has also been described in sympathetic nerve endings, presumably associated with granules containing norepinephrine (93,94). The function of chromogranin A, like SP-I, is unknown.

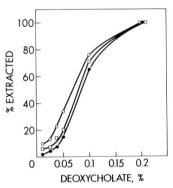

FIG. 18.   Deoxycholate extraction of [^{35}S]methionine-labeled SP-I (○), ProPTH (●), and PTH (□) from parathyroid membranes. From Morrissey *et al.* (60).

TABLE II

Comparison of SP-I and Chromogranins[a]

Properties	SP-I	Chromogranin A
Molecular mass of major compo- nent(s)[b]	70 and 72 kD	70–80 kD
pI	4.5	Acidic
Carbohydrate (μmol/100 mg of protein)		
Mannose	1.1	0.8
Galactose	6.5	6.3
Fucose	0.6	0.6
Glucosamine	0.5	1.1
Galactosamine	1.7	5.4
Sialic acid	Not determined	8.3

[a] Table adapted from Cohn et al. (95).

[b] The best preparations of SP-I and chromogranin A exhibit several minor components.

TABLE III

Amino Acid Composition of Bovine SP-I and Chromogranin A[a]

	Moles per 100 residues	
	SP-I	Chromogranin A
Asx	7.1	8.0
Glx	23.2	22.5
Ser	7.6	7.7
Thr	2.1	2.6
Cys	0.5	0.2
Met	1.6	1.4
Pro	8.7	9.2
Gly	7.9	8.1
Ala	8.9	8.5
Val	3.5	3.9
Leu	7.4	7.3
Ile	1.0	1.4
Phe	1.5	1.7
Tyr	1.0	1.0
Trp	1.1	1.4
Lys	8.7	8.4
His	1.6	1.9
Arg	6.6	6.0

[a] Table adapted from Cohn et al. (95).

SP–I LPVNSPMNKGDTEVMKXIVE....

Ch.A LRVNSPMNKGDTEVMKCIRE....

FIG. 19.   The partial amino acid sequences of bovine SP-I and chromogranin A. Comparison taken from Cohn *et al.* (95).

Recently, it was noted that SP-I and chromogranin A are chemically and physically similar if not identical (95). Table II compares some properties of the purest SP-I and chromogranin A preparations described in the literature. The respective amino acid compositions are provided in

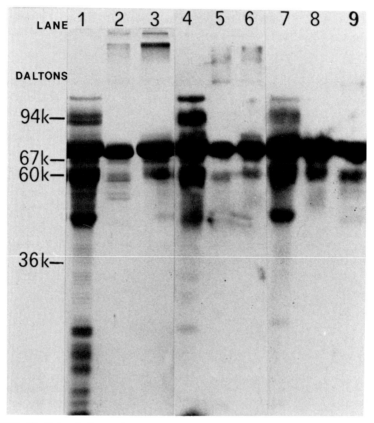

FIG. 20. Slab-gel electrophoresis and immunoreplicas of SP-I and chromogranin A. Daltons are shown ×10⁻³. Lanes 1–3 stained with Coomassie blue. Lanes 4–9 radioautographs of immunoreplicas. Lanes: 1, total soluble lysate of bovine chromaffin granules; 2, SP-I; 3, chromogranin A; 4–6, results of an immunoreplica experiment with antiserum developed against chromogranin A (lane 4, total soluble lysate of bovine chromaffin granules; lane 5, SP-I; lane 6, chromogranin A); 7–9, results of an immunoreplica experiment with antiserum developed against SP-I (lane 7, total soluble lysate of chromaffin granules; lane 8, chromogranin A; lane 9, SP-I). From Cohn *et al.* (95).

Table III and partial amino acid sequences in Fig. 19. The near identities of the molecules are striking. Finally, it has been shown that chromogranin A and SP-I exhibit similar reactivities with antisera generated to the other protein (Fig. 20).

These observations have raised the distinct possibility that the SP-I/chromogranin A species plays a role in the exocytotic process, perhaps in the storage and secretory phases of different classes of substances contained within secretory granules. Takatsuki and his collaborators have conducted a preliminary survey of the distribution of SP-I in other tissues (Table IV). They confirm the existence of a high concentration of immunoactive SP-I in the adrenal medulla and show an elevated presence in other tissues including the anterior pituitary and adrenal cortex. Its amount in other tissues is variable and low. This could mean that SP-I is not functional in all secretory tissues. On the other hand, since SP-I is contained within granules, and the granule content of secretory tissues is not necessarily related to secretory activity (51,90,97), net content of SP-I

TABLE IV

Bovine SP-I Immunoreactivity in Various Bovine Tissues[a]

Tissues	μg/mg Protein
Endocrine	
Adrenal medulla	240
Parathyroid	44
Adrenal cortex	8.3
Pituitary, anterior	5.2
Pituitary, posterior	1.6
Ovary	0.7
Pancreas	0.5
Thyroid	0.03
Nonendocrine	
Renal cortex	0.9
Renal medulla	0.7
Cerebrum	0.2
Cerebellum	0.1
Thymus	0.1
Heart	0.1
Lung	0.04
Muscle	0.04
Liver	Not detectable

[a] K. Takatsuki, T. Takano, M. Yoneda, A. Uchikawa, and A. Tomita, personal communication.

within a gland may not adequately reflect a role for the protein in secretion by the gland. Kinetic studies of its synthesis and secretion are required to answer this question.

At this stage, the manner in which SP-I might act (if it does) in exocytotic process is open to speculation. One possible clue is that SP-I undergoes glycosylation at late stages in its formation (98) and that hexosamine is added to the molecule at or just prior to secretion. Perhaps such a late stage chemical alteration in the molecule could allow the cell to differentiate between the multiple intracellular pools in which SP-I and PTH exist.

VIII. Summary

The study of parathyroid function and chemistry of its secreted proteins has provided substantial insights into several aspects of PTH synthesis, processing, and regulation. The recent characterization of SP-I suggests that future work will provide equally fruitful information on the parathyroid and its hormone and may shed light on the functioning of other secretory tissues, as well.

REFERENCES

1. Copp, D. H. (1970). *Annu. Rev. Physiol.* **32,** 61.
2. Phang, J. M., and Weiss, I. W. (1976). *Handb. Physiol. Sect. 7* **7,** 157.
3. Talmage, R. V., and Meyer, R. A., Jr. (1976). *Handb. Physiol. Sect. 7* **7,** 343.
4. Cohn, D. V., and MacGregor, R. R. (1981). *Endocr. Rev.* **2,** 1.
5. Mayer, G. P. (1979). *In* "Endocrinology" (L. J. DeGrott, ed.), Vol. 2, p. 607. Grune & Stratton, New York.
6. Cohn, D. V., and Wong, G. L. (1979). *In* "Skeletal Research, An Experimental Approach" (D. J. Simmons and A. S. Kunnin, eds.), p. 3. Academic Press, New York.
7. Raisz, L. G. (1976). *Handb. Physiol. Sect. 7* **7,** 117.
8. Handler, P., Cohn, D. V., and DeMaria, W. J. A. (1951). *Am. J. Physiol.* **165,** 434.
9. Handler, P., and Cohn, D. V. (1952). *Am. J. Physiol.* **169,** 188.
10. Levinsky, N. G., and Davidson, D. G. (1957). *Am. J. Physiol.* **191,** 530.
11. Pullman, T. N., Lavender, A. R., Aho, I., and Rasmussen, H. (1960). *Endocrinology* **67,** 570.
12. DeLuca, H. F., and Holick, M. F. (1979). *In* "Endocrinology" (L. J. DeGrott, ed.), Vol. 2, p. 653. Grune & Stratton, New York.
13. Wasserman, R. H., and Taylor, A. N. (1976). *Handb. Physiol. Sect. 7* **7,** 137.
14. Copp, D. H. (1976). *Handb. Physiol. Sect. 7* **7,** 431.
15. Brewer, H. B., and Ronan, R. (1970). *Proc. Natl. Acad. Sci. U.S.A.* **67,** 1862.
16. Niall, H. D., Keutmann, H. T., Sauer, R., Hogan, M., Dawson, B., Aurbach, G. D., and Potts, J. T., Jr. (1970). *Hoppe Seylers Z. Physiol. Chem.* **351,** 1586.
17. Sauer, R. T., Niall, H. D., Hogan, M. L., Keutmann, H. T., O'Riordan, J. L. H., and Potts, J. T., Jr. (1974). *Biochemistry* **13,** 1994.
18. Keutmann, H. T., Sauer, M. M., Hendy, G. N., O'Riordan, J. L. H., and Potts, J. T., Jr. (1978). *Biochemistry* **17,** 5723.
19. Tregear, G. W., van Rietschoten, J., Green, E., Keutman, H. T., Niall, H. D., Reit, B., Parsons, J. A., and Potts, J. T., Jr. (1973). *Endocrinology* **93,** 1349.

20. Keutman, H. T. (1979). *In* "Endocrinology" (L. J. DeGrott, ed.), Vol. 2, p. 593. Grune & Stratton, New York.
21. MacGregor, R. R., Hamilton, J. W., Kent, G. N., Shofstall, R. E., and Cohn, D. V. (1979). *J. Biol. Chem.* **254**, 4428.
22. Cohn, D. V., MacGregor, R. R., Sinha, D., Huang, D. W. Y., Edelhoch, H., and Hamilton, J. W. (1974). *Arch. Biochem. Biophys.* **164**, 669.
23. Fiskin, A. M., Cohn, D. V., and Peterson, G. S. (1977). *J. Biol. Chem.* **252**, 8261.
24. Brewer, H. B., Fairwell, T., Ronan, R., Rittel, W., and Arnaud, C. (1975). *In* "Calcium Regulating Hormones" (R. V. Talmage, M. Owen, and J. A. Parsons, eds.), p. 23. Excerpta Medica, Amsterdam.
25. Edelhoch, H., and Lippoldt, R. E. (1969). *J. Biol. Chem.* **244**, 3876.
26. Chou, P. Y., and Fasman, G. D. (1974). *Biochemistry* **13**, 211.
27. Chou, P. Y., and Fasman, G. D. (1974). *Biochemistry* **13**, 222.
28. Fasman, G. D., Chou, P. Y., and Adler, A. J. (1976). *Biophys. J.* **16**, 1201.
29. Chou, P. Y., and Fasman, G. D. (1977). *J. Mol. Biol.* **115**, 135.
30. Hamilton, J. W., MacGregor, R. R., Chu, L. L. H., and Cohn, D. V. (1971). *Endocrinology* **89**, 1440.
31. Cohn, D. V., MacGregor, R. R., Chu, L. L. H., Kimmel, J. R., and Hamilton, J. W. (1972). *Proc. Natl. Acad. Sci. U.S.A.* **69**, 1521.
32. Kemper, B., Habener, J. R., Potts, J. T., Jr., and Rich, A. (1972). *Proc. Natl. Acad. Sci. U.S.A.* **69**, 643.
33. Hamilton, J. W., Niall, H. D., Jacobs, J. W., Keutmann, H. T., Potts, J. T., Jr., and Cohn, D. V. (1974). *Proc. Natl. Acad. Sci. U.S.A.* **71**, 653.
34. Kemper, B., Habener, J. F., Mulligan, R. C., Potts, J. T., Jr., and Rich, A. (1974). *Proc. Natl. Acad. Sci. U.S.A.* **71**, 3731.
35. Habener, J. F., Kemper, B., Potts, J. T., Jr., and Rich, A. (1975). *Biochem. Biophys. Res. Commun.* **67**, 1114.
36. Kemper, B., Habener, J. F., Potts, J. T., Jr., and Rich, A. (1976). *Biochemistry* **15**, 20.
37. Kemper, B., Habener, J. F., Ernst, M. D., Potts, J. T., Jr., and Rich, A. (1976). *Biochemistry* **15**, 15.
38. Habener, J. F., Rosenblatt, M., Kemper, B., Kronenberg, H. M., Rich, A., and Potts, J. T., Jr. (1978). *Proc. Natl. Acad. Sci. U.S.A.* **75**, 2616.
39. Barker, W. C., and Dayhoff, M. O. (1972). *In* "Atlas of Protein Sequence and Structure" (M. O. Dayhoff, ed.), Vol. 5, p. 101. National Biomedical Research Foundation, Silver Spring, Maryland.
40. Cohn, D. V., Smardo, F. L., and Morrissey, J. J. (1979). *Proc. Natl. Acad. Sci. U.S.A.* **76**, 1469.
41. Palade, G. (1975). *Science* **189**, 347.
42. Habener, J. F., and Potts, J. T., Jr. (1979). *Endocrinology* **104**, 265.
43. Dorner, A. J., and Kemper, B. (1978). *Biochemistry* **17**, 5550.
44. MacGregor, R. R., Chu, L. L. H., Hamilton, J. W., and Cohn, D. V. (1973). *Endocrinology* **93**, 1387.
45. Chu, L. L. H., MacGregor, R. R., Hamilton, J. W., and Cohn, D. V. (1974). *Endocrinology* **95**, 1431.
46. Chu, L. L. H., MacGregor, R. R., and Cohn, D. V. (1977). *J. Cell Biol.* **72**, 1.
47. MacGregor, R. R., Chu, L. L. H., and Cohn, D. V. (1976). *J. Biol. Chem.* **251**, 6711.
48. Habener, J. F., Chang, H. T., and Potts, J. T., Jr. (1977). *Biochemistry* **16**, 3910.
49. MacGregor, R. R., Hamilton, J. W., Cohn, D. V. (1978). *J. Biol. Chem.* **253**, 2012.
50. Nakagami, K., Warshawsky, H., and LeBlond, C. P. (1971). *J. Cell Biol.* **51**, 596.
51. Setoguti, T., Inoue, Y., and Kato, K. (1981). *Cell Tissue Res.* **219**, 457.
52. Sherwood, L. M., Mayer, G. P., Ramberg, C. F., Jr., Kronfeld, D. S., Aurbach, D. G., and Potts, J. T., Jr. (1968). *Endocrinology* **83**, 1043.

53. Mayer, G. P., Habener, J. F., and Potts, J. T., Jr. (1976). *J. Clin. Invest.* **57**, 678.
54. Mayer, G. P., Keaton, J. A., Hurst, J. G., and Habener, J. F. (1979). *Endocrinology* **104**, 1778.
55. Mayer, G. P., and Hurts, J. G. (1978). *Endocrinology* **102**, 1036.
56. Cohn, D. V., MacGregor, R. R., Chu, L. L. H., and Hamilton, J. W. (1972). In "Calcium Parathyroid Hormone and Calcitonin" (R. V. Talmage and P. L. Munson, eds.), p. 173. Excerpta Medica, Amsterdam.
57. Chu, L. L. H., MacGregor, R. R., Liu, P. I., Hamilton, J. W., and Cohn, D. V. (1973). *J. Clin. Invest.* **52**, 3089.
58. Morrissey, J. J., and Cohn, D. V. (1979). *J. Cell Biol.* **83**, 521.
59. Morrissey, J. J., and Cohn, D. V. (1978). *Endocrinology* **103**, 2081.
60. Morrissey, J. J., Shofstall, R. E., Hamilton, J. W., and Cohn, D. V. (1980). *Proc. Natl. Acad. Sci. U.S.A.* **77**, 6406.
61. Abe, M., and Sherwood, L. M. (1972). *Biochem. Biophys. Res. Commun.* **48**, 396.
62. Williams, G. A., Hargis, G. K., Bowser, E. N., Henderson, W. J., and Martinez, N. J. (1973). *Endocrinology* **92**, 687.
63. Brown, E. M., Hurwitz, S., and Aurbach, G. D. (1977). *Endocrinology* **100**, 1696.
64. Brown, E. M., Gardner, D. G., Windeck, R. A., Hurwitz, S., Brennan, M. F., and Aurbach, G. D. (1979). *J. Clin. Endocrinol. Metab.* **48**, 618.
65. Gardner, D. G., Brown, E. M., Windeck, R., and Aurbach, G. D. (1978). *Endocrinology* **103**, 577.
66. Brown, E. M., Gardner, D. G., Windeck, R. A., and Aurbach, G. D. (1978). *Endocrinology* **103**, 2323.
67. Brown, E. M., Hurwitz, S., Woodard, C. J., and Aurbach, G. D. (1977). *Endocrinology* **100**, 1703.
68. Fischer, J. A., Blum, J. W., and Binswanger, U. (1973). *J. Clin. Invest.* **52**, 2434.
69. Blum, J. W., Fischer, J. A., Binswanger, U., Picotti, G. B., and Guillebeau, A. (1978). *J. Clin. Invest.* **61**, 1113.
70. Mayer, G. P., Hurst, J. G., Barto, J. A., Keaton, J. A., and Moore, M. P. (1979). *Endocrinology* **104**, 1181.
71. Morrissey, J. J., and Cohn, D. V. (1979). *J. Cell Biol.* **82**, 93.
72. Oldham, S. M., Lipson, L. G., and Tietjen, G. E. (1982). *Min. Elec. Metab.* **7**, 273.
73. Brown, E. M., Dawson-Hughes, B. F., Wilson, R. E., and Adragna, N. (1981). *J. Clin. Endocrinol. Metab.* **53**, 1064.
74. MacGregor, R. R., Hamilton, J. W., and Cohn, D. V. (1975). *Endocrinology* **97**, 178.
75. Chu, L. L. H., MacGregor, R. R., Anast, C. S., Hamilton, J. W., and Cohn, D. V. (1973). *Endocrinology* **93**, 915.
76. Silverman, R., and Yalow, R. S. (1973). *J. Clin. Invest.* **52**, 1958.
77. Flueck, J. A., Di Bella, F. P., Edis, A. J., Kehrwald, J. M., and Arnaud, C. D. (1977). *J. Clin. Invest.* **60**, 1367.
78. Hanley, D. A., Takatsuki, K., Sultan, J. M., Schneider, A. B., and Sherwood, L. M. (1978). *J. Clin. Invest.* **62**, 1247.
79. Morrissey, J. J., and Hamilton, J. W., MacGregor, R. R., and Cohn, D. V. (1980). *Endocrinology* **107**, 164.
80. MacGregor, R. R., Hamilton, J. W., Shofstall, R. E., and Cohn, D. V. (1979). *J. Biol. Chem.* **254**, 4423.
81. Hamilton, J. W. Personal communication.
82. Judah, J. D., and Foreman, R. C. (1980). *Cienc. Biol. (Coimbra)* **5**, 1.
83. Licata, A. A., Au, W. Y. W., and Raisz, L. G. (1972). *Biochim. Biophys. Acta* **261**, 143.
84. Kemper, B., Habener, J. F., Rich, A., and Potts, J. T., Jr. (1974). *Science* **184**, 167.

85. Morrissey, J. J., Hamilton, J. W., and Cohn, D. V. (1978). *Biochem. Biophys. Res. Commun.* **82**, 1279.
86. Cohn, D. V., Morrissey, J. J., Hamilton, J. W., Shofstall, R. E., Smardo, F. L., and Chu, L. L. H. (1981). *Biochemistry* **20**, 4135.
87. Takatsuki, K., Schneider, A. B., Shin, K. Y., and Sherwood, L. M. (1981). *J. Biol. Chem.* **256**, 2342.
88. Ravazzola, M., Orci, L., Habener, J. F., and Potts, J. T., Jr. (1978). *Lancet* **2**, 371.
89. Winkler, H. (1976). *Neuroscience* **1**, 65.
90. Winkler, H. (1977). *Neuroscience* **2**, 657.
91. Sage, H. J., Smith, W. J., and Kirshner, N. (1967). *Mol. Pharmacol.* **3**, 81.
92. Kirshner, N., Sage, H. J., and Smith, W. J. (1967). *Mol. Pharmacol.* **3**, 254.
93. Banks, P., Helle, K. B., and Mayor, D. (1969). *Mol. Pharmacol.* **5**, 210.
94. DePotter, W. P., Smith, A. D., and DeSchaepdryver, A. F. (1970). *Tissue Cell* **2**, 529.
95. Cohn, D. V., Zangerle, R., Fischer-Colbrie, R., Chu, L. L. H., Elting, J. J., Hamilton, J. W., and Winkler, H. (1982). *Proc. Natl. Acad. Sci. U.S.A.* **79**, 6056.
96. Altenähr, E. (1970). *Virchows Arch. Pathol. Anat.* **351**, 122.
97. Altenähr, E., and Seifert, G. (1971). *Virchows Arch. Pathol. Anat.* **353**, 60.
98. Majzoub, J. A., Dee, P. C., and Habener, J. F. (1982). *J. Biol. Chem.* **257**, 3581.
99. Keutmann, H. T., Niall, H. D., O'Riordan, J. L. H., and Potts, J. T., Jr. (1975). *Biochemistry* **14**, 1842.

DISCUSSION

W. F. Crowley: Another feature that ties parathyroid, pituitary, pancreas, and adrenal together in addition to the multiple endocrine neoplasia syndrome is the pulsatile release of their hormones. Is there anything in the mechanics of packaging, synthesis, or release that you have discovered that could tie this mechanism of secretion together in terms of efficiency of energy in metabolism of release, etc. It seems that it is a sufficiently common enough theme in those organs to have some commonality of explanation.

D. V. Cohn: That is a very astute observation. I really don't have any direct information on the pulsatile nature of PTH secretion. As we know there is always a leak of hormone but these measurements have been integrated over a relatively long time and would not detect what you are referring to. We have wondered in some of the experiments that have been reported by Jan Fisher in Switzerland, in which after two or three injections of epinephrine he found smaller peaks of PTH secreted if he might have been exhausting a pool of granules close to the plasma membrane and available for exocytosis. Now if there were a requirement that a minimum number of granules were required to be close to the plasma membrane before a secretory event could proceed and it took 2–5 minutes for a granule to move from the Golgi zone to the plasma membrane, then one may be able to explain the nature of the secretion in physical terms.

G. D. Aurbach: David, thank you for a very nice presentation. You have shown us that calcium and cyclic AMP produce a bifurcation in the traffic toward synthesis and secretion of parathyroid hormone and it looks like calcium may very well act by degrading newly synthesized hormone. I have a couple of questions: (1) What do you think is the point at which cyclic AMP mediated phenomena occur in terms of secretion. There could be an effect in terms of moving secretory granules toward the surface of the cell, fusion with the cell membrane, or fission of the secretory granule with release of its contents? (2) I was very much interested in your effects of glycosolation at the moment of release of PSP. Are there any data on cyclic AMP mediated phenomena in that regard?

D. V. Cohn: In regard to question (2), the data on glycosylation are fairly recent and we have not had a chance to follow it up, so the answer is negative on that. I was remiss in failing to mention a recent paper from Majgoub *et al.* in which a delayed glycosylation was also reported. However they did not study secretion per se, but cell-free synthesis of SP-I. As far as mechanisms by which cyclic AMP can facilitate secretion, I have considered all of the possibilities you mention but have not been able to test them yet. But, each possibility is certainly viable. The fusion mechanism is the one that would be nice, particularly considering the work of Pollard and his associates who have described a protein *synexin* which produces an aggregation of chromaffin granules in association with this protein. The protein forms chains in the presence of calcium. Whether cyclic AMP plays a role at that point, however, is hard to know, but it would be nice if there were a chemical step in which cyclic AMP is involved and in which there were an interaction between synexin-like protein and glycosylated SP-I leading to exocytosis. I have no evidence for this, of course.

U. Zor: Thank you for the excellent study and presentation. I would like to ask about the mechanism of calcium action. First, in general if you raise the calcium concentration in the medium one can receive an enhancing of the release of pituitary hormones, thyroid and steroid hormone, and parathyroid gland. Therefore it is unique in this respect that if the calcium level is high the secretion is inhibited. Second, in general, cyclic AMP and calcium are working in concert. Rasmussen just published a book about cyclic AMP and calcium as a synactic agent. So in this respect the calcium again is antagonizing the effect of cyclic AMP. So I would like to ask what do you envision the mechanism of calcium action to be and if it works through calmodulin?

D. V. Cohn: Yes. There have been several reports in which a calmodulin-regulated phosphodiesterase has been shown to exist in the parathyroid gland. The explanation for the action of calcium inhibiting secretion would be for the ion to move into the cell raising cytosolic calcium concentration slightly, activating the phosphodiesterase, and then lowering cyclic AMP levels. Since cyclic AMP levels correlate so nicely with secretion at least we can understand how calcium could affect PTH secretion. I can't really discuss whether calcium and cyclic AMP have to work together. Although we can find a ready explanation for how high calcium can inhibit secretion, we have not answered how cyclic AMP works which, of course, brings us back to Dr. Aurbach's question.

U. Zor: Is there some study on the effect of zero calcium in the medium in order to see inhibition of the release of PTH? In another sense, if one could receive biphasic effects (a bell-shaped curve) that is, zero calcium or high concentration of Ca^{2+} inhibition of PTH has occurred. I am not terribly satisfied about the dibutyryl cyclic AMP that you used because you have a lot of hydrolyzed butyrate which may chelate the calcium in the medium. I would prefer to see an experiment done with bromocyclic AMP rather than a dibutyryl cyclic AMP. Does high calcium also inhibit the release of catecholamines from adrenal medulla?

D. V. Cohn: I don't know the answer to that. Maybe someone here knows. As far as the experiments with other derivatives of cyclic AMP and whether dibutyrate exerts its own effects, I would point out that many agents that work on parathyroid receptors such as isoproterenol give the same result without the necessity of worrying about an artifact of lowering calcium in the medium. Since much of the work with cAMP-related PTH secretion was done by Dr. Aurbach, maybe he would like to answer that.

G. D. Aurbach: Yes, in fact 8-bromocyclic AMP will cause release of parathyroid hormone from isolated cells. I should mention also that Dr. Roz Lasker and Allen Spiegel at NIH have recently shown that there is a 14,000, approximately, molecular weight protein in the parathyroid cell membrane that gets phosphorylated in the presence of isoproterenol and also 8-bromol cyclic AMP. So as apparent in almost all phenomena mediated by cAMP, the cyclic nucleotide stimulates a protein kinase causing phosphorylation of one or more proteins in the cell membrane. How that is connected to secretion and what step it is functioning at, seem to be as yet unknown.

L. S. Jacobs: These are very interesting and provocative observations. Obviously, the number of putative roles that one could ascribe to SP-I the secretory protein is legion; among them are some kind of function in packaging or in secretion. The granule is receiving a variety of signals, and interacting with plasma membranes, participating in membrane fusion and fisson reactions, etc. One of the granule membrane constituents that has been described in a number of systems is a band 3-like anion recognition site; in parathyroid cells Pollard and his collaborators have shown that the stilbene disulfonates can influence secretion. These compounds are probes for band 3-like proteins and also interact with components of serotonin, chromaffin, and anterior pituitary granules. Is there conclusive evidence as to the intragranular or membranous localization of SP-I? The fact that it is secreted concordant with PTH and is under calcium control does not tell one where in the granule it is. Even though PTH is probably large enough not to make the granule worry about diffusional loss of secretory product, there may be osmotic reasons for having a binding protein for PTH. This might relate to the number of particles and the energy that would have to be expended to pump water out of the granule. In the pituitary, the concentration of protein secretory produce inside the granule is of the order of magnitude found in the chromaffin granule, which is several hundred millimolar. The parathyroid granule may be similar. I wonder if experiments have been carried out with SP-I to find out if it is capable of binding PTH. Also, is the SP-I in pituitary extracts contained within secretory granules?

D. V. Cohn: Let me see if I can start from the back working forward. To my knowledge the work of Takatsuki and his colleagues was done on whole tissues. Obviously histology has to be done, to determine if SP-I in the pituitary is localized to granules. Regarding the ability of PTH and secretory protein one to bind to each other, we have done some experiments to test that. First we had to consider a technical problem in the purification of SP-I. The procedure for purification of PTH which is a brutal thing was the same one used to extract SP-I. Since this protein is much larger than PTH the first question was whether or not the SP-I produced by the standard isolation procedure could be undenatured. If it was denatured one wouldn't expect anything to happen, so we did develop a more gentle method for extracting SP-I and we published both methods side by side. Rather than urea–HCl we used as the first step the more standard ammonium sulfate precipitations, on extracts of acetone-dried tissue. With this preparation we have not seen any evidence of binding of SP-I to PTH. In that sense we concur with Potts, Kemper, and their group. We have looked for other possible functions as Potts had done without success. At one time we thought SP-I might have enzymatic activity, but could never reproduce those data. I think that now there will be a resurgence of investigation on function of SP-I, particularly by those investigators working on chromaffin granules. The first question you asked is whether we really know that the secretory protein is within the granule. We did some of the standard experiments of isolating membrane and subjecting them to proteolytic activity. The PTH, proPTH, and the SP-I are all pretty well protected until you add Triton or other things to open the granule. That is pretty good evidence, I think, that we are dealing with something contained within a membrane. In one of the figures showing a range of concentrations of deoxycholate you may have noticed that all three proteins were released in the same proportions as the detergent concentration was increased. We think that if SP-I were a surface protein it should have been washed off a little more easily. So that again suggests that it is internal. Further, Dr. Winkler has evidence that chromogranin is totally within the chromaffin granule with nothing of it on the outside.

J. C. Penhos: I have a type of pharmacological question in view of the interrelationship between the calcium and secretory protein. Do you have any information on how calcium entry blockers could affect the release of the parathyroid hormone or the secretory protein?

D. V. Cohn: No I don't have any first-hand information. There have been some experiments in which channel blockers have been shown to interfere with the calcium signal. Perhaps Dr. Aurbach can add to my comment. I'm sure that you have that data.

G. D. Aurbach: Yes, some of the calcium channel blockers do block the effect of calcium in inhibiting parathyroid hormone release. Conversely, the calcium ionophore A 23187 potentiates the effects of calcium on inhibition of secretion.

B. F. Rice: I just have a simple question about the packaging concept and the degragation products. If I understood the figure properly, you have biologically inactive fragments coming out to be degraded and on the clinical side our colleagues tell us that the most important fragment to measure in patients that have clinical primary hyperparathyroidism, is the C terminal fragment that is biologically inactive, and yet obviously they have active hormone in their circulation that is causing their calcium to be very high. Do you have any way to tie that together?

D. V. Cohn: Yes, I think so. There has been some controversy in the field as to whether an amino-terminal assay, which would presumably measure bioactive hormone or a carboxy-terminal assay would give the best results. A few years ago Claude Arnaud correlated whether an assay that would look at carboxy-terminal fragments or amino-terminal fragments would give the better correlation with the clinical picture. He thought that the carboxyl-terminal assay was best. Now if you look at his data, the reason the carboxyl-assay was best, I think, was because it was a more sensitive assay. In general, antisera generated against carboxyl-terminal pieces have a greater sensitivity than amino-terminal antisera. A big problem is that in primary hyperparathyroidism, when we know that the gland is hypersecreting, many N and C-terminal antisera do not report an increased parathyroid hormone level. We have been working at ImmunoNuclear on a way to look at presumed intact PTH to help us detect primary hyperparathyroidism. This is done very simply. You pass the serum through an affinity column which absorbs all the peptides containing the N-terminal region of PTH, including intact PTH. The column is eluted and the eluate measured with a C-terminal or mid-molecule direct antiserum. N-terminal fragments are not measured but intact PTH is. C-terminal fragments were never absorbed on the column and therefore also are not measured. When you do this, you find in every case that there is a substantial elevation of intact PTH or presumed intact PTH in the circulation. The more I have thought about this, the more apparent it is that circulating intact PTH represents a real marker of parathyroid gland secretory activity. One of the reasons that you may have difficulty with a C-terminal region assay is that the gland is secreting both intact PTH and C-terminal fragments. When you turn down the parathyroid gland, less intact but more C-terminal fragments come out. The antisera won't tell the difference between them so that there is a blunting of the final response. Intact PTH, of course, really does move up and down with gland function. That is probably what should be measured and probably is the way to go.

M. B. Nikitovitch-Winer: I'm very interested in your comments about the old and new parathyroid-containing hormone granules. We have worked with prolactin-secreting cells in the pituitary and the concept of an easily releasable pool and a slow releasable pool of prolactin has been proposed by several researchers. Can you tell me how many glands have been described to contain a slow and a fast releasable pool of secretory product. What is your general thinking about the importance of this type of secretory granular storage and release? It seems that a newly synthesized hormone is released first, at least in the two systems where the fast or slow releasable pools of secretion seem to exist.

D. V. Cohn: Well, we're generally talking about the ability of newly made secretory granules to mix with old granules. Marilyn Farquar has worked with the mammotroph and she suggests that there may in fact be two hormone pools but not in the same cell. She has proposed that there may be "slow" cells and "fast" cells. There is also evidence in the pancreatic beta cell that new and old granules may not mix. If you push the beta cells to secrete new insulin comes out relative to old insulin. It may just depend on the gland's architecture. I haven't made a full study of that, but we are aware of other reports containing similar findings. Now whether one can functionally differentiate one pool from another, that is having one pool responsive to one agent and not to another, is another matter. This, to us, was the thing that was unique in the parathyroid. We have wondered why epinephrine, isoproterenol, β-agonists, and so forth will trigger PTH release. Is there any functional significance to this? Is there any reason why in the parathyroid gland circulating epinephrine might trigger parathyroid hormone release? One possibility is that many of the reactions of epinephrine at the target level are related to calcium movement. Also parathyroid hormone has been shown in a number of target tissues to enhance the inflow of calcium to the cell as a primary event. We wondered if PTH and epinephrine might work together in a synergistic fashion. Another point, also worth mentioning, is that in the older literature it is reported that the parathyroid gland is innervated. Nobody these days pays the slightest bit of attention to this. It does raise the question whether stimulation of the sympathetic nervous system might in fact release catecholamines in the parathyroid cell and cause release of PTH. We're looking at that kind of a thing from the standpoint of physiological significance. Much remains for further investigation.

S. Plymate: You said that parathyroid secretory protein (PSP) came out concordant with PTH. Is the molar ratio between the two always the same regardless of the mechanism of stimulation of PTH and PTH secretion continues? Does PSP keep pace with PTH secretion?

D. V. Cohn: Yes, if you calculate you find that about a mole of the secretory protein is made per mole of PTH. But their rates of degradation may differ a bit. We haven't published any of those data yet because they're not solid enough, but the general impression we have is that both SP-I and PTH are being degraded but at slightly different rates. In the secretory the ratios we find are about 0.7–0.8 mole of SP-I to a mole of PTH and that ratio is more or less the same in the medium. We've not been able really to change the ratio under different stimulatory conditions. Over the course of a few hours of incubation these ratios seem to remain the same. So they're made in about the same amount, though they're not made from a common protein, which was one of the questions. The possibility of a common precursor immediately suggested itself.

K. Sterling: In answer to the next to last question that Dr. Nikitovitch-Winer asked, besides the parathyroid gland and the islets producing insulin, the thyroid gland has two separate and distinct pools of thyroxine. This is different altogether, of course, because it is in the colloid space which is an extracellular deposit of thyroglobulin mainly. I enjoyed this paper very much. I was trying to recall à propos of the chromogranin and the secretory protein, the embryology of the two glands. As I recall it, the adrenal medulla probably arises from neurectoderm and the cortex adjeval from mesenchyme, whereas the parathyroid gland is supposed to be pinched off presumably from endoderm near the embryologic thyroid. Dr. Aurbach is shaking his head vigorously in the negative. I didn't really believe that aside from the mesenchymal origin of adrenal medulla—can you help me with this?

G. D. Aurbach: I thought that Dr. Sterling was going to tell us that the main function of the thyroid was to hold up the parathyroid. Actually I don't know. I don't know about the question of neural ectoderm versus mesenchyme. I believe it is mesenchymal origin for parathyroid. The origin of the parathyroid is not the thyroid, I don't think it is pinched off from the thyroid primordia.

K. Sterling: The word means in Greek "like the thyroid," parathyroid.

G. R. Cunha: The parathyroid is derived from the third and fourth pharyngeal pouches which are endodermal in origin.

C. P. Channing: I was really fascinated by the secretory protein made by the parathyroid glands. Maybe we should look for similar secretory proteins in other organs such as the different cells of the pituitary, and such proteins. Perhaps such a protein could help FSH and LH secretion. Is this protein secreted into the blood and does it stabilize the parathyroid hormone during its secretion and/or inhibit its degradation?

D. V. Cohn: Regarding the first part of your question, chromogranin A has been reported to be in sympathetic nerve endings and so when norepinephrine is released, chromogranin A also should be released. Now chromogranin A definitely is released to the blood. In fact there have been two laboratories which have suggested in preliminary reports that the measurement of serum chromogranin will serve as an indicator for pheochromocytoma. The best documented report is by Yamada of Dokkyo University School of Medicine, Japan University who found that the amount of chromogranin in the blood of one patient with pheochromocytoma was as much as 30 times the baseline levels. We've been wondering whether SP-I might reflect excess parathyroid gland function or might be indicative of excessive release of catecholamines from the adrenal medulla, for example, in essential hypertension in cases in which catecholamines are themselves not elevated. Some investigators have measured dopamine β-hydroxylase but this protein is in much smaller amounts in the chromaffin granule and perhaps explains why measure of the hydroxylase has not been picked up as a useful tool. We think that the chromogranin secretory protein radioimmunoassay might prove to be helpful in a number of cases where we suspect glandular excess. We ourselves are now evaluating pheochromocytomas and cases of essential hypertension where one wonders if there could be underlying adrenal tumor. We are also checking medullary thyroid carcinomas involving multiple endocrinopathies. We hope that others will also look and find that the presence of the secretory protein in several tissues is more than an interesting coincidence and that perhaps we are about to uncover an underlying principle of exocytosis.

C. S. Nicoll: With regard to the comments made earlier by Dr. Nikitovitch-Winer on the heterogeneous turnover of prolactin, Dr. Karen Swearingen in my laboratory made observations a number of years ago that the fast turnover component of prolactin secretion is much more sensitive to inhibition by catecholamines than is the total secretion of the hormone. Frabman and Stachura have made similar observations of greater sensitivity of the fast turnover component of growth hormone to the inhibitory effects of somatostatin, so this may be a fairly general phenomenon. This effect may be a reflection of a secretory cycle wherein the cells synthesize and package and then store the hormone, and those cells which have accumulated secretion granules have reduced synthesis and a lower response to certain stimuli as compared to others which have recently unloaded their store of hormone and are beginning the cycle again. The latter may be more sensitive to certain regulators than the former. Perhaps the two pools which you find in the parathyroid that show differential responsiveness to various stimuli reflect populations of cells in different phases of the synthesis–storage–secretion cycle.

D. V. Cohn: Well I think those are reasonable suggestions and interesting thoughts. Certainly we know that during the packaging procedure these granules grow more dense, concentrating its contents, putting more material in, or getting rid of the water. Many things are happening. In the case of the parathyroid granule intercellular degradation of unwanted protein represents a major activity, but in other cases the granule may move onto advanced stages in what you have termed the secretory granular cycle. In truth we don't have as much information on that whole area as we should.

S. Cohen: I've heard that Hector deLuca doesn't think parathyroid hormone has any direct effect on calcium metabolism. Does it effect calcium metabolism only through its formation effects of vitamin D. I wondered do you accept this or can you give me some explanation.

D. V. Cohn: I'm surprised by the thought that parathyroid hormone would have no direct action on calcium metabolism.

S. L. Cohen: Only through the formation of 1,25-vitamin D.

D. V. Cohn: Well, yes. I understand the question. Actually I would say that there is rather convincing evidence that parathyroid hormone can act on its primary target organs— the bone cells—without involving vitamin D metabolism. Certainly the best system to study this is the isolated bone cells that we have worked with—the osteoclast-like and osteoblast-like cells and bone maintained in organ culture. In these experiments one can pretty well control the environment and can demonstrate that the hormone activates cells as far as we know without the intervention of the vitamin D metabolies 1,25-$(OH)_2D_3$ or 25-OH D_3-. Maybe there is something hidden going on within the cell, but I see no evidence to suggest that you have to have a vitamin D metabolite for the hormone to act or that its primary action is only to generate 1,25-dihydroxycholecalciferol in the kidney. So I would have to see those data claiming otherwise and study them very carefully.

S. L. Cohen: I think you are referring primarily to the effects on calcium excretion and phosphate excretion by the kidney.

D. V. Cohn: I have seen no convincing evidence that suggests that. One can readily demonstrate specific effects on tubulary absorption of phosphate by PTH; I haven't seen evidence that convincingly says that you have to have the 1,25-dihydroxycholecalciferol present. I know that Dr. LeLuca has suggested several years ago that PTH won't work in a vitamin D-deficient animal but the data are not strong, in my opinion.

A. D. Kenny: I can contribute somewhat to this discussion. In collaboration with Dr. Peter Pang, we have been oxidizing bPTH (1–34) and bPTH (1–84) with hydrogen peroxide. If we oxidize bPTH (1–84) we decrease or abolish every response that we have looked at except the renal 1-hydroxylase response. Thus, oxidized bPTH (1–84) can stimulate the 1-hydroxylase and yet has little or no hypercalcemic activity in the rat or in the Japanese quail. This, I believe, partially answers Dr. Cohen's question. Incidentally, oxidation abolishes the renal adenylate cyclase response to bPTH (1–84).

J. Larner: I was very interested in the fact that the secretory protein and presumably the chromogranins not only contain carbohydrate but sulfate as well, and I wondered if there was some information regarding the chemistry of the organic sulfate, that is to say, whether it is bound to carbohydrate or bound to the amino acids of the proteins, and, second, if there are any studies with regard to the turnover of the sulfate, in comparison to the turnover of the sugars?

D. V. Cohn: No those experiments were done by adding radioactive sulfate to parathyroid cells and measuring incorporation. We don't have additional information at this time.

J. Larner: It is not known whether the sulfate is bound to the carbohydrate or, for example if it is bound to protein.

D. V. Cohn: I suspect that it is bound to the carbohydrate but it may not be. I can't tell you anything about the chemistry of the linkage at this time.

G. D. Aurbach: Just to go back to a point that was raised a couple of minutes ago about whether parathyroid hormone action must be mediated through a dihydroxy vitamin D. I think it is incontrovertible that parathyroid hormone acts directly on both kidney and bone independently of vitamin D and its metabolites. It is only on gastrointestinal absorption of calcium that parathyroid hormone acts through the intermediation of 1,25-dihydroxy vitamin D formation. You are going to hear tomorrow night from Professor Morel who is going to show you elegant studies of the parathyroid hormone action directly on isolated segments of the kidney tubule.

Gastrointestinal Peptides: The Basis of Action at the Cellular Level

JERRY D. GARDNER AND ROBERT T. JENSEN

Digestive Diseases Branch, National Institute of Arthritis, Diabetes, and Digestive and Kidney Diseases, National Institutes of Health, Bethesda, Maryland

I. Introduction

Historically, it is worth recalling that it was the discovery of the gastrointestinal peptide, secretin, that gave birth to the field of endocrinology. In particular, Bayliss and Starling (1902, 1904) found that instillation of hydrochloric acid into a denervated loop of canine jejunum stimulated pancreatic fluid secretion. Intravenous injection of hydrochloric acid did not stimulate pancreatic secretion, whereas intravenous injection of an aqueous extract of jejunal mucosa did stimulate pancreatic secretion. These observations engendered two concepts. First, Bayliss and Starling postulated the existence of a substance called "secretin." This substance is released by acid from the upper small intestinal mucosa into the blood stream via which the substance is carried to the pancreas and causes stimulation of pancreatic secretion. Second, Bayliss and Starling coined the term "hormone" which is derived from the Greek word meaning "I arouse to activity." It was clear that Bayliss and Starling viewed "hormones" as chemical coordinators of various bodily functions.

Since the experiments of Bayliss and Starling, many other gastrointestinal peptides have been discovered and characterized (Walsh, 1981). In some instances these peptides function as crucial elements in the gastrointestinal endocrine system. As illustrated in Fig. 1, the gastrointestinal endocrine system can be viewed as being designed to regulate the chemical composition of the contents within the lumen of the gastrointestinal tract. Like a conventional endocrine system, there are two major components of the gastrointestinal endocrine system—a production tissue and one or more target tissues. In contrast to the production tissue of a conventional endocrine system in which the cells that are responsible for producing the hormone are organized into a glandular structure, in the

211

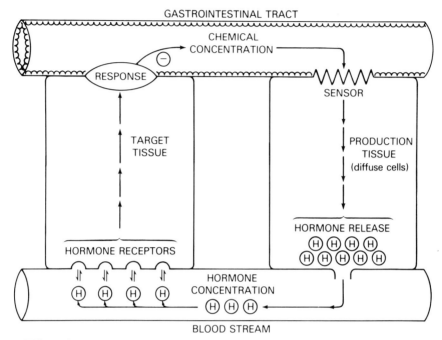

FIG. 1. Schematic diagram of the essential components of the gastrointestinal endocrine system.

gastrointestinal endocrine system the hormone-producing cells are arranged in a diffuse pattern over an area of the gastrointestinal tract (e.g., the first meter of the upper small intestine). The production tissue of the gastrointestinal endocrine system possesses a sensing mechanism that detects changes in the chemical composition of the contents in the lumen of the gastrointestinal tract and a mechanism for synthesizing and releasing the gastrointestinal peptide in response to an appropriate stimulus. The gastrointestinal peptide is released into the blood stream and carried to the target tissue where the peptide interacts with cell surface receptors. This peptide–receptor interaction initiates a series of biochemical changes in the cells that comprise the target tissue and the last of the changes, which is usually referred to as the "hormone response," is one that acts to reverse the stimulus that initiated the release of the peptide from the production tissue. An example of how the gastrointestinal endocrine system operates can be visualized with secretin. Secretion of acid by the stomach increases the concentration of hydrogen ions in the lumen of the upper gastrointestinal tract. This acidification is detected by secretin-producing cells which release secretin into the blood stream. Secretin is carried to the pancreas where the peptide interacts with cell surface receptors and causes a series of changes the last of which is secretion of bicarbonate ions into the lumen of the gastrointestinal tract where they neutralize the hydrogen ions and stop the stimulus to secretin release by the secretin-producing cells.

Although some gastrointestinal peptides clearly function as hormones (e.g., secretin), others function as neurotransmitters (e.g., vasoactive intestinal peptide) and still others function as paracrine regulators of cellular function (e.g., somatostatin).

Another characteristic of the gastrointestinal peptides is that they can exist in multiple chemical forms in the circulation. For example, gastrin can exist in six different molecular forms (Fig. 2). Gastrin has been found to exist in three different molecular sizes: 34 amino acids ("big gastrin" or G-34), 17 amino acids ("little gastrin" or G-17), and 13 amino acids (mini-gastrin or G-13). As illustrated in Fig. 2, G-17 and G-13 can be viewed as C-terminal fragments of G-34. Each of the three different sizes of gastrin can exist in two different forms, with the tyrosine residue sulfated or not sulfated. Figure 2 also gives the structure of "pentagastrin." It is important to note that this peptide, which is used for diagnostic testing of gastric acid secretion, is not the C-terminal five amino acids of gastrin but is the C-terminal tetrapeptide of gastrin with an N-terminal t-BOC-βalanine moiety.

G-17 differs from G-34 and G-13 both in terms of potency for stimulating gastric acid secretion and rate of disappearance from the circulation. In stimulating gastric acid secretion, G-17 is five times more potent than G-34 and 2.5 times more potent than G-13 (Walsh and Grossman, 1975). The plasma half-life of G-17 is approximately 20% of that of G-34 and is approximately the same as that of G-13 (Walsh and Grossman, 1975). Sulfation of the tyrosine residue does not alter the biologic activity of any of the gastrins (Walsh and Grossman, 1975). Because there is no necessary correlation between the ability of a form of gastrin to react with a particular gastrin-specific antiserum and its ability to stimulate gastric acid secretion, total gastrin immunoreactivity determined by radioimmunoassay is only a crude index of biologic activity (Walsh and Grossman, 1975).

Figure 2 also illustrates three different examples of how a particular gastrointestinal peptide can undergo posttranslational modification in its structure. G-34 and G-17 each have an N-terminal pyroglutamic acid residue. In each of the different sizes of gastrin the C-terminal residue is phenylalanine amide and the tyrosine residue can be sulfated.

HUMAN GASTRINS

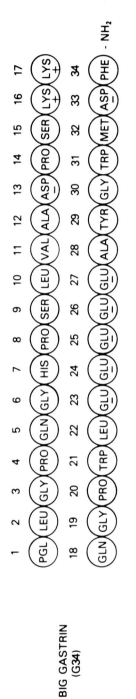

EACH OCCURS IN 2 FORMS: I = UNSULFATED TYROSINE; II = SULFATED TYROSINE

FIG. 2. Amino acid sequences of the different molecular forms of gastrin.

II. Actions of Secretagogues on Pancreatic Acinar Cells

Rather than list all of the known gastrointestinal peptides and their effects on various gastrointestinal target tissues, we have decided to choose one target cell, the pancreatic acinar cell, and examine the cellular basis of action of gastrointestinal peptides on this cell type in some detail. The initial step in the mechanism of action of secretagogues on pancreatic enzyme secretion is reversible binding of the secretagogue to receptors located on the outer surface of the plasma membrane of the pancreatic acinar cells. Binding of the secretagogue to its receptor is both necessary and sufficient to initiate the sequence of events that ultimately causes stimulation of pancreatic enzyme secretion. To date, six different classes of receptors have been described for secretagogues that act on pancreatic acinar cells. As illustrated in Fig. 3, acinar cells possess receptors for muscarinic cholinergic agents, cholecystokinin and structurally related peptides, bombesin and structurally related peptides, physalaemin and structurally related peptides, secretin and vasoactive intestinal peptide (VIP), and cholera toxin.

To date, receptors for muscarinic cholinergic agents have been identified only by the abilities of atropine and other muscarinic antagonists to competitively inhibit the actions of acetylcholine and other muscarinic agonists. Tritrate quinuclidinyl benzilate, [^{3}H]QNB, as well as the iodinated hydroxy derivative of QNB, [^{125}I]OH-QNB, have been used with broken cell preparation from several different tissues (Flanagan and Storni, 1979; Yamamura and Snyder, 1974a,b), including pancreas (Larose *et al.*, 1979; Ng *et al.*, 1979), to detect binding sites that have the properties of muscarinic cholinergic receptors. Because no corresponding agonist-induced functional change has been measured in these broken cell preparations, the conclusion that these binding sites are, in fact, muscarinic cholinergic receptors has been based on functional changes in intact cell preparations incubated under different conditions (Larose *et al.*, 1979; Ng *et al.*, 1979).

Cholecystokinin (CCK) is a peptide that was originally isolated and purified from hog upper small intestine and found to contain 33 amino acid residues (Mutt and Jorpes, 1968, 1971). In the course of investigating the structure of CCK, Mutt and Jorpes (1968) also detected a peptide that differed from CCK in that although it was retained by a CM-cellulose column, it was eluted by 0.2 M but not by 0.02 M ammonium bicarbonate. This peptide, which has been termed "CCK-variant," possesses 39 amino acids. The C-terminal 33 amino acid residues are identical to those of CCK and the N-terminal hexapeptide sequence is Tyr-Ile-Gln-Gln-Ala-Arg (Mutt, 1976). Subsequent studies of the structure of CCK showed

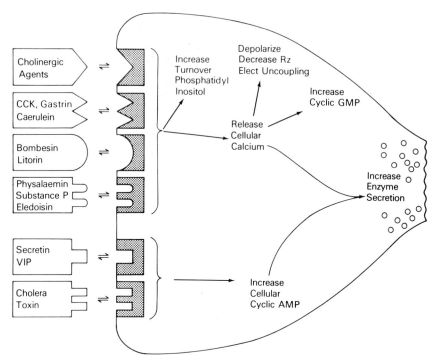

FIG. 3. Cellular basis of action of secretagogues on enzyme secretion from pancreatic acinar cells. There are four classes of receptor for secretagogues that can cause mobilization of cellular calcium and, after a series of undefined steps, stimulation of enzyme secretion. There are two classes of receptors for secretagogues that can cause activation of adenylate cyclase, increased cellular cyclic AMP, activation of cyclic AMP-dependent protein kinase, and, after a series of undefined steps, stimulation of enzyme secretion. Although the two mechanisms of action are initially separate, they converge at some presently undefined step that is distal to the mobilization of calcium and to the generation of cyclic AMP. The nature of this convergence is such that potentiation of enzyme secretion occurs when acinar cells are incubated with a secretagogue that causes release of cellular calcium plus a secretagogue that increases cellular cyclic AMP.

that the C-terminal heptapeptide possessed all of the biological activity of the native peptide and that the C-terminal octapeptide had the same effi- cacy as CCK but was approximately 10-times more potent than CCK (for example, see Jensen *et al.*, 1980; and Sjodin and Gardner, 1977). In CCK as in all of the gastrointestinal peptides that can increase pancreatic en- zyme secretion, the C-terminal amino acid residue is amidated (Figs. 4– 7). As illustrated in Fig. 4, there are two other naturally occurring peptides that are structurally similar to CCK and that stimulate pancreatic enzyme secretion by interacting with the same receptors as CCK: gastrin and caerulein. Gastrin, as mentioned previously, occurs naturally in several different chemical forms (Walsh and Grossman, 1975) and shares a common C-terminal pentapeptide amide sequence with CCK. Gastrin, like CCK, also possesses a sulfated tyrosine residue; however, in CCK the sulfated tyrosine is the seventh residue from the C-terminus, whereas in gastrin the sulfated tyrosine is the sixth residue from the C-terminus (Fig. 4). Caerulein is a decapeptide originally isolated from the skin of the Australian hylid frog *Hyla caerulea* (Anastasi *et al.*, 1968) and found subsequently to share seven of its eight C-terminal amino acids with the C-terminal octapeptide of CCK (Fig. 4). Studies of binding of ^{125}I-labeled CCK to pancreatic acinar cells indicate that CCK receptors have a high affinity for CCK (EC$_{50}$ 2 nM) and caerulein (EC$_{50}$ 0.3 nM) and a low affinity for gastrin (EC$_{50}$ 2 μM).

Another group of naturally occurring peptides that can stimulate pancreatic enzyme secretion comprises bombesin, alytesin, ranatensin, and litorin (Fig. 5). These peptides, like caerulein, were originally isolated from the skins of various frogs and were named after the particular class of frogs from which they were isolated (Erspamer and Melchiorri, 1973). For example, bombesin was isolated from the skin of *Bombina bombina* (Erspamer *et al.*, 1972). Like CCK amd structurally related peptides, the bombesin-related peptides possess a C-terminal amide; however, unlike CCK, which possesses a C-terminal phenylalanine-amide, each of the bombesin-related peptides has a C-terminal methionine-amide (Fig. 5). In bombesin, alytesin, ranatensin, and litorin, seven of their eight C-terminal

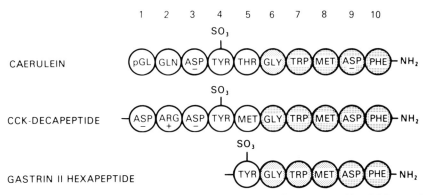

FIG. 4. Amino acid sequences for caerulein, the C-terminal decapeptide of CCK, and the C-terminal hexapeptide of gastrin II. Shaded residues indicate identical corresponding amino acids in each of the three peptides.

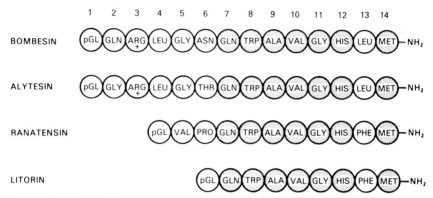

FIG. 5. Amino acid sequences for bombesin, alytesin, ranatensin, and litorin. Shaded residues indicate identical corresponding amino acids in each of the four peptides.

amino acids are identical. In bombesin and alytesin the penultimate C-terminal residue is leucine, whereas in ranatensin and litorin it is phenylalanine (Fig. 5). A mammalian structural counterpart of the bombesin-like peptides is gastrin-releasing peptide (Fig. 6)—a heptacosapeptide with gastrin-releasing action that has been recently isolated from porcine non-antral gastric mucosa (McDonald *et al.*, 1979). A radiolabeled analog of bombesin, ^{125}I-labeled [Tyr[4]]bombesin, can be used to identify binding sites that interact with bombesin and structurally related peptides, but not with other pancreatic secretagogues (Jensen *et al.*, 1978). There is a good correlation between the concentration at which bombesin and related peptides inhibit binding of ^{125}I-labeled [Tyr[4]]bombesin and the concentration at which these same secretagogues produce changes in acinar cell function (Jensen *et al.*, 1978). Each acinar cell has approximately 5000 receptors for bombesin and structurally related peptides and these recep-

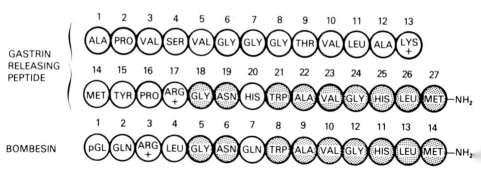

FIG. 6. Amino acid sequences for gastrin-releasing peptide and bombesin. Shaded areas indicate identical corresponding amino acids in both peptides.

tors have a higher affinity for bombesin (EC_{50} 4 nM) than for alytesin (EC_{50} 12 nM), ranatensin (EC_{50} 12 nM), or litorin (EC_{50} 40 nM).

A third group of naturally occurring peptides that can stimulate pancreatic enzyme secretion includes physalaemin, substance P, eledoisin, and kassinin. Physalaemin and kassinin, like caerulein, and the bombesin-related peptides, were originally isolated from frog skin (Anastasi *et al.*, 1964; Erspamer *et al.*, 1977). Eledoisin was originally isolated from the posterior salivary gland of a Mediterranean octopod, *Eledone moschata* (Erspamer and Melchiorri, 1973). Substance P was originally isolated from mammalian gastrointestinal mucosa and brain (v. Euler and Gaddum, 1931). Physalaemin, eledoisin, and kassinin probably represent phylogenetic precursors of substance P just as bombesin, alytesin, ranatensin, and litorin probably represent phylogenetic precursors of gastrin-releasing peptide. The physalaemin-related peptides, like the bombesin-related peptides, have a C-terminal methionine-amide (Fig. 7). In the physalaemin-related peptides, four of the five C-terminal amino acids are identical and each peptide has a hydrophobic residue in the fourth position from the C-terminus (Fig. 7). Radioiodinated physalaemin, ^{125}I-labeled physalaemin, can be used to identify a class of binding sites on pancreatic acinar cells that interact with physalaemin and structurally related peptides but not with other pancreatic secretagogues (Jensen and Gardner, 1979). There is a good correlation between the concentrations at which physalaemin and structurally related peptides inhibit binding of ^{125}I-

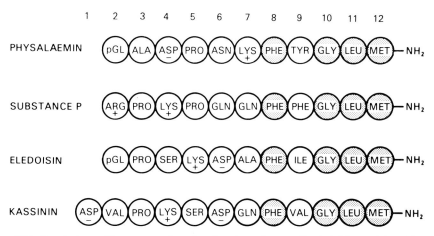

FIG. 7. Amino acid sequences for physalaemin, substance P, eledoisin, and kassinin. Shaded residues indicate identical corresponding amino acids in each of the four peptides.

labeled physalaemin and the concentration at which these same secreta-gogues produce changes in acinar cell function. Each pancreatic acinar cell has approximately 500 receptors for physalaemin and these receptors have a relatively high affinity for physalaemin (EC_{50} 2 nM) and for sub-stance P (EC_{50} 5 nM) and a relatively low affinity for eledoisin (EC_{50} 100 nM) and kassinin (EC_{50} 250 nM).

A fourth class of peptides that can stimulate pancreatic enzyme secre-tion includes VIP and secretin. VIP is an octacosapeptide isolated origi-nally from porcine upper shall intestine and was named for its ability to produce a decrease in blood pressure following intravenous injection of high doses in dogs (Said and Mutt, 1972). Secretin is a heptacosapeptide also originally isolated and characterized from porcine upper small intes-tine (Mutt and Jorpes, 1971). As illustrated in Fig. 8, VIP and secretin resemble the peptides discussed previously in that the C-terminal amino acid residue is amidated. VIP and secretin differ from the peptides dis-cussed previously in that of the nine amino acid identities shared by VIP and secretin, eight are in the N-terminal region of the peptide; one is in the C-terminal region (Fig. 8). The receptors via which VIP and secretin stimulate pancreatic enzyme secretion can be identified using ^{125}I-labeled VIP (Christophe et al., 1976). Each acinar cell possesses approximately 9000 of these receptors which have a high affinity for VIP (EC_{50} 0.7 nM) and a low affinity for secretin (EC_{50} 7 μM).

The final class of receptors illustrated in Fig. 3 interacts with cholera toxin. Cholera toxin is a protein with a molecular weight of about 83,000

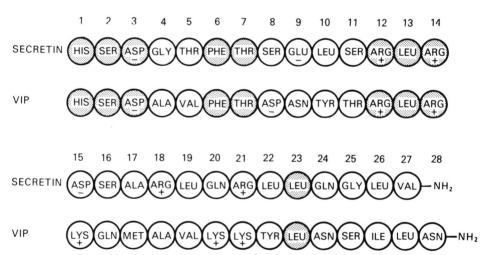

FIG. 8.   Amino acid sequences for secretin and VIP. Shaded residues indicate identical corresponding amino acids in both peptides.

and is composed of three subunits. (For a comprehensive review of the structure and mode of action of cholera toxin see Gill, 1977.) The "B subunit" of cholera toxin, also referred to as "choleragenoid" or "aggregated B subunit," has a molecular weight of approximately 54,000 and is thought to be composed of four to six identical monomers. The "A_1 subunit" has a molecular weight of 23,000 and the "A_2 subunit" has a molecular weight of 6000. A simplified view of the functions of the different portions of the cholera toxin molecule is that the B subunit, which has no intrinsic biologic activity, binds to monosialogangliosides on the outer surface of the plasma membrane. The A_2 subunit, in some unknown way, facilitates the passage of the A_1 subunit across the membrane to its inner surface where the A_1 subunit causes activation of adenylate cyclase. ^{125}I-labeled cholera toxin can be used to identify binding sites on pancreatic acinar cells that interact with cholera toxin but not with other secretagogues (Gardner and Rottman, 1979). There is a good correlation between the concentrations at which cholera toxin produces changes in acinar cell function. Each acinar cell has approximately 21,000 receptors for cholera toxin (EC_{50} 1 nM). Choleragenoid, which unlike the native toxin is devoid of intrinsic efficacy, can also bind to the cholera toxin receptors (EC_{50} 10 nM) and by so doing function as a competitive antagonist of the action of cholera toxin.

Figure 3 illustrates that acinar cells possess two functionally distinct mechanisms by which secretagogues can increase enzyme secretion (for review see Gardner, 1979; Gardner and Jensen, 1980, 1981). One mechanism is activated by occupation of receptors for cholinergic agents, for CCK-related peptides, for bombesin-related peptides or for physalaemin-related peptides. This mechanism involves mobilization of calcium from intracellular stores and, after a series of presently undefined steps, stimulation of enzyme secretion. The other mechanism is activated by VIP, secretin, or cholera toxin and involves activation of adenylate cyclase, increased cellular cyclic AMP, activation of cyclic AMP-dependent protein kinase, and, after a series of undefined steps, stimulation of enzyme secretion. The initial steps in these two pathways are functionally distinct. Secretagogues that cause release of cellular calcium do not increase cyclic AMP and do not alter the increase in cyclic AMP caused by other secretagogues. Similarly, secretagogues that increase cellular cyclic AMP do not alter calcium transport and do not alter the increase in calcium outflux caused by other secretagogues. Although the two different mechanisms for stimulating enzyme secretion have initial steps that are functionally distinct, these two mechanisms do interact at some presently unknown step and one consequence of this interaction is that there is potentiation of enzyme secretion (Gardner, 1979; Gardner and Jensen,

1981). That is, the increase in secretion caused by a secretagogue that increases cellular cyclic AMP plus a secretagogue that increases release of cellular calcium is substantially greater than the sum of the effect of each secretagogue acting alone. Although the biochemical basis of potentiation is not known, this phenomenon serves to amplify the signal generated in response to occupation of a particular class of receptors by a secretagogue.

Figure 3 illustrates that secretagogues that mobilize cellular calcium also alter metabolism of phosphatidylinositol. In the pancreas, CCK and acetylcholine, two agents that cause mobilization of cellular calcium, also increase the turnover of phosphatidylinositol by accelerating its degradation to diacylglycerol and inositolphosphate (Gardner, 1979). Secretin, which increases cyclic AMP, does not alter degradation of phosphatidylinositol. The actions of various agents on phosphatidylinositol turnover persist in tissues incubated in calcium-free solutions. Furthermore, A23187, a divalent cation ionophore, does not accelerate degradation of phosphatidylinositol under conditions where the ionophore causes changes in other cell functions. Thus, in tissues such as the pancreas in which calcium may mediate the actions of various agonists, the change in phosphatidylinositol turnover is thought to precede the change in calcium movement. Whether changes in phosphatidylinositol metabolism in some way mediate the changes in calcium transport remains to be determined. Nevertheless, secretagogue-induced changes in phosphatidylinositol metabolism appear to be one of the earliest changes caused by occupation of receptors by secretagogues that mobilize cellular calcium.

As illustrated in Fig. 3 those pancreatic secretagogues that cause calcium release also cause depolarization of pancreatic acinar cells (Petersen, 1976). This secretagogue-induced depolarization of acinar cells is accompanied by a reduction in the cell surface membrane resistance and by changes in the membrane conductance of sodium, potassium, and chloride ions. The secretagogue-induced electrical changes in pancreatic acinar cells appear to result from the abilities of the secretagogues to cause release of cellular calcium. Muscarinic cholinergic agents, CCK, bombesin, or A23187 cause depolarization and a decrease in the surface membrane resistance of pancreatic acinar cells, whereas secretin, a secretagogue that does not alter calcium transport in acinar cells, does not cause depolarization. The electrical changes caused by various secretagogues do not require extracellular calcium. Because intracellular injection of calcium also causes depolarization and decreased surface membrane resistance, the secretagogue-induced electrical changes probably result from an increased concentration of cytoplasmic calcium caused by secretagogue-induced mobilization of intracellular calcium stores. Thus, the secretagogue-induced electrical changes do not result from the release of cellular calcium per se, but instead, from the consequent increase in the cytoplasmic calcium concentration.

The secretagogue-induced depolarization of pancreatic acinar cells does not of itself stimulate enzyme secretion. High concentrations of extracellular potassium also cause depolarization of pancreatic acinar cells but do not cause stimulation of pancreatic enzyme secretion provided that atropine is added to block the action of acetylcholine released from nerve terminals (Case, 1978). In the presence of depolarizing concentrations of extracellular potassium, the increase in enzyme secretion caused by CCK is the same as it is with normal concentrations of extracellular potassium (Case, 1978). It should be noted that although depolarization of pancreatic acinar cells can be produced by high concentrations of extracellular potassium as well as by those pancreatic secretagogues that cause release of cellular calcium, only the secretagogue-induced depolarization is accompanied by a decrease in the surface membrane resistance.

Pancreatic acinar cells are electrically coupled because the junctional cell membranes have a specific resistance that is substantially lower than that of the surface cell membranes (Petersen, 1976). Furthermore, each acinar cell is electrically coupled to other cells within the same acinus but not to acinar cells in adjacent acini; therefore, from the electrical standpoint each acinus behaves as a single functional unit. At relatively high concentrations, those pancreatic secretagogues that cause depolarization can also cause electrical uncoupling of acinar cells (Petersen, 1976). Repeated injections of intracellular calcium, like high concentrations of secretagogues, also cause electrical uncoupling of pancreatic acinar cells (Petersen, 1976). These findings suggest that at high concentrations, secretagogues may be able to increase the concentration of cytoplasmic calcium to an extent sufficient to cause electrical uncoupling. The functional significance of electrical coupling of pancreatic acinar cells is not known; however, this coupling does provide a potential amplification mechanism whereby signals initiated by interaction of a secretagogue with a few cells could be transmitted to all of the cells within the same acinus. Just as electrical coupling may amplify the response of the system to low secretagogue concentrations, electrical uncoupling could conceivably serve as an attenuation mechanism to buffer the response of the system to high secretagogue concentrations.

Another effect of pancreatic secretagogues that cause release of cellular calcium is that they can also increase cellular cyclic GMP and this increase can occur in a calcium-free incubation solution (Gardner, 1979). There is a close correlation between the time-course for secretagogue-induced mobilization of cellular calcium and that for the effect of the secretagogue on cyclic GMP in that significant increases in both functions can be detected at the earliest time it is technically possible to make measurements. In addition, with muscarinic cholinergic agents, CCK-related peptides, bombesin-related peptides, or physalaemin-related peptides, the dose–response curve for the secretagogue-induced increase in cyclic GMP is the same as that for secretagogue-stimulated calcium outflux. Several findings indicate that secretagogues increase cellular cyclic GMP as a result of their abilities to cause mobilization of cellular calcium. (1) Calcium can influence guanylate cyclase activity in broken cell preparations from various tissues. (2) A23187 increases cellular cyclic GMP in pancreatic acinar cells and this action can occur in a calcium-free medium. (3) 8-Br cyclic GMP does not increase calcium outflux, but does increase enzyme secretion.

Because of the abilities of those secretagogues that cause calcium outflux to increase cellular cyclic GMP, and because of the ability of 8-BR cyclic GMP to increase pancreatic enzyme secretion, cyclic GMP has been proposed to be an intracellular mediator of the actions of secretagogues on pancreatic enzyme secretion. Several types of experimental findings, however, indicate that although some pancreatic secretagogues can increase cyclic GMP, this cyclic nucleotide does not mediate the actions of these secretagogues on enzyme secretion. To date, none of the secretagogues that increases cyclic GMP has been found to increase guanylate cyclase activity in a broken cell preparation. Pancreatic acinar cells have a cyclic GMP-dependent protein kinase activity (Jensen and Gardner, 1978); however, the secretagogues that increase cellular cyclic GMP do not cause endogenous activation of the cyclic GMP-dependent protein kinase (Jensen and Gardner, 1978). When pancreatic acinar cells are incubated with secretagogues such as CCK, all the cyclic GMP is in the extracellular medium after 60 minutes of incubation (Gardner and Rottman, 1980). Although 8-Br cyclic GMP can increase pancreatic enzyme secretion, this action reflects the ability of this cyclic nucleotide derivative to mimic the action of endogenous cyclic AMP (Gardner and Jensen, 1981; Gardner and Rottman, 1980; Peikin et al., 1979). The most compelling argument against cyclic GMP mediating the actions of secretagogues on pancreatic enzyme secretion, has been obtained with agents such as hydroxylamine and sodium nitroprusside, which are able to activate guanylate cyclase in broken cell preparations and to increase cyclic GMP in intact tissues (Mittal and Murad, 1977). In contrast to CCK, which increases cyclic GMP, calcium outflux and enzyme secretion, nitroprusside causes a 70-fold increase in cyclic GMP, but does not alter calcium outflux or enzyme secretion (Gardner and Rottman, 1980). In addition, nitroprusside does not alter the increase in calcium outflux or the increase in enzyme secretion caused by CCK or other secretagogues (Gardner and Rottman, 1980).

For those secretagogues that act by causing mobilization of cellular calcium, the pattern of action of a secretagogue on enzyme secretion differs depending on the particular class of receptors that is activated. As illustrated in Fig. 9, with increasing concentrations of CCK, enzyme secretion increases, becomes maximal and then decreases as the secretagogue concentration is increased further. The dose–response curves for the action of muscarinic cholinergic agents on enzyme secretion, like those for CCK and structurally related peptides, also show submaximal stimulation with supramaximal secretagogue concentrations; however, with cholinergic agents the magnitude of the decrement in the dose–response curve is usually not as great as it is with CCK-related peptides (Fig. 9). Bombesin and structurally related peptides also show a small, but statistically significant decrease in enzyme secretion with supramaximal secretagogue concentrations, but the magnitude of this decrease is substantially less than that which occurs with cholinergic agents or with

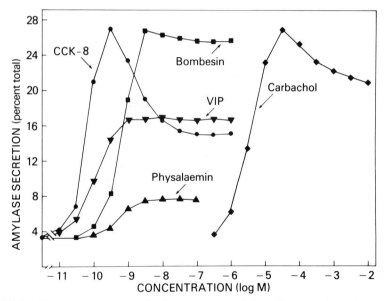

FIG. 9. Dose–response curves for the secretagogue-induced increases in amylase secretion by dispersed acini from guinea pig pancreas. Acini were incubated with the secretagogue specified for 30 minutes at 37°C and amylase secretion is expressed as percentage release. Results are from Gardner and Rottman (1979), Gardner *et al.* (1979, 1980), Jensen and Gardner (1979), Jensen *et al.* (1978, 1980), Peikin *et al.* (1978, 1979), and Uhlemann *et al.* (1979). CCK-8, C-terminal octapeptide of CCK; VIP, vasoactive intestinal peptide.

CCK-related peptides (Fig. 9). As occurs with CCK-related peptides as well as with cholinergic agents, the bombesin-related peptides have different potencies for stimulating enzyme secretion, but are equal in efficacy and the configuration of their dose–response curves is the same as that for bombesin illustrated in Fig. 9. Furthermore, with maximally effective secretagogue concentrations, the increase in enzyme secretion caused by bombesin or one of its structurally related peptides is the same as that caused by a maximally effective concentration of a cholinergic agent or a CCK-related peptide (Fig. 9). The pattern of action of the physalaemin-related peptides on secretion differs in several respects from those for other classes of secretagogues that cause release of cellular calcium. Neither physalaemin nor its structurally related peptides show submaximal stimulation of enzyme secretion with supramaximal concentrations of the secretagogue (Fig. 9). The efficacies of physalaemin and substance P are equal and are approximately 30% less than that of eledoisin (Jensen and Gardner, 1979; Uhlemann et al., 1979). In terms of the maximal increase in amylase secretion caused by CCK, bombesin, or cholinergic agents, the physalaemin-related peptides are substantially less efficacious (Fig. 9). The reduced efficacy with which physalaemin and structurally related peptides stimulate enzyme secretion can be accounted for by the lower efficacies of these peptides for stimulating calcium release (Jensen and Gardner, 1979; May et al., 1978; Uhlemann et al., 1979). On the other hand, the basis for the difference in the configurations of the dose–response curves for CCK-related peptides, bombesin-related peptides, and muscarinic cholinergic agents is not clear. Each of these classes of peptides is equally efficacious in causing mobilization of cellular calcium (Gardner and Jensen, 1981) and the configurations of their dose–response curves for stimulating calcium mobilization are the same (Gardner and Jensen, 1981).

In contrast to those secretagogues that cause release of cellular calcium, the two classes of secretagogues that act by increasing cyclic AMP show the same pattern of action on enzyme secretion. That is, although VIP, secretin, and cholera toxin have different potencies for increasing enzyme secretion, these three secretagogues are equal in efficacy and their dose–response curves have the same configuration as that illustrated for VIP in Fig. 9. The increase in amylase secretion caused by maximally effective concentrations of two secretagogues each of which increases cyclic AMP is the same as that caused by either secretagogue acting alone (Gardner and Jensen, 1981; Peikin et al., 1979). Thus, with secretagogues that increase cyclic AMP, the changes in enzyme secretion are what one would expect from a system that has a common limited effector mechanism that can be activated by multiple agents.

III. Recent Studies with Cholecystokinin

The remainder of this article will focus on some of the more recent studies of the mode of action of CCK-related peptides. To explore the structure–function relationship for CCK, various C-terminal fragments of CCK were tested for their abilities to stimulate enzyme secretion and for their abilities to bind to receptors on pancreatic acinar cells. In terms of the increase in amylase secretion caused by a maximally effective concentration, all C-terminal fragments of CCK tested have the same efficacies (Fig. 10). As illustrated in Fig. 10, C-terminal fragments of CCK varying in length from 4 amino acids (CCK-4) to 10 amino acids (CCK-10) are able to cause an 8-fold increase in amylase secretion from pancreatic acini. In terms of the peptide concentration that causes maximal stimulation of amylase secretion, the relative potencies of the CCK fragments are CCK-10 = CCK-8 > CCK-7 > [desSO$_3$H]CCK-7 > CCK-6 > CCK-5 = CCK-4 (Fig. 10). Each peptide tested had a biphasic dose–response curve for stimulating amylase secretion in that as the peptide concentration in-

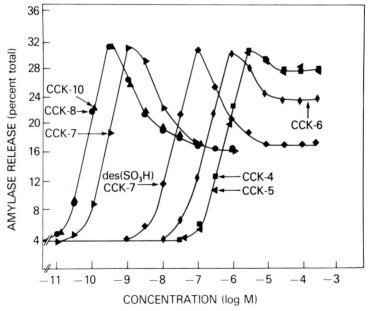

FIG. 10. Effect of various C-terminal fragments of CCK on amylase secretion from pancreatic acini. Acini were incubated with the fragment indicated for 30 minutes at 37°C and amylase secretion is expressed as percentage release. Results are from Jensen *et al.* (1982).

creases, amylase secretion increases, becomes maximal, and then decreases with supramaximal peptide concentrations (Fig. 10). With C-terminal peptides having more than 6 amino acids, the stimulation of
amylase secretion decreases by approximately 50% as the peptide concentration is increased progressively above the maximally effective concentration (Fig. 10). With CCK-6, however, supramaximal concentrations
decrease amylase secretion by only 30% and with CCK-5 and CCK-4,
supramaximal concentrations decrease secretion by only 10% (Fig. 10).

To examine directly the interaction of C-terminal fragments of CCK
with CCK receptors, one can measure the abilities of various CCK fragments to inhibit binding of ^{125}I-labeled CCK to pancreatic acini (Fig. 11).
Each CCK fragment is able to inhibit binding of ^{125}I-labeled CCK and
there is a close correlation between the ability of a fragment to inhibit
binding of labeled CCK (Fig. 11) and the fragment's ability to stimulate
amylase secretion (Fig. 10). Maximal stimulation of enzyme secretion
occurs when 40–50% of the CCK receptors are occupied by a particular
CCK fragment and occupation of the remaining receptors causes a progressive decrease in stimulated amylase secretion (compare Figs. 10
and 11).

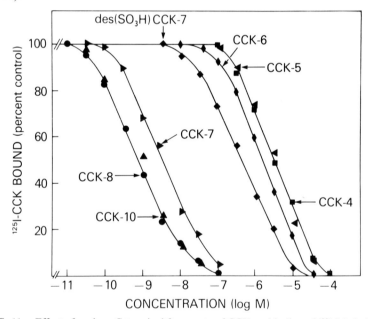

FIG. 11.   Effect of various C-terminal fragments of CCK on binding of ^{125}I-labeled CCK
to pancreatic acini. Values are expressed as the percentage of radioactivity that was sa-
turably bound in the absence of added nonradioactive peptide. Results are from Jensen *et al.*
(1982).

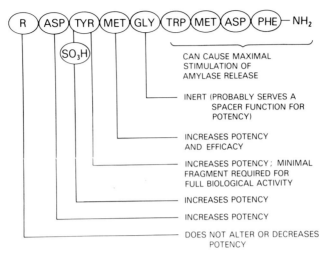

FIG. 12. Summary of the structural requirements for the action of CCK on enzyme secretion from pancreatic acini.

As illustrated in Figs. 9 and 10, the full spectrum of the action of CCK on enzyme secretion from pancreatic acini cells includes an 8-fold maximal stimulation and, with supramaximal concentration, a 50% reduction in secretion. Figure 12 illustrates the relationship between the structure of various C-terminal fragments of CCK and their effects on enzyme secretion. The C-terminal tetrapeptide amide of CCK produces maximal stimulation of enzyme secretion but causes only a small (10%) reduction in secretion with supramaximal concentration. Adding an NH_2-terminal glycine to CCK-4 does not alter the biologic activity of the peptide, suggesting that the glycine residue is inert and functions to produce proper spacing between the COOH-terminal tetrapeptide portion of CCK and the remaining biologically active, NH_2-terminal portion of the peptide. Adding an NH_2-terminal methionine to CCK-5 increases the potency with which the peptide causes maximal stimulation of enzyme secretion and increases the efficacy of the peptide for causing supramaximal inhibition of enzyme secretion. Thus, methionine does not simply serve a spacer function as suggested previously (Christophe *et al.*, 1980) but increases both the potency and supramaximal efficacy of the peptide. Adding an NH_2-terminal tyrosine to CCK-6 increases the potency with which the peptide causes maximal stimulation of enzyme secretion and increases the efficacy of the peptide for causing supramaximal inhibition of secretion. Both the maximal stimulation and the reduction in stimulation seen with supramaximal concentrations of unsulfated CCK-7 are identical with those seen with CCK, thus demonstrating that this peptide is the smallest COOH-terminal peptide that expresses the full spectrum of bio-logic activity of CCK. Adding a sulfate ester to the tyrosine residue of [desSO$_3$H]CCK-7 does not alter the configuration of the dose–response curve but does increase the potency of the peptide. Adding an NH$_2$-terminal aspartyl residue to CCK-7 causes a further 3- to 10-fold increase in potency with no change in the configuration of the dose–response curve. Extending the NH$_2$-terminus of CCK-8 either does not change or reduces by as much as 10-fold (Jensen *et al.*, 1980; Sankaran *et al.*, 1980; Sjodin and Gardner, 1977) the potency with which the peptide stimulates enzyme secretion, but does not alter the configuration of the dose–response curve (Jensen *et al.*, 1980; Sjodin and Gardner, 1977).

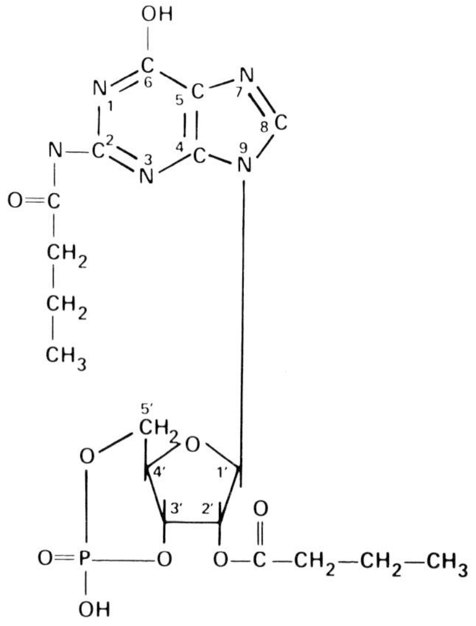

DIBUTYRYL CYCLIC GMP

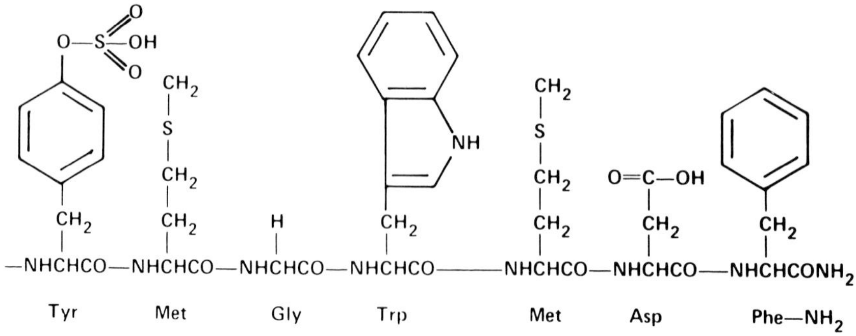

C-TERMINAL HEPTAPEPTIDE OF CCK

FIG. 13.   Structures of dibutyryl cyclic GMP and the C-terminal heptapeptide of CCK.

In general, the structural requirements for occupation of a peptide hormone receptor are quite stringent in that only other peptides will bind to the hormone receptor and the peptides that do bind are usually fragments of the hormone or analogs with a similar chemical structure. One striking exception to this general pattern occurs with the opiate receptors (Goldstein, 1976; Snyder, 1977). These receptors can interact not only with peptides (the enkephalins and other opioid peptides) but also with morphine and structurally related alkaloid compounds. A second apparent exception to the general principle that only peptides will bind to peptide hormone receptors is the finding that dibutyryl cyclic GMP (Fig. 13) can competitively inhibit the interaction of CCK and structurally related peptides with their receptors on pancreatic acinar cells (Jensen et al., 1980; Peikin et al., 1979).

Figure 14 illustrates that dibutyryl cyclic GMP, as well as each of the monobutyryl derivatives of cyclic GMP, inhibit binding of ^{125}I-labeled CCK to pancreatic acini and produce a corresponding decrease in both

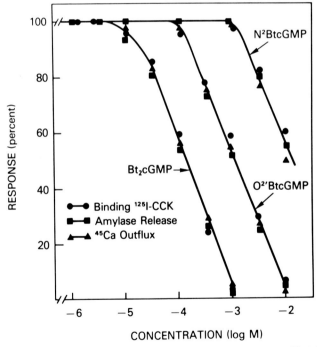

FIG. 14.   Effect of butyryl derivatives of cyclic GMP on binding of ^{125}I-labeled CCK, CCK-stimulated amylase secretion, and CCK-stimulated calcium outflux in dispersed acini from guinea pig pancreas. All incubations contained 1 nM CCK. Results are expressed as the percentage of the value obtained with no cyclic nucleotide. Results are from Jensen et al. (1980). BtcGMP, monobutyryl cyclic GMP; Bt$_2$cGMP, dibutyryl cyclic GMP.

CCK-stimulated calcium outflux and CCK-stimulated amylase release. Derivatives of cyclic AMP and cyclic IMP can also inhibit binding of CCK as well as its action on acinar cell function (Barlas *et al.*, 1982). Moreover, the inhibition caused by cyclic nucleotide derivatives does not require the presence of a butyryl moiety because certain 8-bromo-cyclic nucleotides can also inhibit the interaction of CCK with its receptors (Barlas *et al.*, 1982). Table I illustrates that the inhibitory action of dibutyryl cyclic GMP is specific for those peptides that interact with the CCK receptor (i.e., CCK, cerulein, and C-terminal fragments of CCK). Dibutyryl cyclic GMP does not alter the action of bombesin, physalaemin, A23187, carbachol, secretin, or VIP. Finally, the inhibition of the action of CCK by derivatives of cyclic nucleotides is of the competitive type because increasing concentrations of a cyclic nucleotide produce a progressive rightward shift in the CCK dose–response curve (Peikin *et al.*, 1979).

A second class of nonpeptide, antagonists of the interaction of CCK with its cell surface receptors is composed of proglumide (DL-4-benzamido-*N*,*N*-dipropylglutaramic acid) and benzotript (*N*-*p*-chlorobenzoyl-L-tryptophan) (Fig. 15). Like dibutyryl cyclic GMP, proglumide and benzotript inhibit binding of ^{125}I-labeled CCK to pancreatic acini and pro-

TABLE I

Effect of Dibutyryl Cyclic GMP on the Stimulation of Amylase Secretion by Various Secretagogues[a]

	Amylase release (% total)	
Secretagogue	Alone	+Bt$_2$cGMP (2.5 mM)
None	4.5	4.5
CCK-7 (0.3 nM)	53.2	6.5
CCK-8 (0.3 nM)	55.2	5.3
CCK-10 (1 nM)	57.0	5.2
CCK-33 (3 nM)	44.4	12.2
CCK-7 (desSO$_3$) (0.3 nM)	53.5	7.2
CCK-7 (Ser-SO$_3$) (1 μM)	52.7	6.2
Caerulein (0.3 nM)	53.2	6.4
Bombesin (10 nM)	43.7	39.3
Physalaemin (10 nM)	13.6	13.9
A23187 (3 μM)	15.1	14.5
Carbachol (10 μM)	50.0	52.2
Secretin (0.2 μM)	29.0	30.3
VIP (10 nM)	27.9	27.3

[a] Results are from Peikin *et al.* (1979). Bt$_2$cGMP, dibutyryl cyclic GMP.

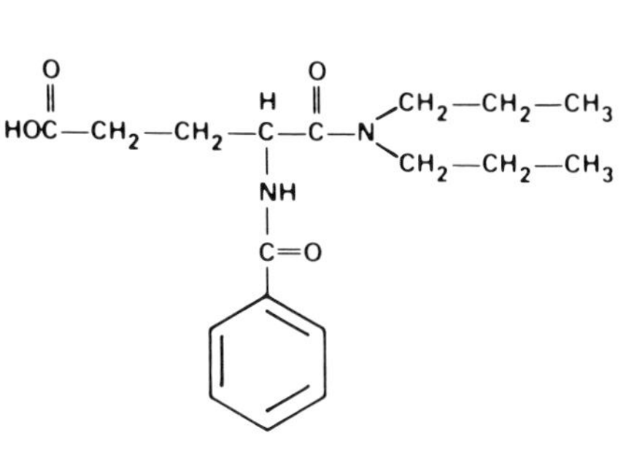

PROGLUMIDE

(DL-4-benzamido-N, N-dipropylglutaramic acid)

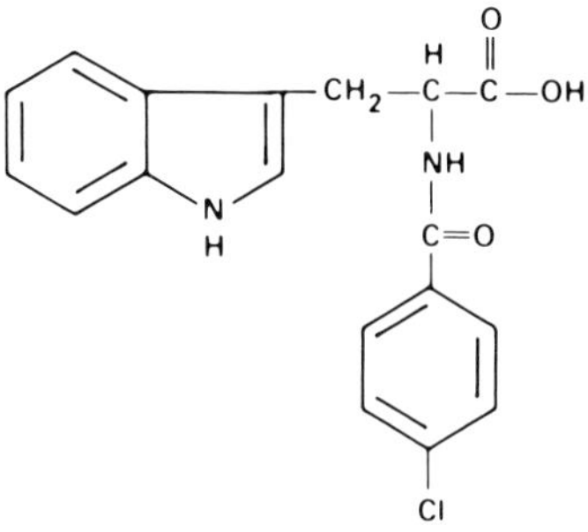

BENZOTRIPT

(N-p-chlorobenzoyl-L-tryptophan)

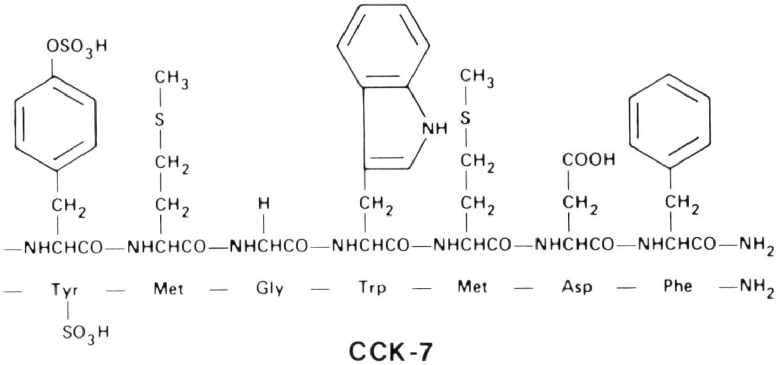

CCK-7

(C-terminal heptapeptide of cholecystokinin)

FIG. 15.   Structure of proglumide, benzotript, and the C-terminal heptapeptide of CCK.

duce a corresponding decrease in both CCK-stimulated calcium outflux and CCK-stimulated amylase release (Fig. 16). The actions of proglumide and benzotript are specific for those secretagogues that interact with the CCK receptor and are of the competitive type because increasing concentrations of proglumide and benzotript produce a progressive rightward shift in the CCK dose–response curve (Hahne *et al.*, 1981).

When pancreatic acini are first incubated with relatively high concentrations of CCK-octapeptide, washed to remove the free secretagogue and then reincubated in fresh, secretagogue-free incubation solution, there is significant residual stimulation of enzyme secretion measured during the second incubation (Fig. 17). Although the spontaneous rate of reversal of CCK-induced residual stimulation is slow, this residual stimu-

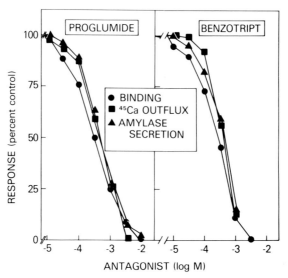

FIG. 16. Effect of proglumide and benzotript on binding of ^{125}I-labeled CCK-stimulated calcium outflux and CCK-stimulated amylase secretion in dispersed acini from guinea pig pancreas. All incubations contained 1 nM CCK. Results are expressed as the percentage of the value obtained with no proglumide or benzotript. Results are from Hahne *et al.* (1981).

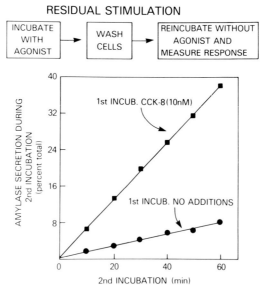

FIG. 17. CCK-induced residual stimulation of enzyme secretion from dispersed acini from guinea pig pancreas. Amylase secretion is expressed as the percentage of the amylase activity in the acini at the beginning of the second incubation that was released into the extracellular medium during the second incubation. Results are from Collins *et al.* (1981a). CCK-8, C-terminal octapeptide of CCK.

lation can be reversed immediately by adding a CCK-receptor antagonist such as dibutyryl cyclic GMP (Fig. 18).

Figure 19 illustrates how the C-terminal octapeptide of CCK (CCK-OP) might interact with CCK receptors on pancreatic acini to cause residual stimulation of enzyme secretion. The essential features of this hypothesis are as follows. (1) Each CCK receptor has two distinct binding sites (sites 1 and 2). (2) Site 1 has a high affinity for CCK-OP and occupation of this site is a prerequisite for occupation of site 2 by CCK-OP. That is, the peptide can bind to site 2 when site 1 is also occupied. (3) The dissociation of CCK-OP from site 1 is rapid. (4) The dissociation of CCK-OP from site 2 is rapid when site 1 is occupied but is slow when site 1 is vacant. Low concentrations of CCK-OP (up to 0.3 nM) cause occupation of site 1 (Fig. 19). This single-ligand–receptor complex exists in a rapidly dissociating state, and, when the acini are washed, bound CCK-OP dissociates completely during the wash procedure, thus accounting for the inability of concentrations of CCK-OP up to 0.3 nM to cause residual stimulation of enzyme secretion (Fig. 19). This single-ligand–receptor complex has full or maximal efficacy for stimulating enzyme secretion and produces the upstroke of the dose–response curve for CCK-OP-stimulated amylase release illustrated in Figs. 9 and 10. Concentrations of CCK-OP above 0.3

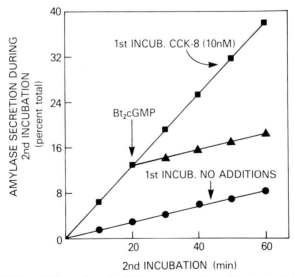

FIG. 18. Ability of dibutyryl cyclic GMP to reverse the residual stimulation of enzyme secretion caused by CCK. The experimental conditions were the same as those for the experiment illustrated in Fig. 17 except that dibutyryl cyclic GMP was added after 20 minutes of the second incubation. Results are from Collins *et al.* (1981b). CCK-8, C-terminal octapeptide of CCK; Bt$_2$cGMP, dibutyryl cyclic GMP.

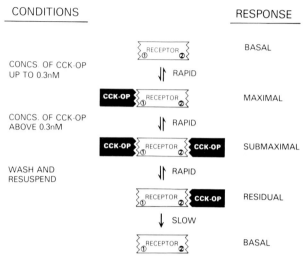

FIG. 19.   Illustration of a mechanism by which octapeptide of cholecystokinin (CCK-OP) might interact with CCK receptors in pancreatic acini to cause residual stimulation of enzyme secretion. Each CCK receptor is viewed as having two distinct binding sites (sites 1 and 2). Site 1 has a high affinity for CCK-OP, and occupation of site 1 is a prerequisite for occupation of site 2 by CCK-OP. Dissociation of CCK-OP from site 1 is rapid. Dissociation of CCK-OP from site 2 is rapid when site 1 is occupied but is slow when site 1 is vacant. Concentrations of CCK-OP up to 0.3 nM cause occupation of site 1, and this single-ligand–receptor complex has full efficacy for stimulating enzyme secretion. Concentrations of CCK-OP above 0.3 nM cause occupation of both sites 1 and 2, and double-ligand–receptor complex has submaximal efficacy for stimulating enzyme secretion. When acini are first incubated with high concentrations of CCK-OP and then washed, CCK-OP that is bound in rapidly dissociating form is lost from receptors during wash procedure. During a subsequent incubation, remaining CCK-OP, which is bound to site 2 in a slowly dissociating state, produces residual stimulation of enzyme secretion.

nM cause occupation of the second binding site on the CCK receptors. This double-ligand–receptor complex has partial or submaximal efficacy for stimulating enzyme secretion and produces the downstroke of the dose–response curve for CCK-OP-stimulated amylase release illustrated in Figs. 9 and 10. When the acini are washed, the CCK-OP that is bound in a rapidly dissociating form is lost from the receptor during the wash procedure, and, during a second incubation, the remaining CCK-OP, which is bound to site 2 in a slowly dissociating state, produces residual stimulation of enzyme secretion. Although the mechanism proposed in Fig. 19 obviously needs confirmation by direct examination of binding of CCK to its receptors on pancreatic acini, this hypothesis accounts for the present findings and, in addition, can serve as a useful guide to future experiments.

Figure 20 illustrates a mechanism that can account for the ability of dibutyryl cyclic GMP to function as a competitive antagonist of the CCK-OP and the ability of the nucleotide to reverse the residual stimulation caused by CCK-OP. The essential features of this proposal are as follows. (1) Each CCK receptor has two distinct CCK binding sites (sites 1 and 2), each of which can interact reversibly with dibutyryl cyclic GMP. (2) Occupation of site 1 is a prerequisite for occupation of site 2. (3) The nucleotide, when bound to either binding site, has no efficacy for stimulating amylase release and exists in a rapidly dissociating state. Because dibutyryl cyclic GMP can interact with each CCK receptor binding site, the nucleotide will function as a fully competitive antagonist of the action of CCK and structurally related peptides when the nucleotide and the secretagogue are added to the incubation simultaneously (Jensen *et al.*, 1980;

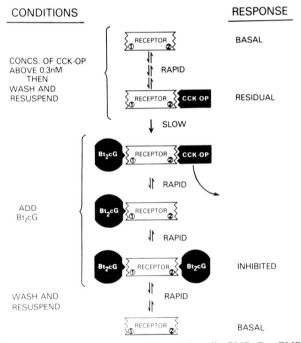

FIG. 20. Hypothesis to explain action of dibutyryl cyclic GMP (Bt₂cGMP) on residual stimulation of enzyme secretion caused by octapeptide of cholecystokinin (CCK-OP). Residual stimulation of enzyme secretion is attributed to persistent occupation of 1 of 2 CCK receptor binding sites by CCK-OP. When dibutyryl cyclic GMP is added, it interacts with vacant receptor binding sites and converts sites that are occupied by CCK-OP to a rapidly dissociating state. This conversion causes displacement of CCK-OP followed by binding of dibutyryl cyclic GMP is bound in rapidly dissociating state; therefore, when acini are washed, nucleotide dissociates, and CCK receptors are restored to their basal state.

Peikin *et al.*, 1979). Because dibutyryl cyclic GMP is bound in a rapidly dissociating state, the nucleotide does not cause residual inhibition of CCK-OP-stimulated amylase release in acini that have been first incubated with the nucleotide, then washed, and reincubated with CCK-OP (Collins *et al.*, 1981a,b). As illustrated in Fig. 20, when dibutyryl cyclic GMP is added to acini that have been first incubated with high concentrations of CCK-OP and then washed, the nucleotide interacts with site 1, converts the sites that are occupied by CCK-OP to a rapidly dissociating state, and thereby causes displacement of CCK-OP from the receptor. Dibutyryl cyclic GMP then binds to the sites from which CCK-OP has dissociated, and the receptor exists in a fully inhibited state. Because dibutyryl cyclic GMP is bound in a rapidly dissociating state, when the acini are washed, the nucleotide dissociates and the CCK receptors are restored to their basal state. This ability of dibutyryl cyclic GMP to restore the CCK receptors to a basal state is consistent with the finding that the nucleotide-induced reversal of residual stimulation of amylase release is accompanied by restoration of full responsiveness to CCK-OP (Collins *et al.*, 1981a,b).

ACKNOWLEDGMENTS

We thank Mary O'Shaughnessy for preparing this manuscript for publication and the members of the Digestive Diseases Branch for helpful discussions.

REFERENCES

Anastasi, A., Erspamer, V., and Cei, J. M. (1964). *Arch. Biochem. Biophys.* **108,** 341.
Anastasi, A., Erspamer, V., and Endean, R. (1968). *Arch. Biochem. Biophys.* **125,** 57.
Barlas, N., Jensen, R. T., Beinfeld, M. C., and Gardner, J. D. (1982). *Am. J. Physiol.* **242,** G161.
Bayliss, W. M., and Starling, E. H. (1902). *J. Physiol. (London)* **28,** 325.
Bayliss, W. M., and Starling, E. H. (1904). *Proc. R. Soc.* **73,** 310.
Case, R. M. (1978). *Biol. Rev.* **53,** 211.
Christophe, J. P., Conlon, T. P., and Gardner, J. D. (1976). *J. Biol. Chem.* **251,** 4629.
Christophe, J., Svoboda, M., Calderon-Attas, P., Lambert, M., Vandermeers-Piret, M. C., Vandermeers, A., Deschodt-Lanckman, M., and Robberecht, P. (1980). *In* "Gastrointestinal Hormones" (G. B. Jerzy-Glass, ed.), p. 451. Raven, New York.
Collins, S. M., Abdelmoumene, S., Jensen, R. T., and Gardner, J. D. (1981a). *Am. J. Physiol.* **240,** G459.
Collins, S. M., Abdelmoumene, S., Jensen, R. T., and Gardner, J. D. (1981b). *Am. J. Physiol.* **240,** G466.
Erspamer, V., and Melchiorri, P. (1973). *Pure Appl. Chem.* **35,** 463.
Erspamer, V., Falconieri-Erspamer, G., Inselvini, M., and Negri, L. (1972). *Brit. J. Pharmacol.* **45,** 333.
Erspamer, V., Erspamer, G. F., and Linari, G. (1977). *In* "Substance P" (U.S. v. Euler and B. Pernow, eds.), p. 67. Raven, New York.

Flanagan, S. D., and Storni, A. (1979). *Brain Res.* **168**, 261.

Gardner, J. D. (1979). *Annu. Rev. Physiol.* **41**, 55.

Gardner, J. D., and Jensen, R. T. (1980). *Am. J. Physiol.* **238**, G63.

Gardner, J. D., and Jensen, R. T. (1981). *In* "Physiology of the Gastrointestinal Tract" (L. R. Johnson, ed.), Vol. 2, p. 831. Raven, New York.

Gardner, J. D., and Rottman, A. J. (1979). *Biochim. Biophys. Acta* **585**, 250.

Gardner, J. D., and Rottman, A. J. (1980). *Biochim. Biophys. Acta* **627**, 230.

Gardner, J. D., Rottman, A. J., Natarajan, S., and Bodanszky, M. (1979). *Biochim. Biophys. Acta* **583**, 491.

Gardner, J. D., Walker, M. D., and Rottman, A. J. (1980). *Am. J. Physiol.* **238**, G458.

Gill, D. M. (1977). *In* "Advances in Cyclic Nucleotide Research" (P. Greengard and G. A. Robinson, eds.), Vol. 8, p. 85. Raven, New York.

Goldstein, A. (1976). *Science* **193**, 1081.

Hahne, W. F., Jensen, R. T., Lemp, G. F., and Gardner, J. D. (1981). *Proc. Natl. Acad. Sci. U.S.A.* **78**, 6304.

Jensen, R. T., and Gardner, J. D. (1978). *Gastroenterology* **75**, 806.

Jensen, R. T., and Gardner, J. D. (1979). *Proc. Natl. Acad. Sci. U.S.A.* **76**, 5679.

Jensen, R. T., Moody, T., Pert, C., Rivier, J. E., and Gardner, J. D. (1978). *Proc. Natl. Acad. Sci. U.S.A.* **75**, 6139.

Jensen, R. T., Lemp, G. F., and Gardner, J. D. (1980). *Proc. Natl. Acad. Sci. U.S.A.* **77**, 2079.

Jensen, R. T., Lemp, G. F., and Gardner, J. D. (1982). *J. Biol. Chem.* **257**, 5554.

Larose, L., Lanoe, J., Morrisset, J., Geoffrion, L., Dumont, Y., Lord, A., and Poirier, G. G. (1979). *In* "Hormone Receptors in Digestion and Nutrition" (G. Rosselin, P. Fromageot, and S. Bonfils, eds.), p. 229. Elsevier, Amsterdam.

McDonald, T. J., Jornvall, H., Nilsson, G., Vagne, M., Ghatei, M., Bloom, S. R., and Mutt, V. (1979). *Biochem. Biophys. Res. Commun.* **90**, 227.

May, R. J., Conlon, T. P., Erspamer, V., and Gardner, J. D. (1978). *Am. J. Physiol.* **235**, E112.

Mittal, C. K., and Murad, F. (1977). *J. Cyclic Nucleotide Res.* **3**, 381.

Mutt, V. (1976). *Clin. Endocrinol.* **5** (Suppl.), 175s.

Mutt, V., and Jorpes, J. E. (1968). *Eur. J. Biochem.* **6**, 156.

Mutt, V., and Jorpes, E. (1971). *Biochem. J.* **125**, 57.

Ng, K. H., Morrisset, J., and Poirier, G. G. (1979). *Pharmacology* **18**, 263.

Peikin, S. R., Rottman, A. J., Batzri, S., and Gardner, J. D. (1978). *Am. J. Physiol.* **235**, E743.

Peikin, S. R., Costenbader, C. L., and Gardner, J. D. (1979). *J. Biol. Chem.* **254**, 5321.

Petersen, O. H. (1976). *Physiol. Rev.* **56**, 535.

Said, S. I., and Mutt, V. (1972). *Eur. J. Biochem.* **28**, 199.

Sankaran, H., Goldfine, I. D., Deveney, C. W., Wong, K-Y., and Williams, J. A. (1980). *J. Biol. Chem.* **255**, 1849.

Sjodin, L., and Gardner, J. D. (1977). *Gastroenterology* **73**, 1015.

Snyder, S. H. (1977). *New Engl. J. Med.* **296**, 266.

Uhlemann, E. R., Rottman, A. J., and Gardner, J. D. (1979). *Am. J. Physiol.* **236**, E571.

v. Euler, U. S., and Gaddum, J. H. (1931). *J. Physiol. (London)* **72**, 74.

Walsh, J. H. (1981). *In* "Physiology of the Gastrointestinal Tract" (L. R. Johnson, ed.), p. 59. Raven, New York.

Walsh, J. H., and Grossman, M. I. (1975). *New Engl. J. Med.* **292**, 1324, 1377.

Yamamura, H. I., and Snyder, S. H. (1974a). *Mol. Pharmacol.* **10**, 861.

Yamamura, H. I., and Snyder, S. H. (1974b). *Proc. Natl. Acad. Sci. U.S.A.* **71**, 1725.

DISCUSSION

L. S. Jacobs: If it is true that all the various enzymes produced by the pancreatic acivar cell are co-packaged in individual secretory granules, it is possible that specificity of enzyme secretory response to nutrients could somehow be related to the large array of different receptor types you have shown? It's a little difficult to see how the pancreas can release more amylase, say, and less chymotrypsinogen in response to nutrient loads of different composition if all the enzymes are in all the granules.

J. Gardner: Nutrients have two roles in influencing pancreatic enzyme secretion. On a long-term basis they modify the relative proportions of various digestive enzymes. On a short-term basis they cause release of various gastrointestinal peptides, of which the most important for pancreatic enzyme secretion is cholecystokinin, and by so doing stimulate enzyme secretion.

L. S. Jacobs: Is it in fact the case that all the granules contain all the enzymes?

J. Gardner: Our current thinking is that every zymogen granule contains every digestive enzyme. However, as I mentioned, the relative proportions of the various digestive enzymes within a zymogen granule is influenced by the composition of the diet.

A. D. Kenny: I notice that most of the GI peptides, especially those that work through the calcium release mechanism, contain methionine. Have you ever tested the effect of hydrogen peroxide oxidation on biological activity or binding?

J. Gardner: Cholecystokinin has two methionine residues in the biologically active, C-terminal portion of the molecule. Oxidation of these residues by incubation with hydrogen peroxide markedly reduces the affinity of the peptide for its receptor and its ability to stimulate enzyme secretion.

E. Rall: With your two site models for the biphasic action of CCK you should be able to see some evidence of that from either Scatchard plots if the two sites had different association constants. However, if the two sites have different dissociation rates you ought to see something from the kinetics of either binding or debinding with or without stable peptide. Have you done those experiments? The second question which you have somewhat alluded to with reference to how you can change the enzyme content of the granules depending on prior dict—do you have any data that would indicate that those hormones which act through calcium have any different effect in terms of the long-term stimulation of protein synthesis, or perhaps even stimulation of cell division versus those that act through cyclic AMP? There are a number of polypeptide hormones that have an immediate secretory effect through adenylate cyclase, but which also have an effect on protein synthesis generally and may even have an effect on cell division.

J. Gardner: Our stoichiometric studies of binding of ^{125}I-labeled cholecystokinin give rise to a curvilinear Scatchard plot. As you suggest, we should be able to distinguish this hypothetical two-site model on the basis of dissociation kinetics; however, we have not yet done these experiments. Those peptides that act to release cellular calcium as well as those that act to increase cellular cyclic AMP not only stimulate enzyme secretion but also cause substantial hypertrophy of the pancreatic acinar cell mass.

C. S. Nicoll: Can you tell us whether these peptides that you described from frog skin are found in the skin of other aquatic vertebrates or invertebrates?

J. Gardner: I don't know.

C. S. Nicoll: It would be interesting to find out if they do because these skin peptides may have been of significance to the evolution of hormonal control of the functions of the digestive tract and its associated glands. We can speculate that in an earlier stage of evolution when one aquatic species ingested another, the peptides from the skin of the ingested activated the digestive functions of the ingestor. Later in evolution a series of gut peptides evolved which had structures and gut-regulatory actions similar to those of the skin peptides of the ingestees.

J. R. Gill: I was very interested in the observation that dibutyryl cyclic GMP was a very effective competitive antagonist of cholecystokinin. In this regard is dibutyryl cyclic GMP detected by an antibody to cholecystokinin during radioimmunoassay? That is to say, are the reactive sites that are important for cholecystokinin binding to its receptor similar in configuration to that of cyclic GMP in solution?

J. Gardner: Robberecht and colleagues at the Free University of Brussels as well as our group have shown that dibutyryl cyclic GMP will inhibit binding of ^{125}I-labeled cholecystokinin to antibodies that recognize the C-terminal portion of the molecule. This is the strongest evidence available to date that there are structural similarities between dibutyryl cyclic GMP and the C-terminal portion of cholecystokinin.

M. Saffran: I'm struck by so many similarities between the acinar cell system and the system I know best, the adrenal cortical cell, including the electrical response to peptide hormone. Have you used the change in membrane potential as one of the responses that you can follow?

J. Gardner: We have not measured the electrophysiological changes in pancreatic acinar cells but Petersen and colleagues in the Department of Physiology at the University of Liverpool have and have found that those secretagogues that cause mobilization of cellular calcium produce concentration-dependent changes in the electrophysiological properties of pancreatic acinar cells.

M. Saffran: The advantage in following electrical changes is that you can do so on a second-by-second basis and get the speed of response to activators and also to inhibitors.

J. Gardner: I agree and this is precisely what Petersen and colleagues have done.

G. D. Aurbach: How do you propose that interaction of CCK with the cell membrane controls release of calcium from intracellular compartments? Does the inhibitory function of CCK also influence the release of intracellular calcium?

J. Gardner: We actually do not know the mechanism by which certain pancreatic secretagogues cause release of calcium from intracellular stores. In fact, we do not know the subcellular site from which the calcium is released. Some have postulated that secretagogues cause release of calcium from the plasma membrane, whereas others have proposed that the calcium is released from endoplasmic reticulum. We do not know what causes the downstroke of the dose–response curve for cholecystokinin-stimulated enzyme secretion. The downstroke of the amylase dose–response curve does not correlate with the ability of cholecystokinin to stimulate outflux of calcium from pancreatic acinar cells.

M. I. New: Is much known about the developmental biology of these peptides? Are they all present in the newborn? I ask you this because the newborn is known not to digest many substances very well.

J. Gardner: Very little is known about the developmental biology of the various gastrointestinal peptides. What we do know about the developmental biology of the pancreas would suggest that impaired digestion in the newborn probably results, at least in part, from an impaired ability of the pancreas to secrete digestive enzymes in response to various secretagogues.

S. Cohen: Can you first tell me does the pancreatic secretion always have the same content regardless of the diet?

J. Gardner: No, the relative proportions of various digestive enzymes varies depending on the composition of the diet. For example, eating a high protein diet increases the proportion of proteolytic enzymes in the pancreas.

S. Cohen: How is this related to the hormone stimulation?

J. Gardner: Insofar as we know gastrointestinal peptides appear to cause release of the various digestive enzymes in the same proportion that they are present in the pancreas.

S. Cohen: Is the GMP formation by calcium specific for GMP or is AMP also effected?

J. Gardner: Changes in cellular calcium do not alter cyclic AMP or the increase in cyclic AMP caused by various secretagogues. Similarly, changes in cellular cyclic AMP do not alter cellular calcium or the changes in cellular calcium caused by various secretagogues.

S. Cohen: Do the calcium changes in the cell involve the reaction of calmodulin?

J. Gardner: Although pancreatic acinar cells do contain calmodulin, it is not known whether or not calmodulin is involved in the action of those secretagogues that mobilize cellular calcium. Phenothiazines can inhibit the increase in enzyme secretion caused by cholecystokinin but this may reflect an action of the phenothiazine on phospholipid-requiring, calcium-sensitive protein kinase rather than on calmodulin.

J. C. Beck: You have rather studiously avoided mentioning the ubiquitous distribution of these materials, outside of the gut, particularly in the central nervous system, and I wonder whether you have any insight into why some of these compounds are there; in particular does secreting play a role in regulating appetite?

J. Gardner: Insofar as I am aware we do not know what functions are influenced by the various gastrointestinal peptides that are present in the central nervous system. It is known that cholecystokinin can cause satiety in animals as well as man; however, recent studies by Gibbs and Smith at Cornell University School of Medicine indicate that cholecystokinin causes satiety in animals through a peripheral action. In particular, the satiety effect of cholecystokinin can be abolished by a diaphragmatic vagotomy.

M. B. Nikitovitch-Winer: I am curious about the release of pancreatic enzymes. Are they all dumped out of the pancreas into the duodenum together regardless of the composition of the meal?

J. Gardner: In a word, yes. If ingestion of a meal causes stimulation of pancreatic enzyme secretion, the enzymes will be released in roughly the same proportions that they are present in the pancreas. As I mentioned previously, however, the relative proportion of the various digestive enzymes in the pancreas is influenced on a relatively long-term basis by the composition of the diet.

M. B. Nikitovitch-Winer: Then you are saying that the granules really do not all contain all of the enzymes, that there is a change in their composition as they age, comparerd to the newly formed granules?

J. Gardner: No. Insofar as we know every enzyme granule contains every digestive enzyme; however, the proportions of the enzymes within the granule are determined by the composition of the diet.

P. Robel: Is there any indication that the gastrointestinal peptide receptors can undergo internalization or desensitization?

J. Gardner: Carbamylcholine, cholecystokinin, and bombesin can each cause desensitization. No studies have been done on the internalization of muscarinic cholinergic agents. Preliminary studies from Williams at the University of California at San Francisco indicate that cholecystokinin is internalized by pancreatic acinar cells, but it is not known whether or not this internalization causes desensitization. Recent studies from our laboratory by Drs. Steven Pandol and Robert Jensen indicate that bombesin is internalized and that this internalization correlates with bombesin-induced desensitization.

B. M. Dobyns: I have recently encountered over several years a family with multiple endocrine neoplasia. There were six parathyroid neoplasms in the family. More recently, two identical twins in the family have turned up with pancreatic tumors which on secretin challenge yielded high VIP and PP in particular and also glucagon. The rise in gastrin was not particularly dramatic. The watery diarrhea is quite extreme. The twins' mother, a grandmother of four children of the two identical twins, has recently developed severe diarrhea but not been studied yet. When I see the very slight variations in structure of your formulas of the peptides, I see how such a single tumor might produce a variety of effects. I wonder if you could comment on the experience you may have had with some of the islet cell pancreatic tumors which have caused a variety of symptoms. This family of tumors is not producing insulin and only slight amounts of gastrin.

J. Gardner: The usual pancreatic hormone-producing tumor that is found in patients with multiple endocrine neoplasia type I is a gastrinoma. Tumors producing vasoactive intestinal peptide are usually sporadic and not part of the multiple endocrine neoplasia syndrome.

Chemical and Biological Characterization of Corticotropin Releasing Factor

WYLIE VALE, CATHERINE RIVIER, MARVIN R. BROWN,
JOACHIM SPIESS, GEORGE KOOB,* LARRY SWANSON,†
LOUISE BILEZIKJIAN, FLOYD BLOOM,* AND JEAN RIVIER

*Peptide Biology Laboratory, *Behavioral Neurobiology Laboratory, and †Developmental Neurobiology Laboratory, The Salk Institute, La Jolla, California*

The development of concepts of the neuroendocrine regulation of the pituitary by Harris, the Scharrers, and others in the 1930s and the 1940s together with the demonstration of adrenal cortical activation following electrical stimulation of the hypothalamus led Harris to postulate in 1950 that the hypothalamus liberates a substance into the hypophysial portal blood that stimulates the adrenocorticotrophic activity of the pituitary. The activity of this corticotropin releasing factor (CRF) was subsequently observed directly in *in vitro* studies of Guillemin and Rosenberg (1955) and Saffran and Schally (1955).

Several known naturally occurring substances including vasopressin, oxytocin, norepinephrine, epinephrine, and angiotensin II have been found to stimulate ACTH secretion (reviews Vale *et al.,* 1977, 1980; Vale and Rivier, 1977; Gaillard *et al.,* 1981; Yasuda *et al.,* 1982). Partially purified hypothalamic or neurohypophysial fractions have been reported by numerous workers to possess peptides with ACTH releasing activity. Some have been partially (Guillemin, 1964; Schally *et al.,* 1968) or fully characterized (Schally *et al.,* 1978; Knudsen *et al.,* 1978). Yet for various reasons, none of the known peptides met the criteria expected of the principal hypothalamic ACTH releasing factor (reviews Vale *et al.,* 1977; Vale and Rivier, 1977, Yasuda *et al.,* 1982). Thus a full understanding of the neuroregulation of ACTH secretion required the characterization of the putative CRF.

In view of the observations of Selye (1936) that environmental stimuli activates the pituitary adrenocortical axis, it was considered that the putative CRF would mediate this effect of stress and might play a major role in the "general adaptation syndrome."

Further interest in CRF was generated with the demonstration that partially purified preparations of CRF would stimulate the secretion of a

245

number of peptides derived from the proopiomelanocortin (POMC) precursor including the opioid peptide, β-endorphin.

Finally, based upon experience with other regulatory peptides, it was realized that CRF was likely to be distributed outside of the hypothalamus and to possess extrahypophysiotropic actions.

In 1981 we reported the isolation, sequence, synthesis, and biological activity of the synthetic replicate of a 41 amino acid ovine hypothalamic corticotropin releasing factor (CRF) (Vale *et al.*, 1981; Spiess *et al.*, 1981; C. Rivier *et al.*, 1982a). As will be discussed below, it is likely that this peptide, which will be referred to as CRF, is a major neuroregulator of adenohypophysial ACTH production.

The more than 25 year delay in the characterization of CRF since its discovery can be attributed to several factors. The bioassays were a problem. *In vivo* methods lacked sufficient sensitivity and some of them were susceptible to responding to any brain mediated stressor. The development of *in vitro* assays using acutely dissociated pituitary cells (Portanova and Sayers, 1973; Lowry, 1974) or cell cultures by our (Vale *et al.*, 1972, 1975) and Greer's groups (Takebe *et al.*, 1975) provided the basis of sensitive quantitative, valid bioassays. With antisera initially from J. P. Felber and M. Aubert, and later from D. Orth (1979), the ACTH radioimmunoassay became the other essential ingredient of our bioassay. Even the best *in vitro* assays could be complicated by numerous substances (such as vasopressin and epinephrine) that could release ACTH on their own and strongly potentiate CRF. Furthermore, most hypothalamic extracts contain ACTH which could initially be mistaken for CRF. Also, since the sizes of CRF (41 amino acids) and ACTH (39 amino acids) are similar, the two peptides are not separated by gel filtration chromatography. Thus the CRF-like activity of those fractions shown to contain ACTH may have been overlooked. Finally *in vitro* systems are vulnerable to nonspecific secretagogs in extracts including myelin basic protein, histones, potassium ion, and the components of various buffers and solvents.

Generally only picomole levels or less of CRF are present in each hypothalamic fragment necessitating large amounts of starting material, good recoveries during purification, sensitive sequencing, or some combination of the three.

I. Characterization of CRF

The approach taken during the purification of CRF is shown in Fig. 1. Almost one-half million sheep hypothalamic fragments were extracted with ethanol/acetic acid, defatted, and partitioned by bulk shake out in the

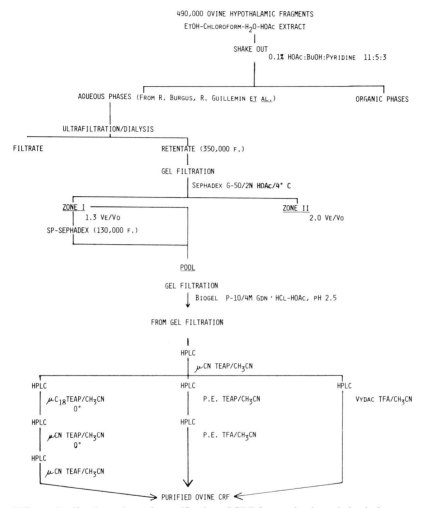

FIG. 1.   Purification scheme for purification of CRF from ovine hypothalamic fragments as described in Vale *et al.* (1981).

Laboratories for Neuroendocrinology (Burgus *et al.*, 1976). The organic phases were then used in the purification of ovine GnRH and somatostatin. This fraction contained the majority of the CRF activity but was no longer available. The aqueous phase also contained some CRF activity and was provided to us by Roger R. Burgus, M. Amoss, and R. Guillemin.

This fraction was ultrafiltered and the activity retained. The retentates were then gel filtered on Sephadex G-50 yielding two zones of activity (Vale and Rivier, 1977), one eluting just after the void volume at about 1.3

V_e/V_0 and another at about 2 V_e/V_0. Multiple ACTH-releasing zones, including "large CRFs," have been described by various workers (Porter and Rumsfeld, 1959; Schally *et al.*, 1960; Dhariwal *et al.*, 1966; Jones *et al.*, 1967; Chan *et al.*, 1969; Cooper *et al.*, 1976; Gillies and Lowry, 1979; Sayers *et al.*, 1980; Schally *et al.*, 1981). The two zones showed different intrinsic activities in that the earlier larger molecular weight zone elicited a much higher secretory V_{max} (secretory rate at maximum concentration of added substance) than did the later zone. The activity in the later zone was similar to that of vasopressin, and expectedly, further purification of the ACTH-releasing activity of this zone yielded an active fraction with the same amino acid composition as [Arg^8]-vasopressin (Vale *et al.*, 1981). Because of the high intrinsic activity of the earlier zone and encouraging results of a series of *in vitro* studies, we focused on the further purification of the ACTH-releasing substances in this higher molecular weight fraction (Vale and Rivier, 1977; Vale *et al.*, 1981).

The purification of zone 1 was accomplished by a series of traditional steps and ultimately by high-pressure liquid chromatography (HPLC) (Vale *et al.*, 1981; J. Rivier *et al.*, 1982a). Initially, multiple HPLC steps were required, however, with the development of improved columns with large pore size (300–330 Å), small particle size, and monolayered, end capped octadecyl silica, final purification could be accomplished with two HPLC steps. With the various procedures we ended up with approximately 90 μg (ca. 20 nmole) of CRF of greater than 80% purity.

The primary structure of the major component was determined by Edman degradation with the use of a Beckman 890C spinning cup sequencer modified according to Wittmann-Liebold. The phenylthiohydantoin derivatives of the amino acids were identified by reverse phase HPLC. Several analyses of 0.6 to 3.6 nmole of peptide were performed. The initial sequencing attempts were carried out at a low level of peptide revealed that most of the sample was not N-terminally blocked and 27 residues of the sequence were determined. Subsequently, the analysis of 3.6 nmole of peptide confirmed the previous run yielded the sequence of residues 28–39. Residue 40 (Ile) was established by spinning cup sequencing of the tryptic digest of the peptide. The COOH-terminal alaninamide was identified by HPLC after digestion of CRF with thermolysin and carboxypeptidase Y and confirmed by COOH-terminal tritiation experiments (Spiess *et al.*, 1981). The primary sequence of ovine CRF was thus determined to be a 41 residue straight chain C-terminally amidated peptide (Fig. 2).

Ovine CRF is homologous with several known peptides including sauvagine and urotensin I (Fig. 2). Sauvagine was isolated from the skin of the frog, *Phylomedusa sauvagei*, and characterized by Erspamer and colleagues (Montecucchi *et al.*, 1979; Erspamer and Melchiorri, 1980).

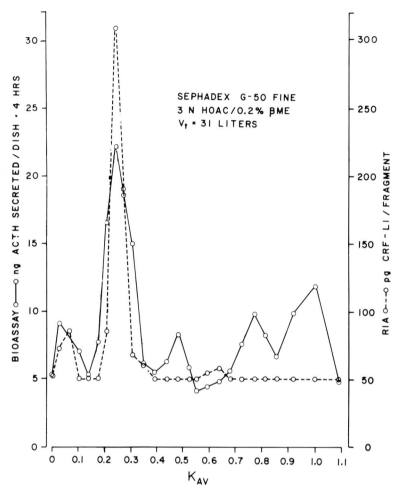

FIG. 2.   Elution profile of CRF like immunoactivity ◯---◯ or ACTH releasing activity ◯——◯ from Sephadex-G-50 chromatography of acid extract of rat hypothalamic fragments.

Over 50% of the residues in sauvagine are identical to those in CRF; the majority remaining are conservative substitutions. Sauvagine had been reported to produce hypotension, antidiuresis, and a variety of pituitary effects including the release of ACTH and β-endorphin and the inhibition of growth hormone, TSH, and prolactin secretion (Montecucchi *et al.,* 1979; Erspamer and Melchiorri, 1980; Erspamer *et al.,* 1981). Both sauvagine and CRF are closely related to a third peptide, urotensin-I, isolated from the urohyphysis of two species of fish, cyprimus C. and catostomus

C. (MacCannell and Lederis, 1977; Lederis et al., 1982). All three produce hypotension when injected peripherally by dilating the superior mesenteric bed and increasing blood flow to the GI tract (Erspamer et al., 1981; MacCannell et al., 1982; Brown et al., 1982a,b).

CRF also shows some homology with calmodulin and with angiotensinogen. The tetrapeptide Phe-His-Leu-Leu is common to both angiotensinogen (Skeggs et al., 1957) and CRF (Vale et al., 1981) and is the site in angiotensinogen of renin and converting enzyme cleavage. Perhaps this homology reflects a distant ancestral relationship between angiotensinogen and CRF—each of which ultimately regulates the adrenal cortex.

This peptide was synthesized (Vale et al., 1981) by solid phase methodology (Marki et al., 1981) and established to be a potent stimulator of ACTH secretion in the cell culture assay used throughout its isolation. The minimal effective concentration of CRF in this assay is generally less than 10 pM and the EC_{50} is observed at approximately 100 pM. The plateau response occurs at approximately 1 nM and is equivalent to that seen with high concentrations of 8-Br-3′,5′ cyclic AMP.

The specificity of CRF is demonstrated by our finding little effect of CRF at concentrations $\leq$100 nM on the basal secretion of TSH, LH, FSH, or GH or on the GnRH mediated secretion of LH or FSH, the TRF mediated secretion of TSH, 8-Br-3′,5′-cyclic AMP, or synthetic human pancreatic GRF mediated secretion of GH (J. Rivier et al., 1982b) or the somatostatin mediated inhibition of GH secretion (Vale et al., 1982).

As expected from the mode of biosynthesis of ACTH (Eipper and Mains, 1981) and from earlier studies (Vale et al., 1978), CRF releases both ACTH and β-endorphin-like immunoactivity, about one-third of which cochromatographs with synthetic β-endorphin (Vale et al., 1981, 1982). CRF stimulates the production of other POMC-derived peptides including those related to MSH (Ling et al., 1982).

Synthetic CRF has been shown to be a potent stimulator of ACTH, β-endorphin, and glucocorticoid production in vivo in several species including the rat (C. Rivier et al., 1982a; Turkelson et al., 1981), dog (Brown et al., 1982a,b), monkey (Schulte et al., 1982), and human (Orth et al., 1982; Grossman et al., 1982). In the rat, CRF is effective (Vale et al., 1981; C. Rivier et al., 1982a) in releasing ACTH in unanesthetized animals with indwelling venous cannulas or in rats whose response to stress is blocked, either pharmacologically or by hypothalamic knife cuts (Palkovits, 1977).

A comparison of the biologic activities and HPLC behavior of the synthetic CRF and that isolated from the sheep revealed that in the sheep derived peptide, the methionine residue was oxidized to its sulfoxide form

(Vale *et al.*, 1981). The oxidation of CRF presumably occurred during the decade between the extraction of the tissues and the characterization of CRF.

One of the questions raised by the size of CRF is the possibility that we had isolated a pro-hormone. Against this hypothesis is the finding that several shortened analogs of CRF are much less active (Vale *et al.*, 1981; Rivier and Vale, 1983). At the C-terminus, simply deamidating the peptide decreases potency to less than 0.1%. Retaining the C-terminal amide but shortening by one or two residues, again results in drastic reduction of potency. There is more flexibility at the N-terminus, where the first three residues can be removed with no decrease in potency, the first six with retention of 25% activity. The deletion of nine N-terminal amino acids reduces potency by more than 1000-fold. It is thus unlikely that a form of CRF that is very much smaller than this one will be found with high activity. Cleavage of the molecule at the Phe^{12}-His^{13}, Leu^{14}-Leu^{15} bonds or in the region of Arg^{35}-Lys^{36} yields inactive peptides (Rivier and Vale, unpublished results).

The three closely related peptides, CRF, sauvagine, and urotensin I, exhibit similar potencies to stimulate ACTH and β-endorphin secretion *in vitro* and *in vivo* (Brown *et al.*, 1982a,b; C. Rivier *et al.*, 1982a). It is interesting that CRF appears less potent than the other two to cause hypotension (Brown *et al.*, 1982a,b). Perhaps it has been adaptive in the higher vertebrates for the extra pituitary actions of CRF to be diminished. The possibility that other CRF-like molecules more closely related to sauvagine or urotensin I exist in the gastrointestinal tract or other peripheral sites of mammals is under investigation.

The existence of the three naturally occurring peptides with similar ACTH releasing potencies has saved a great deal of time for those interested in structure–function relationships. Only 17 residues out of 41 are in common. The fact that many others are very conservative substitutions not withstanding, this provides real insight concerning the residues responsible for biological activities. From several analogs with alanine substitutions made and tested in our group, it appears that the double leucine residues are positions 14 and 15 and at 37 and 38 are critical as are the basic groups at 16 and 35.

Drs. Murray Goodman and Peter Pallai and colleagues have applied Chou and Fassman's predictions to CRF's primary sequence and found a high probability for an α-helix from residues 5–30 followed by a β-bend encompassing residues 31–35. CD analysis has confirmed the presence of considerable helical content (Pallai *et al.*, 1983). It is possible that conformationally these three peptides are much more closely related than is apparent from their primary structures.

II. Development of CRF Antisera and Radioimmunoassays

Our CRF radioimmunoassays employ either HPLC purified ^{125}I-labeled CRF, ^{125}I-labeled [Nle^{21},Tyr^{32}]-CRF, or ^{125}I-labeled [Tyr^{13},Nle^{21}]-CRF as a radioligand. Rabbits were immunized with three different immunogens (Vale *et al.*, 1982; Swanson *et al.*, 1982) (Fig. 1). One rabbit immunized with [Tyr^{22},Gly^{23}]-CRF-(1–23) coupled by bis-diazotized benzidine to human α-globulins produced antibodies directed against the N-terminal region (residues 4–20) of CRF. Radioimmunoassays using this antiserum, called C-24, can be used to detect CRF-like immunoactivity (CRF-LI) in the hypothalamus/median eminence/pituitary of sheep, dog, rat, monkey, and human (Vale *et al.*, 1982). Antibodies produced in rabbits immunized with CRF coupled by glutaraldehyde to human α-globulins or with CRF polymerized with 1-ethyl-3-(3-dimethylaminopropyl)carbodiimide are directed toward the middle or C-terminal region of CRF. Radioimmunoassays with these sera read sheep very well but detect rat, dog, and human

TABLE I

Summary of CRF Antisera

Rabbit number	Immunogen	RIA specificity (approximate)	Titer[a]	Note
24	[Tyr^{22},Gly^{23}]-CRF(1–23) conjugated to human α-globulin with bis-diazetized benzidine	CRF (4–20)	1/230,000	RIA detects rat and human CRF. Good for immunohisto-chemistry of rat brain
28	CRF conjugated to human α-globulin with glutaraldehyde	CRF (10–41)	1/74,000	Good for immunohisto-chemistry of rat brain
29	Same as 28	CRF (23–41)	1/147,000	
30	Same as 28	CRF (33–42)	1/168,000	Excellent for immuno-histochemistry of rat brain
31	Same as 28	CRF (10–41)	1/135,000	
33	poly-CRF (polymerized with ethylene diaminocarbodiimide)	CRF (10–41)	1/104,000	
35	Same as 33	CRF (33–41)	1/28,000	

[a] Dilution of antiserum that binds 50% of intact, HPLC purified tracer in radioimmunoassay. RIA schedule is as follows: day 1, standards and unknowns added to phosphosaline buffer containing antiserum, 0.1% bovine serum albumin and 0.1% Triton X-100; day 2, ^{125}I-labeled CRF tracer added; day 3, bound from free counts separated by fixed Staph A precipitation of antibody.

very poorly (Vale *et al.*, 1982). These immunological results suggested that sheep CRF is different from the CRF of those other species (Table I).

In order to provide the tools for studying the role of CRF in the rat, and to evaluate CRF-like molecules in fresh extracts, we decided to purify CRF from rat hypothalamus. As starting material, we have used rat hypothalamic powder provided by Dr. A. Parlow under the aegis of the National Hormone and Pituitary Program.

Acidic, defatted extracts of rat hypothalamic fragments were applied to a Sephadex G-50 fine column. The eluted fractions were bioassayed for the ability to release ACTH *in vitro* and radioimmunoassayed with our N-terminally directed CRF radioimmunoassay using C-24 (Fig. 3). We detected the major peak of both biological and immunological activity in the 4K–5K size range. A smaller peak with biological and immunological activities representing perhaps a CRF precursor was seen close to the void volume. Additional zones of biological activity without immunological activity were seen in the smaller molecular weight areas. In subsequent studies none of these exhibited the high intrinsic activity of CRF.

The major peak of biological and immunological activity has been purified further using preparative, semipreparative, and analytical HPLC steps, yielding ca. 50% pure rat CRF. We observed that this CRF elutes later than did an ovine CRF marker. Sequence analysis of this fraction revealed that rat CRF is a 41 amino acid peptide that differs from ovine CRF by 7 residues with substitutions occurring at positions 2, 22, 23, 25, 38, 39, and 41 (Fig. 3).

III. Hypothalamic Distribution of CRF

CRF-like immunoactivity has been detected by radioimmunoassay in the stalk median eminence area of several species. In the rat we measure 1–2 ng CRF-LI/medial basal hypothalamus (Vale *et al.*, 1982). This value increases around 2-fold in chronically adrenalectomized rats (Bruhn and Vale, 1983). In collaboration with F. Bloom and associates (Bloom *et al.*, 1982), CRF staining has been observed in the external zone of the median eminence—the staging area for transport of hypophysiotropic substances to the pituitary gland. Cell bodies of these terminals have been identified in the paraventricular nucleus of the sheep, dog, monkey, and colchicine-treated rat (Bloom *et al.*, 1982; Bugnon *et al.*, 1982; Paull *et al.*, 1982). In normal and adrenalectomized rats CRF-containing fibers in the neurohemal zone of the median eminence arise predominantly in parvocellular parts of the paraventricular nucleus of the hypothalamus (Swanson *et al.*, 1982). Most CRF-stained cells are only visible in colchicine-pretreated intact animals, and cell counts indicated that about 2000 such neurons are

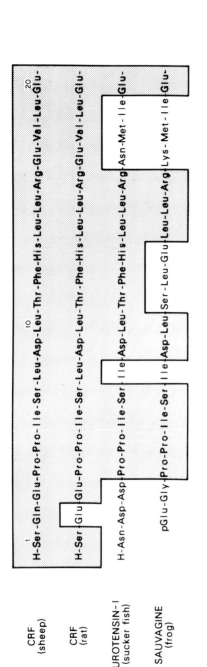
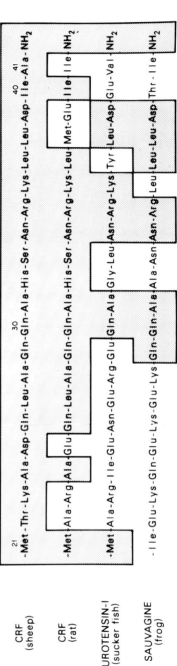

FIG. 3. Amino acid sequences of sheet CRF, rat CRF (Spiess, Rivier, and Vale, in preparation), urotensin I from catostomus carpi (Lederis et al., 1982), and sauvagine.

distributed throughout all 8 parts of the PVH (Swanson and Kuypers, 1980), although they are concentrated in the dorsal medial parvocellular part. From the lateral tip of the PVH, CRF-stained fibers arch laterally and ventrally around the fornix and then the ventromedial nucleus to enter the lateral edge of the median eminence. Interestingly, a cluster of about 750 CRF-stained neurons was clearly visible in the dorsomedial PVH of adrenalectomized animals that were not treated with colchicine. These cells clearly gave rise to a labeled pathway to the median eminence, and appeared to be the only cells in the brain affected by adrenalectomy. Further double-immunostaining experiments on individual sections (Swanson et al., 1982; Sawchenko and Swanson, unpublished observations) indicate that some CRF-stained cells in the PVH also contain oxytocin, while other contain neurotensin; from the distribution of these doubly labeled cells, it appears that the former group may project to the posterior pituitary (Bloom et al., 1982), while the latter may project to the median eminence.

The localization of the paraventricular nucleus as the site of CRF cell bodies is consistent with physiologic studies of Dunn and Critchlow (1973) and Malakara and Palkovitz (review Palkovitz, 1977) and others that have emphasized the importance of this region for the regulation of ACTH secretion.

In addition to median eminence, CRF and paraventricular nucleus immunostaining is found in other hypothalamic regions including the periventricular nucleus of the monkey and in both the paraventricular and supraoptic nuclei of the sheep and in the vicinity of basal hypothalamic cells which contain proopiomelanocortin (POMC) derivatives (Bloom et al., 1982).

IV. CRF in Portal Blood

Dan Gibbs of the University of California, San Diego collected portal blood from the transsected hypophysial stalk of pentobarbital anesthetized rats. We extracted the CRF-like activity by adsorption onto C_{18} Bond Elut cartridges. After elution, the samples were assayed by an RIA that detects 1 fmole ovine CRF. We found that extracted portal plasma was detected by this assay—giving a response parallel to that of either synthetic ovine CRF or highly purified rat CRF (Gibbs and Vale, 1982). Based upon the ovine standard, around 100 pM CRF-LI was found in portal blood. Since we suspect that this RIA underreads rat CRF, the actual concentration of rat CRF is somewhat higher. Peripheral rat blood extracted and assayed in the same way contained undetectable (<20 pM) CRF-LI. Because concentrations of from 100 to 500 pM CRF are highly activity *in vitro,* these results suggest that physiologically significant levels of CRF are present in the blood supplying the anterior pituitary.

We have also examined CRF-like immunoactivity in the portal blood of a cat provided by Paul Plotsky. In this sample, around 1 nM CRF was detected based upon the ovine standard.

V. Passive Immunization

Perhaps the most definitive approach to the question of the role of endogenous CRF in ACTH secretion is provided by passive immunization experiments. We have examined the effects of administration of antiserum against CRF to freely moving catheterized adrenalectomized rats. This anti-CRF serum dramatically reduced plasma ACTH levels to around 10–25% of that of rats receiving normal rabbit serum (C. Rivier *et al.,* 1982b). Thus, in adrenalectomized rats the secretion of ACTH appears to be highly dependent upon endogenous CRF.

The effect of anti-CRF serum on the secretion of ACTH during ether stress was also studied. The administration of anti-CRF serum to catheterized rats blocked most of the ACTH response to either CRF or to ether stress (C. Rivier *et al.,* 1982b). However, it must be pointed out that significant residual (ca. 10–25%) release of ACTH due to stress remained in multiple experiments. Either we have failed to neutralize all endogenous CRF or other factors contribute to the stress response. Even so, the fact that anti-CRF serum typically presents 70–90% of the amount of ACTH released due to stress provides strong support for the physiological role of a peptide immunologically related to CRF.

VI. Interactions between CRF and Neurohypophysial Peptides

In the past vasopressin has been considered as a candidate CRF (Buckingham, 1980). However, various studies including those carried out in the vasopressin-deficient Brattleboro rat have indicated that although vasopressin is not the CRF it nonetheless may play a role in the regulation of ACTH secretion.

In vitro, vasopressin and oxytocin stimulate ACTH and β-endorphin secretion yet exhibit lower potency and intrinsic activity does CRF. Figure 4A presents the ACTH released by rat anterior pituitary cells in cultured in response to a full range of CRF in the presence and absence of vasopressin or oxytocin. CRF and either neurohypophysial peptide exhibit an "effect additive" (Poch, 1982) interaction in that at plateau concentrations of CRF, the coaddition of vasopressin or oxytocin will elicit additional increases in ACTH or β-End-LI secretory rates. This enhancement can be quite marked at "physiologic" concentrations of CRF and

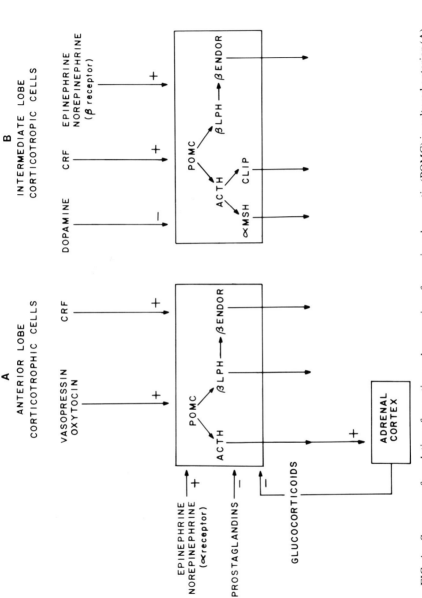

FIG. 4. Summary of regulation of secretion and processing of proopiomelanocortin (POMC) in cultured anterior (A) and intermediate (B) lobe cells of the pituitary.

vasopressin that are in the range of those found in pituitary portal blood. For example, 2 nM vasopressin can double the ACTH secretory rate of cells treated with 0.3 nM CRF.

Vasopressin can also be a powerful ACTH secretagog at the high doses that elevate blood pressure and cause apparent distress in the rat. We have found that the release of ACTH due to vasopressin is considerably attenuated in rats given antiCRF serum (J. Rivier and Vale, 1983). These results suggest that the action of vasopressin in this model is dependent upon CRF. Consistently, in rats pretreated with morphine-nembutal and chlorapromazine which act centrally to prevent stress-induced secretion of ACTH, CRF is a much more efficacious stimulator of ACTH secretion than is vasopressin. It is hypothesized that in the absence of CRF, vasopressin is a weak secretagog *in vitro* and *in vivo,* and that vasopressin can act *in vivo* both to trigger CRF release from the hypothalamus (Yates and Maran, 1974) as well as to then potentiate the action of CRF at the pituitary level.

Concerning a possible role of vasopressin in stress, we have found that the administration of 1 mg of vasopressin antagonist, which completely blocks the response to up to 3 μg exogenous vasopressin has only a slight (ca. 20%) inhibitory effect on the amount of ACTH released by rats in response to ether stress. These data do not support an essential role of the neurohypophysial peptide in mediating stress-induced ACTH secretion (Rivier and Vale, 1983).

VII. Interaction between CRF and Catecholamines

Epinephrine, norepinephrine, and other α-adrenergic agonists stimulate ACTH and β-End-LI secretion *in vitro* showing lower potency and intrinsic activity than does CRF (Vale and Rivier, 1977; Vale *et al.,* 1980; Giuere *et al.,* 1980). Both epinephrine and norepinephrine exhibit "effect additivity" with CRF. This enhancement is observed with concentrations of catecholamines as low as 10 nM, levels which are reached in the blood during stressful circumstances. The administration of chlorisondamine, a ganglionic blocker that inhibits peripheral production of epinephrine and norepinephrine, reduces the amount of ACTH released by the rat during ether stress by 40–60% (C. Rivier and Vale, 1983). These results support a role of peripheral catecholamines in mediating the release of ACTH due to ether stress.

The rise in plasma ACTH levels in the ether-stressed rat can be totally abolished by the administration of a combination of anti-CRF serum, and chlorisondamine (C. Rivier and Vale, unpublished). It can be argued therefore that the rise in ACTH induced by ether stress in the rat is mediated by the interaction of CRF and catecholamines. ACTH regulation under various circumstances may differ; for example, anti-CRF serum completely abolishes ACTH rises in rats being restrained by the tail (Brown and Vale, unpublished) so presumably only CRF mediates ACTH release due to that stress. Likewise, as described above, the elevated ACTH secretion following adrenalectomy seems to be highly CRF dependent.

Under other conditions, additional putative ACTH regulators may become involved, such as angiotensin II. This peptide is a very weak ACTH secretagog (Gaillard et al., 1981) that also exhibits effect additivity with CRF (Vale et al., 1982).

VIII. Interaction between CRF and Glucocorticoids

Of major significance in the regulation of ACTH secretion are the glucocorticoids. Experimental evidence has implicated both pituitary and brain sites of action for the well-established negative feedback effects of glucocorticoids on ACTH secretion (reviews, Vale and Rivier, 1977; Buckingham, 1980). Hypothalamic CRF levels as monitored by radioimmunoassay or immunofluorescence have been observed to increase in response to long-term adrenalectomy (Bruhn and Vale, 1983; Swanson et al., 1982). These results do not establish CRF production rates, however, but would support the possibility that part of the action of glucocorticoids on ACTH secretion could be mediated through changes in CRF secretion.

Glucocorticoids can undoubtedly modulate the response of pituitary cells to CRF or other secretagogs in vivo and in vitro (Vale et al., 1981, 1982; C. Rivier et al., 1982a; Giguere et al., 1982). The pretreatment of animals or pituitary cells with glucocorticoids such as dexamethasone, corticosterone, or cortisol inhibits the release of ACTH and β-End-LI due to CRF. Maximal inhibition of CRF-mediated ACTH secretion is observed after a delay of several hours pretreatment with glucocorticoids as is typically seen with other transcriptionally mediated steroid effects. When pituitary cells are pretreated with glucocorticoids, the CRF dose–response curve is shifted to the right and the release rate at plateau CRF levels is reduced (Vale et al., 1982). A family of curves is obtained in which alteration of either CRF or steroid results in a new secretion rate of ACTH or β-End-LI. CRF can be viewed as having altered the set point for glucocorticoid inhibition or vice versa. The glucocorticoid inhibition of CRF's action is noncompetitive in that the plateau response is reduced. It is noteworthy that even at highest doses of dexamethasone, CRF can still elicit some stimulation of hormone secretion. Thus in this system, when CRF is high, ACTH production can be elevated even when glucocorticoids are high. These observations are consistent with the possibility that failure of glucocorticoids to completely suppress ACTH secretion in some clinical conditions such as Cushing's disease or in affective disorders like depression could be CRF mediated.

IX. Mode of Action of CRF

The initial step in the action of CRF on pituitary cells probably involves an interaction with plasma membrane receptors. Consistently, ^{125}I-labeled CRF binds to purified bovine membranes with high affinity ($K_d = 1$ nM) (Perrin, Rivier, and Vale, unpublished results).

The similar maximal effects of CRF and cyclic AMP derivatives, the ACTH releasing actions of agents known to elevate intracellular cyclic AMP such as phosphodiesterase inhibitors (isobutylmethylxanthine, theophylline), cholera toxin, and forskolin have suggested to various investigators (Fleisher et al., 1969; Hedge, 1971; Vale et al., 1976, 1978; Vale and Rivier, 1977; Raymond et al., 1979) an involvement of the adenylate cyclase system in ACTH secretion. Labrie et al. (1982) and we (Vale et al., 1982; Bilezikjian and Vale, 1983) have found that CRF rapidly elevates intracellular and secretion $3',5'$ cyclic AMP levels in anterior pituitary cell cultures. In contrast to the report of Giguere et al. (1982) we find that glucocorticoid pretreatment strongly inhibits CRF-mediated increases in intracellular cyclic AMP concentrations and consider that part of the effects of glucocorticoids may be mediated by altering cyclic AMP levels (Bilezikjian and Vale, 1982). Both groups observe, however, that glucocorticoids can inhibit ACTH secretion due to exogenous 8-Br-$3',5'$ cyclic AMP, a result that suggests that glucocorticoids also act in part beyond the cyclic AMP generating steps in their inhibition of CRF action.

The secretion of ACTH due to CRF is calcium dependent as shown by the observation that incubation of pituitary cells with either cobalt or in low calcium medium strongly attenuates the secretory response to CRF (Vale et al., 1981, 1982; Bilezikjian and Vale, 1982).

The acute response to CRF results in release of stored ACTH/β-End-LI contents associated with a considerable decrease in intracellular ACTH levels after 24 hours of continuous exposure. Cellular ACTH contents are virtually replenished after 8 days CRF treatment while secretory rates remain elevated. Since purified (Vale and Rivier, 1977) or synthetic CRF increases total (cells + medium) ACTH content of the cultures (Vale et al., 1982) it is likely that the hypothalamic peptide can increase rates of ACTH synthesis. In earlier studies we have shown that other secretagogs such as PMA can also increase total ACTH content (Vale and Rivier, 1977). Subsequently, we have observed that CRF and other secretagogs increase levels of proopiomelanocortin (POMC) messenger RNA in the cultures (Sutton *et al.*, 1982a), an effect that is attenuated by glucocorticoids. Effects on hormonal synthesis may be a direct consequence of the enhanced secretory rates.

X. CRF on Intermediate Lobe

The intermediate lobe of the pituitary gland contains primarily corticotropic cells which secrete a variety of peptides derived from POMC. The processing of the POMC precursor in anterior lobe differs from that in the intermediate lobe where the bulk of the ACTH is processed to MSH and the β-LPH is cleaved to β-endorphin and its acetylated forms (reviews Vale *et al.*, 1980; Eipper and Mains, 1981).

Cultures of dissociated neurointermediate lobe cells secrete large quantities of β-endorphin-like immunoactivity spontaneously. CRF can further increase β-End-LI secretion rates although in our studies the dose–response curve is shifted to the right of that seen with anterior lobe cultures (Vale *et al.*, 1982). The EC_{50} for CRF mediated β-End-LI secretion by intermediate lobe cells is observed to be between 1 and 10 nM. The β-End-LI secretory rate at plateau concentrations of CRF is less than that induced by 8-Br-3',5' cyclic AMP. In our previous experiments with purified CRF on neurointermediate lobe cells (Vale *et al.*, 1980) we found no effect on secretion of β-End-LI probably because we were giving insufficient amounts of CRF in the (then precious) native CRF preparations.

Epinephrine and other β-adrenergic agonists such as isoproterenol markedly stimulate intermediate lobe secretion of POMC products (Bower *et al.*, 1974; Tilders *et al.*, 1980; Pettibone and Mueller, 1982; Cote *et al.*, 1980) and, in contract to CRF, will elicit a secretory response as great as that due to 8-Br-3',5' cyclic AMP (Vale *et al.*, 1982).

The intermediate lobe is innervated by fibers containing dopamine, which is probably a major physiologic regulator of those cells. Dopamine and a variety of dopaminergic agonists, apomorphine, bromocriptine, and pergolide, are powerful inhibitors of β-End-LI secretion by cultured intermediate lobe cells (Vale *et al.*, 1980; Eipper and Mains, 1981; Munemura *et al.*, 1980). Dopamine noncompetitively inhibits the response to CRF; CRF can partially overcome the inhibitory effects of moderate doses of dopamine but has little effect on high concentrations of dopamine (Vale *et al.*, 1982). Thus, anterior and intermediate lobe corticotropic cells differ with respect to their processing of the POMC precursor (Eipper and Mains, 1981) as well as in their sensitivities to physiologic regulators such as glucocorticoids and dopamine. The fact that CRF modulates secretion by both cell types raises the possibility that cells producing POMC-derived products such as β-endorphin found in the central nervous system and other regions might be similarly responsive to CRF.

XI. Brain Distribution and Actions of CRF

In keeping with experience with other hypothalamic hypophysiotropic peptides, it was considered that CRF might have multiple roles within the central nervous system (CNS). Indeed, in addition to the paraventriculoinfundibular pathway described above, we localized CRF immunoreactivity in two other CNS systems of the colchicine-treated rat (Fig. 5) (Swanson *et al.*, 1982). The first consists of stained cell bodies, fiber tracts, and terminal fields in neural systems that are known to regulate the autonomic nervous system. CRF-stained cells and terminals fields were found in the amygdala (central nucleus), septum (bed nucleus of the stria terminalis), lateral hypothalamus, central gray, parabrachial nucleus, and dorsal vagal complex, as well as in the two major fiber tracts that interconnect them, the medial forebrain and the periventricular system. This autonomic-related system is quite complex, as the two fiber tracts just mentioned appear to contain both ascending as well as descending CRF-stained projections. The second major CRF system appears to consist of interneurons in the cerebral cortex. Most of these cells resemble small bipolar neurons in superficial layers (II and III) of all cortical areas, although they are concentrated in parts of the cingulate gyrus and the prefrontal region.

Extrahypothalamic CRF has also been observed in the normal sheep brain by radioimmunoassay (Palkovitz *et al.*, 1983) and immunohistochemistry (Bloom *et al.*, 1983). According to these immunohistochemical studies in the sheep, a major projection links the hypothalamic neurons with the limbic system, particularly the connecting pathway termed the stria terminalis; through this pathway, the hypothalamus as well as the central and medial nuclei of the amygdala are linked (the amygdala has been loosely associated with emotional regulation). The hypothalamic CRF neurons, primarily of the parvocellular (or small cell), also project toward the mid-brain and pons, where they innervate the parabrachial nuclei (visceral, taste nuclei) as well as the monoaminergic (norepinephrine, serotonin) neurons of the locus coeruleus and raphe. A separate lower brain stem group of immunoreactive CRF neurons in the midline raphe innervate the inferior olivary complex, where it could interact with spinal and cerebellar proprioceptive feedback systems.

In the sheep forebrain, CRF immunoreactive neurons are found within the regions which are thought to furnish some selective projections to cerebral cortex, again focusing on cortical regions which are associated with visceral or emotional function [olfactory tubercle, in medial amygdala, and in the temperal (insular) cortex]. In the latter zone, the in-

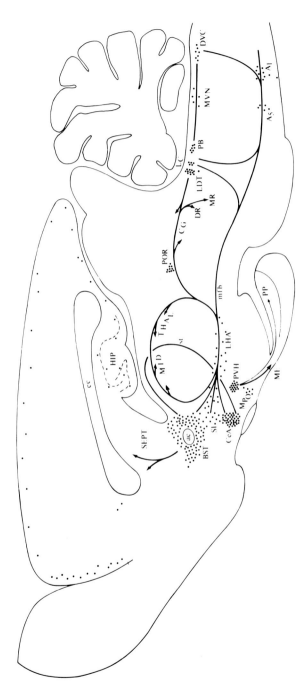

FIG. 5.   Summary of distribution of CRF immunoreactive CRF cell bodies (dots) and fibers (lines) in the colchicine rat brain (Swanson *et al.*, 1982).

creased density of the fibers ending in the outer molecular layer suggests that CRF may also function as an intracortical transmitter.

In summary, the anatomical evidence suggests that CRF-immunoreactive systems in the brain may play an important role in neuroendocrine regulation, in modulating the output of the autonomic nervous system, and perhaps in cortical integrative mechanisms as well.

These findings that CRF is distributed throughout various brain regions (Bloom *et al.*, 1982; Swanson *et al.*, 1982) suggested that CRF might have effects within the central nervous system. Siggins and colleagues, using intracellular recording of hypocampal slices, have observed that CRF depolarizes both CA1 and CA3 pyramidal neurons, accompanied by elevations in spontaneous firing rate (Aldenhoff *et al.*, 1982). We have observed that CRF acting through a calcium-dependent mechanism can stimulate the secretion of somatostatin by cultured rat hypothalamic and cerebral cortical cells (Peterfreund and Vale, 1982). These studies demonstrate a direct effect of CRF on brain cells.

In considering the possibility that CRF might have functions beyond the activation of the pituitary–adrenal axis, we were led to examine the effects of this new peptide on other visceral mechanisms involved in an animal's responses to stress; particular emphasis was placed on evaluating the relationship between CRF and the sympathetic nervous system.

CRF given into the lateral ventricle of the rat or the third ventricle of the dog produces an acute and prolonged elevation of plasma catecholamines (Brown *et al.*, 1982a,b). In the rat, CRF elevates plasma norepinephrine to a greater extent than epinephrine (Brown *et al.*, 1982a,b). This is in contrast to other peptides such as bombesin which act within the central nervous system to influence the sympathetic nervous system to have more prominent effects on adrenal epinephrine secretion (Brown *et al.*, 1979). CRF given into the third ventricle of the dog elevates plasma concentrations of vasopressin. However CRF does not elevate plasma vasopressin levels in the rat (Brown *et al.*, 1982a,b). The site of action of CRF to act within the brain to influence the sympathetic nervous system or vasopressin secretion is as yet undetermined.

The intracranial administration of somatostatin-28 and certain somatostatin analogs (e.g., desAA1,2,4,5,12,13[D-Trp^8]-somatostatin-14 blocks the stress mediated increase in plasma epinephrine but not norepinephrine. Likewise, CRF-induced elevations in epinephrine but not norepinephrine are blocked by somatostatin-28.

Activation of the sympathetic nervous system by CRF results in increased concentrations of plasma glucagon and glucose and an increase in heart rate and mean arterial pressure in both the rat and the dog (Brown *et al.*, 1982a,b; Fisher *et al.*, 1982, 1983). Effects of CRF in both the rat and dog on metabolic and cardiovascular changes can be abolished by the ganglionic blocker, chlorisondamine, that prevents the elevation of peripheral catecholamines (Brown *et al.*, 1982; Fisher *et al.*, 1982, 1983). Administration of antagonists of the renin angiotensin system and vasopressin or hypophysectomy and adrenalectomy do not prevent CRF-induced metabolic or cardiovascular changes (Fisher *et al.*, 1983).

Thus, CRF is capable of acting within the brain to activate the sympathetic nervous system in a fashion similar to that occurring with many forms of stress.

We hypothesized that the CRF neuronal system might mediate multiple brain responses to stress including behavior. We have demonstrated that CRF injected intracerebroventricularly (icv) in rats produces a dose-dependent locomotor activation in rats that could not be reproduced by peripheral injection (Sutton *et al.*, 1982a). This activation, particularly at lower doses (0.015–0.15 nmole), was characterized by increased locomotion and sniffing, grooming, and rearing, behavior consistent with a general arousal. The icv administration of similar doses of CRF caused electroencephalographic changes associated with marked arousal (Ehlers *et al.*, 1982). At higher doses (≥ 1.5 nmole) of CRF more bizarre behavioral effects were observed including elevated walking, repetitive locomotion such as moving forward and backward in a straight line and pawing rapidly against the sides of the cage.

Although other peptides such as endorphins and ACTH have been shown to produce increases in spontaneous behavioral activity, the nature of the CRF response differed substantially from the responses observed with these other peptides (Segal *et al.*, 1982). CRF does not produce the initial depressant phase followed by bursts of locomotor activity that characterizes icv injections of opioid peptides; nor does the opiate antagonist naloxone antagonize these effects (Koob, Rivier, and Vale, unpublished results). In contrast, the activation by CRF at the lower doses appeared to be an exaggeration of the normal activation produced by introduction of the animal into a familiar environment. This activation appears to be at least partially independent of the pituitary adrenal system in that hypophysectomized rats show consistent responses to CRF (Koob, Rivier and Vale, unpublished results) although significantly more CRF (approximately 10 times) is required to produce the same behavioral activation as seen in sham-operated rats. Whether this difference reflects a partial mediatory or permissive contribution of the pituitary adrenal axis or the general debilitation of the hypophysectomized rats is unknown at this time.

Perhaps of more importance for the conceptualization of CRF as a peptide involved in the organism's behavioral response to stress are the studies where animals are exposed to a novel, presumably aversive, environment following pretreatment with CRF. Rats tested in a novel open field following icv injection of doses of CRF (0.0015–0.15 nmol) showed responses that were consistent with an increased emotionality or increased sensitivity to the stressful aspects of the situation. Here the rats showed decreases in locomotion and rearing. Typically a rat injected with 0.15 nmole of CRF and placed 60 minutes later in the open field moves hesitantly to the outer squares and then either circled the open field remaining close to the floor or remained in one of the corners grooming or hesitantly moving forward and backward. In contrast, saline-injected animals rapidly circled the open field rearing and exploring and eventually made forays into the inner squares of the center of the open field (Sutton *et al.*, 1982a).

Similar results have been observed in open field conflict test (Britton *et al.*, 1982) previously shown to be sensitive to both anxiolytic drugs as well as treatments which increase neophobia (Britton and Britton, 1981). Here, rats were deprived of food for 24 hours and then placed in a highly illuminated circular open field when a single food pellet was secured to a pedestal in the center of the open field. CRF, again injected 1 hour prior to the test in doses of 0.0015–0.15 nmole, produced a dose-dependent change in behavior consistent with an increase in the aversiveness of the situation. CRF caused decreases in the number of approaches to the food pellet, decreases in the amount of food eaten per approach to the food pedestal, and an increase in grooming (Britton *et al.*, 1982). These results are the opposite to those observed with benzodiazepine treatment and are consistent with the hypothesis that CRF augments the stressfulness of a novel environment.

These results showing EEG arousal, general behavioral activation, and stress-enhancing actions all point to a possible role for CRF in a basic and fundamental activating system. The functional significance of this system may have developed as a means for an organism to mobilize not only the pituitary adrenal system but also the central nervous system in response to environmental challenge. Indeed, preliminary results in our laboratory suggest that treatment with CRF can improve learning in both aversively and appetitively motivated tasks (Koob, Le Moal, Bloom, Rivier, and Vale, unpublished results). Clearly, a hypothetical central nervous system activation system definitively linked to the pituitary adrenal system, that can improve behavioral performance at low levels of output but disrupt behavioral performance at high levels of output, has important implications for anxiety disorders and other psychopathology.

In conclusion, the evidence strongly supports CRF or a closely related peptide in the neuroregulation of the pituitary corticotropic cells. Broader roles of CRF within the brain as a transsynaptic or paracrine mediator of endocrine and visceral functions and behavior, particularly under stressful circumstances, are suggested and require further investigation. Fundamental and applied studies of this new regulatory peptide may improve our understanding of the brain and endocrine system and lead to improved means of diagnosis and management of human disease.

ACKNOWLEDGMENTS

The authors wish to acknowledge the contributions of the numerous collaborators sited in this article. Research was supported by NIH grants AM26741, HD13527, and AA03504 and by grants from The Rockefeller and Texas Salk Institute Foundation. Research conducted in part by The Clayton Foundation for Research, California Division. Drs. W. Vale, C. Rivier, and J. Spiess are Clayton Foundation Investigators. Thanks to Susan O. McCall for manuscript preparation.

REFERENCES

Aldenhoff, J. B., Groul, D., Siggins, G., Rivier, J., and Vale, W. (1982). In preparation.

Arimura, A., Saito, T., and Schally, A. V. (1967). *Endocrinology 81,* 235.

Bilezikjian, L., and Vale, W. (1983). *Endocrinology,* in press.

Bloom, F. E., Battenberg, E. L. F., Rivier, J., and Vale, W. (1982). *Reg. Peptides* **4,** 43.

Bloom, F. E., Morrison, A., Battenberg, J., Rivier, J., and Vale, W. (1983). In preparation.

Bower, A., Hadley, M. E., and Hruby, V. J. *Science* (1974). **184,** 70.

Britton, D. R., and Britton, K. T. (1981). *Pharm. Biochem. Behav.* **15,** 577.

Britton, D. R., Koob, G. F., Rivier, J., and Vale, W. (1982). *Life Sci.* **31,** 363.

Brown, M. R., Rivier, J., and Vale, W. (1979). *Endocrinology* **104,** 1709.

Brown, M. R., Fisher, L. A., Spiess, J., Rivier, C., Rivier, J., and Vale, W. (1982a). *Endocrinology* **111,** 928.

Brown, M. R., Fisher, L. A., Spiess, J., Rivier, J., Rivier, C., and Vale, W. (1982b). *Reg. Peptides* **4,** 107.

Brown, M., Rivier, C., Rivier, J., and Vale, W. (1983). In preparation.

Bruhn, T., and Vale, W. (1983). In preparation.

Buckingham, J., *Pharmacol. Rev.* (1980). **31,** 253.

Bugnon, C., Fellmann, D., Gouget, A., and Cardot, J. (1982). *Nature (London)* **298,** 159.

Burgus, R. *et al.* (1976). "Hypothalamus and Endocrine Functions." Plenum, New York.

Chan, L. T., Schaal, M., and Saffran, M. (1969). *Endocrinology* **85,** 644.

Cooper, D. M. F., Synetos, D., Cristie, R. B., and Schulster, D. (1976). *J. Endocrinol.* **71,** 171.

Cote, T., Munemura, M., Eskay, R., and Kebabian, J., (1980). *Endocrinology* **107,** 108.

Dhariwal, A. P. S., Rodriques, J. A., Reeser, F., Chowers, L., and McCann, S. M., (1966). *Proc. Soc. Exp. Biol. Med.* **121,** 8.

Dunn, J., and Critchlow, V. (1973). *Endocrinology* **93,** 835.

Ehlers, C. H., Henriksen, S. J., Bloom, F. E., Rivier, J., and Vale, W. W. (1982). *Soc. Neurosci. Ann. Mtg.,* Oct. 31–Nov. 5 (Abstr.).

Eipper, B., and Mains, R. (1981). *Endocrine Rev.* **1,** 1.

Erspamer, V., and Melchiorri, P. (1980). *Trends Pharmacol. Sci.* **20,** 391.

Erspamer, V., Melchiorri, P., Broccardo, M., Erspamer, G. F., Falaschi, P., Improta, G., Negri, L., and Renda, T. (1981). *Peptides* **2**, 7.

Fisher, L. A., Rivier, J., Rivier, C., Spiess, J., Vale, W., and Brown, M. (1982). *Endocrinology* **110**, 2222.

Fisher, L. A. *et al.* (1983).

Fleischer, N., Donald, R., and Butcher, R., *Am. J. Physiol.* (1969). **217**, 1287.

Gaillard, R. C., Grossman, A., Gillies, G., Rees, L. H., and Besser, G. M. (1981). *Clin. Endocrinol.* **15**.

Gibbs, D. M., and Vale, W. (1982). *Endocrinology* **111**, 1418.

Giguere, V., Cote, J., and Labrie, F. (1980). *Endocrinology* **110**, 1225.

Giguere, V., Labrie, F., Cote, J., Coy, D., Sueiras-Diaz, J., and Schally, A. (1982). *Proc. Natl. Acad. Sci. U.S.A.* **79**, 3466.

Gillies, G., and Lowry, P. (1979). *Nature (London)* **278**, 463.

Grossman, A., Perry, L., Schally, A. V., Nieuwenhuyzen-Kruseman, A. C., Tomlin, S., Coy, D. H., Comaru-Schally, A. M., and Besser, G. M. (1982). *Lancet* 922.

Guillemin, R., *Recent Prog. Horm. Res.* (1964). **20**, 89.

Guillemin, R., and Rosenberg, B. (1955). *Endocrinology* **57**, 599.

Harris, G. W., (1948). *Physiol. Rev.* **28**, 139.

Hedge, G., (1971). *Endocrinology* **89**, 500.

Jones, M. T., Gillham, B., and Hillhouse, E. W. (1967). *Fed. Proc. Fed. Am. Soc. Exp. Biol. Med.* **36**, 2104.

Knudsen, J., Lam, Y., Frick, W., Daves, G., Barofsky, D., Bowers, C., and Folkers, K. (1978). *Biochem. Biophys. Res. Commun.* **80**, 735.

Koob, G. F., LeMoal, M., Bloom, F. E., Sutton, R. E., Rivier, J., and Vale, W. (1982). *Soc. for Neurosci.* (Abstr.) **8**, 41.

Labrie, F., Veilleux, R., LeFerre, G., Coy, D., Sueiras-Diaz, J., and Schally, A. V. (1982). *Science* **216**, 1007.

Lederis, K., Vale, W., Rivier, J., MacCannell, K. L., McMaster, D., Kobayashi, Y., Suess, U., and Lawrence, J. (1982). *Proc. Western Pharmacol. Soc.,* in press.

Lowry, P. J., *J. Endocrinol.* (1974). **62**, 163.

MacCannell, K., and Lederis, K. (1977). *J. Pharmacol. Exp. Ther.* **203**, 38.

MacCannell, K. L., Lederis, K., Hamilton, P. L., and Rivier, J. (1982). *Pharmacology,* in press.

Marki, W., Spiess, J., Tache, Y., Brown, M., and Rivier, J. (1981). *J. Am. Chem. Soc.* **103**, 3178.

Montecucchi, P. C., Henschen, A., and Erspamer, V. (1979). *Hoppe-Seyler's Z. Phisiol. Chem.* **360**, 1178.

Munemura, M., Cote, T., Tsuruta, K., Eskay, R. and Kebabian, J. (1980). *Endocrinology* **107**, 1676.

Orth, D. (1979). "Methods of Hormone Radioimmunoassay," p. 245. Academic Press, New York.

Orth, D. N., DeBold, C. R., DeCherney, G. S., Jackson, R. V., Alexander, A. N., Rivier, J., Rivier, C., Spiess, J., and Vale, W. (1982). *J. Clin. Endocrinol. Metabol.,* submitted.

Palkovits, M. (1977). *Ann. N.Y. Acad. Sci.* **297**, 455.

Palkovits, M., Brownstein, M., and Vale, W. (1983). In preparation.

Pallai, P., Rivier, J., Vale, W., and Goodman, M. (1983). In preparation.

Paull, W., Schöler, J., Arimura, A., Meyers, C., Chang, J., Chang, D., and Shimizu, M. (1982). *Peptides* **1**, 183.

Peterfreund, R. A., and Vale, W. W. (1982). *Endocrinology,* submitted.

Pettibone, D., and Mueller, G. (1982). *J. Pharmacol. Exp. Ther.* **222,** 103.

Poch, G. (1982). *Trends Pharmacol. Sci.* 256.

Portanova, R., and Sayers, G. (1973). *Proc. Soc. Exp. Biol. Med.* **143,** 661.

Porter, J., and Rumsfeld, H. W., Jr. (1959). *Endocrinology* **64,** 948.

Raymond, V., Lepine, J., Cote, J., and Labrie, F. (1979). *Mol. Cell Endocrinol.* **16,** 113.

Rivier, C., and Vale, W. (1983). In preparation.

Rivier, C., Brownstein, M., Spiess, J., Rivier, J., and Vale, W. (1982a). *Endocrinology* **110,** 272.

Rivier, C., Rivier, J., and Vale, W. (1982b). *Science* **218,** 377.

Rivier, C., Rivier, J., Lederis, K., and Vale, W. (1983). In preparation.

Rivier, J., Rivier, C., Branton, D., Millar, R., Spiess, J., and Vale, W. (1982a). "Peptides: Synthesis, Structure, Function," p. 771. Pierce Chemical Company.

Rivier, J., Spiess, J., Thorner, M., and Vale, W. (1982b). *Nature (London)* **300,** 276.

Saffran, M., and Schally, A. V. (1955). *Can. J. Biochem. Physiol.* **33,** 408.

Sayers, G., Hanzmann, E., and Bodansky, M. (1980). *FEBS Lett.* **116,** 3.

Schally, A. V., Andersen, R. N., Lipscomb, H. S., Long, J. M., and Guillemin, R. (1960). *Nature (London)* **188,** 1192.

Schally, A. V., Arimura, A., Bowers, C. Y., Kastin, A. J., Sawano, S., Redding, T. W. (1968). *Nature (London)* **24,** 497.

Schally, A. V., Huang, W. Y., Redding, T. W., Arimura, A., Coy, D. H., Chihara, K., Raymond, V., and Labrie, F. (1978). *Biochem. Biophys. Res. Commun.* **82,** 582.

Schally, A. V., Chang, R. C., Arimura, A., Redding, T. W., Fishback, J., and Vigh, S. (1981). *Proc. Natl. Acad. Sci. U.S.A.* **78,** 5197.

Schulte, H., Chrousos, G., Gold, P., Oldfields, E., Philips, J., Munson, P., Cutler, G., and Loriaux, D. (1982). *J. Clin. Endocrinol. Metab.* **55,** 1023.

Segal, D. S., Browne, R. G., Arnsten, A., Derrington, D. C., Bloom, F. E., Guillemin, R., and Ling, N. (1982). *In* "Endorphins in Mental Health Research" (E. Usdin, W. E. Bunney, Jr., and N. S. Kline, eds.), p. 331. Macmillan, London.

Selye, H. (1936). *Br. J. Exp. Pathol.* **17,** 234.

Skeggs, L. T., Kahn, J. R., Lentz, K., and Shumway, N. P. (1957). *J. Exp. Med.* **106,** 439.

Spiess, J., Rivier, J., Rivier, C., and Vale, W. (1981). *Proc. Natl. Acad. Sci. U.S.A.* **78,** 6517.

Sutton, R., Kobb, G. F., LeMoal, M., Rivier, J., and Vale, W. (1982a). *Nature (London)* **297,** 331.

Sutton, R., Birnberg, N., Evans, R., Rosenfeld, G., Rivier, J., and Vale, W. (1982b). Submitted.

Swanson, L. W., and Kuypers, H. G. J. M. (1980). *J. Comp. Neurol.* **194,** 555.

Swanson, L. W., Sawchenko, P. E., Rivier, J., and Vale, W. W. (1982). *Neuroendocrinology,* in press.

Takebe, K., Yasuda, N. G., and Greer, M. A. (1975). *Endocrinology* **97,** 1248.

Tilders, F. J. H., Berkenbosch, F., and Smelik, P. G. (1980). "Catecholamines and Stress Recent Advances," p. 125. North Holland, Amsterdam.

Turkelson, C. M., Arimura, A., Culler, M. D., and Shimizu, M. (1981). *Peptides* **2,** 425.

Vale, W., Grant, G., Amoss, M., Blackwell, R., and Guillemin, R. (1972). *Endocrinology* **91,** 562.

Vale, W. *et al.* (1976). "Hypothalamus and Endocrine Functions." Plenum, New York.

Vale, W., and Rivier, C. (1977). *Fed. Proc. Fed. Am. Soc. Exp. Biol.* **36,** 8.

Vale, W., Rivier, C., and Brown, M. (1977). *Annu. Rev. Physiol.* **29,** 473.

Vale, W., Rivier, J., and Rivier, C. (1980). "The Role of Peptides in Neuronal Function," p. 432. Dekker, New York.

Vale, W., Rivier, C., Yang, L., Minick, S., and Guillemin, R. (1978). *Endocrinology* **103,** 1910.

Vale, W., Spiess, J., Rivier, C., and Rivier, J. (1981). *Science* **213,** 1394.

Vale, W., Rivier, C., Spiess, J., Brown, M., and Rivier, J. (1982). *In* "Brain Peptides" (D. Krieger, M. Bownstein, and J. Martin, eds.). Wiley, New York, in press.

Vale, W., Bruhn, T., Douglas, C., Yamamoto, G., Vaughan, J., and Rivier, J. (1983a). In preparation.

Vale, W., Vaughan, J., Smith, M., Yamamoto, G., Rivier, J., and Rivier, C. (1983b). *Endocrinology,* in press.

Yasuda, N., Greer, M. A., and T. Aizawa (1982). *Endocrine Reviews* **3,** 123.

Yates, F. E., and Maran, J. W. (1974). "Handbook of Physiology," Vol. 4, section 7.

RECENT PROGRESS IN HORMONE RESEARCH, VOL. 39

Regulation of Kidney Functions by Hormones: A New Approach

F. MOREL

Laboratoire de Physiologie Cellulaire, Collège de France, Paris, France

I. Introduction

Among the numerous hormones which act on the kidneys, many modify urine composition and regulate the excretion rate of definite ion or solute species, so as to ensure body fluid homeostasis. In fact, urine elaboration consists of a number of specific tubular reabsorption (and excretion) processes which progressively alter the volume and composition of tubular fluid as it flows along the successive nephron portions. The transport and permeability characteristics of the epithelial cells lining the tubules are entirely responsible for these reabsorption processes. The only manner in which hormones can selectively regulate the urinary output of specific ions or solutes is by controlling the functioning of the tubular cells which, in the nephron, have the capacity of generating transepithelial net fluxes of these ions and solutes. It is necessary, therefore, to precisely know where and how hormones act in the nephron, to better understand the mechanisms whereby they regulate kidney functions.

Unfortunately, the kidney is a highly complex organ as regards both its structural organization and functioning, so that the physiological methods in use for measuring whole kidney functions *in vivo* are not appropriate for analyzing the sites and mechanisms of hormone actions on the cell scale. I would like to show in this article how progress was recently achieved by using a completely different approach to the problem. In fact, it is now possible to investigate *in vitro* the sites and mechanisms of hormone action in single, well-localized pieces of kidney tubules, by combining nephron microdissection and adequate biochemical or physiological micromethods.

We have limited our discussion to the case of hormones which act on their target cells in the kidney by stimulating cyclic AMP generation. But a similar approach can also be used for hormones acting via other mechanisms, such as corticoid hormones. Moreover, we shall focus attention on the results obtained in two animal species only: the rabbit kidney, because hormonal effects could be analyzed *in vitro* in this species by micro-

271

perfusing single pieces of tubule, and the rat kidney, because hormone-dependent adenylate cyclase activity, as observed in the diluting segment of the rat nephron, raised a problem of general physiological importance, and helped to define new experimental conditions, appropriate for observing hormonal effects in this nephron segment in *in vivo* micropuncture experiments.

For the two animal species, we first examine the distribution of hormone action sites along the nephron, as revealed by an adenylate cyclase microassay; then we discuss the nature of the corresponding biological responses, when they have been established.

II. Cyclic AMP as a Second Messenger of Hormone Action in the Kidney

As early as 1962, Orloff and Handler reported that cAMP mimics the physiological effects of vasopressin on isolated toad bladders.

These authors then observed that vasopressin or theophyllin, when applied *in vitro* to incubated toad bladders, may induce an increase in the cyclic AMP content of the epithelial cells (Handler *et al.*, 1965). One year later, Grantham and Burg (1966) reported that vasopressin added *in vitro* to the fluid bathing microperfused collecting tubules from rabbit enhanced the cell permeability to water in this structure. Addition of exogenous cAMP instead of hormone produced the same response. This was the first evidence demonstrating that the well-known antidiuretic action of vasopressin was actually cAMP mediated. Further evidence supporting this mechanism of ADH action accumulated rapidly, as reviewed by Strewler and Orloff (1977) and Handler and Orloff (1981).

Chase and Aurbach (1967), using homogenates from kidney tissue, observed that vasopressin (AVP) and parathyroid hormone (PTH) stimulated the adenylate cyclase activity in cell membrane fractions; most of the vasopressin effect (Chase and Aurbach, 1968) was obtained in homogenate from the kidney medulla, whereas the PTH effect predominated in homogenates from the cortex. These results demonstrated that cAMP is the second messenger of PTH action in the kidney. Moreover, they provided additional evidence that proximal tubules constitute the main site of PTH action in the kidney and collecting tubules, the main site of vasopressin action. Later experiments showed that other hormones as well, such as calcitonin (Marcus and Aurbach, 1969; Melson *et al.*, 1970; Murad *et al.*, 1970), β-adrenergic agonists (Bell, 1974; Kurokawa and Massry, 1973), and glucagon (Marcus and Aurbach, 1969; Melson *et al.*, 1970) also stimulate adenylate cyclase activity in kidney tissue homogenates, indicating that many hormones act in the kidney via the general cell mechanism discovered by Sutherland and associates.

However, both the kidney cortex and medulla are highly heterogeneous tissues and contain, in addition to interstitial and vascular cells, a large number of different epithelial cell types corresponding to the successive tubular portions forming the nephron. Homogenates or membrane fractions prepared from kidney cortex contain, therefore, a mixture of membranes from proximal tubules mainly, but also from glomeruli, distal tubules, cortical collecting tubules, etc. Homogenates from kidney medulla contain membranes from loops of Henle (thick and thin limbs) and straight proximal tubules, in addition to those from medullary collecting tubules. The observation that several hormones stimulated adenylate cyclase preferentially in homogenates either from cortical or medullary kidney areas indicated some specificity of action sites. But this approach did not make it possible to ascribe the observed effects to precisely localized nephron portions or well-defined cell types in the kidney, owing to the above mentioned tissue heterogeneity. Obviously, new experimental approaches had to be developed to further investigate this important and difficult matter. The method had to combine the following two main prerequisites: (1) it had to provide samples containing a single, well-localized epithelial cell type, and (2) to preserve the high chemical specificity of the adenylate cyclase enzymatic assay. At first sight cell sorting should be a method fulfilling these requirements, but unfortunately does not yet work at sufficient resolution in the case of kidney cells (Vandewalle and Heidrich, 1980; Endou et al., 1982).

Another approach was to isolate well-localized pieces of tubule by microdissecting collagenase-treated kidney tissue (Burg et al., 1966). In principle, nearly all nephron segments should be separated by this method, even though some of them may still be heterogeneous at cell level. One millimeter of kidney tubule contains about 0.1 to 0.2 μg whole proteins, depending on the nephron segment (Morel et al., 1977). Therefore, in order to measure adenylate cyclase activity with good accuracy in such microdissected nephron segments, it would be necessary either to pool a large number of homologous pieces of tubule in each sample, or to develop an enzyme microassay of a high enough sensitivity to measure adenylate cyclase activity in samples containing a single piece of tubule (50 to 100 ng of proteins). The second strategy was adopted and allowed a number of observations, as will be discussed in subsequent sections.

III. The Single Tubule Adenylate Cyclase Microassay

The micromethod developed (Imbert et al., 1975a; Morel et al., 1977) includes two main steps: (1) sampling of well-localized single pieces of tubule by kidney tissue microdissection, and (2) measurement of adenylate cyclase activity in such tiny samples.

Adenylate cyclase activity itself is determined from the rate of [α-^{32}P]ATP conversion into [^{32}P]cyclic AMP by incubating the samples under appropriate conditions. Highly improved sensitivity of the assay is obtained by using [α-^{32}P]ATP of high specific activity and by reducing the incubation volume to 2.5 μl per sample. Otherwise, the conditions adopted for the enzyme assay and for recovering the [^{32}P]cAMP formed during the incubation period are similar to those generally used for measuring adenylate cyclase in tissue homogenates (Salomon et al., 1979): incubate containing ATP (0.3 mM), labeled with [α-^{32}P]ATP (about 1 μCi per sample), an ATP regenerating system (phosphocreatine–creatine kinase), cold cAMP (1 mM), Mg^{2+} (4 mM), and Tris buffer (100 mM), pH 7.4; cAMP isolation by double filtration on Dowex and alumin columns after addition to the samples of an excess of cold ATP and cAMP, plus a tracer amount of [^{3}H]cAMP in order to measure the yield of [^{32}P]cAMP recovery.

Only a few main points are briefly recalled here, as regards nephron microdissection and tubule sampling, since all the steps in this micromethod are documented in detail elsewhere (Imbert et al., 1975a; Morel et al., 1977). Pretreatment of the kidney tissue with collagenase includes immediate perfusion of the organ with a physiological solution containing the enzyme followed by incubation of large kidney slices in the same solution. Microdissection of the incubated slices is performed by hand at about 4°C, under stereomicroscopic control. All nephron portions can be easily recognized and isolated for sampling in rabbit kidney tissue. Microdissection of nephrons is also possible in collagenase-treated kidneys from other species of mammals, including man (Chabardès et al., 1980), but certain segments are often difficult to obtain, in particular the middle portion of distal convoluted tubules in the rat (Morel, 1981) and man (Chabardès, et al., 1980). Each isolated piece of the required segments is transferred with a small droplet of microdissection solution into the hollow of a bacteriological glass slide, tightly covered, photographed (for subsequent measurement of its length), and kept at ice cold temperature until adenylate cyclase activity assay. The membranes of the tubular cells are disrupted before the enzyme microassay by successively applying to the samples a hypoosmotic shock and a short freezing period. The final incubation is performed under the conditions already specified, for a 30-minute period at 30°C, either in the absence (basal activity) or in the presence of the required hormone (stimulated activity). Since the protein content of the piece of tubule cannot be measured in all samples, the results are expressed by using the unit of tubular length as reference (femtomoles cAMP formed during 30 minute incubation at 30°C, per millimeter of tubule). It was checked that the amount of cAMP formed per millimeter of tubule increased linearly as a function of the incubation time for at least 1 hour under the conditions of the microassay. It was also checked that the enzyme activity was proportional to the length of the tubule present in the samples (Imbert *et al.*, 1975a; Imbert-Teboul *et al.*, 1978). Examples of linearity between tubular length per sample and amount of cAMP formed during 30 minute incubation are shown in Fig. 1 for the two main vasopressin sensitive segments of the rat kidney medulla, namely, the medullary collecting tubule (MCT) and the medullary portion of the thick ascending limb of the loop of Henle (MAL). A low arginine-vasopressin (AVP) concentration was present in the incubate in this experiment. The linearity observed in Fig. 1 indicates that (1) the ATP concentration was kept adequately constant in the incubate by the ATP regenerating system, and (2) no large inactivation or degradation of the hormone by the tissue occurred during the incubation period.

More generally, the reproducibility of the results is reasonably good, when several replicate samples are measured under the same conditions

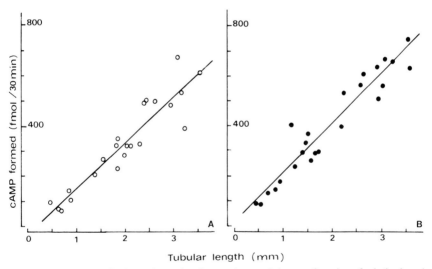

FIG. 1.   Vasopressin-dependent adenylate cyclase activity as a function of tubular length in the samples. Samples containing different lengths of tubule were incubated for 30 minutes in the presence of arginine-vasopressin (AVP) under the conditions indicated in the text. The ordinates give the adenylate cyclase activity measured per sample as a function of the corresponding length of tubule, shown in abscissa. All samples were microdissected from the same rat kidney. (A) MCT, samples of rat medullary collecting tubules (AVP concentration, 10^{-10} M); regression line of the data: $y = 186x - 54$, $n = 24$, $r = 0.93$. (B) MAL, samples of rat medullary thick ascending limbs (AVP concentration, 10^{-9} M); regression line of the data: $y = 198x + 14$, $n = 24$, $r = 0.95$. (Redrawn from Imbert-Teboul *et al. Endocrinology* **102**, 1254–1261, 1978, with permission.)

(each replicate containing a homologous segment isolated from a different nephron). Thus, the standard error of the mean (SEM) usually ranges between 8 and 12% of the mean value when six replicates are used, as discussed in detail by Morel *et al.* (1977).

Basal adenylate cyclase activities are very low in most nephron segments (10 to 30 fmol/mm/30 minutes) except in distal convoluted tubules, where higher values are found (Figs. 3, 4, and 6). In contrast, in the presence of hormone, huge values are obtained in the responsive segments: stimulated activities as high as 10- to 50-fold basal activities are generally observed, depending on segments and hormones. The sensitivity of the responsive segments to a hormone can be estimated by establishing dose–response curves. Four to six replicate samples are measured for each hormonal concentration tested, so that about 40 to 50 samples per segment have to be prepared from the same kidney in order to obtain a single dose–response curve. Figure 2 shows examples of dose–response curves established in one experiment for the two main vasopressin-responsive segments of the rat kidney medulla (MCT and MAL). It is apparent from the figure that vasopressin stimulated adenylate cyclase in a lower concentration range in collecting tubules (MCT, 10^{-11} to 10^{-9} M) than in thick ascending limbs (MAL, 10^{-10} to 10^{-8} M). Half-maximal stimulations of the enzyme corresponded to about 2×10^{-10} M AVP in MCT and to about 10^{-9} M in MAL in this experiment. The difference in apparent K_A for activation between the two structures was a reproducible observation (Imbert-Teboul *et al.*, 1978). Figure 2 also indicates that the 10^{-11} M AVP concentration induced a statistically significant (more than 2-fold) stimulation of adenylate cyclase in collecting tubules. Such a low threshold concentration is of physiological relevance, since it is equivalent to about 5 μU AVP/ml, a value falling into the range of those measured by radioimmunoassay in blood plasma from dehydrated rats (Robertson, 1977). High sensitivity was also observed for other hormones when tested on their respective target segments.

Adenylate cyclase activity must necessarily be measured under standard conditions quite different from those prevailing in the living tissue. It may be assumed, nevertheless, that the information obtained by using the single tubule microassay is of physiological value and reveals the presence of specific membrane-bound hormonal receptors coupled to adenylate cyclase, on the basis of the following evidence: (1) little scatter of values is noted when either basal or hormone-stimulated activities are measured in replicate samples, i.e., in samples containing homologous portions from different nephrons; (2) adenylate cyclase activations achieved by a hormone on its responsive nephron segments correspond to very high stimulated over basal activity ratios; and, even more important,

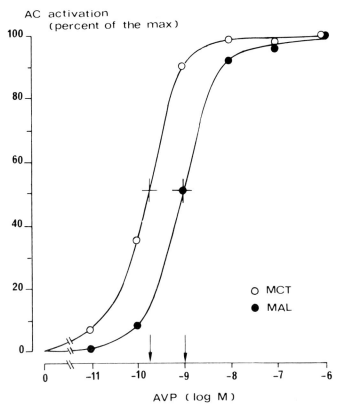

FIG. 2. Vasopressin dose–response curves. All points correspond to the mean values of four to six replicate samples of tubule from the same rat kidney; MCT, medullary collecting tubules; MAL, medullary thick ascending limbs. Abscissa, the arginine-vasopressin concentration in the incubate (log scale). Ordinate, the cyclase response to the hormone (stimulated minus basal activities) is expressed as percentage of the maximal response obtained in the corresponding segment (V_{max} values were 602.9 and 323.8 fmol/mm/30 minutes in MCT and MAL, respectively). (Redrawn from Imbert-Teboul *et al. Endocrinology* **102,** 1254–1261, 1978, with permission.)

(3) the sensitivity of the enzyme to low hormonal concentrations is well preserved under the conditions used.

IV. Sites of Hormone Action Along the Rabbit Nephron

The distribution along the nephron of hormone receptors coupled to adenylate cyclase was first investigated in the kidney of the rabbit, for two reasons. One reason was technical: nephron microdissection is relatively easy in the rabbit, as already mentioned. The other was more general: isolated pieces of rabbit kidney tubules have been widely used for many years under *in vitro* microperfusion conditions to analyze the permeability and transport characteristics specific to various nephron segments (Chonko *et al.,* 1977). It was anticipated, therefore, that the single tubule microperfusion technique, in spite of its technical difficulties and limitations, would permit new insight into the nature of the effects induced by hormones via cAMP in well-localized nephron segments.

A. SEGMENTATION OF THE RABBIT NEPHRON

The nephron portions systematically used to investigate the distribution of hormone-dependent adenylate cyclase activity in the rabbit kidney are the following, starting from the glomerulus (see also Figs. 3 and 4, and the upper left panel of Fig. 5): the first portion (S_1) of the proximal convoluted tubule (PCT), the end portion of the proximal straight tubule (the Pars Recta, PR) located in the outer medulla, the thin descending limb (TDL) and thin ascending limb (TAL) of the loop of Henle, the medullary portion of the thick ascending limb (MAL) located in the outer medulla, and the cortical portion of the thick ascending limb (CAL) located in the cortex. As will appear from the data, the distal convoluted tubule (DCT) had to be subdivided into an early, "bright" portion, DCT_b, and a late "granular" portion, DCT_g. The cortical collecting tubule (CCT) was also subdivided into CCT_g, the "granular" portion which in the rabbit kidney cortex forms the arcades, and CCT_1, the straight collecting portion, of "light" appearance, located in the medullary rays of the cortex. Finally, the medullary collecting tubule (MCT) is the portion located in the outer medulla.

Subdivision of distal convoluted tubules and of cortical collecting tubules was justified on the basis of morphological and biochemical evidence (Morel *et al.,* 1976): the so-called distal convoluted tubule, namely, the nephron portion included between the Macula densa and the first branching with another tubule, did not exhibit a uniform appearance under stereomicroscopic observation. We called the early portion DCT_b, in view of its bright appearance, and the late portion DCT_g, because of its granular appearance resembling that of the adjacent collecting tubule (CCT_g). More important, when these successive nephron portions were isolated from each other and sampled separately in order to measure adenylate cyclase activity, they exhibited quite different responses to hormones. Parathyroid hormone (PTH), for example, produced no cyclase activation either in the early distal convoluted tubule (DCT_b) or in the straight collecting tubule (CCT_1). In contrast, PTH stimulated to a large and almost similar extent the enzyme present in the granular portions of the distal tubule (DCT_g) and collecting tubule (CCT_g). Other hormones, such as isoproterenol (see Fig. 3) and calcitonin (Fig. 4) also revealed a clear-cut functional segmentation of hormone-dependent adenylate cyclase activity in distal and collecting tubules, which was superimposable on the above described morphological segmentation. Moreover, sharp transitions were noted between responsive and nonresponsive successive portions (Morel *et al.*, 1976). It must be pointed out, however, that such morphological and functional segmentation of the distal nephron was observed only in the rabbit kidney. It was no longer as

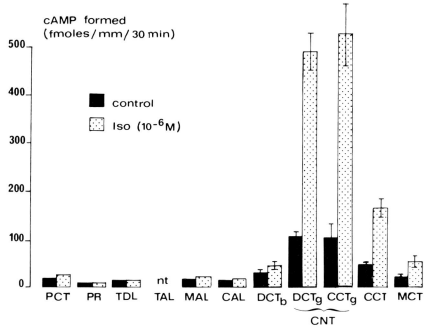

FIG. 3.   Distribution of isoproterenol-sensitive cyclase along the rabbit nephon. Adenylate cyclase activity was measured either in the absence (basal activities, black bars) or in the presence of 10^{-6} M isoproterenol (stimulated activities, dotted bars), in samples containing a single piece of microdissected tubule from various rabbit nephron segments: PCT, proximal convoluted tubules; PR, straight proximal tubules; TDL, thin descending limbs of the loop of Henle; TAL, thin ascending limbs of the loop of Henle; MAL, medullary portion and CAL, cortical portion of thick ascending limbs of the loop of Henle. DCT_b, "bright" portion and DCT_g, "granular" portion of distal convoluted tubules; CCT_g, "granular" portion of cortical collecting tubules (arcades); CCT_1, "light" portion of cortical collecting tubules; MCT, medullary collecting tubules. As specified in the text, DCT_g and CCT_g are the two parts of a single functional segment, the connecting tubule (CNT). Isoproterenol-dependent cyclase activity was not tested (nt) in TAL. (Modified from Chabardès *et al.*, 1975b.)

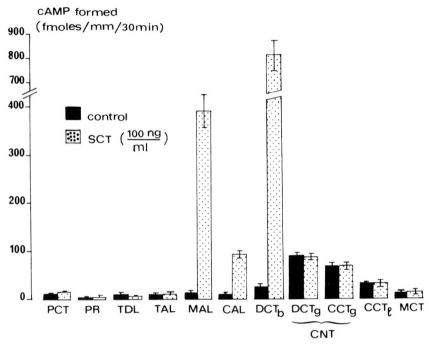

FIG. 4.   Distribution of calcitonin-sensitive cyclase along the rabbit nephron. Adenylate cyclase activity was measured either in the absence (basal activities, black bars) or in the presence of salmon calcitonin (10^{-6} M synthetic SCT, stimulated activities, dotted bars) in samples from successive rabbit nephron segments (abscissa). For definition of segment abbreviations, see text or legend to Fig. 3. (Drawn from Table I, Chabardès *et al.*, 1976b.)

clearly apparent in other species, like mouse (Chabardès *et al.*, 1978a,b), rat (Morel *et al.*, 1978b), or man (Chabardès *et al.*, 1980).

B. ISOPROTERENOL (Iso)

By using the single tubule adenylate cyclase microassay it became possible to demonstrate that β-adrenergic receptors (coupled to adenylate cyclase) are not simply present in vascular smooth muscle cells in the kidney, but also in the membrane of some tubular epithelial cells. Figure 3 illustrates the distribution of isoproterenol-sensitive cyclase activity along the rabbit nephron as measured by Chabardès *et al.*, (1975b). Three portions were responsive to the β-agonist, namely the granular portions of the distal convoluted tubule (DCT_g) and of the collecting tubule (CCT_g), and, to a lesser extent, the light cortical collecting tubule (CCT_l). These isoproterenol-induced effects were blocked in the presence of propranolol but not of phentolamine (Chabardès *et al.*, 1975b). The apparent K_A of activation was about 3×10^{-8} M, and the 10^{-8} M isoproterenol concentration induced a more than 2-fold stimulation of cyclase activity (compared to basal activity) in the responsive segments, indicating a relatively well-preserved sensitivity of cell membranes to β-agonists under the conditions of the microassay (Chabardès *et al.*, 1975b).

C. CALCITONIN (SCT)

Figure 4 illustrates the distribution along the rabbit nephron of the calcitonin-sensitive adenylate cyclase [synthetic salmon calcitonin, SCT, 100 ng/ml, Chabardès *et al.* (1976b)]. Three nephron portions were responsive to this hormone: the medullary and cortical portions of the thick ascending limb (MAL and CAL) and the bright portion of the distal convoluted tubule (DCT_b). The magnitude of the maximal response to calcitonin was lower in CAL than in the two other portions (Fig. 4). In the responsive segments, half-maximal stimulation was obtained with about 0.3 ng/ml, i.e. about 10^{-10} M calcitonin. It must be stressed that the distribution of hormone action sites in the rabbit nephron is quite different for calcitonin and isoproterenol (compare Figs. 3 and 4).

D. PARATHYROID HORMONE (PTH)

Parathyroid hormone (1–34 synthetic fragment of bovine PTH, 1–10 U/ml) stimulates adenylate cyclase activity all along the proximal tubule, although the induced response is of a higher magnitude in S_1 and S_2 (the convoluted segment) than in S_3 (the last portion of the straight segment) (Morel *et al.*, 1978a). In addition to proximal tubules, PTH was observed to stimulate cyclase activity in three other portions of the rabbit nephron: the cortical portion of the thick ascending limb, CAL (the medullary portion of this segment, MAL, is PTH unresponsive) (Chabardès *et al.*, 1975a), and the granular portions of distal convoluted tubules (DCT_g) and cortical collecting tubules (CCT_g) (Morel *et al.*, 1976). These results are summarized in a semiquantitative way in Fig. 5. Half-maximal cyclase stimulation was obtained with PTH concentrations of about 100 to 200 mU/ml ($2-4 \times 10^{-8}$ M) in PCT, CAL, and DCT_g (Chabardès *et al.*, 1976a).

Finally, the cyclase response elicited by PTH either in PCT or in β-blocked DCT_g was not inhibited by the α-agonist, norepinephrine (10^{-6} M), even in the presence of added GTP (10^{-4} M) (Morel *et al.*, 1980b). Thus, under the conditions of the enzyme microassay using single tubules with disrupted cells, α-adrenergic agonists no longer inhibited the effects of PTH on cyclase activity as they did for *in vivo* cAMP cell accumulation

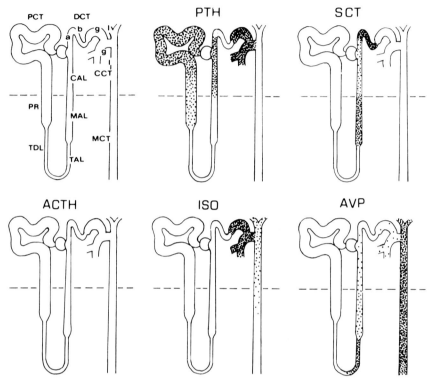

FIG. 5. Pattern of cyclase activation by various hormones along the rabbit nephron. Upper left panel: abbreviations for nephron portions, as follows: PCT and PR, convoluted and straight portions of proximal tubule; TDL and TAL, descending and ascending limbs of thin segment; MAL and CAL, medullary and cortical portions of thick ascending limb; DCT, distal convoluted tubule including a bright (b) and a granular (g) portion; CCT, cortical collecting tubule, including a granular (g) and a light (l) portion; MCT, medullary collecting tubule. In the other five panels, dot density in tubules is proportional to the increase in adenylate cyclase activity induced by the corresponding hormones (stimulated minus basal activities). PTH, 1–34 synthetic fragment of bovine parathyroid hormone, 1–10 U/ml; SCT, synthetic salmon calcitonin, 10–100 ng/ml; Iso, isoproterenol, 10^{-6} M; AVP, arginine-vasopressin, 10^{-6} M. (Reproduced from Morel, 1981b, *Am. J. Physiol.* **240**, F159–F164, with permission.)

in cortical tubule suspensions in the presence of theophyllin (Guder and Rupprecht, 1975).

E. ARGININE-VASOPRESSIN (AVP)

The distribution along rabbit nephrons of adenylate cyclase responsive to vasopressin (AVP, 10^{-6} M) is also shown in Fig. 5. As expected, the enzyme contained in collecting tubules was highly responsive to this hormone (K_A, 10^{-9} M, threshold response below the 10^{-11} M AVP, Imbert *et al.*, 1975b). In the collecting system located within the kidney cortex, however, the sensitivity to vasopressin was present in the light portion only (CCT$_1$), whereas the granular collecting tubule (CCT$_g$) was almost insensitive to this hormone (Morel *et al.*, 1976). This observation indicates that arcades (CCT$_g$) and true collecting tubules (CCT$_1$) have different functional properties and might correspond to different nephron segments in the rabbit. Neither the bright nor the granular portions of distal convoluted tubule responded to vasopressin in the rabbit kidney. The same holds for the proximal tubule and the thin descending limb of the loop of Henle (TDL). In contrast, the enzyme present in the thin ascending limb (TAL) was responsive to vasopressin (Imbert *et al.*, 1975c). The magnitude of the stimulation obtained per millimeter of the tubule was much lower in TAL than in collecting tubules (MCT), but the difference may largely be accounted for by the differences in diameter and protein content which exist between these two nephron portions. AVP (10^{-6} M) induced, on an average, 8- to 10-fold stimulation compared to basal values in thin ascending limbs (TAL), whereas the corresponding descending thin segments of the same loops were completely unresponsive (Imbert *et al.*, 1975c). Finally, the medullary portion (MAL) and, to a lesser extent, the cortical portion (CAL) of the thick ascending limb were also responsive to vasopressin, although the magnitude of the responses was low in the rabbit compared to that obtained in the rat, and varied from one experiment to another for as yet unknown reasons (Imbert *et al.*, 1975b, see also, Morel *et al.*, 1981a).

F. OTHER HORMONES

ACTH (when not contaminated with traces of vasopressin) had no effect on cyclase activity in rabbit nephron segments (Fig. 5). Porcine glucagon (10^{-6} M) was also inactive, except for a very low and poorly reproducible cyclase stimulation noted in the thick ascending limb.

G. PATTERN OF CYCLASE RESPONSIVENESS: FUNCTIONAL ASPECTS

Examination of Fig. 5 calls for a few general comments. Clearly, each of the active hormones tested up to now (vasopressin, calcitonin, parathyroid hormone, and isoproterenol) stimulated cyclase activity not only in one but in several nephron portions, according to a pattern which was highly reproducible and specific for the hormone. The nephron portions obviously differ from each other as regards the epithelial cell types they contain and their physiological permeability and transport properties. It is well documented that the physiological responses induced by hormones via cAMP in a given target cell type result from phosphorylation reactions catalyzed by cAMP-dependent protein kinases. The nature of the final response varies from one cell type to another because the proteins which are substrates of these phosphorylation reactions are different in each cell type. In other words, the specificity of hormone recognition by the target cell is made possible by the presence in cell membranes of the corresponding molecular receptors, whereas the specificity of the hormonal response is established by the differentiation of the cell itself. Therefore, one would expect each of the above listed hormones to induce as many different tubular effects in the kidney as it activates cyclase in different tubular cell types. As an example, PTH should elicit different physiological responses in proximal tubules (PCT), cortical thick ascending limbs (CAL), and connecting tubules (DCT_g + CCT_G), respectively.

As regards the functional segmentation of the rabbit nephron, it is apparent from Fig. 5 that the usual segmentation, based on anatomical criteria, is no longer sufficient to account for the data obtained in thick ascending limbs and distal tubules.

Thus, the medullary (MAL) and cortical (CAL) portions of the thick ascending limb contain cyclase exhibiting different responsiveness to hormones: the differences are not only quantitative (vasopressin, calcitonin), but even qualitative (PTH is inactive in MAL and active in CAL). In spite of these differences the two portions of thick limbs contain cell types of a similar general organization, judging from electron microscopy (Kaissling and Kriz, 1979) and exhibit roughly the same physiological properties, judging from *in vitro* experiments (Burg and Green, 1973; Rocha and Kokko, 1973). Therefore, both portions might also exhibit the same final responses to hormones, even though the active hormones are not the same in each of them.

The situation is different as regards the granular portions of distal (DCT_g) and collecting tubules (CCT_g). They both contain adenylate cyclase responsive to PTH and to isoproterenol. When tested together these two hormones induced fully additive effects in DCT_g samples (Chabardès *et al.*, 1975b), an observation suggesting that each hormone might stimulate a different pool of adenylate cyclase in the structure, and consequently might activate a different cell type and induce a different physiological response. This conclusion is supported by morphological observations by Kaissling and Kriz (1979), who showed that the granular distal tubule of the rabbit is heterogeneous and contains at least two cell types, i.e., light cells and dark cells. One of these cell types might be responsive to PTH and the other to isoproterenol.

On the other hand, the granular portions of the distal convoluted tubule (DCT_g) and of the collecting tubule (CCT_g) almost certainly represent the two parts of a single functional segment of the rabbit nephron, on the basis of the following evidence (Morel *et al.*, 1976; Imai, 1979; Kaissling and Kritz, 1979): (1) where present, the two granular portions are always in anatomical continuity; (2) both portions contain the same two cell types, according to electron microscopy; and (3) the cyclase present in the two portions is quantitatively and qualitatively responsive to the same hormones (PTH and isoproterenol). It has been suggested that this DCT_g + CCT_g nephron segment corresponds to the "connecting segment" (Morel *et al.*, 1976) and should therefore be called "connecting tubule" (CNT) (Kaissling and Kriz, 1979; Imai, 1979). According to this definition, the connecting tubule would be a well-delineated nephron portion of the rabbit kidney cortex; rabbit CNT includes the last portion of most distal convoluted tubules and the arcades to which they are branched; sharp transitions exist between CNT and the adjacent bright portion of the distal tubule at one end, and the light cortical collecting tubule at the other. In the kidney of other species of mammals, however, the morphological and functional organization of this part of the nephron is quite different: transitions between adjacent portions are no longer sharp, but rather progressive; arcades are poorly developed and have a light and not a granular appearance, similar to that of light collecting tubules. Finally, the distribution in this nephron area of the hormone-dependent adenylate cyclase activity is also quite different in these other species compared to rabbit, as illustrated by Fig. 7 for the rat nephron. Therefore, the connecting tubule is no longer a well-delineated nephron segment in many species of mammals as it is in the rabbit kidney.

V. Biological Effects of Hormones on Microperfused Rabbit Kidney Tubules

The adenylate cyclase microassay enabled the precise action sites of several hormones to be established along nephrons. But, as already mentioned, other experimental approaches are required in order to investigate the nature of the physiological effects elicited by these hormones on their respective nephron target sites. The *in vitro* single tubule microperfusion technique developed by Burg *et al.* (1966) appears well suited for this purpose. The technique makes possible, under controlled *in vitro* conditions, measurements of the changes in transport characteristics induced by hormones in well-localized pieces of tubules. Unfortunately, tubules microdissected without pretreatment of the kidney tissue with collagenase have to be used, a condition which can routinely be fulfilled in rabbit kidneys only. Even in this species, the technique remains laborious and difficult to handle, so that the data available in the literature are still scant. A few points, nonetheless, have been clarified and deserve mention here (see reviews by Grantham et al., 1981, and by Jacobson, 1981).

EFFECT OF HORMONES ACTING VIA cAMP

1. Vasopressin

The antidiuretic action of vasopressin in cortical (CCT$_1$) and medullary collecting tubules (MCT) is well established and documented (Burg et al., 1968; Handler and Orloff, 1981; Grantham et al., 1978). In this recent progress series, Andreoli and Schafer (1977) reviewed the mechanism whereby ADH and cAMP increase hydraulic conductance across the apical membrane of collecting epithelial cells. In contrast, no clear-cut effect was reported up to now for the rabbit as regards the vasopressin action either in microperfused thin ascending limbs (TAL) (Imai and Kokko, 1974; Imai, 1977) or in microperfused medullary thick ascending limbs (MAL) (Sasaki and Imai, 1980). In microperfused MAL of the mouse, however, vasopressin was observed to increase the lumen-positive transepithelial potential difference (PD) and to stimulate the uphill net reabsorption of Na$^+$ and Cl$^-$ ions (Hall and Varney, 1980; Hebert et al., 1981a,b,c). The species difference noted between rabbit and mouse regarding the vasopressin action on NaCl reabsorption in MAL might be related to the much weaker effect of the hormone on MAL cyclase in the rabbit compared to the mouse (Chabardès et al., 1978b). There is no report available concerning a possible action of vasopressin on the reabsorption fluxes of other ion species, in particular calcium and magnesium, either in rabbit or mouse MAL.

2. Parathyroid Hormone

The biological responses elicited by PTH in microperfused rabbit proximal tubules are well documented and were reviewed by Dennis et al. (1979). In addition to metabolic effects (see reviews by Brown and Aurbach, 1980, and by Amiel et al., 1981), PTH inhibits isoosmotic fluid reabsorption and, in particular, phosphate reabsorption in this segment. The component of phosphate reabsorption reduced by this hormone is the uphill phosphate entry across brush border membranes by a sodium-dependent cotransport mechanism (Evers et al., 1978). Heterogeneity along rabbit proximal tubules was noted in microperfusion experiments as regards these two reabsorption processes. Thus, PTH inhibited fluid reabsorption mainly in the convoluted segment, but phosphate transport in the straight proximal segment only (Dennis et al., 1977, 1979).

Concordant evidence is now available from microperfused thick ascending limbs showing that parathyroid hormone stimulates calcium and magnesium transport in the cortical portion of this segment (CAL) (Bourdeau and Burg, 1980; Sharegi and Agus, 1979; Suki et al., 1980; Imai, 1978); cyclic AMP and cAMP derivatives produce the same effect. In contrast, PTH is inactive in the medullary portion (MAL) (Sharegi and Agus, 1979). These observations agree with the presence of PTH sensitive adenylate cyclase in CAL and its absence in MAL (Fig. 5).

Finally, PTH was also observed to stimulate calcium reabsorption in microperfused connecting tubules without inducing changes in transepithelial PD (Sharegi and Stoner, 1978; Imai, 1981), whereas it had no effect on either calcium or phosphate transport in collecting tubules (CCT$_1$) (Imai, 1981; Dennis et al., 1977).

3. Isoproterenol

Isoproterenol was also tested on microperfused rabbit connecting tubules (Imai, 1979): it decreased the lumen-negative transepithelial PD without affecting calcium fluxes. Thus, PTH and isoproterenol elicited distinct physiological responses in CNT, an observation suggesting that each hormone activated a different cell type in this heterogeneous segment. This hypothesis is supported by the additional observation that cAMP, when added to the bathing solution, induced both the electrical depolarization and the increase in calcium transport (Imai, 1981). These physiological results fit with the already mentioned additivity of PTH and isoproterenol effects on cyclase activity in rabbit connecting tubules.

Isoproterenol was also reported to decrease the transepithelial lumen-negative PD and to stimulate chloride reabsorption in perfused cortical collecting tubules (CCT$_1$) (Iino et al., 1981). These effects were inhibited by acetazolamide, but not by ouabain.

4. Calcitonin

Calcitonin was tested on microperfused rabbit thick ascending limbs; it stimulated calcium transport in the medullary portion of this segment (MAL) but was inactive in the cortical portion (CAL) (Suki and Rouse, 1981), in accordance with the more marked adenylate cyclase stimulation observed in MAL than CAL (Figs. 4 and 5). The calcitonin action on microperfused bright distal convoluted tubules (DCT$_b$) remains to be investigated. No effect of either vasopressin or isoproterenol was observed in this nephron portion (Gross et al., 1975; Imai, 1979). In fact, rabbit DCT$_b$ contains adenylate cyclase responsive to calcitonin only (Fig. 5).

To conclude this brief survey of the literature, it may be pointed out that several hormones were recently shown to regulate transport properties in various rabbit nephron portions, in addition to the well-established action of PTH on proximal tubules and of ADH on collecting tubules. Although still scant, such physiological studies using isolated perfused tubules demonstrate hormonal effects in those rabbit nephron segments which contain adenylate cyclase responsive to the corresponding hormones and not in the others. Moreover, the same effects were elicited by applying exogenous cAMP or cAMP derivatives instead of hormones. There is, therefore, good evidence that hormone-dependent adenylate cyclase is involved in the cell mechanisms through which many hormones regulate tubular functions. On the other hand, the effects induced by a given hormone varied depending on the segment of tubule used, in accordance with the principle that each hormone should elicit a different biological response in each of its different target cell types along the nephron (Morel *et al.*, 1981).

VI. Sites of Hormone Actions along the Rat Nephron

As already mentioned, marked species differences appeared in the results, when single tubule adenylate cyclase microassay was applied to collagenase-treated kidney tissue from mice (Chabardès *et al.*, 1978a,b; Imbert-Teboul *et al.*, 1980), rats (Morel *et al.*, 1978b), or humans (Chabardès *et al.*, 1980) instead of rabbits. Consequently, the data summarized in Fig. 5 cannot be extrapolated to other species without great caution. The differences mainly concerned the distal nephron portions (diluting segment, distal convoluted tubule, and cortical collecting tubule), where not only the distribution of action sites, but (in a few instances) even the nature of the active hormones varied from species to species. We focus here on the results obtained with the rat kidney, since they raise a problem of general importance for kidney physiology.

It must first be recalled that microdissection of tubules is more difficult in rat than in rabbit, even after treatment of the kidney tissue with collagenase. In fact, the middle portion of distal convoluted tubules could not be sampled and studied in the rat. Hormone-dependent adenylate cyclase activity, however, was investigated in all the other nephron portions.

A. HORMONES STIMULATING CYCLASE ACTIVITY

1. Glucagon

As an example, Fig. 6 illustrates the results obtained in the presence of glucagon, a hormone which was virtually inactive on the cyclase of rabbit nephrons. In the rat, glucagon (porcine hormone, 10^{-6} M) stimulated cyclase activity to a huge extent in the diluting segment (MAL and CAL)

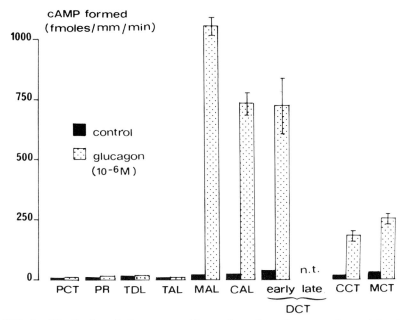

FIG. 6. Distribution of glucagon-sensitive cyclase along the rat nephron. Adenylate cyclase activity was measured either in the absence (basal activities, black bars) or presence of glucagon (porcine hormone, 10^{-6} M, stimulated activities, dotted bars) in samples from successive rat nephron segments (abscissa). Segment abbreviations as in Fig. 3. (Constructed from Bailly *et al.*, 1980, Table I.)

and the early distal convoluted tubule, and to a lesser extent in the collecting tubules (CCT and MCT) (Bailly *et al.*, 1980). The sensitivity of the enzyme to glucagon in the responsive segments was similar to that reported for liver membranes (K_A value of 5×10^{-9} M in MAL).

The pattern of cyclase activation along the rat nephron obtained with six different hormones is given in Fig. 7. Compared to the rabbit (Fig. 5), the following main differences are noted in the rat.

2. Isoproterenol

In rat distal tubules, isoproterenol (10^{-6} M) induces responses of a lower magnitude than in rabbit CNT, but the nephron area sensitive to the hormone is larger and includes the early DCT portion and the cortical portion of thick ascending limbs (CAL) (Morel *et al.*, 1979).

3. Calcitonin

Calcitonin sensitive cyclase activity, in contrast, extends more distally in the rat than in rabbit, and includes all accessible portions of distal

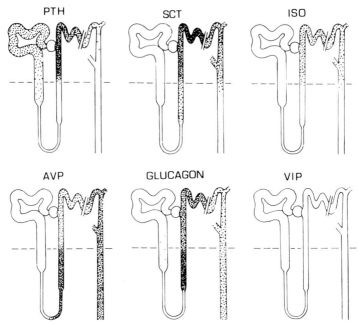

FIG. 7.   Pattern of cyclase activation by various hormones along the rat nephron. For dot density in tubules, see legend to Fig. 5. Hormone abbreviations and concentrations used, as in Fig. 5. VIP, vasoactive intestinal peptide, 10^{-6} M; glucagon, porcine hormone, 10^{-6} M. Note that the cyclase response to hormones could not be measured in the middle portion of distal convoluted tubules. (Reproduced from Morel, 1981b, *Am. J. Physiol.* **240,** F159–F164, with permission.)

convoluted tubules, as well as cortical collecting tubules. In the rat diluting segment, the cortical portion (CAL) is more responsive than the medullary portion (MAL), whereas the opposite holds for the rabbit.

4. Parathyroid Hormone

PTH action sites are roughly distributed in the same way in both species; the response of the cyclase to PTH decreases progressively along all accessible portions of distal convoluted tubules in the rat, whereas it is confined to the connecting tubule in the rabbit. Moreover, the cortical thick ascending limb (CAL) is much more responsive to PTH in rat than in rabbit.

5. Vasopressin

AVP highly stimulates the cyclase contained in collecting tubules of both species. The response to AVP in MAL and CAL, respectively, are much higher in rats than rabbits (Morel *et al.*, 1978). In addition, AVP stimulates the enzyme along rat distal tubules, whereas it is inactive in rabbit DCT_b and DCT_g.

As mentioned in Section III and shown by Fig. 2, the sensitivity of the cyclase to vasopressin was higher in rat collecting tubules (MCT) than in rat medullary thick ascending limbs (MAL). Higher K_A values for adenylate cyclase activation in MAL than in MCT do not necessarily indicate a difference in the binding affinity of vasopressin for its specific molecular receptors in the cell membranes of the two structures. In fact, when vasopressin and structural analogs were tested on the two nephron portions in the same experiments, the analogs induced the same relative activation of cyclase in both segments as vasopressin (Imbert-Teboul *et al.*, 1978). In addition, experiments measuring the kinetics of [³H]lysine-vasopressin binding to membrane fractions prepared from homogenates of rat kidney medulla demonstrated a single, homogeneous class of specific binding sites (Bockaert *et al.*, 1973; Rajerison *et al.*, 1976). Therefore, the molecular receptors of vasopressin are probably the same in MAL- and MCT-responsive cells. The difference in K_A values for cyclase activation probably results from a difference in coupling efficiency between receptors and cyclase moieties in the membranes of the two nephron portions. The observed difference in K_A should be expected if, for example, the numbers of vasopressin receptors per cyclase unit were larger in MCT membranes than in MAL membranes. In the presence of "spare" receptors, lower hormonal concentrations are needed to obtain the same steady-state concentration of hormone-receptor complexes in the membrane and thus to induce similar cyclase activations.

Prostaglandins (PGE_1, PGE_2, $PGF_{2\alpha}$), when tested in concentrations ranging from 10^{-9} to 10^{-6} M, had little effect either on basal or on vasopressin-stimulated adenylate cyclase activities of MAL or MCT samples under the conditions of our microassay (see, for example, Imbert-Teboul *et al.*, 1979). Torikai and Kurokawa (1981a), however, reported that 10^{-6} to 10^{-5} M PGE_2 induced a selective stimulation of basal cyclase activity in rat thin descending limbs. Although of limited magnitude, this effect of PGE_2 deserves mention, since the cyclase contained in thin descending limbs was responsive to none of the hormones tested up to now (see Fig. 7).

B. CYCLASE RESPONSIVENESS TO HORMONES IN DISTAL CONVOLUTED TUBULES

Figure 7 clearly shows that the rat distal convoluted tubule (even though its middle portion could not be analyzed) does not, unlike rabbit DCT, comprise two successive portions separated by a sharp transition, each portion containing cyclase whose responsiveness to hormones is quite different. Moreover, there is no well-delineated granular portion including the arcades of the cortical collecting system. In contrast, the changes in hormonal effects are progressive along the rat distal convoluted tubule, and the end portion of this segment contains cyclase qualitatively and quantitatively responsive to the same hormones as that of the adjacent straight collecting tubules (Fig. 7). Electron microscopy also revealed (Kriz *et al.*, 1978) that, in rats, the distal convoluted tubule is highly heterogeneous at cell level and contains several intermingled cell types, whose respective proportions change gradually along the length of the structure. Any speculation regarding which of these cell types might be responsive to each of the various hormones stimulating cyclase in rat distal convoluted tubules would be unwarranted and premature.

C. CYCLASE RESPONSIVENESS TO HORMONES IN THICK ASCENDING LIMBS

The hormone-dependent adenylate cyclase activity observed in the medullary and cortical portions of rat thick ascending limbs (MAL and CAL) raises a question of major physiological importance. Either portion is relatively homogeneous at cell level, and mainly contains a single cell type (Allen and Tischer, 1976; Kriz *et al.*, 1978). However, each portion contains adenylate cyclase responsive to several hormones in the rat, as clearly shown by Fig. 7. This is particularly striking for the cortical portion (CAL), where five different hormones were observed to stimulate the enzyme, PTH, calcitonin, and glucagon to a great extent, and vasopressin and isoproterenol to a lesser extent. In the medullary portion (MAL), the cyclase was responsive to three of these hormones, namely, glucagon, vasopressin, and calcitonin.

Additivity experiments were performed in order to investigate whether these various hormones all activate a single pool of cyclase in each of the two structures, or activate segregated pools of the enzyme. When high hormone concentrations (i.e., concentrations inducing maximal cyclase responses) of glucagon, calcitonin, or PTH were tested on CAL samples either separately or in combination, the effects were never additive (Morel *et al.*, 1980a, 1982; Torikai *et al.*, 1981). When low hormonal concentrations were used, however (i.e., concentrations inducing submaximal responses), partial or full additivity was observed. An example of such additivity experiments is given in Fig. 8 for PTH and calcitonin. Thus, in rat cortical thick ascending limbs (CAL), the maximal effects induced by glucagon, calcitonin, or PTH were clearly not additive when these hormones were tested together. It was not possible to establish whether the same also holds for isoproterenol and/or vasopressin, due to

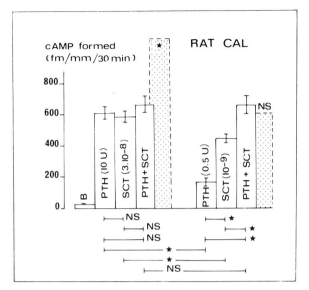

FIG. 8. Combined effects of calcitonin and PTH on cyclase in rat diluting segments. Each open bar gives adenylate cyclase activity (mean value for five to six replicate samples, ±SEM) measured under the conditions indicated (B, basal activity; PTH, units per ml; SCT, salmon calcitonin, moles per liter; PTH + SCT, the two hormones present in the incubate at the same concentrations as for the two left adjacent columns). Dotted bars indicate the calculated cyclase activity for fully additive hormonal effects. All tubular samples were cortical thick ascending limbs (CAL) microdissected from the same rat kidney. Statistics: *, $p < 0.05$; NS, not significant; dotted bar values are compared to the corresponding values measured in the presence of both hormones. Note that effects were not additive at the high hormone concentrations (left panel), whereas the submaximal effects induced by low concentrations were fully additive (right panel). (Modified from Morel *et al. Kidney Int.* **21** (Suppl. 11), S58, 1982, with permission.)

technical limitations (in fact, the maximal responses elicited in rat CAL by these two hormones are much lower than those produced by the three others). Absence of additivity of hormonal effects indicates that (1) the tested hormones competed to activate the same pool of adenylate cyclase in the structure, and (2) the V_{max} of this pool of enzyme itself—and not the number of receptors specific for each hormone—acted as the limiting factor of the response under the conditions of the assay.

Similar experiments were also performed with vasopressin, glucagon, and calcitonin in samples of rat medullary thick ascending limbs (MAL) (Morel *et al.,* 1982). The results are averaged in Table I. When tested separately, the three hormones induced different maximal responses in MAL (glucagon > vasopressin > calcitonin). When glucagon and vasopressin were both present in the incubate, their respective effects were

TABLE I

Hormonal Additivity in Rat Mal[a,b]

Condition[c]	cAMP formed (fmol/mm/30 minutes)	ΔcAMP due to AVP
Basal	15.2 ± 2.5 (7)[d]	588.3 ± 46.6 (7)
AVP	603.5 ± 47.9 (7)	
SCT	220.4 ± 42.5 (7)	581.3 ± 69.5 (7)
AVP + SCT	801.7 ± 69.9 (7)	
Calculated additivity	802.7 ± 69.1 (7)	
Basal	17.0 ± 2.6 (5)	915.9 ± 80.3 (5)
AVP	932.9 ± 82.6 (5)	
GLU	1080.7 ± 104.2 (5)	235.3 ± 91.8 (5)
AVP + GLU	1316.0 ± 163.1 (5)	
Calculated additivity	1996.6 ± 173.8 (5)	

[a] From Morel *et al.* (1982). *Kidney Int.* **21** (Suppl. 11), S59, reprinted with permission.

[b] The table gives average values (±SEM) for two series of seven and five experiments, respectively, in which the additivity of the effects either of vasopressin (10^{-6} M) and salmon calcitonin (3×10^{-8} M), or of vasopressin (10^{-6} M) and porcine glucagon (10^{-5} M) was tested in samples of rat medullary thick ascending limbs (MAL). Note that vasopressin alone induced a higher average response in the glucagon than in the calcitonin series. Clearly, the effects of calcitonin and vasopressin were fully additive, whereas those of glucagon and vasopressin were only partly additive, compared to the corresponding calculated values for fully additive effects. Note also that the response obtained with the combination of vasopressin and calcitonin was lower than that measured with glucagon alone.

[c] AVP, arginine vasopressin, 10^{-6} M; SCT, salmon calcitonin, 3×10^{-8} M; GLU, porcine glucagon, 10^{-5} M.

[d] Values in parentheses are number of experiments.

only partly additive. When vasopressin and calcitonin were combined, their respective effects were fully additive, but the cyclase activity obtained was still lower than that measured in the presence of glucagon alone, or glucagon plus vasopressin (Table I). The data indicate, therefore, that in rat MAL, none of the three active hormones, when tested alone, was able to fully stimulate adenylate cyclase up to V_{max}. Moreover, the absence of full additivity of glucagon and vasopressin effects clearly indicates that both hormones competed to stimulate the same pool of enzyme. The full additivity observed for the effects of vasopressin and calcitonin is not conclusive in this respect, since the V_{max} of the cyclase was not reached in the presence of these two hormones. However, calcitonin is likely to stimulate the same cyclase units as glucagon and vasopressin in MAL, since calcitonin and glucagon effects are not additive in CAL.

The observation that several hormones might stimulate a single pool of adenylate cyclase in rat CAL and MAL, respectively, is obviously of physiological significance. It indicates that, in both portions, the membrane receptors specific for the corresponding active hormones are all coupled to the same cyclase moieties. In other words, in either portion, all active hormones would stimulate the same cells, and therefore should induce the same physiological response in that portion. As stressed earlier (Morel *et al.*, 1980a), this prediction is valid only as long as the primary mechanism of action of these different hormones on their common target cells does not involve some yet unknown molecular transduction step independent of cyclase activation.

In principle, the nature of the physiological response induced by these hormones might be different in MAL and CAL, if the permeability and transport properties of epithelial cells were different in the two portions (the specificity of cAMP-mediated cell responses is established by the cell differentiation itself). However, it must be recalled at this point that MAL and CAL (although they contain cyclase of a somewhat distinct responsiveness to hormones) exhibit almost the same main morphological and physiological characteristics: their cells have a roughly similar general organization, as shown by electron microscopy (Kriz *et al.*, 1978), and the same, very characteristic permeability and transport properties, as demonstrated by rabbit tubule microperfusion experiments (Burg and Green, 1973; Rocha and Kokko, 1973): finally, as mentioned before, calcitonin (in MAL) and PTH (in CAL) were observed to elicit the same effect in the two thick ascending limb portions of the rabbit, namely, to stimulate calcium transport.

In view of such similarities, glucagon, calcitonin, parathyroid hormone, and vasopressin should all induce the same biological effect(s) in the thick ascending limb of the rat kidney, even though these effects are not evenly distributed for each hormone along the medullary (MAL) and cortical (CAL) portions of the "diluting segment."

Appropriate physiological approaches are obviously required to substantiate these predictions and establish the nature of the responses induced by these hormones in the rat diluting segment.

VII. Biological Effects of Hormones on the Rat Kidney *in Vivo*

Unfortunately, the *in vitro* single tubule microperfusion technique cannot be used for the rat as for the rabbit, because microdissection of kidney tissue without pretreatment with collagenase is hardly feasible in the rat. As a consequence, the literature hardly contains any reports concerning hormonal actions studied on isolated rat tubules *in vitro*.

In contrast, a large number of *in vivo* experiments using either whole kidney clearance or micropuncture techniques were performed to investigate the effects of various hormones on kidney functions in the rat. When the many available data concerning tubular effects of hormones are analyzed and compared [see reviews by Katz and Lintzheimer (1977), Dennis *et al.*, (1979), Amiel *et al.*, (1981)], the overall result is rather disappointing. It is generally agreed that, among the various hormones known to stimulate adenylate cyclase in the kidney, only two induce clear reproducible effects, namely, PTH, which inhibits phosphate reabsorption in proximal tubules (phosphaturic effect), and vasopressin, which increases osmotic permeability to water in collecting tubules (antidiuretic effect). In contrast, the evidence concerning other possible actions of these two hormones is rather uncertain or equivocal. The same holds for the tubular effects produced in the rat kidney by other hormones, like glucagon, calcitonin, or β-adrenergic agonists. We are therefore confronted with a puzzling situation: on the one hand, the biochemical approach suggests that each of these hormones should induce effects via cAMP in several well-defined portions of the rat nephron; on the other hand, the physiological approach failed to prove clear-cut biological responses to any of these hormones in the rat kidney, except for the proximal phosphaturic action of PTH and the antidiuretic action of AVP. Careful examination of Fig. 7 may help to account for this major discrepancy and to define new experimental conditions, more appropriate for observing hormonal effects on the rat kidney *in vivo*. Indeed, Fig. 7 shows that most of the rat nephron portions contain adenylate cyclase responsive, not to a single hormone only, but to several hormones simultaneously. The main exceptions are precisely the proximal tubule, in which the enzyme is stimulated by PTH only, and the medullary collecting tubule, in which the enzyme is highly stimulated by AVP only.[1]

---

[1] Cyclase in rat medullary collecting tubules is also responsive to some extent to glucagon (Figs. 6 and 7), but vasopressin and glucagon might stimulate different cell types and elicit different final responses in this structure, on the basis of the following evidence: (1) collecting tubules contain principal light cells and intercalated dark cells and (2) when perfused to Brattleboro rats, glucagon does not increase the permeability of collection tubules to water, whereas vasopressin does (Amiel and associates, personal communication).

In studies investigating the effects of a given hormone on the rat kidney *in vivo,* the conditions determined are usually such that only the concentration of this hormone is experimentally controlled in blood plasma (by appropriate suppression and then perfusion of the hormone), and little attention is given to the other hormones. Obviously, such conditions are adequate to induce and observe effects on those cell types containing cyclase which responds only to the hormone tested (proximal cells for PTH and collecting cells for ADH). However, they might no longer suffice to obtain effects on cell types containing cyclase responsive to several hormones, because, when only one hormone is suppressed, the presence in blood plasma of the other active hormones should largely or even fully sustain the corresponding cell responses. This is particularly true of the rat diluting segment (CAL + MAL), where several hormones were assumed to induce the same common biological responses, in view of the absence of additivity characterizing their effects on adenylate cyclase activity in CAL and MAL, respectively, as already noted. The situation would be very different in *in vivo* biological studies if the following conditions were adopted (Morel, 1982): as a first step, all the hormones presumed to control the diluting segment functioning via cAMP should be experimentally suppressed in the blood. Then, in rats thus acutely and simultaneously deprived of several hormones, perfusion of physiological doses of a single hormone should allow induction and observation of its actions on the diluting segment. In addition, such experiments should indicate whether or not each active hormone in fact induces the same biological response in the diluting segment *in vivo,* as postulated from the *in vitro* adenylate cyclase data.

Experiments of this type are in progress in two laboratories and the results obtained so far fully support the above expectations. C. de Rouffignac and associates, and Cl. Amiel and associates were kind enough to let me report here the main as yet unpublished results they have obtained up to now. The experimental conditions they chose are, briefly, as follows: Brattleboro rats (i.e., rats with permanent diabetes insipidus due to genetic lack of vasopressin production) were used, in order to suppress ADH actions in the kidneys. These animals were acutely thyroparathyroidectomized to suppress PTH and calcitonin. Finally, either glucose or, better, somatostatin was perfused in appropriate doses, in order to reduce or suppress endogenous glucagon secretion. Whole kidney clearance and micropuncture experiments were then performed on these hormone-deprived rats, either without additional hormone administration (controls) or during intravenous perfusion of a physiological dose of vasopressin, parathyroid hormone, calcitonin, or glucagon. The experiments included successive clearance periods in which the glomerular filtration rate and urine flow rate were measured, as well as the Ca^{2+}, Mg^{2+}, K^+, Na^+, Cl^-, and phosphate concentrations in blood plasma and urine samples. Paired micropuncture samples of tubular fluid were collected from the kidney surface in the last accessible convolution of proximal tubules and in the early accessible distal site of the same nephrons, in order to analyze the hormonal effects occurring between these two nephron sites, i.e., in the loop of Henle (which includes the diluting segment). Na^+, K^+, Ca^{2+}, Mg^{2+}, Cl^-, and phosphorus concentrations in the micropuncture samples and in plasma ultrafiltrates were measured by electron probe analysis (Morel and Roinel, 1969; Morel et al., 1969); the single glomerular filtration rate and water reabsorption in the punctured nephrons were calculated from the [³H]inulin concentration in the collected samples ([³H]inulin was perfused throughout the experiments).

Under these experimental conditions, the hormone-suppressed controls excreted a large amount of hypoosmotic urine (ADH suppression) with a low phosphate content (PTH suppression). Calcium and magnesium fractional excretions in the urine were very high. In the hormone-deprived rats perfused with PTH, the phosphaturic effect of the hormone (of proximal origin) was obtained as expected, but, in addition, the urinary output of calcium and magnesium decreased markedly. When vasopressin (¹deamino-⁸D-arginine-vasopressin) was perfused, the expected antidiuretic effect of the hormone was induced, but calcium and magnesium excretion also decreased markedly. Perfusion of either calcitonin or glucagon again induced a marked fall in Mg^{2+} and Ca^{2+} urinary output. The micropuncture data clearly show that, when perfused into such hormone-deprived rats, each of the four hormones markedly reduced the concentrations of calcium, magnesium, and potassium ions in the early distal fluid samples (tubular fluid flowing out of the diluting segment) whereas, in the late proximal samples (fluid entering Henle's loop), the concentration of these ion species was not modified by the hormone, compared to the controls. These results, therefore, demonstrate that each of the four hormones tested has the ability to stimulate in vivo calcium, magnesium, and potassium reabsorption by the thick ascending limb of the loop of Henle in the rat kidney. It is worthwhile recalling at this point that, as already mentioned, PTH and calcitonin were also shown to stimulate divalent cation reabsorption in microperfused rabbit diluting segments.

Obviously, the observations made by C. de Rouffignac and associates and Cl. Amiel and associates will do much to clarify the problem of how and where polypeptide hormones regulate kidney functions in vivo in the rat. In addition, their studies validate and complete the biochemical in vitro measurements made of hormone-dependent adenylate cyclase activity in single rat kidney tubules. Finally, the observation that four different hormones may all contribute to ensure cation reabsorption by the diluting segment of the rat kidney might explain why this biological effect is so difficult to obtain with a single hormone when the three other active hormones are already present in body fluids.

VIII. Conclusion

In concluding this article, I am fully aware of the many simplifications introduced in my description of the sites and actions of hormones in the successive portions of rabbit and rat nephrons. Obviously, the overall physiological action induced by a hormone in the living kidney is not simply the algebraic sum of definite tubular effects elicited in well-delineated nephron portions. Many other factors, which were omitted here, should be considered. Under *in vivo* physiological conditions, the hormonal concentrations prevailing in body fluids are several orders of magnitude lower than those inducing maximal effects on adenylate cyclase *in vitro*. Even maximal biological responses are obtained *in vivo* with hormonal concentrations much lower than those required to fully activate the enzyme *in vitro*. Therefore, recognition and transduction of hormonal signals by cell membranes occur *in vivo* at concentrations closed to the threshold *in vitro* levels and are likely to exhibit kinetic and interaction properties very different from those measured *in vitro* with broken cell systems. In addition, a number of microenvironment factors such as physicochemical gradients across membranes, turnover rates of membrane receptors and components, availability of metabolic substrates, prostaglandin synthesis, and calcium or adenosine concentrations, may affect cell responsiveness to hormones locally.

It is also well established that external messengers can modulate the responses induced by a given hormone, either by increasing the responsiveness of its target cells (as, for example, in the case of the permissive action exerted by corticoids), or by producing inhibitory effects like those exerted by α-adrenergic agonists.

Finally, the successive nephron portions do not function independently. In any segment, the rate of specific transport fluxes depends on the tubular fluid composition and flow rate in the tubular lumen. When hormones alter transport fluxes in a given nephron portion, therefore, functioning of more distally located portions may be indirectly affected. The same holds when hormones change the glomerular filtration rate or blood flow distribution in the kidney. Obviously, almost none of the specific excretory functions accomplished by the kidney can be accounted for in terms of cell physiology. All of them result from the integration of cell processes on the scale of the organ. The vasopressin-dependent mechanism of urine concentration by the kidney is a well-known example of such an integrated function involving the overall organization of both medulla and cortex.

Nevertheless, if we wish to acquire a better understanding of the intricate machinery of the kidneys, we must in any case start by further analyzing the properties of all its component parts.

REFERENCES

Allen, F., and Fischer, C. G. (1976). *Kidney Int.* **9**, 8.

Amiel, C., Chabardès, D., and Bailly, C. (1981). *Actual. Nephrol. Hop. Necker* p. 21.

Andreoli, T. E., and Schafer, J. A. (1977). *Recent Prog. Horm. Res.* **33**, 387.

Bailly, C., Imbert-Teboul, M., Chabardès, D., Hus-Citharel, A., Montegut, M., Clique, A., and Morel, F. (1980). *Proc. Natl. Acad. Sci. U.S.A.* **77**, 3422.

Bell, N. H. (1974). *Acta Endocrinol (Copenhagen)* **77**, 604.

Bockaert, J., Roy, C., Rajerison, R., and Jard, S. (1973). *J. Biol. Chem.* **248**, 5922.

Bourdeau, J. E., and Burg, M. B. (1980). *Am. J. Physiol.* **239**, F121.

Brown, E. M., and Aurbach, G. D. (1980). *Vitam. Horm.* **38**, 205.

Burg, M. B., and Green, N. (1973). *Am. J. Physiol.* **224**, 659.

Burg, M., Grantham, J. J., Abramow, M., and Orloff, J. (1966). *Am. J. Physiol.* **210**, 1293.

Burg, M., Helman, S., Grantham, J. J., and Orloff, J. (1968). *In* "Urea and the Kidney" (B. Schmidt Nielsen and D. W. S. Kerr, eds.), p. 193. Excerpta Medica, Amsterdam.

Chabardès, D., Imbert, M., Clique, A., Montegut, M., and Morel, F. (1975a). Pflugers Arch. **354**, 229.

Chabardès, D., Imbert-Teboul, M., Montegut, M., Clique, A., and Morel, F. (1975b). Pflugers Arch. **361**, 9.

Chabardès, D., Imbert, M., and Morel, F. (1976a). *Int. Workshop Phosphate Metab. Kidney Bone.*

Chabardès, D., Imbert-Teboul, M., Montegut, M., Clique, A., and Morel, F. (1976b). *Proc. Natl. Acad. Sci. U.S.A.* **73**, 3608.

Chabardès, D., Imbert-Teboul, M., Gagnan-Brunette, M., and Morel, F. (1978a). *Proc. Parathyroid Cont., 6th, Excerpta Med. Int. Congr. Ser.* N°421, 209.

Chabardès, D., Imbert-Teboul, M., Gagnan-Brunette, M., and Morel, F. (1978b). *Biochem. Nephrol. Current Probl. Clin. Biochem.* **8**, 447.

Chabardès, D., Gagnan-Brunette, M., Imbert-Teboul, M., Gontcharevskaia, O., Clique, A., and Morel, F. (1980). *J. Clin. Inest.* **65**, 439.

Chase, R. L., and Aurbach, G. D. (1967). *Proc. Natl. Acad. Sci. U.S.A.* **58**, 518.

Chase, R. L., and Aurbach, G. D. (1968). *Science* **159**, 545.

Chonko, A. M., Irish, J. M., III, and Welling, D. J. (1977). *Methods Pharmacol.* **4B**, 297–334.

Dennis, V. W., Bello Reuss, E., and Robinson, R. R. (1977). *Am. J. Physiol.* **233**, F29.

Dennis, V. W., Stead, W. W., and Myers, L. (1979). *Annu. Rev. Physiol.* **41**, 257.

Endou, H., Koseki, C., Kimura, K., Yokokura, Y., Fukuda, S., and Sakai, F. (1982). *In* "Biochemistry of Kidney Functions" (F. Morel, ed.), p. 69. Elsevier, Amsterdam.

Evers, C., Murer, H., and Kinne, R. (1978). *Biochem. J.* **172**, 49.

Grantham, J. J., and Burg, M. (1966). *Am. J. Physiol.* **211**, 255.

Grantham, J. J., Irish, M., III, and Hall, D. A. (1978). *Annu. Rev. Physiol.* **40**, 249.

Gross, J. B., Imai, M., and Kokko, J. P. (1975). *J. Clin. Invest.* **55,** 1284.

Guder, W. G., and Rupprecht, A. (1975). *Pflugers Arch.* **354,** 177.

Hall, D. A., and Varney, D. M. (1980). *J. Clin. Invest.* **66,** 792.

Handler, J. S., and Orloff, J. (1981). *Annu. Rev. Physiol.* **43,** 611.

Handler, J. S., Butcher, R. W., Sutherland, E. W., and Orloff, J. (1965). *J. Biol. Chem.* **240,** 4524.

Hebert, S. C., Culpepper, R. M., and Andreoli, T. E. (1981a) *Am. J. Physiol.* **241,** F412.

Hebert, S. C., Culpepper, R. M., and Andreoli, T. E. (1981b). *Am. J. Physiol.* **241,** F432.

Hebert, S. C., Culpepper, R. M., and Andreoli, T. E. (1981c). *Am. J. Physiol.* **241,** F443.

Iino, K., Troy, J. L., and Brenner, B. M. (1981). *J. Membr. Biol.* **6,** 67.

Imai, M. (1977). *Am. J. Physiol.* **232,** F201.

Imai, M. (1978). *Pflugers Arch.* **374,** 255.

Imai, M. (1979). *Kidney Int.* **15,** 346.

Imai, M. (1981). *Pflugers Arch.* **390,** 145.

Imai, M., and Kokko, J. P. (1974). *J. Clin. Invest.* **53,** 393.

Imbert, M., Chabardès, D., Montegut, M., Clique, A., and Morel, F. (1975a). *Pflugers Arch.* **354,** 213.

Imbert, M., Chabardès, D., Montegut, M., Clique, A., and Morel, F. (1975b). *Pflugers Arch.* **357,** 173.

Imbert, M., Chabardès, D., Montegut, M., Clique, A., and Morel, F. (1975c). *C.R. Acad. Sci. Paris* **280,** 2129.

Imbert-Teboul, M., Chabardès, D., Montegut, M., Clique, A., and Morel, F. (1978). *Endocrinology* **102,** 1254.

Imbert-Teboul, M., Chabardès, D. and Morel, D. (1979). *Upsala J. Med. Sci. Suppl.* **26,** Abstr. 53.

Imbert-Teboul, M., Chabardès, D., and Morel, F. (1980). *Contrib. Nephrol.* **21,** 41.

Jacobson, H. R. (1981). *Am. J. Physiol.* **241,** F203.

Kaissling, B., and Kriz, W. (1979). *Adv. Anat. Embryol. Cell Biol.* **56,** 1.

Katz, A. I., and Lindheimer, M. D. (1977). *Annu. Rev. Physiol.* **39,** 97.

Kriz, W., Kaissling, B., and Pszolla, M. (1978). *In* "New Aspects of Renal Functions" (H. G. Vogel and K. J. Ullrich, eds.), p. 67. Excerpta Medica, Amsterdam.

Kurokawa, K., and Massry, S. G. (1973). *Proc. Soc. Exp. Biol.* **143,** 126.

Marcus, R., and Aurbach, G. D. (1969). *Endocrinology* **85,** 801.

Melson, G. L., Chase, L. R., and Aurbach, G. D. (1970). *Endocrinology* **86,** 511.

Morel, F. (1981). *Am. J. Physiol.* **240,** F159.

Morel, F. (1982). *Q. J. Exp. Physiol.* **67,** 387.

Morel, F., and Roinel, N. (1969). *J. Chim. Phys.* **66,** 1084.

Morel, F., Roinel, N., and Le Grimellec, C. (1969). *Nephron* **6,** 350.

Morel, F., Chabardès, D., and Imbert, M. (1976). *Kidney Int.* **9,** 264.

Morel, F., Chabardès, D., and Imbert-Teboul, M. (1977). *Methods Pharmacol.* **4B,** 297.

Morel, F., Chabardès, D., and Imbert-Teboul, M. (1978a) *In* "Renal Function" (G. H. Giebisch and E. F. Purcell, eds.), p. 275. Josia Macy Foundation, New York.

Morel, F., Chabardès, D., and Imbert-Teboul, M. (1978b). *Proc. Int. Congr. Nephrol., 7th Montreal* p. 209.

Morel, F., Chabardès, D., and Imbert-Teboul, M. (1979). *Upsala J. Med. Sci. Suppl.* **26,** Abstr. 53.

Morel, F., Chabardès, D., and Imbert-Teboul, M. (1980a). *Current Top. Membr. Transp.* **13,** 415.

Morel, F., Imbert-Teboul, M., and Chabardès, D. (1980b). *Adv. Cyclic Nucleotide Res.* **12,** 301.

Morel, F., Chabardès, D., and Imbert-Teboul, M. (1981a). *J. Physiol. (Paris)* **77**, 615.

Morel, F., Imbert-Teboul, M., and Chabardès, D. (1981b). *Annu. Rev. Physiol.* **43**, 569.

Morel, F., Chabardès, D., Imbert-Teboul, M., Le Bouffant, F., Hus-Citharel, A., and Montegut, M. (1982). *Kidney Int. Suppl.* **11**, S55.

Murad, F., Brewer, M. B., Jr., and Vauhan, M. (1970). *Proc. Natl. Acad. Sci. U.S.A.* **65**, 446.

Orloff, J., and Handler, J. S. (1962). *J. Clin. Invest.* **41**, 702.

Rajerison, R. M., Butlen, D., and Jard, S. (1976). *Mol. Cell. Endocrinol.* **4**, 271.

Robertson, G. L. (1977). *Recent Prog. Horm. Res.* **33**, 333.

Rocha, A. S., and Kokko, J. P. (1973). *J. Clin. Invest.* **52**, 612.

Salomon, Y., Londos, C., and Rodbell, M. (1974). *Anal. Biochem.* **58**, 541.

Sasaki, S., and Imai, M. (1980). *Pflugers Arch.* **383**, 215.

Shareghi, G. R. and Agus, Z. S. (1979). *Kidney Int.* **16**, Abstr. 837.

Shareghi, G. R., and Stoner, Z. S. (1978). *Am. J. Physiol.* **235**, F367.

Strewler, G. J., and Orloff, J. (1977). *Adv. Cyclic Nucleotide Res.* **8**, 311.

Suki, W. N., and Rouse, D. (1981). *Am. J. Physiol.* **241**, F171.

Suki, W. N., Rouse, D., Ng, R. C. K., and Kokko, J. P. (1980). *J. Clin. Invest.* **66**, 1004.

Torikai, S., and Kurokawa, K. (1981). *Prostaglandins* **21**, 427.

Torikai, S., Wang, M. S., Klein, K. L., and Kurokawa, K. (1981). *Kidney Int.* **20**, 649.

Vandewalle, A., and Heidrich, H. G. (1980). *Int. J. Biochem.* **12**, 61.

DISCUSSION

G. D. Aurbach: Thank you Professor Morel for a very interesting and stimulating talk. You have demonstrated, I think for the first time, overlap of hormone action within the nephron, particularly in terms of reabsorption of calcium, sodium, and magnesium. Your beautiful paper is now open for discussion.

A. L. Goodman: One of the characteristics of cells comprising transporting epithelia is their morphological asymmetry. Hormone acting on the kidney can reach these cells either through the tubular fluid, because these are small molecules that presumably would be filtered quite readily at the glomerulus, or they could reach the cells through the vasa in the interstitial fluid. What would be the primary source of the hormonal signal to these cells? Would it be hormones in the tubular fluid or hormones in the interstitial fluid?

F. Morel: The hormonal signal certainly reaches the epithelial cells from the peritubular side, on the basis of the following evidence: (1) in *in vitro* single tubule microperfusion experiments, the hormones are much more active when added into the bath than when they are added to the perfusate, and (2) after appropriate isolation of the two membrane fractions, it was shown that adenylate cyclase activity is located in basolateral membranes, and not in luminal membranes.

A. D. Kenny: I would like to suggest to Dr. Morel that he consider testing the effect of the following probe in his system, namely the oxidized form of bPTH (1–34). We have found that if we oxidize bPTH (1–34) with hydrogen peroxide (0.3% for 30 minutes at 25°C), in contrast to the effect on bPTH (1–84), the hypercalcemic, hypocalciuric, and renal 25-hydroxyvitamin D 3-1-hydroxylase responses remain unaffected. On the other hand oxidation of bPTH (1–34) destroys, or at least markedly decreases (we have not done full dose–response curves in most instances), all other responses to bPTH (1–34) so far tested. Note that the renal adenylate cyclase response is decreased or abolished and that the hyperphosphaturic response is also eliminated. Thus, the oxidized form of bPTH (1–34) still has hypocalciuric and renal 1-hydroxylase stimulating activities but does not have any marked hyperphosphaturic of renal adenylate cyclase stimulating activities. It would be interesting to test this probe in your beautiful system.

F. Morel: We used only the 1–34 synthetic bovine PTH fragment. In view of your data, it would be of interest to test the action of the oxydized derivatives on the different PTH target sites of the kidney by using our microassay in order to see whether their relative activity on the cyclase is similar to that of the 1–34 native fragment, or different.

G. D. Aurbach: Dr. Kenny raised the issue of the 1-hydroxylase in the kidney, perhaps Professor Morel could comment about the localization of the 1-hydroxylase and its sensitivity to parathyroid hormone within the nephron.

F. Morel: We have no personal experience of this problem, but it was recently shown by using the microdissection techniques that the PTH-dependent site of vitamin D 1-hydroxylation is located in the proximal tubule.

C. S. Nicoll: There has been much discussion in recent years about the possible role of prolactin in mammalian renal function. Have you had any occasion to test a "good" prolactin preparation on your kidney system? By "good" I mean a preparation lacking vasopressin. I would also like to have your comments on the work that has been done on prolactin's action on the mammalian kidney.

F. Morel: I agree with you that the problem of the relationship between prolactin and the kidney is an interesting and important one. We did not test prolactin up to now however, since in other target tissues prolactin does generally not stimulate adenylate cyclase activity.

F. C. Bartter: Thank you Dr. Morel for a delightful presentation. We have been teaching that vasopressin has no function in the distal convoluted tubule, since the appearance of the work of Gross and Kokko reporting this. I realized when you spoke how fortunate we were that they had studied the rabbit, which is like man in this respect. The teaching would presumably be in error had they studied the rat, since you report a cyclase response in man similar to that in the rabbit and not that in the rat. May I ask you for one more bit of information even after the feast you have given us. At about the same time Gross and Kokko reported these results, they reported also that aldosterone had no function in the distal convoluted tubules, as had been widely taught. We are now assuming that aldosterone has no function in the distal convoluted tubule. Can you tell us whether this is a reasonable conclusion for man, in view of what your studies have shown?

F. Morel: As regards the sites of aldosterone action in the rabbit kidney, two kinds of experimental evidence suggest that the collecting tubule is the main target segment for this hormone: (1) tritiated aldosterone binds preferentially and with a high affinity to collecting tubules as compared to the other nephron segments and (2) after adrenalectomy, there is a big decrease in Na–K-ATPase activity in this nephron portion which is specifically and rapidly restored by the administration of low doses of aldosterone. I am not sure, however, that these data which were obtained in the rabbit, can be extrapolated to the human kidney, since large species differences exist between rabbit and mouse for example, as regards the effects of aldosterone on Na–K-ATPase activity in collecting tubules.

G. D. Aurbach: In the golden hamster it has been shown that parathyroidectomy causes a huge loss of calcium into the urine. The hypocalcemia that develops shortly after parathyroidectomy in that species can be accounted for almost entirely by the amount of calcium excreted in the urine. Thus the hamster kidney is particularly sensitive to the calcium reabsorption effects of parathyroid hormone. The golden hamster is like the desert rat in that it has an unusually long renal papilla and loop of Henle. It is possible that the PTH-sensitive calcium transport portion of the nephron in the hamster extends much further down into the medullary portion?

F. Morel: We have investigated the PTH action in isolated nephron portions of the golden hamster for the reason you just mentioned. We found that the cortical portion, but not the medullary portion of the thick ascending limb was responsive to PTH in this species, as it is in the rabbit, the rat, and the mouse. In addition, the cyclase stimulation was not much higher, in this cortical portion, in the golden hamster than in the rat, for example. The only species in which we found a cyclase responsiveness extending in the medullary portion of the thick ascending limb is the human kidney. Some other factor(s) than cyclase responsiveness to PTH itself might therefore contribute to marked calciuria induced by parathyroidectomy in golden hamsters.

G. D. Aurbach: So that is still an enigma, an unanswered question.

Calcitonin, Prolactin, and Growth Hormone Gene Expression as Model Systems for the Characterization of Neuroendocrine Regulation

MICHAEL G. ROSENFELD,* SUSAN G. AMARA,* NEIL C. BIRNBERG,†
JEAN-JACQUES MERMOD,* GEOFFREY H. MURDOCH,*
AND RONALD M. EVANS†

* *University of California, San Diego, School of Medicine, La Jolla, California, and*
† Tumor Virology Laboratory, The Salk Institute, La Jolla, California

I. Introduction

The study of the regulation of three neuroendocrine genes has provided evidence for developmental regulation of RNA processing events, and defined the rapid transcriptional regulation of specific neuroendocrine genes by both polypeptide and steroid hormones.

A. CALCITONIN GENE EXPRESSION

1. The calcitonin gene provides the initial example of developmentally regulated tissue-specific RNA processing events in the neuroendocrine system, but the underlying mechanisms are postulated to be responsible for the developmental alterations in the expression of many genes.

2. The consequence of these events in the case of calcitonin gene expression is the production of distinct mRNAs encoding the hormone calcitonin in the thyroidal "C" cells, and a novel 37 amino acid predicted neuropeptide, referred to as calcitonin gene related peptide (CGRP), in the brain.

3. The predicted neuropeptide, CGRP, is distributed in a fashion which suggests its function in ingestive behavior, nosioception, and cardiovascular regulation. The methodology used to identify CGRP in the brain should be prototypic for identification of other novel neuropeptides predicted as a result of recombinant DNA analysis.

4. The mechanism of the developmental regulation of exon usage in calcitonin gene expression involves alternative poly(A) site selection within a single transcription unit.

305

5. The CGRP peptide itself is a member of a gene family. A second gene, exhibiting an entirely different organization, encodes a polypeptide product differing from CGRP at only a single amino acid residue.

6. Whatever the evolutionary processes, whether convergent or divergent, by which the calcitonin and CGRP exons became linked in a single transcription unit, a similar genomic arrangement appears to occur in the human calcitonin gene.

7. The calcitonin gene is regulated at a transcriptional level by both polypeptide hormones (e.g., glucagon) and steroid hormones (e.g., glucocorticoids, vitamin D).

8. The RNA processing regulatory events observed in the case of genes of the neuroendocrine and immune systems are likely to be prototypic for events in other gene systems in which diversity offers biological advantages.

B. PROLACTIN GENE EXPRESSION

1. Three polypeptide hormones, thyrotropin releasing hormone (TRH), epidermal growth factor (EGF), and bombesin, exert rapid transcriptional effects on the apparently unique prolactin gene. These data directly demonstrate that the transcriptional effects of polypeptide hormones can entirely account for the observed effects on mRNA accumulation or/and biosynthesis.

2. Elevation of the intracellular level of cAMP rapidly increases prolactin gene transcription; cAMP, therefore, exerts direct transcriptional effects in higher eukaryotes.

3. The positive effects of EGF, TRH, and cAMP on prolactin gene transcription are closely correlated with the phosphorylation of a novel 23,000 dalton basic chromatin-associated protein, referred to as BRP. TRH transcriptional effects are not mediated by cAMP.

4. TRH exerts rapid, transient effects over an unexpectedly broad subpopulation of polymerase II transcription units.

C. GROWTH HORMONE GENE EXPRESSION

1. Thyroid hormones and glucocorticoids rapidly increase the transcription of the growth hormone gene in cultured, clonal rat pituitary cell lines. These transcriptional effects are sufficient to account for the observed induction of growth hormone mRNA and the encoded protein.

2. Glucocorticoids exert transcriptional regulation of pituitary growth hormone gene expression *in vivo* and *in vitro*.

3. The determinants of glucocorticoid regulation of growth hormone gene expression reside in the gene itself, because such regulation is transferred by transfection of eukaryotic cells with the growth hormone gene cloned into various vectors.

4. Introduction of a hybrid gene containing the mouse metallothionine promoter fused to the rat growth hormone gene into the pronucleus of the fertilized mouse eggs results in mice carrying and expressing the fusion gene in specific tissues, including the liver. These mice have extraordinarily high levels of circulatory rat growth hormone and exhibit gigantism. These data suggest an experimental approach for introduction and expression of regulatory peptides into recipients deficient in specific gene products, and imply that specific genomic sequences may exert critical roles in determining the developmental, regulated, tissue-specific distribution of neuroendocrine gene expression.

II. Experimental Data and Background

The complex events required for development and for physiological homeostasis in higher eukaryotes requires a system of intricate communication via regulatory signals, which are largely subserved by the neuroendocrine system. The diversity of regulatory signals within this system permits the control of specific gene expression and provides the specificity of intercellular communication within and between organs. The nuance and subtlety of this system is analogous to that of verbal communication. Thus, in order to understand the neuroendocrine system one must first learn the vocabulary, which is likely to include extensive numbers of polypeptide hormones and neuropeptides, and define the rules of syntax; that is, the molecular mechanisms by which specific gene expression is regulated. The elegance of phraseology is specified by overlapping regulatory interactions on gene expression.

In this article, the regulation of three neuroendocrine genes—calcitonin, growth hormone, and prolactin—is presented as model systems which further the understanding of both neuroendocrine communication and the molecular definition and regulation of eukaryotic transcription units. The calcitonin gene utilizes a novel tissue-specific mechanism which increases diversity of gene expression in the neuroendocrine system. Studies of prolactin gene expression provide insight into the mechanism of action of polypeptide hormones on neuroendocrine gene expression and the nature of hormonal interactions on gene transcription. Finally, the study of growth hormone gene expression provides insight into the genomic determinants and mechanisms of transcriptional regulation.

A. CALCITONIN GENE EXPRESSION

1. Origins of Polypeptide Hormone Diversity

The neuroendocrine system requires enormous diversity to subserve the biological demands of progressively more complex organisms. Three mechanisms account for this diversity of polypeptide regulators in the neuroendocrine systems. The first two mechanisms reflect the initial concept that one gene generates a single mRNA, encoding one protein. In the case of the larger polypeptide hormones, the product of mRNA translation may encode a single protein product; however, in the case of small polypeptide hormones, proteolytic processing serves to excise a series of mature hormones from the larger protein precursors which represent the initial products of mRNA translation. An example of this type of event is provided by the generation of ACTH, MSH, and β-endorphin from the primary translation product of the proopiomelanocortin mRNA (Eipper and Mains, 1978; Roberts et al., 1978, 1979; Nakanishi et al., 1979), and such a mechanism operates in the case of many neuroendocrine genes (Patzelt et al., 1979; Lund et al. 1981; Noyes et al., 1979; Shields, 1980; Hobart et al., 1980; Goodman et al., 1980; Schally et al., 1980; Lin et al., 1979; Gubler et al., 1982; Comb et al., 1982; Noda et al., 1982; Kakidini et al., 1982; Noe and Bauer, 1971; Amara et al., 1980b; Jacobs et al., 1981). Indeed, modification of component peptides may increase even further the number of functionally distinct products generated by translation of a single mRNA. A second mechanism involves the processes of gene duplication and diversification, generating families of related genes, encoding similar but nonidentical peptide products. The third mechanism for generating the observed diversity involves the generation of more than one messenger mRNA, each encoding discrete component neuropeptides, from a single genomic locus. This can arise via use of alternative splice sites within a single exon (Early et al., 1980; Wallis, 1980; De Noto et al., 1981) or can be consequential to the alternative inclusion of exons encoding specific component polypeptide hormones. The operation of the latter mechanism was implicit in the structure of eukaryotic genes (Chow and Broker, 1978; Klessig, 1977; Sambrook, 1977; Jeffries and Flavell, 1977; Tilghman et al., 1978; Darnell, 1978, 1982; Gilbert, 1978). As shown in the schematic representation in Fig. 1, most eukaryotic genes contain component regions, referred to as exons, which are destined for inclusion in the mature mRNA, separated by intervening sequences which are excised by

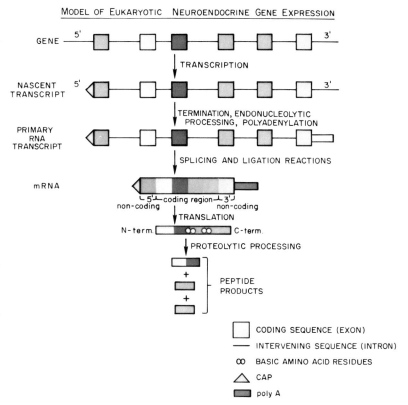

FIG. 1.   Schematic representation of the neuroendocrine genes. Boxes represent exons; the solid lines, the intervening sequences (introns). In this representative model, several exons encode component, excisable peptides from the precursor protein.

RNA processing events. The initial transcript of the gene is processed by enzymatic addition of a unique 5' nucleotide, referred to as the 5' cap. The 3' terminus of the mRNA is determined by a site-specific endonucleotypic cleavage, presumably directed by a specific signal sequence(s) or/and RNA secondary structural considerations (Darnell, 1978, 1979; Ziff, 1980; Ford and Hsu, 1978; Hofer and Darnell, 1981). A poly(A) tract is then enzymatically added at the 3' terminus following an AAUAAA signal sequence. Intervening sequences are then removed as a consequence of endonucleolytic cleavage at intron/exon borders, and ligation of component exons in a semiprocessive and generally precise fashion, to generate mature mRNAs (Lewin, 1980; Sharp, 1981). The discovery of the discontinuity of DNA sequences encoding the mature mRNA and definition of the structure of mRNA precursors (hnRNA) raises the possibility of regulation at the level of posttranscriptional processing of initial mRNA transcripts. While intervening sequences (introns) and RNA splicing have been suggested to have evolutionary significance (Gilbert, 1978; Doolittle, 1978; Darnell, 1979), they probably have other functions in the expression of many genes (Gruss *et al.*, 1979; Hamer and Leder, 1979).

Recent studies of viral and eukaryotic gene expression demonstrate that multiple mature RNAs can be generated from a single transcriptional unit (for reviews see Darnell, 1978; Ziff, 1980). In many cases this polymorphism results from the choice of 3' polyadenylation sites, which can be used to direct alternative splicing choices (Darnell, 1978; Ziff, 1980; Nevins and Darnell, 1978). Definition of calcitonin gene expression demonstrates the role of posttranscriptional RNA processing events in increasing the diversity of neuroendocrine gene expression (Rosenfeld *et al.*, 1981; Amara *et al.*, 1982b). In those neuroendocrine genes in which the component peptides present in the protein precursor are encoded by discrete exons, selective inclusion of one or more of the component exons could generate, by differential RNA processing, a series of mRNAs encoding both shared and unique component neuropeptides. Alternative expression of these RNA products from a single gene would result in a physiological phenomena which we refer to as "peptide switching," the consequence of selective exon inclusion. Calcitonin gene expression provides the initial evidence that precisely such a mechanism operates in expression of certain neuroendocrine genes. The ability to generate multiple mRNAs from a single genomic locus again multiplies the number of hormones which can be generated from a fixed amount of genetic material.

2. Calcitonin cDNA Structure

The biosynthesis of calcitonin in serially transplanted rat medullary thyroid carcinomas (MTCs) has provided an experimental system for definition of "peptide switching" events. Calcitonin is a 32 amino acid polypeptide synthesized by thyroid parafollicular C cells in mammals and is proposed to function as a physiological regulator of calcium homeostasis (Austen and Heath, 1981). The major effects of calcitonin are inhibition of reabsorption of the organic phase of bone, stimulation of the urinary excretion of calcium and phosphorus, and possibly physiological gastrointestinal effects. Calcitonin is almost certain to have additional target tissues (Austen and Heath, 1981), which might be postulated to include the brain.

Molecular cloning of calcitonin cDNA and DNA sequence analysis demonstrated that the calcitonin information is present in a 17,400 dalton precursor containing 136 amino acids and is flanked by basic di- and triamino acid residues (Amara *et al.*, 1980, Fig. 2). Its excision should generate a 16 amino acid C-terminal peptide, referred to as CCP, and an 85 amino acid N'-terminal peptide (Amara *et al.*, 1980, 1981; Jacobs *et al.*, 1981; Birnbaum *et al.*, 1982). The sequence Gly-Lys-Lys-Arg in the precursor following the carboxyl-terminal proline of calcitonin is proposed to contain signals both for amidation and for proteolytic processing. Thus, the organization of the calcitonin precursor is analogous to that described initially for preproinsulin and later for proopiomelanocortin (Nakanishi *et*

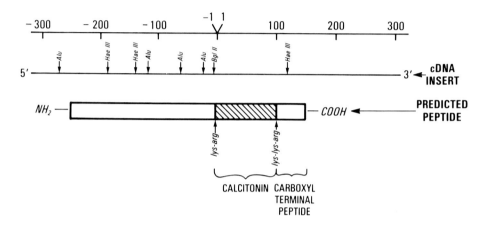

FIG. 2. Molecular cloning of DNA complementary to rat calcitonin mRNA. A schematic diagram shows the organization of the predicted peptide, and the sequence of the cDNA insert.

al., 1979; Roberts *et al.,* 1978; Eipper and Mains, 1978; Steiner *et al.,* 1971).

3. Polymorphism of Calcitonin Gene Expression

The production of multiple calcitonin-related mRNAs was first noted during the spontaneous and permanent "switching" of serially transplanted rat MTCs (Roos *et al.,* 1979) from states of "high" to "low" calcitonin production (Rosenfeld *et al.,* 1979, 1981; Amara *et al.,* 1982). The unexpected explanation for these events were revealed by analysis of the new calcitonin cDNA-reactive RNAs, which established that transcription of the calcitonin cDNA-reactive RNAs apparently continues after the "switch" to states of low calcitonin production, but that a series of new, structurally related mRNAs 50–200 nucleotides larger than calcitonin mRNA, are generated (Rosenfeld *et al.,* 1979, Fig. 3A). These are referred to as calcitonin gene-related product mRNAs (CGRP mRNAs). Associated with these events is a concomitant, marked decrease in calcitonin mRNA levels and a marked increase in specific reactive nuclear RNA species (Rosenfeld *et al.,* 1979) (Fig. 2). The CGRP mRNAs are present on polyribosomes and encode unique proteins as determined by positive selection and immunoprecipitation of mRNA-treated *in vitro* translation products. A new 16,000 dalton protein is the major cell-free translation product directed by one of the CGRP mRNAs (Rosenfeld, 1981); this protein does not contain immunoreactive calcitonin (Fig. 3B and C). On the basis of these data, we suggested that the most likely of several possible explanations was that calcium and CGRP mRNAs were generated by differential RNA processing of a single gene. The corollaries of this model are that (1) the entire sequence of both calcitonin and CGRP mRNAs should be linked within a discrete genomic locus, and the sequences found in genomic DNA should be identical to those of the mRNAs, (2) the function of the common and diverged sequence in calcitonin and CGRP mRNAs should correspond to intron · exon junctions, and (3) the events predict the potential physiological occurrence of "peptide switching" events. To determine the molecular events responsible for CGRP mRNA expression and to examine the possibility that exon selection might be involved, DNA clones complementary to CGRP mRNA and a copy of the apparently unique calcitonin gene cloned into λCH4A were isolated and characterized (Amara *et al.,* 1982b; Rosenfeld *et al.,* 1981). Sequence analysis establishes that CGRP RNA contains sequence identity with calcitonin mRNA through nucleotide 727 of the coding region, predicting that the initial 72 N′-terminal amino acids are identical to those in the calcitonin mRNA-encoded precursor. The mRNA subsequently diverges entirely in nucleotide sequence, encoding a

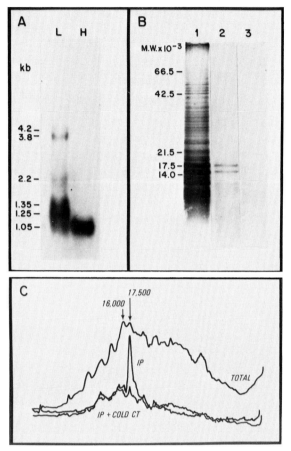

FIG. 3. (A) RNA blot analysis of total rat cellular MTC RNA. Poly(A)-rich RNA from a rat MTC tumor line which switched from a state of high calcitonin production (H) to a state of low calcitonin production (L) was fractionated by electrophoresis under denaturing conditions, transferred to "diazotyzed" cellulose, and hybridized to ^{32}P-labeled cloned calcitonin cDNA probe (Rosenfeld et al., 1980). The autoradiograph reveals bands characteristic of calcitonin mRNA in "H," and CGRP mRNAs in "L." (B) Positive selection and translation of CGRP mRNAs. A mixture of mRNAs from "H" and "L" were hybridized to an immobilized calcitonin cDNA clone. The eluted RNA was used to direct cell-free protein synthesis and the products of translation were displayed on SDS–polyacrylamide gels. Autoradiographs show (1) total mRNA directed translation products; (2 and 3) hybridization-selected RNA-directed protein synthesis using CGRP plasmids (2) or pBR322 (3). Calcitonin mRNA directs the synthesis of a 17.5 kd protein (upper band); CGRP mRNA directs the synthesis of a 16 kd protein (lower band). (C) Immunoprecipitation of the primary mRNA translation products. Calcitonin antisera immunoprecipitates the 17.5 kd protein product of calcitonin mRNA translation, but not the 16 kd protein product directed by CGRP mRNA. The upper quantitative densinometric scan is of total mRNA-directed translation products fractionated using SDS–polyacrylamide gel electrophoresis. The lower scans show the products immunoprecipitated by calcitonin antiserum in the presence and in the absence of excess unlabeled salmon calcitonin (CT).

unique 46 amino acid carboxy-terminal peptide. Although structurally unrelated to calcitonin, the peptide product of CGRP mRNA translation shares a C'-terminal organization remarkably similar to that of the calcitonin precursor. Processing signals within this C'-terminal region predict the excision and C'-terminal amidation of a 37 amino acid polypeptide, referred to as calcitonin gene related peptide (CGRP). A schematic representation of calcitonin and CGRP protein precursors is shown in Fig. 4. On the basis of extensive genomic mapping data there appears to be a unique rat calcitonin gene and the isolated rat calcitonin genomic clone contains all of the sequences present in both the calcitonin and CGRP mRNA sequences (Amara *et al.*, 1982b). Furthermore, identification of the intron/exon boundaries establishes that the calcitonin and CGRP domains are discrete exons within a single gene whose exons correspond precisely in sequence to the cloned cDNAs (Amara *et al.*, 1982a). A schematic representation of the structural organization of the rat calcitonin gene is shown in Fig. 5 (Amara *et al.*, 1983). These data suggest a model whereby both calcitonin and CGRP mRNAs arise from a single genomic locus as a consequence of alternative RNA processing events, resulting in selection of discrete exons for inclusion in the mature mRNAs.

4. Mechanisms Responsible for Exon Selection and Peptide Switching

There are several plausible mechanisms by which the unique calcitonin gene could direct the alternative expression of Cal and CGRP mRNAs. First, there could be two overlapping transcription units with different cap and poly(A) sites. Second, there could be one transcription unit having a single promoter and a single site for initiation of RNA synthesis, but with two or more poly(A) addition sites. Third, there could be a small rearrangement or modification of gene structure during development or differentiation (on one or both alleles) affecting a splice site or polyadenylation signal, directly or consequential to alteration of the transcriptional termination site. Finally, there could be true regulation of processing of the product(s) of a single transcription unit.

Several approaches were used to distinguish between the alternative mechanisms. In one experiment an oligonucleotide was synthesized and used to determine the length and sequence of the 5' termini of both calcitonin and CGRP mRNAs by primer extension methodology. The surprising result of this analysis was that, although the two mRNAs apparently used identical transcriptional initiation sites, there was actually an alternative internal splice site on the 5' terminal nonconding exon used in generation of both calcitonin and CGRP mRNAs (Amara *et al.*, unpub-

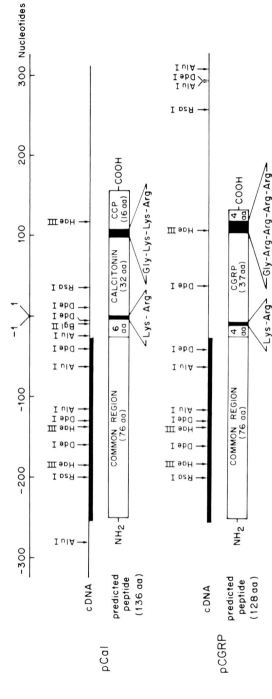

FIG. 4. Schematic representation of calcitonin and CGRP cDNAs, with a partial restriction map, and a schematic drawing of the structure of the predicted primary translation products. The dark bar shows the region of structural identity in the two cDNA clones.

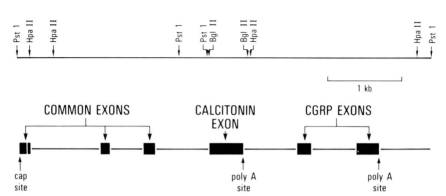

FIG. 5. Schematic representation of the rat calcitonin gene. The organization was determined by mapping and DNA sequence analyses of fragments and overlapping subclones of
genomic DNA inserted in the single-stranded bacteriophage, M13.

lished data). The use of alternative splice sites within an exon has been
observed in immunoglobulin $\mu_m \rightarrow \mu_s$ switching (Early *et al.*, 1980) in the
expression of human growth hormone gene expression, where a portion
of exon 3, encoding amino acids 22–43 of the hormone, is deleted approximately 15% of the time (Wallis, 1980; DeNoto *et al.*, 1981). Similarly,
such alternative splicing choice can involve extremely proximal nucleotides adjacent to an intron, exon border (Sakano *et al.*, 1979; Weigert *et
al.*, 1978; Max, 1979; Taylor *et al.*, 1981; Cooke and Baxter, 1982).

   In the case of calcitonin gene expression, use of two alternative donor
sites within a single exon generates mRNAs with polymorphism of the 5′
noncoding region but encoding the identical mature protein. Thus, selection of the 5′ cap site and the 5′ exon splicing site do not appear to account
for the observed "peptide switching" events. On the basis of restriction
map analysis, no detectable rearrangements within the *Eco*RI fragment
containing the calcitonin gene have been identified (Amara *et al.*, unpublished data). Genomic sequence analysis did reveal a signal sequence
(AATAAA) associated with polyadenylation at the 3′ terminus of the calcitonin exon, and extensive sequence and S1 mapping data predict that
this site is used as the 3′ terminus of calcitonin mRNA. In contrast, the
3′ terminus of CGRP occurs two exons 3′ to the calcitonin/CCP exon.
Therefore, poly(A) site selection appears to dictate alternative exon usage. In this regard, similar mechanisms appear to account for alternative
exon usage in expression of genes of the immune system (Alt *et al.*, 1980;
Early *et al.*, 1980; Maki *et al.*, 1981; Chang *et al.*, 1982) and of the
neuroendocrine system. The critical mechanistic event requiring explica-
tion is the biochemical process(es) which determines poly(A) site selection. It is suggested that this regulation is mediated by a "factor" which

could either direct selection of termination site(s) used, directly or indirectly, or could direct the initial endonucleolytic cleavage to a site adjacent to one of the two possible poly(A) addition sites. The function of such a putative factor, of course, could itself be directed by or produce covalent modification(s) of the calcitonin genomic DNA. These issues are the subjects of current investigation.

5. Calcitonin Gene Expression in the Brain

The next critical question was whether these events are restricted to tumor biology, or reflect their physiological occurrence. To examine this question, RNAs from various tissues were screened using exon-specific probes. This analysis revealed the presence of RNA homologous to CGRP in the hypothalamus (Amara *et al.*, 1982a) (Fig. 6). Therefore, the apparent physiological consequence of these events, in the case of the calcitonin gene, is that expression of a single neuroendocrine gene produces one hormone in thyroidal "C" cells and a second, putative neuro-

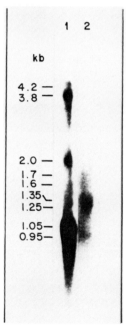

FIG. 6. Presence of CGRP cDNA-reactive RNA in the brain. Poly(A$^+$) RNA from rat thyroid glands (1) or size-selected (9–13 S) poly(A$^+$) RNA from rat hypothalamus (2) was size fractionated under denaturing conditions, blotted onto nitrocellulose, and hybridized to [^{32}P]CGRP cloned insert (Amara *et al.*, 1982). The autoradiograph shows reactive RNA species in each tissue.

peptide in the brain. A model of the predicted, tissue-specific regulation of calcitonin gene expression is shown in Fig. 7.

This prediction, based upon RNA blotting technology, could be tested using an approach identical to that which we utilized to document the physiological occurrence of a peptide CCP (Amara *et al.,* 1982b). Using this method, a synthetic peptide predicted by the cDNA sequence analysis is selected to generate specific antisera. The 37 amino acid CGRP peptide is predicted to terminate in a C'-terminal Phe-amide (Fig. 8) and for reasons of specificity the appropriate region to select for specific antibody generation was the C'-terminus. This peptide, with an added N'-terminal tyrosine residue to permit linkage and iodination, was synthe-

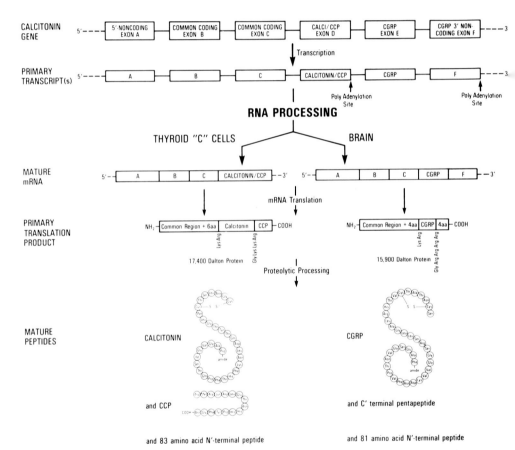

FIG. 7.   Model of tissue-specific neuropeptide production in calcitonin gene expression. The precise exon organization is correctly diagrammed in Fig. 5; this schematic represents the model of tissue-specific exon choice. The poly(A) site following the calcitonin exon has been demonstrated to be utilized in generation of calcitonin mRNA.

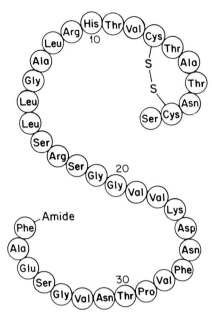

FIG. 8. The predicted sequence of CGRP, based upon the sequence of CGRP mRNA.

sized and an antibody raised (as illustrated in the schematic diagram represented in Fig. 9). Using this antisera immunohistochemistry of the brain revealed staining of regions including neurons and projections subserving sensory, integrative, and motor functions (Rosenfeld *et al.*, 1983). The detailed analysis of Drs. Larry Swanson and Paul Sawchenko revealed that a subset of the fibers and neurons in each region enumerated below demonstrated specific positive immunoreactivity. The positive sensory regions include neurons and small diameter fibers in the trigeminal ganglion and nerve, projecting to the spinal nucleus (subserving pain and/ or temperature), and a similar pattern in all spinal sensory ganglia; vagal and glossopharangeal nuclei to the nucleus of the solitary tract (visceral and taste information), parabranchial nucleus projecting to the thalamic taste nucleus; and primary olfactory, auditory, and vestibular fibers. The integrative regions with anti-CGRP reactivity include projections from the parabranchial nucleus and peripeduncular nucleus, projecting via the medial forebrain bundle to the limbic system (septum, prefrontal cortex, lateral hypothalamus, and central nucleus of the amygdala). The positive motor regions include the facial nerve (muscles of mastication), hypoglossal nerve (motor functions of the tongue), and nucleus ambiguus (one of two motor nuclei innervating heart and/or muscles of the pharynx and throat), and a subset of anterior horn cells in the spinal cord. CGRP staining is observed in both sympathetic and parasympathetic nervous

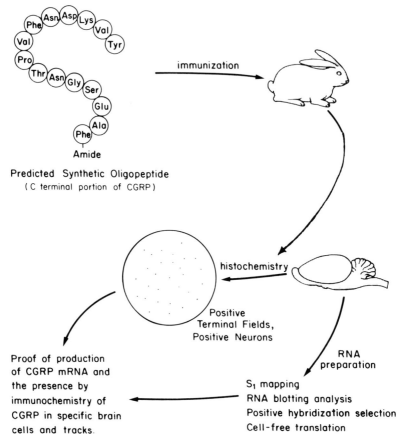

FIG. 9. Schematic diagram of the experimental approach used to identify the production of bona fide CGRP in the brain. Immunohistochemical, S1 nuclease, RNA blotting, and positive selection, translation methodologies were utilized to document the production of CGRP mRNA and CGRP peptide in the brain. CGRP 23-27 was synthesized by Dr. Jean Rivier.

systems, including a widespread distribution in arterioles. Physiological function common to and subserved by these positive regions predicts that CGRP is involved with ingestive behavior, nociception (pain), and vascular function. In addition, the presence of CGRP in adrenal medullary chromaffin cells, in pancreatic islets, and in pulmonary bronchiolar cells suggests hormonal (endocrine) functions for the peptide.

Once peptide reactivity is established immunologically, unequivocal proof of the presence of a predicted peptide has previously required its isolation and protein sequencing, a difficult and often impossible task.

Therefore, a modified S1 nuclease assay, permitting the precise simultaneous identification of CGRP and calcitonin mRNA, was used to map the neuronal sites of CGRP synthesis, and to provide, by inference, a direct sequence confirmation of the immunohistochemical findings (Rosenfeld *et al.*, 1983). Using this technology, the presence of CGRP mRNA was established in the specific neurons in the hypothalamus, midbrain, spinal tract, and trigeminal ganglia. No calcitonin mRNA was detected in these regions, nor was CGRP mRNA present in a region(s) containing only terminal fields, such as the central nucleus of the amygdala. Finally, CGRP gene expression in the brain was quantitated by analysis of nascent polymerase II-catalyzed transcripts in the trigeminal ganglia.

Functional cell lines derived from rat MTC tumors have been established in the laboratory of Dr. Roos. We have established that dexamethasone, cAMP analogs, glucagon, and vitamin D increase transcription of the calcitonin gene in these cell lines, providing evidence that this transcription unit is under complex hormonal regulation (Mermod *et al.*, 1983).

Finally, CGRP has been established to be a member of a gene family (unpublished data). We have isolated and sequenced a cDNA clone which contains a region of homology to CGRP mRNA, flanked by regions of entirely unrelated sequence. This mRNA predicts that a series of polypeptide products will be generated, one of which is a CGRP-related peptide which differs in only a single C'-terminal amino acid from CGRP. The N'-terminal region common to calcitonin and CGRP mRNA and calcitonin coding sequences are apparently not present in this mRNA.

The apparent tissue specificity of the observed RNA processing events in calcitonin gene expression implies developmental regulation of these processes. Calcitonin gene expression therefore represents a model system for exploring the mechanisms responsible for both transcriptional and RNA processing regulation of specific genes during development. Whatever the responsible biochemical reactions, the unexpected consequence of these RNA processing events is that the same gene which generates the hormone calcitonin in thyroid "C" cells is apparently responsible for expression of a new neuropeptide, CGRP, in the brain. Based upon the structure of this gene, and two of its polymorphic RNA products, we propose a model in which genomic regions represent discrete hormone-encoding domains whose ultimate expression is dependent upon differential RNA processing events. It is tempting to speculate (Fig. 10) that alternative exon selection operates in a group of genes encoding small regulatory peptides, including neurotransmitter or releasing factors, and further, that the events in neuroendocrine and immune gene expression are prototypic for other genes, which encode proteins which are com-

A

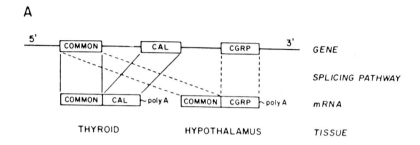

B

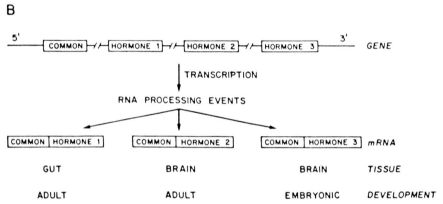

FIG. 10. Model of the potential application of "peptide switching" events in the case of genes encoding other neuropeptides. A similar mechanism may operate with respect to genes encoding other proteins containing domains in which diversity is biologically required. (A) Calcitonin switching; (B) Hypothetical structure of a gene encoding polymorphic products.

posed of functional domains, such as hormone receptors, and in which polymorphism in ligand binding or response would be advantageous.

B. PROLACTIN GENE EXPRESSION

1. Mediation of Polypeptide Hormone Action

The mechanisms by which hypophysiotropic regulators and neuropeptides exert their effects on specific gene expression was investigated using the hormonally regulated biosynthesis of prolactin in a functional clonal rat pituitary cell line (GH) as a model system (Tashjian et al., 1968; Martin and Tashjian, 1977; Bancroft et al., 1979). Both prolactin and growth hormone biosynthesis are under complex hormonal regulation in these cells (Martin and Tashjian, 1977). The mechanisms by which polypeptide hormones act is considerably more complex than was initially appreciated, and there are several possible consequences of their initial binding to receptor (Fig. 11). Understanding the mechanisms by which polypeptide hormones regulate specific gene expression requires definition of the sites at which regulation is accomplished, identification of which second messengers or effectors are generated as a consequence of receptor–hormone interaction mediate this effect, and characterization of the precise biochemical reactions responsible for the observed regulation. Definition of the structure of the prolactin gene (Gubbins *et al.*, 1980; Chien and Thompson, 1980; Cooke and Baxter, 1982) and its nuclear RNA transcript (Maurer *et al.*, 1980; Hoffman *et al.*, 1981; Potter *et al.*, 1981) provided the experimental basis for further analyses.

While it is likely that many of the intracellular effects produced by a hormone are regulated by a single mediator, there is overwhelming evidence that, in accord with the redundancy of nature, a series of intracellular modulators or second messengers can be generated by the initial interactions of a polypeptide hormone with its membrane receptors. It is

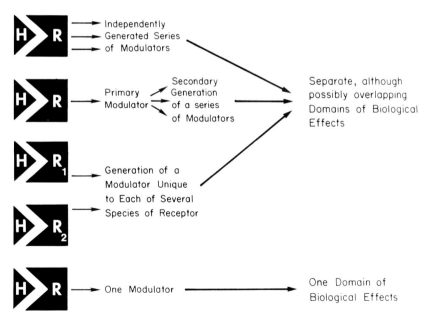

FIG. 11.   Potential modulation of intracellular effects of hormone–receptor interactions. The diversity of intracellular effects may reflect simultaneous or sequential elaboration of a series of so-called second messengers, as diagrammatically outlined.

unknown how proximal to the initial hormone–receptor interactions the putative second messengers are generated. As shown in Fig. 11, such a diversity of second messengers could result from functional polymorphism of receptors, multiple effects of allosteric modification of a single receptor, or a cascade of events rapidly following generation of a primary effector. It is tempting to speculate that each effector pathway will simultaneously govern a domain of biological actions. Therefore, in order to understand any single regulated process, such as the stimulation of specific gene expression, the nature of the regulated site must be defined before the potential effector mediation is identified.

2. TRH Regulation of Prolactin Gene Expression

In the case of prolactin gene expression, the tripeptide thyrotropin releasing hormone (TRH) (Pyro Glu · His · Pro · amide) stimulates the biosynthesis of prolactin as a result of TRH binding to its plasma membrane receptor (Hinkle and Tashjian, 1973). With prolonged exposure to TRH, down-regulation of TRH receptors is noted (Hinkle and Tashjian, 1975). There is a close correlation between prolactin biosynthesis and prolactin mRNA sequence levels (Evans et al., 1976, 1979; Murdoch et al., 1982c). It is therefore postulated that prolactin mRNA concentration determines the biosynthesis of prolactin. The kinetics of TRH stimulation of prolactin biosynthesis and levels characteristically reach the maximal stimulation by 15–36 hours, followed by a progressive attenuation which could reflect receptor down regulation or/and attenuation of intracellular effects (Potter et al., 1981). The site at which TRH acts to increase prolactin mRNA accumulation appears to be gene transcription, as determined by (1) quantitation of the primary nuclear transcript (Potter et al., 1981) and (2) direct quantitation of prolactin gene transcription by measurement of nascent RNA transcripts. TRH addition increases the mass of the putative primary RNA transcript >10-fold by 1 hour (Fig. 12), with a $t_{\frac{1}{2}}$ to maximal stimulation of <20 minutes, with a subsequent attenuation of effects (Murdoch et al., 1982c). TRH is reported to increase nuclear prolactin RNA content using R_0t analysis (Biswas et al., 1982). Measurement of prolactin gene transcription by quantitation of nascent RNA transcripts elongated by incubation of isolated nuclei in the presence of radiolabeled nucleotide, by hybridization to an immobilized gene-specific intervening sequence clones under conditions of DNA excess. TRH increases polymerase II-dependent prolactin gene transcription within minutes, with maximal effects (7- to 12-fold stimulation) by 15–30 minutes (Fig. 13) (Murdoch et al., 1983). After 1 hour there is a rapid, persistent attenuation of TRH transcriptional effects. The kinetic and quantitative effects of TRH on prolactin gene transcription are entirely sufficient to account for

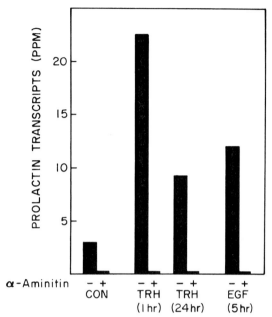

FIG. 12. Effects of TRH and EGF on prolactin gene transcription. Addition of TRH (10^{-7} M) or EGF (2×10^{-8} M) to GH4 cell cultures increases prolactin gene transcription. The inhibition by α-amanitin (0.8 μg/ml) of *in vitro* chain elongation suggests that the transcription of the prolactin gene is catalyzed by RNA polymerase II.

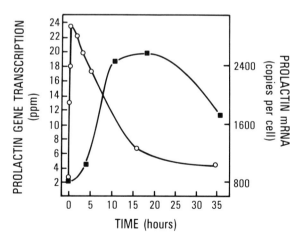

FIG. 13. TRH rapidly increases the rate of prolactin gene transcription (○———○) as quantitated by DNA excess hybridization of nascent chains radiolabeled by chain elongation *in vitro*, using isolated nuclei and increases accumulation of cytoplasmic prolactin mRNA sequences (■———■).

both the magnitude (2- to 3-fold) and the kinetics of prolactin mRNA accumulation (Potter *et al.*, 1981; Murdoch *et al.*, 1982a, 1983c). Therefore, it is postulated that TRH exerts rapid transcriptional effects to account for its regulation of prolactin biosynthesis, and that the "burst, attenuation" effects on transcription is an important characteristic of polypeptide hormone action. These data establish the fact that polypeptide hormones can regulate expression of specific genes by rapidly increasing their transcription.

3. Modulation of TRH Transcriptional Effects

The very rapid transcriptional effects of TRH, with a $t_{\frac{1}{2}}$ to maximum actually faster than that for prolactin secretion, helps to exclude one possible mechanism of transcriptional regulation of secreted hormones, namely, that secretion is the stimulus for specific gene transcription via "push–pull" mechanism. This conclusion is further supported by the observation that several agents (50 *mM* K^+, calcium ionophores) which stimulate prolactin secretion in pituitary lactotrophs and GH cells fail to increase prolactin gene transcription (Murdoch *et al.*, 1983b). Secretion and specific gene transcription, therefore, appear to reflect two unlinked cellular effects. Thus, one must consider it likely that different molecular events mediate TRH stimulation of prolactin secretion and regulation of prolactin gene transcription. In fact, on the basis of pharmacological data it has been previously proposed that two separate TRH receptors were responsible for secretion and synthetic effects (Dannies and Tashjian, 1976). The mediators of TRH are unproven, but the candidates, including elevation of intracellular cAMP levels, activation of a number of protein kinase activities (cAMP-dependent and cAMP-independent kinases), modifications of plasmid membrane lipids, alterations in Ca^{2+} flux, or/and intracellular distribution (Martin and Tashjian, 1977; Drust *et al.*, 1982; Sutton and Martin, 1982; Tan and Tashjian, 1982; Gershengorn, 1980; Taraskivich and Douglas, 1977; Kidokoro, 1975; Gershengorn, 1980; Ozawa and Kimura, 1979; White, *et al.*, 1981; Drust and Martin, 1982). Finally, and with slower kinetics, there is an internalization of the TRH receptor complex. The challenge, then, is to determine which of the many potential intracellular effectors of hormone–receptor interaction exert regulatory effects on a specific biochemical event, such as transcription of the prolactin gene. In the absence of any readily applicable genetic approach, a pharmacological approach was initially utilized to generate a model which could then be biochemically tested. The addition of cobalt, a Ca^{2+} channel blocker, entirely abolished the TRH effects on prolactin gene transcription at 1 hour following its addition; no effect on total transcription or upon growth hormone gene transcription was observed

(Murdoch *et al.*, 1983b). Pimozide, a diphenylbutylpiperidine likely to bind a number of Ca^{2+}-binding calmodulin-like proteins, perhaps including the phospholipid regulated membrane kinase, the so-called "C" kinase, inhibited TRH transcriptional effects approximately 40–50%. The half-maximal inhibition was observed at concentrations of $<10^{-7} M$, indicating that this effect was due to the effects other than effects on inhibition of calmodulin activity (Murdoch *et al.*, 1983). Neither calcium ionophores nor pharmacological agents causing redistribution of intracellular calcium increased prolactin gene transcription (Murdoch *et al.*, 1983a).

As seen in Fig. 14, cAMP analogs (8-bromo-cAMP, dibutyryl cAMP) stimulate prolactin gene transcription 4- to 6-fold, but to levels only 40–50% those observed by TRH (Murdoch *et al.*, 1982). At high concentrations of cAMP analogs, or following the addition of the diterpene, forskolin, which specifically and rapidly activates the catalytic subunit of adenylate cyclase producing large increases in intracellular cAMP concentrations, a 4- to 6-fold stimulation of prolactin gene transcription was the maximal effect observed. This fold stimulation was virtually identical for each agent. As shown in Fig. 14B, the kinetics of stimulation are extremely rapid, with a $t_{\frac{1}{2}}$ to maximal effect of less than 3 minutes following addition. Recent evidence suggests this induction may begin within seconds to minutes, suggesting a direct cAMP effect rather than a process secondary to cAMP-induced alteration of cell metabolism. In contrast to the "burst, attenuation" effects of TRH on prolactin gene transcription, there is an attenuation of effects following elevation of intracellular cAMP levels over the initial 10 hours. Finally, as shown in Fig. 14C, the consequence of this cAMP-induced increased prolactin gene transcription is the elevation of prolactin mRNA levels with a kinetics of accumulation and the final level of stimulation of prolactin mRNA levels (3- to 7-fold stimulation), comparable to that observed in response to TRH. Therefore, the sustained stimulation of prolactin gene transcription, though at a lower level, is equally as productive as the "burst, attenuation" pattern characteristic of TRH action. The steady-state stimulation of transcription in response to cAMP enables one to infer that the $t_{\frac{1}{2}}$ to maximal mRNA accumulation, approximately 6 hours, corresponds to the prolactin mRNA half-life in the cAMP-induced cells. These data are consistent with the postulate that increased intracellular cAMP concentrations produce rapid transcriptional effects on specific genes, as occurs in prokaryotes. This postulate is supported by the observations that cAMP can overcome the inhibitory transcriptional effects of dopamine (Maurer *et al.*, 1981) and that administration of dibutyryl cAMP *in vivo* increases liver PEPCK gene transcription (Lamers *et al.*, 1982).

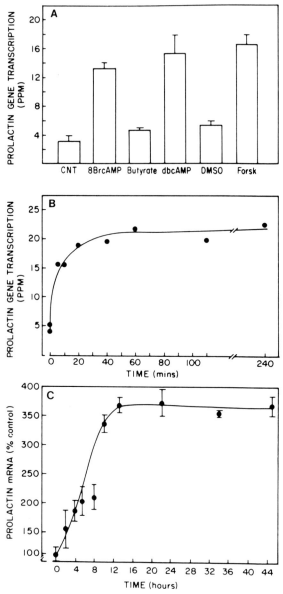

FIG. 14. Effects of cAMP analogs and forskolin on prolactin gene expression in GH$_4$ cell cultures. (A) Effects of cAMP analogs and forskolin on prolactin gene transcription. Agents were added 50 minutes prior to harvest. (B) Kinetic analysis of the transcriptional effects of forskolin (10^{-6} M) addition. (C) Prolactin mRNA accumulation following addition of forskolin (10^{-6} M) to GH4 cell cultures.

If cAMP alone cannot mimic the full TRH effects on prolactin gene transcription, then either cAMP does not mediate TRH action or it is only one component of the TRH effects. While pharmacological approaches alone cannot answer this question, based upon a series of pharmacological experiments (Murdoch *et al.*, 1983), we propose that TRH stimulates prolactin gene transcription as a consequence of the activation of both C kinase and a second protein kinase, while cAMP exerts effects via a cAMP-dependent protein kinase-mediated phosphorylation of a phosphatase inhibitor. Such a model is consistent with the data that calcium deprivation may decrease prolactin gene expression (White *et al.*, 1982). There are no data that Ca^{2+} itself directly mediates TRH actions; indeed, TRH and EGF exert their effects in cells following 4 days of serum-free, calcium-free cell culture conditions (Waterman *et al.*, 1983).

If TRH and cAMP exert transcriptional effects within seconds to minutes, it is logical to predict that mediation of the rapid nuclear hormonal effects might be modification (e.g., phosphorylation) of a nuclear protein. Thus far, we can identify only one nuclear chromatin-associated protein which is phosphorylated in response to TRH. This protein is a basic, chromatin-associated, 23,000 dalton phosphoprotein, the phosphorylation of which can be stimulated as much as 10- to 12-fold by TRH or cAMP (Murdoch *et al.*, 1982, 1983). The mass of this protein is approximately 1/100 of that of the major H1 histone species, and this protein appears to differ from the known histone isotypes or the so-called HMG proteins. Figure 15 shows autoradiograms of basic nuclear proteins following 20 minutes of exposure to TRH or cAMP and subject to analysis using two-dimensional gel analysis (Murdoch *et al.*, 1982b). TRH stimulates phosphorylation of this protein 5- to 10-fold; calcium ionophores actually decrease phosphorylation below that in unstimulated cells, while addition of cobalt virtually abolishes its phosphorylation. We refer to this basic chromatin-associated regulated protein as BRP. BRP appears to have an exclusively nuclear location. Two types of data closely correlate BRP phosphorylation with increased prolactin gene transcription. The first type of evidence is pharmacological, with precise correspondence between the effects of various agents and hormones on prolactin gene transcription and BRP phosphorylation (Murdoch *et al.*, 1983a). The second type of evidence is based upon a detailed kinetic analysis of phosphorylation of BRP and prolactin gene transcription following addition of TRH, which reveals a totally parallel rapid increase in BRP phosphorylation and prolactin gene transcription with a $t_{\frac{1}{2}}$ to maximal effect of approximately 1.5–3 minutes (Murdoch *et al.*, 1982c). There are several conclusions from these analyses. First, polypeptide hormones maximally stimulate specific

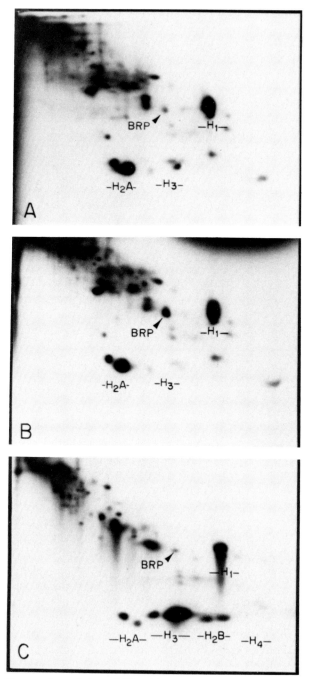

FIG. 15. Hormonal regulation of "BRP" phosphorylation. Phosphorylation of acid-soluble nuclear proteins in unstimulated (A) or TRH-stimulated (20 minutes) (B) GH_4 cell cultures (for details see Murdoch 1982b,c). (C) Phosphorylation of chromatin basic proteins by purified cAMP-dependent protein kinase (see Murdoch, 1982b).

gene transcription with such rapidity that events such as receptor internalization become unlikely mediators of the nuclear effects, since the observed kinetics exceed that of hormone–receptor internalization. Thus, a signal must either activate a nuclear protein kinase or translocation of a protein kinase must occur within seconds to minutes in order to produce BRP phosphorylation. The close correlation between hormone-stimulated BRP phosphorylation and increased prolactin gene transcription permits one to propose that BRP modification could itself represent a biochemical event which regulates prolactin gene transcription. It is further observed that BRP contains at least four phosphorylation sites, and preliminary data support the notion that at least two discrete protein kinases independently regulate its function.

Because BRP is present on chromatin, and would be expected to exhibit a fairly general genomic distribution, it is possible that its phosphorylation could regulate a wide variety of genes, rather than the putatively more limited domain classically considered under regulation by a specific hormone (Ivarie and O'Farrell, 1978; Garrels and Schubert, 1979; Steinberg and Coffino, 1979; Rosenfeld and Barrieux, 1979). The pleiotropic domain of TRH genomic effects was therefore investigated; surprisingly, TRH was found to rapidly, although transiently, stimulate polymerase II-dependent transcription of up to 20% of actively transcribing genes, an unusually large domain (Murdoch et al., 1983a). These transcriptional effects were generally maximal by 20–30 minutes and attenuated by 60–90 minutes. This massive extent of transcriptional effects further supports the possible functional significance of hormone-dependent BRP modification, and emphasizes that all effects of hormones occurring after 30 minutes are potentially consequential to the expression of these ''early'' transcriptional events.

4. EGF Stimulates Prolactin Gene Transcription

Several laboratories independently reported that EGF increased prolactin secretion and biosynthesis (Schonbrunn et al., 1980; Johnson et al., 1980). We have demonstrated that EGF increased both the level of nuclear prolactin precursors (Fig. 16) and rapidly increased the transcription of the prolactin gene (Fig. 16, Murdoch et al., 1982a). EGF in parallel increased prolactin gene transcription greater than 8-fold, the mass of the primary nuclear transcript (6- to 8-fold), and prolactin mRNA accumulation. EGF also stimulates BRP phosphorylation (Murdoch et al., unpublished data). The kinetics of the EGF attenuation events depend upon culture conditions.

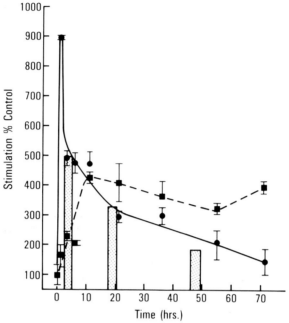

FIG. 16. Kinetic effects of EGF addition to GH4 cultures upon prolactin mRNA
(■——■), prolactin primary RNA transcript levels (hatched bars), and prolactin gene transcription (●——●).

5. Interactive Hormonal Actions on Prolactin Gene Transcription

Because both TRH and EGF stimulate transcription of the prolactin
gene and because, on the basis of Southern genomic mapping data, there
appears to be a unique prolactin gene, the question arises whether there
are two independent "sites" regulated by each polypeptide hormone, or
whether their effects converge at a single regulatory site. TRH and EGF,
each at concentrations well above those producing maximal transcriptional effects, can exert additive effects on prolactin gene transcription
(Waterman *et al.*, 1983) (Fig. 17). Furthermore, following attenuation of
TRH effects, EGF can still stimulate gene transcription (>8-fold). Hence,
EGF and TRH cannot entirely share an identical mechanism of action;
and attenuation of the effects of one polypeptide hormone does not interrupt actions of a second polypeptide hormone in prolactin gene expression.

In the case of steroid hormones, estrogen which also stimulates prolactin biosynthesis, has been shown to increase estrogen mRNA levels
(Maurer *et al.*, 1976; Shupnik *et al.*, 1979), and by Maurer (1982) to

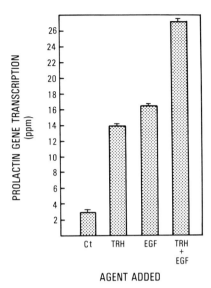

FIG. 17. Hormonal interactions on prolactin gene expression. Additive effects of TRH and EGF on prolactin gene transcription are observed after hormonal additions to GH4 cell culture.

increase prolactin gene transcription following its *in vivo* administration. However, because estrogen acutely decreases dopamine concentration in the portal circulation, the acute action of estrogen could be partially or entirely indirect. In GH cell cultures estrogen does exert transcriptional effects on prolactin gene transcription (Waterman *et al.*, 1983) confirming the expected transcriptional site of action. A combinatorial analysis reveals that the effects of estrogen, TRH, and EGF exert direct additive effects on prolactin gene transcription and upon the accumulation of the primary transcript. Finally, GH cells have been shown to contain vitamin D receptors, and to respond to vitamin D with induction of specific proteins (Murdoch and Rosenfeld, 1980). Vitamin D produces a series of effects including modification of the attenuation of TRH genomic effects, producing stimulatory effects on prolactin mRNA induction and prolactin gene transcription in combinatorial analysis with other hormones (Fig. 18, Murdoch and Rosenfeld, 1980; Murdoch *et al.*, unpublished data). Therefore, a single transcription unit (Supowit *et al.*, unpublished data) in the unique prolactin gene can be regulated in an additive fashion by two steroid hormones and two polypeptide hormones. A critical question is whether these agents exert their effects at one or more genomic sites, and whether each agent affects transcriptional initiation or/and other transcriptional events. In order to approach these questions, a hybrid gene

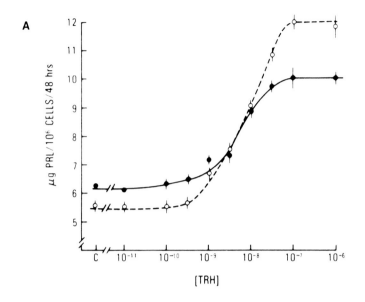

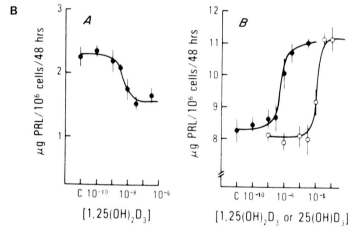

FIG. 18.   Modulation of TRH stimulation of prolactin by 1,25(OH₂)D₃. (A) GH4 cell
cultures were incubated for 48 hours in the presence (○——○) or absence (●——●) of
1,25(OH₂)D₃ (10⁻⁷ M) and the indicated concentration of TRH. (B) *A*: Effect of 1,25(OH₂)D₃
on basal prolactin production. *B*: Effect of TRH- (3 × 10⁻⁷ M) stimulated prolactin production of 1,25(OH₂)D₃ (●——●) or 25(OH₂)D₃ (○——○).

construction containing the 5′ portion of the prolactin gene fused to other genes was transfected into a series of eukaryotic cell lines. The transcriptional regulation by cyclic nucleotides and polypeptide hormones of the transfected gene provides evidence consistent with the postulate that specific 5′ genomic sequences transfer responsivity to polypeptide hormones (Supowit et al., unpublished data).

C. REGULATION OF GROWTH HORMONE GENE EXPRESSION

Growth hormone is a pituitary polypeptide important during adolescence but produced throughout the life span of all mammals (Samuels, 1978; Felig et al., 1981). It is necessary for normal growth and development, and abnormal production is associated with numerous disease states including various forms of dwarfism and normal variant short stature syndrome. The growth hormone gene serves as an excellent model for studying complex control mechanisms because it, like prolactin, is expressed and regulated in the clonal rat pituitary cell lines G/C and GH_3 (Tashjian et al., 1968; Bancroft et al., 1969). In these cells it has been established that growth hormone biosynthesis is induced by glucocorticoids and by thyroid hormone and this induction is apparently the consequence of hormonal stimulation of growth hormone mRNA levels (Tashinski, 1977; Martial et al., 1977; Samuels et al., 1977, Seeburg et al., 1977; Harpold et al., 1979). The regulation of specific gene expression by glucocorticoids, and related steroid hormones, is postulated to be mediated by specific soluble receptors which bind the hormone, undergo allosteric modification, and become associated with nuclear chromatin complexes (Yamamoto and Alberts, 1976; Samuels and Shapiro, 1967). Thyroid hormone is postulated to interact with nuclear thyroid hormone receptors, and thyroid hormone receptors are present in the nuclei of these cultured pituitary cells (Samuels and Shapiro, 1976). The cloning of growth hormone cDNA in a number of laboratories, and the isolation of the growth hormone genomic clone (Cooke and Baxter, 1981; Page et al., 1981; Chien and Thompson, 1980; Gubbins et al., 1980; Deehmer et al., 1982). In order to define the biochemical reactions modulating the unique rat growth hormone gene expression, it is critical to first define the sites of action of each hormone. Analysis of the effects of the synthetic glucocorticoid, dexamethasone, or the accumulation of pulse-labeled growth hormone mRNA by increasing its rate of synthesis suggests that the primary site of action is nuclear (Evans et al., 1982). A series of studies which tentatively identify the growth hormone mRNA nuclear precursors (Harpold et al., 1979; Maurer et al., 1981; Dobner et al., 1981; Evans et al.,

1982) permitted a demonstration that dexamethasone promotes an increase in growth hormone nuclear RNA precursors in proportion to its induction of mRNA levels (Dobner *et al.*, 1981; Evans *et al.*, 1982). These results provide compelling evidence that the growth hormone gene is the target of steroid hormone action, and are consistent with the proposed mechanism of mouse mammary tumor virus and α_2-euglobin and metallothionein gene transcriptional regulation by glucocorticoids (Huang *et al.*, 1981; Lee *et al.*, 1981; Kurtz, 1981; Buetti and Diggelman, 1980).

1. Glucocorticoids Regulate Growth Hormone Gene Transcription

The induction of both mRNA and nuclear precursors suggests that glucocorticoids act by increasing the rate of transcription of the growth hormone gene. Transcription rates of the growth hormone gene were assessed by quantitation under DNA excess hybridization conditions of the number of nascent transcripts labeled with [^{32}P]UTP following digestion in isolated nuclei (Evans *et al.*, 1982). The results shown in Fig. 15 demonstrate the 3- to 4-fold increase in the transcription rate of the rGH gene in GC cells following addition of dexamethasone; this increase is virtually identical to the increase in levels of GH nuclear RNA precursors and GH mRNA produced by dexamethasone. Addition of dexamethasone has no effect on the transcription of at least two other specific gene products and actually decreased prolactin gene transcription. Induction is apparently maximal by 1 hour and at least 15 hours (Fig. 19). In order to address the question of whether thyroid hormone and glucocorticoids can

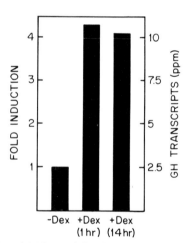

FIG. 19.   Effects at 1 and 14 hours following addition of dexamethasone to G/C cell cultures on the transcription of the hormone gene.

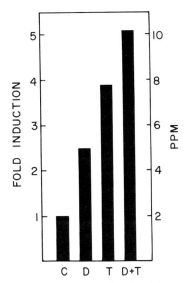

FIG. 20.   Effects of thyroid hormone [T3 10^{-7} (T)] and dexamethasone (dexamethasone 10^{-6} *M*) on G/C cells under conditions of serum-free culture. Transcriptional rates were quantitated 5 hours after hormonal addition (Evans *et al.*, 1982).

independently regulate growth hormone gene transcription, hormonal effects were evaluated in cells grown in serum-free conditions. The results presented in Fig. 20 establish that within 4 hours of its addition to cells in serum-free medium, either dexamethasone or T3 can act independently to transcriptionally regulate the growth hormone gene. Simultaneous addition of both hormones results in a transcriptional stimulation greater than that produced by either agent alone.

2. Glucocorticoid Regulation of Growth Hormone Gene Transcription in Vivo

The physiological relevance of this regulation was evaluated by measuring the effects of glucocorticoids on the growth hormone gene expression in the animal. The effects of dexamethasone were determined by measuring the rates of GH gene transcription in nuclei isolated from anterior pituitaries at various times following hormone administration to chronically adrenalectomized animals. The results shown in Fig. 21 demonstrate a rapid transcriptional response evident by 15 minutes, the earliest time analyzed, and progressively rising from 27 to 107 ppm in a 2-hour time period. This 4-fold induction is virtually identical to that observed with the G/C cell cultures in response to dexamethasone.

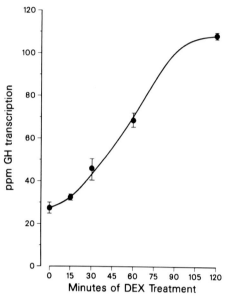

FIG. 21. Effect of dexamethasone administration *in vivo* to chronically adrenalecto-mized rats on growth hormone gene transcription in pituitary somatotrophs, as quantitated by analysis of nascent RNA transcripts (Evans *et al.*, 1982).

3. The Rat Growth Hormone Gene Contains Determinants Which Transfer Glucocorticoid Regulation

The ability to introduce purified eukaryotic genes into heterologous eukaryotic cells provides a powerful method for both selecting genes and for studying their regulation in a new cellular environment (Wigler *et al.*, 1979; Pellicer *et al.*, 1980; Buetti and Diggelman, 1981; Lee *et al.*, 1980; Kurtz, 1981; Lai *et al.*, 1980). Because glucocorticoids regulate growth hormone gene expression by exerting transcriptional regulation, it is critical to establish whether this regulation can be transferred by the growth hormone gene itself. In order to use DNA-mediated gene transfer to assess the functional significance of sequences involved in the expression and regulation of the growth hormone gene, the GH gene was introduced into mouse 3T3 cells using a plasmic vector which contains the entire genome of Maloney mouse sarcoma virus (Mo-MSV) (Fig. 22). The ability of the molecularly cloned MSV DNA to transform mouse fibroblasts was used as a dominant selective marker to construct mouse cell lines containing the rGH gene. Analyses of several lines of transformed cells suggested that most of the GH-related sequences had become chromosomally inte-

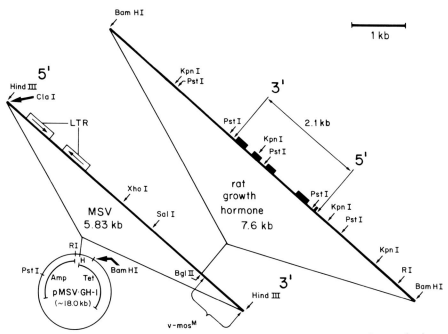

FIG. 22. Construction of the rat growth hormone Mo-MSV vector use in transfection experiments (Doehmer *et al.*, 1982).

grated and the restriction endonuclease pattern of reactive fragments remained stable for successive generations, with independent transformants containing between 3 and 20 gene copies (Doehmer *et al.*, 1982). These cells were found to synthesize an mRNA approximately 250 nucleotides larger than its bona fide rat pituitary counterpart, but which encoded and generated the authentic growth hormone peptide which was actually secreted by the 3T3 cells (Doehmer *et al.*, 1982). Since the mouse 3T3 fibroblasts contain glucocorticoid receptors, and since the transfected growth hormone gene contained at least 2 kb of both 5' and 3' flanking sequence information, the potential effects of the synthetic glucocorticoid, dexamethasone, on GH production was examined. As shown in Fig. 23, addition of dexamethasone increased growth hormone production approximately 2.5-fold above that produced in unstimulated cells. This is similar to the effects of dexamethasone on GC cell cultures. Similar transfer of regulation has been observed in the case of the human growth hormone gene (Robins *et al.*, 1982). The ability to obtain regulated expression of the rGH gene in heterologous cells suggests that hormonal respon-

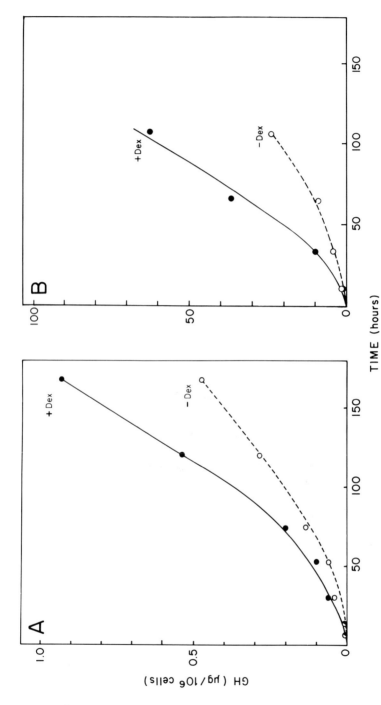

FIG. 23.   Effect of dexamethasone on production of GH in cells transformed with pMSV-GH1 (A) and GC cells (B) (1 × 10⁷/140-mm dish) in 25 ml of synthetic medium without serum were incubated with and without 5 μM dexamethasone.

siveness is intrinsic to the structure of the gene or its RNA products and permits further investigation into the nature of hormonally inducible control elements.

4. Expression of the Transfected Growth Hormone Gene in Vivo: Accelerated Growth of Mice from Eggs Microinjected with Metallothionein–Growth Hormone Fusion Genes

The ability of the growth hormone gene to be expressed and regulated following transfection in heterologous cells suggested the possibility that introducing the cloned gene into the germ lines of heterologous species could provide further insight into eukaryotic gene regulation. The introduction and expression of specific genes in mammalian embryos could potentially provide a useful approach to the study of both gene regulation and the genetic basis of development. Recent studies have clearly established the feasibility of introducing foreign DNA into the mammalian genome by microinjection of DNA molecules of interest into the pronuclei of fertilized eggs followed by insertion of the eggs into the reproductive tracts of foster mothers (Gordon *et al.*, 1980; Brinster *et al.*, 1981; Wagner *et al.*, 1981, 1982; Constantini and Lacy, 1981; Harbers *et al.*, 1981; Rusconi and Schaffner, 1981). The possibility of introducing genes encoding secreted regulatory peptides into animals via this technology has a number of potential applications. The growth hormone gene whose product has profound developmental effects provides a particularly convenient and biologically potent molecule to model this approach. In a series of collaborative studies, such an approach was initiated, by construction of a hybrid gene containing the mouse metallothionein promoter fused to the rat growth hormone gene (Fig. 24; Palmiter *et al.*, 1983); this hybrid

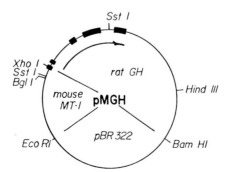

FIG. 24. Schematic diagram of the construction of fused genes containing a mouse metallothionein 1 (MT-1) promoter region and the rat growth hormone gene. The fused gene contains 68 bases of the MT-1 promotor and the entire rat growth hormone gene beginning at nucleotide 7 of the coding sequence.

gene is referred to as MGH. Palmiter *et al.*, (1980) have reported that the metallothionine gene promoter did function in transgenic mice when fused to the structural portion of the herpes TK gene. Injection of the hybrid gene construction (MGH) into fertilized mice eggs by Dr. Brinster and his colleagues generated mice developing from these injected eggs which were significantly larger than their litter mates (up to 1.8-fold) and contained integrated copies of MGH in their genome.

5. *Expression of the MGH Gene in the Livers of Transgenic Mice*

Evaluation of MGH gene expression in these so-called transgenic animals was initiated by analysis of its activity in liver. Figure 25 shows the results of RNA blot hybridization analysis, which revealed significant levels of reactive RNA. The level of MGH mRNA expression in the liver of the largest animals was unexpectedly high (800–3000 copies/cell) and correlated with the growth of the transgenic mice. The authenticity of the hybridized RNA as MGH RNA was confirmed by RNA blotting and S1 nuclease analyses. The correlation between MGH mRNA levels and growth of the mice suggests that expression of the MGH gene accounts for the observed biological consequences and predict that circulating levels of GH should be elevated. The plasma GH values for four of the largest transgenic mice are 100 to 800 times greater than levels in control

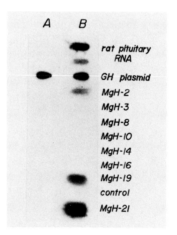

FIG. 25.   Blot analysis of liver RNAs from transgenic mice. Hybridization of ^{32}P-labeled growth hormone cDNA to 25 μg of immobilized liver RNA (untreated, B; base hydrolyzed, A) from a series of transgenic mice. The animals MGH-2, 19, and 21 were the largest animals, up to 1.8-fold heavier than littermate controls. Other animals exhibited lesser growth stimulation. Rat pituitary RNA provides a positive control, and the GH cDNA plasmid documents the validity of the base hydrolysis assay.

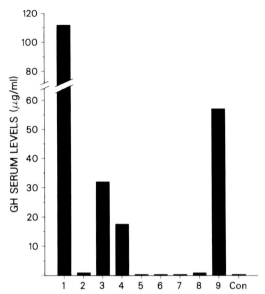

FIG. 26.   Blood GH levels in transgenic mice. Animals 1, 3, and 9 represented the three animals showing most accelerated growth and highest content of GH mRNA in their livers.

litter mates (Fig. 26). One mouse had 112 μg/ml of GH in its serum, literally 3 orders of magnitude above physiological levels.

These data strongly suggest that the altered phenotype of these mice is a direct result of the integration and expression of the metallothionein–growth hormone fusion gene. In addition to the potential practical applications of this approach it provides a tool to study the molecular basis of tissue-specific gene expression. This question is a long-standing issue in developmental biology. One possibility is that such developmental specificity is determined, in part or totally, by specific sequences flanking the gene. This postulate can be directly tested by analysis of the developmental expression of introduced genetic material. To address this question we have initiated studies designed to analyze the tissue specificity of MGH gene expression. In fact, striking tissue specificity of MGH gene expression is observed, compatible with the postulate that expression of the introduced gene is determined, at least in part, by sequences present in the introduced gene. These experiments have implications in the use of introduced genes to complement or replace deficient gene products in a recipient animal. Clearly, more knowledge is required with respect to the determinants of tissue-specific gene expression, efficiency of replication, and heritability to deduce how to optimally design hybrid genes for such a purpose.

III. Future Perspectives

The critical challenges are to define in minute detail biochemical reactions and requisite 5' genomic sequences required for hormonal regulation of gene transcription, and to further define the rules determining tissue-specific gene expression. On the basis of initial studies, we propose that sequences 5' of the cap site are critical determinants of the specificity of gene expression. The 3' portion of genes are also postulated to provide critical regulatory information, perhaps directing the alternative RNA processing events observed in the case of calcitonin gene expression. The precise molecular determinant of such termination regulation requires further definition. Finally, the predicted biological actions in ingestive behavior of the novel neuropeptide CGRP require experimental evaluation.

ACKNOWLEDGMENTS

Individuals in the laboratory who have made invaluable contributions to this or related research areas include Marcia Barinage, Rodrigo Franco, Vivian Jonas, Chijen Lin, Kathryn Nicolaisen, Estelita Ong, Ellen Potter, Lana Stolarsky, Scott Supowit, and Marian Waterman. We particularly wish to acknowledge our close collaborators Dr. Bernard Roos and members of his laboratory (Case Western Reserve) whose studies of the biology of rat MTCs and of calcitonin production were prerequisite for elucidation of the switching events, and whose participation and discussions have been invaluable to the completion of many of the reported experiments regarding calcitonin gene expression, Dr. Wylie Vale and Dr. Jean Rivier (Salk Institute) for their synthesis of a series of polypeptides and invaluable aid in evaluation of their physiological importance, as well as for many fruitful and critical discussions, and Dr. Larry Swanson (Salk Institute) for stimulating discussions and for his extraordinary histochemical and interpretive analysis of CGRP in the brain. We thank Margaret Richards for typing, and retyping, this manuscript. Experiments reported were supported by grants from the American Cancer Society and from The National Institutes of Health.

REFERENCES

Abelson, J. (1979). *Ann. Rev. Biochem.* **48,** 1035–1069.
Alt, F. W., Bothwell, A. L., Kapp, M., Siden, E., Mather, G., Koshland, M., and Baltimore, D. (1980). *Cell* **20,** 293–301.
Amara, S. G., Rosenfeld, M. G., Birnbaum, R. S., and Roos, B. A. (1980a). *J. Biol. Chem.* **255,** 2645–2648.
Amara, S. G., David, D. D., Rosenfeld, M. G., Roos, B. A., and Evans, R. M. (1980b). *Proc. Natl. Acad. Sci. U.S.A.* **77,** 4444–4448.
Amara, S. G., Jones, V., O'Neil, J. A., Vale, W., Rivier, J., Roos, B. A., Evans, R. M., and Rosenfeld, M. G. (1982a). *J. Biol. Chem.* **257,** 2129–2132.
Amara, S. G., Jones, V., Rosenfeld, M. G., Ong, E. S., and Evans, R. M. (1982b). *Nature (London)* **298,** 240–244.
Amara, S. G., Jonas, V., Evans, R. M., and Rosenfeld, M. G. (1983). In preparation.

Bancroft, F. C., Levine, L., and Tashjian, A. H., Jr. (1969). *J. Cell. Biol.* **43**, 432–441.

Barta, A., Richards, R., Baxter, J. D., and Shine, J. (1981). *Proc. Natl. Acad. Sci. U.S.A.* **78**, 4867–4871.

Biswas, D. K., Hanes, S. D., and Brennessel, B. A. (1982). *Proc. Natl. Acad. Sci. U.S.A.* **79**, 66–70.

Brinster, R. L., Chen, H. Y., Trumbauer, M., Senear, A. W., Warren, R., and Palmiter, R. D. (1981). *Cell* **27**, 223–231.

Buetti, E., and Diggleman, H. (1981). *Cell* **23**, 335.

Castagna, M., Palmer, W. K., and Walsh, D. A. (1975). *Eur. J. Biochem.* **55**, 193–199.

Chien, Y. H., and Thompson, E. B. (1980). *Proc. Natl. Acad. Sci. U.S.A.* **77**, 4583.

Cheng, H. L., Blattner, F. R., Titzmaurice, L., Mushinski, J. F., and Tucker, P. W. (1982). *Nature (London)* **296**, 410–415.

Chow, L. T., and Broker, T. R. (1978). *Cell* **15**, 497–510.

Comb, M., Seeburg, P. H., Adelman, J., Eiden, L., and Herbert, E. (1982). *Nature (London)* **295**, 663–666.

Constantini, F., and Lacy, E. (1981). *Nature (London)* **295**, 92–94.

Cooke, N. E., and Baxter, J. D. (1982). *Nature (London)* **297**, 603–606.

Dannies, P. S., and Tashjian, A. H., Jr. (1976). *Biochem. Biophys. Res. Commun.* **70**, 1180–1189.

Dannies, P. S., and Tashjian, A. H., Jr. (1973). *J. Biol. Chem.* **248**, 6174.

Dannies, P. S., and Tashjian, A. H., Jr. (1976). *Nature (London)* **261**, 707–710.

Darnell, J. E. (1978). *Science* **202**, 1257–2360.

Darnell, J. E. (1979). *Prog. Nucleic Acid Res. Mol. Biol.* **22**, 327–357.

Darnell, J. E., Jr. (1982). *Nature (London)* **297**, 365–371.

DeNoto, F. M., Moore, D. D., and Goodman, H. M. (1981). *Nucleic Acids Res.* **9**, 3719.

Dobner, P. R., Kawasaki, E. S., Yu, L. Y., and Bancroft, F. C. (1981). *Proc. Natl. Acad. Sci. U.S.A.* **78**, 2230–2234.

Doehmer, J., Barinaga, M., Vale, W., Rosenfeld, M. G., Verma, I. M., and Evans, R. M. (1982). *Proc. Natl. Acad. Sci. U.S.A.* **79**, 2268–2272.

Doolittle, R. (1978). *Nature (London)* **272**, 581–582.

Drust, D. S., and Martin, T. F. J. (1982). *J. Biol. Chem.* **257**, 7566–7573.

Drust, D. S., Sutton, C. A., and Martin, T. F. J. (1982). *J. Biol. Chem.* **257**, 3306–3312.

Early, P., Rogers, J., Davis, M., Calame, K., Bond, M., Wall, R., and Hood, L. (1980). *Cell* **20**, 313–319.

Eipper, B. A., and Mains, R. E. (1978). *J. Biol. Chem.* **253**, 5732–5744.

Evans, G. A., and Rosenfeld, M. G. (1976). *J. Biol. Chem.* **251**, 2842–2847.

Evans, G. A., and Rosenfeld, M. G. (1978). *Proc. Natl. Acad. Sci. U.S.A.* **75**, 1294–1298.

Evans, G. A., and Rosenfeld, M. G. (1979). *J. Biol. Chem.* **254**, 8023–8030.

Evans, R. M., Birnberg, N. C., and Rosenfeld, M. G. (1982). *Proc. Natl. Acad. Sci. U.S.A.,* in press.

Ford, J. P., and Hsu, M. T. (1978). *J. Virol.* **28**, 795–801.

Geras, E., and Rebecchi, M. J. (1982). *Endocrinology* **110**, 901–906.

Gershengorn, M. C. (1980). *J. Biol. Chem.* **255**, 1801–1803.

Gilbert, W. (1978). *Nature (London)* **271**, 501.

Giudice, L. C., and Chaiken, I. M. (1979). *Proc. Natl. Acad. Sci. U.S.A.* **76**, 3800–3804.

Goodman, R. H., Jacobs, J. W., Chin, W. W., Lund, P. K., Dee, P. C., and Habener, J. F. (1980). *Proc. Natl. Acad. Sci. U.S.A.* **77**, 5869–5873.

Gordon, J. W., Scangos, G. A., Plotkin, D. J., Barbosa, J. A., and Ruddle, F. (1980). *Proc. Natl. Acad. Sci. U.S.A.* **77**, 7380–7384.

Gruss, P., Lai, C.-J., Dhar, R., and Khoury, G. (1979). *Proc. Natl. Acad. Sci. U.S.A.* **76**, 4317–4321.

Gubbins, E. J., Maurer, R. A., Lagrimini, M., Erwin, C. R., and Donelson, J. E. (1980). *J. Biol. Chem.* **235**, 8655–8662.

Gubler, U., Seeburg, P., Hoffman, B. J., Gage, L. P., and Udenfriend, S. (1982). *Nature (London)* **295**, 206–208.

Guidice, L. C., and Chaiken, I. M. (1979). *Proc. Natl. Acad. Sci. U.S.A.* **76**, 3800–3804.

Habener, J. F., Kemper, B., Potts, J. T., Jr., and Rich, A. (1975). *J. Clin. Invest.* **56**, 1328–1333.

Hamer, D., and Leder, P. (1979). *Cell* **18**, 1299–1302.

Harbers, K., Johner, J. D., and Jaenisch, R. (1981). *Nature (London)* **292**, 540–542.

Harpold, M., Dobner, P., Evans, R. M., and Bancroft, F. C. (1978). *Nucleic Acids Res.* **5**, 2039–2053.

Harpold, M. M., Dobner, P. R., Evans, R., Bancroft, F. C., and Darnell, J. D. (1979). *Nucleic Acids Res.* **6**, 3133–3144.

Hinkle, P. M., and Tashjian, A. H., Jr. (1973). *J. Biol. Chem.* **17**, 6180–6186.

Hinkle, P. M., and Tashjian, A. H., Jr. (1975). *Biochemistry* **14**, 3845–3850.

Hobart, P., Crawford, R., Shin, L., Pictect, R., and Rutter, W. J. (1980). *Nature (London)* **288**, 137–141.

Hofer, E., and Darnell, J. E. (1981). *Cell* **23**, 585–593.

Hoffman, L. M., Fritsch, M. K., and Gorski, J. (1981). *J. Biol. Chem.* **256**, 2597–2600.

Ivarie, R. D., and O'Farrell, P. H. (1978). *Cell* **13**, 41–55.

Jacobs, J. W., Goodman, R. H., Chin, W. W., Dee, P. C., Habener, J. F., Bell, N. H., and Potts, J. T., Jr. (1981). *Science* **213**, 457–459.

Johnson, L. K., Baxter, J. D., Vladvasky, I., and Gospodarowicz, D. (1980). *Proc. Natl. Acad. Sci. U.S.A.* **77**, 394–398.

Kakidani, H., Furitani, Y., Takahashi, H., Noda, M., Morimoto, Y., Hirose, T., Asia, M., Inayama, S., and Numa, S. (1982). *Nature (London)* **298**, 245–249.

Kidokoro, Y. (1975). *Nature (London)* **258**, 741–742.

Kurtz, D. T. (1981). *Nature (London)* **291**, 629.

Lai, E. C., Woo, S. L. C., Bordelon-Riser, M. E., Fraser, T. H., and O'Malley, B. W. (1980). *Proc. Natl. Acad. Sci. U.S.A.* **77**, 244–248.

Lamers, W. H., Hanson, R. W., and Meisner, H. M. (1982). *Proc. Natl. Acad. Sci. U.S.A.* **79**, 5137–5141.

Lee, F., Mulligan, R., Berg, P., and Ringold, G. (1981). *Nature (London)* **294**, 228.

Lin, C., Joseph-Bravo, T., Sherman, T., Chan, L., and McKelvy, J. F. (1979). *Biochem. Biophys. Res. Commun.* **89**, 943–950.

Lewin, B. (1980). *Cell* **22**, 327.

Lund, P. K., Goodman, R. H., and Habener, R. F. (1981). *J. Biol. Chem.* **256**, 6515–6518.

Maki, R., Roeder, W., Traunecker, A., Sidman, C., Wabl, M., Raschke, W., and Tonegawa, S. (1981). *Cell* **24**, 353–365.

Martial, J. A., Baxter, J. D., Goodman, H. M., and Seeburg, P. H. (1977). *Proc. Natl. Acad. Sci. U.S.A.* **74**, 1816–1820.

Martin, T. F. J., and Tashjian, A. H., Jr. (1977). *In* "Biochemical Actions of Hormones" (G. Litwack, ed.), pp. 270–317. Academic Press, New York.

Maurer, R. A. (1980). *J. Biol. Chem.* **255**, 8092–8097.

Maurer, R. A. (1981). *Nature (London)* **294**, 94–97.

Maurer, R. A. (1982). *J. Biol. Chem.* **257**, 2133–2136.

Maurer, R. A., Gubbins, E. J., Erwin, C. R., and Donelson, J. E. (1981). *J. Biol. Chem.* **255,** 2243–2246.

Maurer, R. A., Stone, R., and Gorski, J. (1976). *J. Biol. Chem.* **251,** 2801–2807.

Max, E. (1979). *Proc. Natl. Acad. Sci. U.S.A.* **76,** 3450–3454.

Mermod, J.-J., Nicolaisen, A. K., Roos, B. A., Evans, R. M., and Rosenfeld, M. G. (1982). In preparation.

Murdoch, G. H., and Rosenfeld, M. G. (1981). *J. Biol. Chem.* **256,** 4050–4055.

Murdoch, G. H., Potter, E., Nicoliasin, K., Swans, R., and Rosenfeld, M. G. (1982a). *Nature (London)* **300,** 192–194.

Murdoch, G. H., Rosenfeld, M. G., and Evans, R. M. (1982b). *Science,* in press.

Murdoch, G. H., Franco, R., Evans, R. M., and Rosenfeld, M. G. (1982c). Submitted.

Murdoch, G. H., Waterman, M., Evans, R. M., and Rosenfeld, M. G. (1983). In preparation.

Nakanishi, S., Inoue, A., Kita, T., Nakamura, M., Chang, A. C. Y., Cohen, S. N., and Numa, S. (1979). *Nature (London)* **278,** 423–427.

Nevins, J. R., and Darnell, J. E., Jr. (1978). *Cell* **15,** 1477–1493.

Noda, M., Furutani, Y., Takahashi, H., Toyosato, M., Hirose, T., Inayama, S., Nakanishi, S., and Numa, S. (1982). *Nature (London)* **295,** 202–206.

Noe, B. D., and Bauer, G. E. (1971). *Endocrinology* **89,** 642–651.

Noyes, B., Meverech, M., Stein, R., and Agarwal, K. (1979). *Proc. Natl. Acad. Sci. U.S.A.* **76,** 1770–1774.

Ozawa, S., and Kimura, N. (1979). *Proc. Natl. Acad. Sci. U.S.A.* **76,** 6017–6020.

Page, G., Smith, S., and Goodman, H. (1981). *Nucl. Acids Res.* **9,** 2087–2104.

Palmiter, R. D., Chen, H. Y., and Brinster, R. L. (1982). *Cell* **29,** 701–710.

Palmiter, R. D., Brinster, R. L., Hammer, R. E., Trumbauer, M. E., Rosenfeld, M. G., Birnberg, N. C., and Evans, R. M. (1982). *Nature (London),* in press.

Patzelt, C., Tager, H. S., Carrol, R. J., and Steiner, D. F. (1979). *Nature (London)* **282,** 260–266.

Potter, E., Nicolaisen, K. A., Ong, E. S., Evans, R. M., and Rosenfeld, M. G. (1981). *Proc. Natl. Acad. Sci. U.S.A.* **78,** 6662–6666.

Roberts, J. L., Phillips, M., Rosa, P. A., and Herbert, E. (1978). *Biochemistry* **17,** 3609–3618.

Roberts, J. L., Seeberg, P. H., Shine, J., Herbert, E., Baxter, J. D., and Goodman, H. M. (1979). *Proc. Natl. Acad. Sci. U.S.A.* **76,** 2153–2157.

Robins, D. M., Paek, I., Seeburg, P. N., and Axel, R. (1982). *Cell* **29,** 623.

Roos, B. A., Yoon, M. J., Frelinger, A. L., Pensky, A. C., Birnbaum, R. S., and Lambert, P. W. (1979). *Endocrinology* **105,** 27–32.

Rosenfeld, M. G., Amara, S. G., Roos, B. A., Ong, E. S., and Evans, R. M. (1981). *Nature (London)* **290,** 63–65.

Rosenfeld, M. G., Lin, C. R., Amara, S. G., Stolarsky, L., Roos, B. A., Ong, E. S., and Evans, R. M. (1982). *Proc. Natl. Acad. Sci. U.S.A.* **79,** 1717–1721.

Rosenfeld, M. G., Mermod, J.-J., Amara, S. G., Swanson, L., Sawchenko, P., Rivier, J., Vale, W., and Evans, R. M. (1983). In press.

Rusconi, S., and Schaffner, W. (1981). *Proc. Natl. Acad. Sci. U.S.A.* **78,** 5051–5055.

Samuels, H. H., and Shapiro, L. E. (1978). *In* "Receptors and Hormone Action" (L. Birnbaumer and B. N. O'Malley, eds.), Vol. 13, pp. 35–75. Academic Press, New York.

Shapiro, L. E., Samuels, H. H., and Yaffee, B. M. (1978). *Proc. Natl. Acad. Sci. U.S.A.* **75,** 45–49.

Schally, A. V., Huang, W., Chang, R. C. C., Arimura, A., Redding, T. W., Miller, R. F., Hunkapiller. M. W., and Hood, L. E. (1980). *Proc. Natl. Acad. Sci. U.S.A.* **77,** 4489–4493.

Schonbrunn, A., Krasnoff, M., Westendorf, J. M., and Tashjina, A. H., Jr. (1980). *J. Cell Biol.* **85,** 786–797.

Seo, H., Refetoff, S., Vassart, G., and Brocas, H. (1980). *Proc. Natl. Acad. Sci. U.S.A.* **76,** 824–828.

Sharp, P. A. (1981). *Cell* **23,** 643–646.

Shields, D. (1980). *Proc. Natl. Acad. Sci. U.S.A.* **77,** 4074–4078.

Shupnik, M. A., Baxter, L. A., French, L. R., and Gorski, J. (1979). *Endocrinology* **101,** 729–735.

Steiner, D. F., Cho, S., Oyer, P. E., Terris, S., Peterson, J. D., and Rubenstein, A. H. (1971). *J. Biol. Chem.* **246,** 1365–1374.

Sussman, P. M., Tushinski, R. J., and Bancroft, F. C. (1976). *Proc. Natl. Acad. Sci. U.S.A.* **73,** 29–33.

Sutton, C. A., and Martin, T. F. J. (1982). *Endocrinology* **110,** 109–127.

Tan, K. N., and Tashjian, A. H., Jr. (1981). *J. Biol. Chem.* **256,** 8994–9002.

Tashjian, A. H., Jr., Yasumura, Y., Levine, L., Sato, G. H., and Parker, M. L. (1968). *Endocrinology* **82,** 342–352.

Taylor, W. L., Collier, K. J., Weith, H. L., and Dixon, J. E. (1981). *Biochem. Biophys. Res. Commun.* **102,** 1071–1077.

Taraskevich, P. S., and Douglas, W. W. (1977). *Proc. Natl. Acad. Sci. U.S.A.* **74,** 4064–4067.

Tushinski, R. J., Sussman, P. M., Yu, L. Y., and Bancroft, F. C. (1977). *Proc. Natl. Acad. Sci. U.S.A.* **74,** 2357–2361.

Wagner, E., Stewart, T., and Mintz, B. (1981). *Proc. Natl. Acad. Sci. U.S.A.* **78,** 5016–5020.

Wagner, T. E., Hoppe, P. C., Jollick, J. D., Scholl, D. R., Hodinka, R. L., and Gault, J. B. (1981). *Proc. Natl. Acad. Sci. U.S.A.* **78,** 6376–6380.

Wallis, M. (1980). *Nature (London)* **284,** 512–516.

Waterman, M., Murdoch, G. H., Potter, E., Nicolaisen, A. K., Evans, R. M., and Rosenfeld, M. G. (1982). Submitted.

White, B. A., Bauerle, L. R., and Bancroft, F. C. (1981). *J. Biol. Chem.* **256,** 5942–5945.

Williams, J. G., Tsang, A. S., and Mahbubani, H. (1980). *Proc. Natl. Acad. Sci. U.S.A.* **77,** 7171–7175.

Yamamoto, K. R., and Alberts, B. M. (1976). *Annu. Rev. Biochem.* **45,** 721–746.

White, B. A., Bauerle, L. R., and Bancroft, F. C. (1981). *J. Biol. Chem.* **256,** 5942–5945.

Ziff, E., and Evans, R. M. (1978). *Cell* **15,** 1463–1475.

Ziff, E. B. (1980). *Nature (London)* **287,** 491–499.

DISCUSSION

V. C. Jordan: Thank you, Dr. Rosenfeld, that was an excellent presentation. I would like to focus for a few moments on the effects of steroid hormones on prolactin synthesis. For the past 3 years I have been collaborating with Drs. Mara Lieberman and Jack Gorski at the University of Wisconsin. We have been studying the direct effects of estrogens and antiestrogens on the synthesis of prolactin by normal rat pituitary cells in culture in order to compare our results with similar studies using the GH3 and GH4 cell lines. Our aim is to define a model for the interaction of different estrogens and antiestrogens with the estrogen receptor which results in the stimulation or inhibition of prolactin synthesis. The unique finding with these experiments is that the nonsteroidal antiestrogens, which are partial estrogen agonists *in vivo,* are complete inhibitors of estradiol-stimulated prolactin synthesis *in vitro* and do not stimulate prolactin synthesis when studied alone. We made a preliminary report of our findings at the Endocrine Society Meeting in San Francisco. I should point out that antiestrogen action in this system is fully competitive with estradiol and the suppressive effects produced by several days of exposure to antiestrogens alone can be "rescued" by the addition of increasing concentrations of estradiol. Overall the potency of the estrogens and antiestrogens is dependent upon the binding affinity of the compound for the estrogen receptor. I would like to ask whether you have studied the effects of antiestrogens in your system. I would be particularly interested to learn whether antiestrogens can inhibit the stimulatory effects of TRH in your cells.

M. G. Rosenfeld: Well, first the history of the use of estrogen analogs in GH cells, as you know but I will remind everyone else, was explored in detail by Priscilla Dannies and Armen Tashjian in the GH cells. Their unexpected observation, one winter day, was that estrogen no longer stimulated the prolactin gene expression in their cells but in fact a so-called estrogen antagonist, or I should say partial agonist, did stimulate prolactin gene transcription. Now at that time, not aware of the results from Boston, our cells were responding to estrogen in a stimulatory fashion. As soon as their article appeared, our cells, as expected of them, stopped responding to estrogen. In fact we analyzed the effects of estrogen and estrogen antagonists on prolactin gene expression, and the results of these observations were that neither exerted effects. Subsequently by modifying conditions of culture, estrogen effects on prolactin gene transcription. The effects are seen only after long lay periods such that they may be directly steroid hormone receptor mediated or secondary to the transcriptional effects of the complex on yet another gene. Now with respect to your question about interactions with other hormones, the answer is quite clear. Estrogen exerts an additive effect with respect to TRH and EGF.

V. C. Jordan: Yes, we were fascinated by the same report by Dr. Dannies. In her study she measured the accumulation of prolactin in the medium. In our studies with GH4 cells we have confirmed her observation but we can detect estradiol stimulated-prolactin synthesis within the cells. It appears that the antiestrogens cause a secretion of estradiol-stimulated prolactin into the medium, but cause an apparent reduction of prolactin synthesis within the cell. It is possible that we are each dealing with different variants of the original tumor cells that have independently changed their hormone sensitivity during prolonged cell culture.

T. Spelsberg: I had two questions: in the first part of your lecture—the poly(A)sites selectivity—you have a nice potential model of RNA processing. Really though have you ruled out the transcriptional possibilities where you could have, let's say, terminating proteins on the DNA that would terminate the RNA polymerase?

M. G. Rosenfeld: Yes, the transcriptional analysis that was done using probes along the calcitonin genes and the results of this analysis were that in tissues which selectively produce only calcitonin and in tissues which selectively produce only CGRP transcription proceeds past both the calcitonin and CGRP exons to a site approximately 2 kilobases downstream of the 3' end of all the coding exons. This does not exclude the possibility that there are two closely linked or closely situated termination sites, but it excludes the possibility that termination occurs in the intervening sequence between calcitonin and CGRP exons.

T. Spelsberg: Right, but there still could be a control at the transcriptional level.

M. G. Rosenfeld: Transcription does not correlate with processing.

T. Spelsberg: One last quick question. Your BRP protein, a phosphorylated basic protein—do you know the p*I* of this protein. Could it be H1 histone?

M. G. Rosenfeld: It is not an HI histone. Our analysis so far reveals that this protein is similar neither to any of the described histones nor to any of the described HMG proteins. BRP thus represents an uncharacterized protein which will require full sequence analysis to structurally define.

T. Spelsberg: Is it abundant?

M. G. Rosenfeld: Thank you for asking that question. Its abundance is approximately 1% that of the major HI species; that is, relatively similar in abundance to HMG14 and HMG17.

J. Larner: In order to further develop the biochemical basis of the effects it would be very nice if you could obtain effects on isolated nuclei, particularly since you have evidence of regulation by both cyclic AMP and calcium. Of course it is known classically that they interact in a number of biochemical systems. Have you tried to get effects of these agents on isolated nuclei?

M. G. Rosenfeld: The answer is yes, but allow me to elaborate. First, there has been a recent report regarding the prolactin regulation of casein gene transcription in isolated nuclei. For the sake of formal discussion, I should state that these data must still be viewed with great caution and I would appreciate a comment from John Baxter regarding this point. The methods of analysis used to imply that a second messenger generated from membranes as a consequence of prolactin binding exerted an effect on casein gene transcription were insensitive and possibly ineffective. Therefore, this model is yet unproven. In attempting to do this type of experiment in GH cells, there is a very simple and very major technical problem. Initiation of transcription is very inefficient in isolated nuclei, probably because DNases digest the gene. Thus, while representing an apparently very simple and logical approach, it presents a great technical challenge.

J. D. Baxter: I've heard these data too, and I haven't really digested it properly.

J. Larner: I wanted to ask whether you had identified the amino acid site of phosphorylation in the BRP protein?

M. G. Rosenfeld: No, we are in the process of analyzing tryptic digestion products; the preliminary data indicate that at least one serine residue can be phosphorylated, but obviously it becomes critical to ascertain whether, in a case of EGF, there could be a phosphotyrosine residue.

G. D. Aurbach: You've shown that calcium-mediated phenomenon, cyclic AMP-mediated phenomenon, glucocorticoids, estrogens, and EGF all can regulate transcription of prolactin message in these cells and this is putatively all through phosphorylation of BRP protein. How do you visualize messages from the interaction of all of these different types of factors filtering down to phosphorylation of one protein?

M. G. Rosenfeld: Allow me to clarify a misconception which I must have inadvertently created. I do not suspect that steroid hormones act through BRP, nor have we so demonstrated. I would wonder whether steroid hormones can regulate the mass of such a protein, modify its distribution, and/or effect the synthesis of alternative members of a related gene family, but I doubt steroid hormones regulate the phosphorylation of BRP. The evidence for this statement is based upon the observation that there is an additive effect of estrogens and the peptide hormones on gene transcription. The additivity of actions imply that they cannot phosphorylate an identical site on this protein; hence, I believe that BRP modification can explain only a portion of hormone-mediated transcriptional effect. These data point out the complexity of transcriptional regulation by hormones. Therefore, I would suggest that though all hormonal agents act at a transcriptional site, and within a single genomic code, they have both common and discrete mechanisms, and differ in the sites of their action. The analysis is consistent with the notion that the transcriptional effects alone account for specific messenger RNA stimulation and subsequent stimulated biosynthesis of both prolactin and growth hormone. There have been arguments supporting so-called translational control and hormonally regulated mRNA stability as sites of hormone action, and one can be relatively certain on a theoretical basis that such sites for hormone action must exist. I would like to propose, however, that neither site has been unequivocally proven in any model system for either steroid or peptide hormone, and, therefore, these sites must still be regarded as possible, or putative, sites of hormone action.

Expression of Cloned Growth Hormone and Metallothionein Genes in Heterologous Cells

GEORGE N. PAVLAKIS AND DEAN H. HAMER

Laboratory of Biochemistry, National Cancer Institute, National Institutes of Health, Bethesda, Maryland

I. Introduction

Recombinant DNA technology has already had a significant impact on modern endocrinology. The cloning of genes in bacteria has been essential to understanding the structure and evolution of both hormone-coding and hormone-responsive genes and will probably soon lead to important new insights on the receptors and other factors that mediate the interaction between hormones and their target cells. But experiments performed in prokaryotes are not capable of addressing certain key points: How do hormones increase or decrease the transcription rates of specific genes? Is RNA processing involved in hormonal regulation? How is hormone release related to posttranslational modifications such as glycosylation and signal sequence cleavage? One approach to answer these questions is to return the genes of interest to eukaryotic cells that contain the complex machinery required for appropriate transcription, RNA processing, and secretion.

With this aim in mind, we have used DNA tumor virus vectors to transfer cloned human growth hormone (hGH) genes, and mutants derived from them, into cultured monkey kidney and mouse fibroblast cells. We have also studied the expression of a hybrid gene in which hGH structural sequences are fused to the promoter from the mouse metallothionein-I (MT-I) gene, a sequence that is naturally inducible by glucocorticoids. Finally, we have devised a new dominant selective cloning system that may eventually allow us to transfer such genes into a wider variety of cell types than can be used with current vectors.

Human growth hormone is normally produced by the acidophil cells of the anterior pituitary. Like all known polypeptide hormones, it is synthesized as a prehormone containing a hydrophobic, amino-terminal signal sequence that is removed during secretion. The mature hormone exhibits multiple biological effects *in vivo* including diabetogenic, insulin-like, lactogenic, and growth-promoting activities (reviewed in Raiti, 1973). Most hGH preparations can be separated into multiple bands by high-resolution isoelectric focusing or gel electrophoresis (Bala *et al.*, 1973; Cheever and Lewis, 1969; Chrambach *et al.*, 1973). Some of these appear to result from posttranslational modification (Lewis and Cheever, 1965; Lewis *et al.*, 1970) and others represent primary sequence variants. The best studied of these is the M_r 20,000 ("20K") variant, which is a single polypeptide chain identical to the major form of hGH except that it lacks amino acid residues 32–46 (Lewis *et al.*, 1978, 1980). It is also known that hGH exists in heterogeneous forms in human plasma with respect to molecular size and biological properties (Gorden *et al.*, 1973, 1976; Goodman *et al.*, 1972).

Recent DNA cloning experiments show that the human genome contains several different hGH-related genes (Fiddes *et al.*, 1979; Moore *et al.*, 1982; Seeburg, 1982). One of these, designated here as the hGH1 gene, has been shown by sequence analysis to be capable of encoding the predominant form of pituitary hGH (DeNoto *et al.*, 1981). A second gene, referred to as the hGH2 gene, is highly homologous to the hGH1 gene but contains 13 point mutations that are expected to lead to amino acid substitutions in the mature hormone (Seeburg, 1982). This suggests that some of the heterogeneity of hGH might be due to the expression of multiple closely related but nonidentical genes. At the present time we do not know whether the hGH2 gene is expressed in humans and what the function of this protein might be.

The mouse metallothionein-I gene is of interest because it is known to be transcriptionally regulated by glucocorticoids as well as heavy metals (Karin *et al.*, 1980; Durnam and Palmiter, 1981; Hager and Palmiter, 1981; Mayo and Palmiter, 1981). The physiological basis for hormonal induction is unknown, and in general the response is less than that observed with metals; nevertheless, the system offers an interesting opportunity to study how a single gene responds to two very different classes of inducers. Moreover, because metallothioneins can chelate and, therefore, confer resistance to toxic heavy metals such as cadmium, it seemed possible that the MT-I gene might be used as a dominant selective marker to transfer other genes to a variety of different cell types.

II. Techniques Used for Gene Transfer

We have utilized three different methods to introduce cloned genes into cultured mammalian cells.

A. INFECTION WITH SIMIAN VIRUS 40 VIRIONS

In this method the hGH gene was inserted into the late region of the simian virus 40 (SV40) genome. Since the recombinant molecule lacks the late functions necessary for encapsidation, we provided these functions in *trans* by means of an early region-defective SV40 DNA as helper. The recombinant and the helper DNA were introduced into monkey kidney cells, the permissive host for SV40, by the DEAE-dextran technique (McCutchan and Pagano, 1968). After approximately 3 weeks the cell monolayer was completely lysed and a mixture of recombinant and helper virions was released into the medium. All subsequent experiments were performed by infecting fresh cell monolayers of monkey kidney cells with the virus stock.

B. ACUTE TRANSFECTION WITH SIMIAN VIRUS 40 PLASMID RECOMBINANTS

This method does not require the construction of recombinant virions. It consists of transfecting the cells with a recombinant plasmid containing the SV40 origin and early region, allowing approximately 50 hours for the replication and expression of the foreign DNA, and then harvesting the cells and analyzing the products of expression. The advantages of this method are that there is no size limit for the recombinant molecules, since encapsidation into SV40 virions is not required, and that the experiment is completed within days instead of weeks. However, since only a small percentage of the cells are transfected this is a very inefficient process compared to viral infection.

C. TRANSFORMATION WITH BOVINE PAPILLOMA VIRUS RECOMBINANTS

Bovine papilloma virus (BPV) and BPV recombinants can transform mouse cells in tissue culture. The virus replicates in mouse cells as an episome and no integrated copies are required for transformation (Law *et al.*, 1981). The main advantage of this system is that, in contrast to the SV40 systems, stable transformed cell lines containing the recombinant molecules can be isolated and grown indefinitely.

All three of these methods are expected to maintain the inserted DNA in an episomal status in the cell nucleus where it is presumably associated with histones and regulatory factors. This offers unique opportunities to study gene expression and regulation and to isolate potential regulatory factors associated with the DNA. We assume that the environment of the multiple copies of the nonintegrated, episomal genes is more homogeneous than when integrated in various places into the genome as occurs with direct DNA transformation or microinjection. This makes the interpretation of the results simpler since it eliminates the variability in the behavior of transfered genes caused by position effects.

III. Synthesis, Processing, and Secretion of hGH in Monkey Cells Infected with SV40 Recombinants

The two human growth hormone genes utilized in this work were originally cloned in phage λ as 2.6 kilobase pair (kb) *Eco*RI fragments (Fiddes *et al.*, 1979). The two genes are approximately 95% homologous but can be readily distinguished from one another because hGH2 contains one extra *Bam*HI site (indicated in Fig. 1) and one extra *Pst*I site. DNA sequence analysis shows that both the gene 1 and gene 2 *Eco*RI fragments contain approximately 500 base pairs (bp) of 5' flanking sequences and 550 bp of 3' flanking sequences as well as five hGH structural sequences (exons) separated by four intervening sequences (introns) (Fig. 1). The coding sequences of hGH1 are identical to those in cloned hGH complementary DNA (cDNA) suggesting that this gene is expressed into the major form of pituitary hGH (Martial *et al.*, 1979; DeNoto *et al.*, 1981). In contrast, the hGH2 gene differs from the cDNA by several base changes, 13 of which are expected to lead to amino acid substitutions in the mature hormone (Seeburg, 1982).

The two different 2.6 kb hGH gene fragments were inserted, in both possible orientations, into an SV40 vector that retains the origin of viral DNA replication, a functional early gene region and the extreme 5' and 3' termini of the late gene region (Fig. 2). In the SVhGH(L) recombinants the hGH1 and hGH2 genes are in the same orientation as SV40 late gene transcription whereas in the SVhGH(E) recombinants they are in the opposite or early orientation. These recombinant molecules were constructed by cloning in *Escherichia coli* then propagated in monkey kidney cells as virions by mixed transfections with a temperature-sensitive early gene mutant of SV40 (SV40 *tsA*$_{239}$) as helper (Chow and Martin, 1974). The resulting stocks of virus contained approximately 10% SV40–hGH recombinant genomes and 90% helper genomes. These viral stocks were used to infect fresh monolayers of primary monkey kidney cells for all subsequent studies. The ability of these recombinants to direct the synthesis of hGH was tested by labeling infected cells with [^{3}H]leucine and analyzing the cellular proteins by immunoprecipitation and acrylamide–

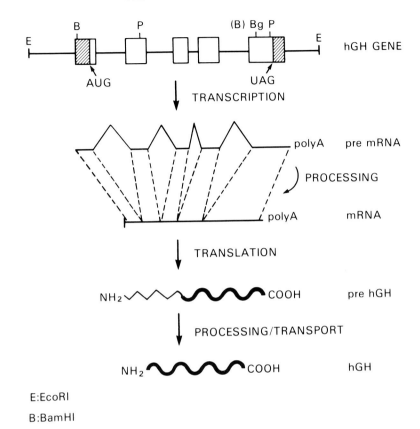

E:EcoRI

B:BamHI

Bg:BglII

P:PvuII

FIG. 1.   Structure of the hGH gene and its products. The top drawing shows the general structure of the hGH1 and hGH2 genes; boxes indicate coding sequences, cross-hatched regions indicate the 5' and 3' untranslated regions, and thin lines indicate flanking and intervening sequences. The gene is transcribed into a colinear pre-mRNA that is spliced and polyadenylated to yield hGH mRNA. This is translated into pre-hGH containing an amino-terminal signal sequence of 26 amino acids. The signal sequence is removed during secretion. The *Bam*HI site that exists only in the hGH2 gene is indicated in parentheses.

SDS gel electrophoresis. As shown in Fig. 3A, cells infected with each of the four recombinants synthesized a protein that comigrated with authentic pituitary hGH and was absent from uninfected and wild type SV40-infected controls. The amount of this protein synthesized was similar for SVhGH1(L) compared to SVhGH2(L) and for SVhGH1(E) compared to SVhGH2(E); in both cases about 3-fold more polypeptide was made in the late (L) than the early (E) orientation. Thus the two genes

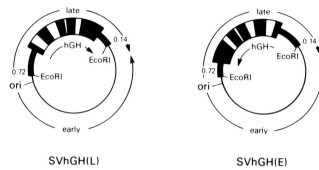

SVhGH(L)   SVhGH(E)

FIG. 2. SV40–hGH viral recombinants. The two hGH genes were inserted, in both possible orientations, into an SV40 vector (thin lines) extending clockwise from the *Bam*HI site at 0.14 map units to the *Hpa*II site at 0.72 map units. Both vector sites were converted to *Eco*RI sites by using oligonucleotide linkers. *ori,* origin of replication. (From Pavlakis *et al.,* 1981.)

function equally well, but the level of expression depends upon their orientation relative to the vector.

To determine whether the hGH was secreted from monkey cells, we repeated the immunoprecipitation and gel analysis on the media from the control and recombinant-infected cells. Figure 3 shows that both the hGH1 and hGH2 proteins are present in the media. Quantitation of the gel lanes by microdensitometry showed that the secreted material represents approximately 80% of the total hGH synthesized in a 3-hour pulse with [³H]leucine. To exclude the possibility of cell leakiness or lysis, as compared to active transport, we also analyzed the total intracellular and media proteins without immunoprecipitation (Fig. 3B). The cell extract showed a complex array of bands, as expected from the fact that SV40 does not shut down host cell synthesis, and it was not possible to resolve hGH from the background of cellular proteins. In contrast, the media contained a much more discrete set of proteins, and hGH could readily be visualized as a predominant band in the recombinant-infected samples but not in the controls. No SV40 capsid proteins were detected in the media, indicating that cell lysis was not occurring at the time of labeling (40 hours after infection).

These results show that both hGH1 and hGH2 are specifically and efficiently secreted from infected monkey cells. Appropriate removal of the hydrophobic leader sequence was not unexpected because the necessary enzymes are present in a variety of cell types and species (Blobel *et al.,* 1979). Also, evidence has been presented (Gruss and Khoury, 1981) that preproinsulin is processed to proinsulin in monkey cells infected with an SV40 insulin gene recombinant; however, the mature hormone was not

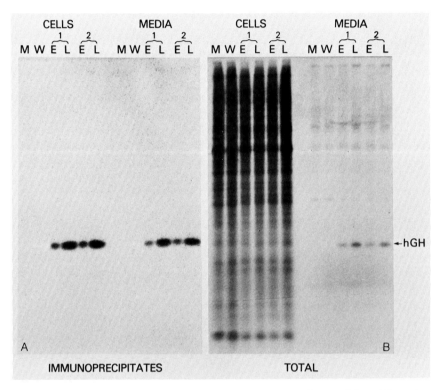

FIG. 3. Synthesis of hGH in infected monkey cells. Monolayers of 2×10^7 monkey kidney cells were labeled with [^{3}H]leucine (200 μCi/ml) at 40–43 hours after infection. Cellular and media proteins were analyzed by electrophoresis through 20% acrylamide–SDS gels. (A) Proteins immunoprecipitated with excess anti-hGH antibody; (B) total proteins. Each set of six lanes shows samples from M, mock-infected cells; W, wild-type SV40-infected cells; 1E, SVhGH1(E)-infected cells; 1L, SVhGH1(L)-infected cells; 2E, SVhGH2(E)-infected cells; 2L, SVhGH2(L)-infected cells. (From Pavlakis *et al.*, 1981.)

produced due to the inability of the kidney cells to remove the internal C peptide. In pituitary cells hGH is sequestered into secretory granules prior to release into the bloodstream. We do not have any evidence of delayed secretion of hGH from monkey cells or from mouse cells transformed with BPV–hGH recombinants (see below). The storage of hGH into secretory granules may require expression of specific proteins (D. Cohn, this volume). This storage may be an important step for additional regulation and/or fine tuning of the physiological levels of growth hormone. The specific and efficient secretion of hGH from monkey kidney cells, which lack these granules, suggests that they are not essential for transport across the cell membrane. Two distinct pathways for the

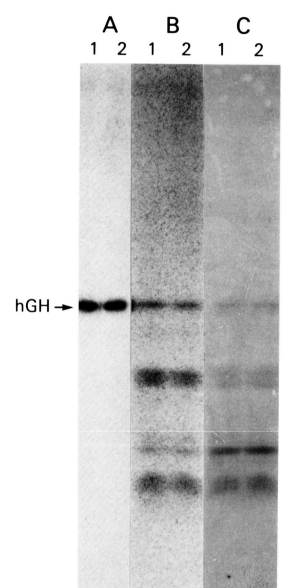

transport of ACTH have been shown recently in AtT-20 pituitary tumor cell line (Gumbiner and Kelly, 1982). Secretion of mature ACTH sequestered into secretory vesicles is delayed and cAMP-dependent, while there is constitutive rapid and cAMP-independent secretion in the same cells.

By analogy, somatostatin, which is known to inhibit hGH secretion (Vale *et al.*, 1973), may act at a level similar to the one affected by cAMP in AtT-20 cells. We have studied the effects of somatostatin on the secretion of hGH from monkey kidney cells infected with the SV40 recombinants. We did not detect any inhibition by somatostatin in these experiments which is consistent with the hypothesis that somatostatin may act on the secretion granule pathway; however, this is not the only possible explanation of this result since we do not know whether functional somatostatin receptors exist on monkey kidney cells.

IV. hGH1 and hGH2 are Very Similar but Distinct Molecules

The structure of the secreted hGH1 and hGH2 was analyzed by partial chymotrypsin digestion of the SDS–denatured proteins followed by acrylamide–SDS gel electrophoresis. Figure 4 shows that both proteins gave rise to identical [³H]leucine-containing chymotryptic peptides and that these comigrated with the peptides obtained from unlabeled pituitary hGH. These data, in conjunction with the fact that the intact proteins comigrate with pituitary hGH on SDS gels, suggest that the amino-terminal signal sequences have been appropriately removed. The hGH1 protein also comigrated with pituitary hGH in isoelectric focusing (O'Farrell, 1975) and nonequilibrium pH gradient electrophoresis gels (O'Farrell *et al.*, 1977), but hGH2 could not be resolved in either system. This indicates that hGH2, although very similar, is not identical to hGH1 protein. This is in agreement with the DNA sequencing data (Seeburg, 1982).

We next studied the interaction of the hGH1 and hGH2 protein with specific antibodies and cell surface receptors. Figure 5 shows double antibody radioimmunoassays of the media from SVhGH1- and SVhGH2-infected cells using either rabbit (A) or guinea pig (B) anti-hGH antibody. In order to ensure that we compared equal quantities of hGH1 and hGH2

FIG. 4.   Partial chymotrypsin digests. [³H]Leucine-labeled hGH1 and hGH2 were purified by immunoprecipitation of the media from cells infected with SVhGH1(L) or SVhGH2(L). The precipitated proteins were eluted by boiling in SDS, mixed with 20 μg of unlabeled pituitary hGH, partially digested with chymotrypsin, and analyzed by 20% acrylamide–SDS gel electrophoresis. (A) Fluorogram of undigested samples. (B) Fluorogram of chymotrypsin-digested samples. (C) Photograph of panel B stained with Coomassie brilliant blue. In each panel lane 1 represents hGH1 and lane 2 represents hGH2. (From Pavlakis *et al.*, 1981.)

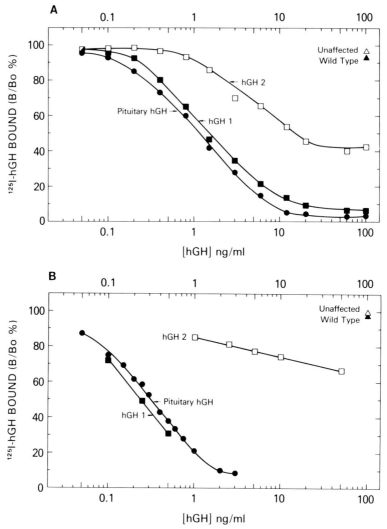

FIG. 5. Radioimmunoassay of hGH preparations. In (A) a rabbit anti-hGH serum was used and in (B) a guinea pig anti-hGH serum was used. For the assay shown in (B) the standard ^{125}I-labeled hGH (^{125}I-hGH, specific activity ~30 μCi/μg) was the same as used in the radioreceptor assays shown in Fig. 6. The media used in this experiment were collected from approximately 2×10^7 cells that had been infected with SVhGH1(L) or SVhGH2(L) and labeled in 20 ml of medium containing [^{3}H]leucine at 20 μCi/ml from 24 to 48 hours after infection. Analysis of these samples by acrylamide–SDS gel electrophoresis and fluorography showed that they contained approximately equal amounts of [^{3}H]leucine-labeled hGH. The lower scale refers to the concentration of pituitary hGH standard added to the assay and the upper scale refers to the amount of infected cell medium added. The total sample volume was 100 μl in all assays. Controls of medium from cells incubated without virus ("Unaffected") and cells infected with SV40 containing no insert ("Wild Type") are shown. B, ^{125}I-hGH bound; B$_0$, ^{125}I-hGH bound in the absence of competitor. (From Pavlakis *et al.*, 1981.)

polypeptides, the media used in this experiment were collected from cells uniformly labeled with [³H]leucine. Scans of the SDS gel fluorograms showed that the SVhGH1 and SVhGH2 samples contained equal amounts of hGH polypeptide. The dose–response curves for hGH1 were parallel to the pituitary hGH standard in both assays. In contrast, hGH2 gave non-parallel curves with both antisera and it reacted less with the guinea pig antibody than with the rabbit antibody. Because of the nonidentical crossreactivity the most dilute samples of hGH2 give the highest values in radioimmunoassay. Under these conditions hGH2 had approximately 10% the immunoactivity of hGH1 with the rabbit antibody and less than 5% with the guinea pig antibody.

The ability of hGH1 and hGH2 to bind to hGH cell surface receptors was tested by radioreceptor assays using either the human lymphocyte line IM9 (Eastman et al., 1979) or pregnant rabbit liver membranes (Tsushima and Friesen, 1973) as the receptor sources. In both systems hGH1 was indistinguishable from pituitary hGH (Fig. 6). Surprisingly, hGH2 was 50% as active as hGH1 in the lymphocyte assay and 100% as active in the liver membrane assay and gave dose–response curves paral-lel to the standard in both systems. Thus the ratio of receptor to immu-noassay activity is approximately 1 for hGH1 whereas it is 10 or greater for hGH2. The 20K variant was 30% as active as hGH in the radioimmu-noassay and 30–40% as active in the radioreceptor assays (Hizuka et al., 1982). Therefore, although both assays give lower potencies, the ratio of RRA to RIA is close to 1. Since the 20K variant is identical to the major form of hGH except for an internal deletion of amino acids 32–46, it has been suggested that this protein may result from alternative splicing of hGH mRNA (Wallis, 1980; DeNoto et al., 1981). We have not been able to detect this protein in SVhGH-infected monkey cells. Therefore, it ap-pears that these cells differ from pituitary cells in their splicing character-istics. An alternative although less likely explanation is that the 20K variant is the product of yet another hGH gene.

These results show that, at least in the heterologous SV40 monkey cell system, gene 2 can be expressed into a novel variant form of hGH. Whether or not the gene 2 product has biological activity in vivo is un-known; we refer to it as a "growth hormone" simply because of its homology to pituitary hGH and its ability to bind to hGH receptors. We also do not know whether the hGH2 gene is expressed in humans; how-ever, it is interesting to note that there are some clinical situations that could, in principle, be explained by the existence of primary sequence variants of hGH such as hGH2. In acromegalic patients it has been found that the major hGH component of plasma ("little hGH") has a higher receptor to immunoassay ratio than the material purified from normal

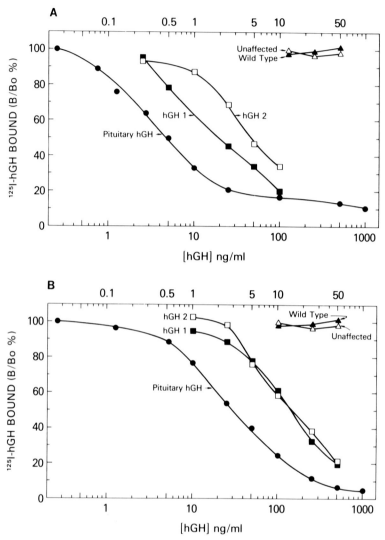

FIG. 6. Radioreceptor assay of hGH preparations. In (A) data from the IM-9 cultured human lymphocyte assay are shown and in (B) data from the pregnant rabbit liver membranes assay are shown. In each instance the assay contained the receptor preparation, ^{125}I-hGH, and various amounts of the unknown hGH preparation. These ingredients were diluted in buffer to a final volume of 500 μl and the incubation and separation of the bound and free components were carried out as described (Eastman *et al.*, 1979; Tsushima and Friesen, 1973). The media were the same samples used in Fig. 4. Note that the relationship of the lower and upper scales is different from that in Fig. 4. (From Pavlakis *et al.*, 1981.)

serum (Gorden *et al.*, 1976). It is apparent from our results that this could be accounted for by the presence of hGH2 in the acromegalic serum. Thus, an increase in an hGH form similar to hGH2 would produce a greater bioactive effect (as predicted from receptor activity) than would be predicted from the immunoreactive hGH concentration.

Although the potency of an hGH preparation in the IM-9 cultured lymphocyte radioreceptor assay correlates well with the bioactivity of the preparation as measured in the classic rat bioassay, other circumstances could exist *in vivo* (Lesniak *et al.*, 1974). For instance, a genetic variant of insulin has been described in a patient exhibiting insulin resistance (Given *et al.*, 1980). In this case the abnormal insulin molecule has decreased bioactivity but, more important, it acts as a partial agonist at the level of the insulin receptor and results in a shift in the insulin dose–response to the right. Whether a similar situation exists for variant short stature, a condition in which appropriate plasma concentrations of immunoreactive hGH fail to produce an appropriate tissue response, is presently unknown. Phillips *et al.* (1981) have studied a Swiss family with isolated hGH deficiency and they concluded that the affected members are missing the hGH1 gene while the hGH2 gene appears to be intact. This indicates that hGH2 cannot replace hGH1 but it does not exclude the possibility that hGH2 is an agonist of hGH since the pattern of expression of the hGH2 gene may be completely different.

Radioimmunoassays (Fig. 5) show that SVhGH-infected monkey kidney cells produce as much as 50 μg per 2×10^7 cells per day (8×10^7 molecules per cell per day) of hGH, a level that compares favorably with cultured pituitary cells. Furthermore, because the monkey cells export only a small fraction of their own proteins, the hGH2 polypeptide can be collected from the medium in highly enriched form. The ability to produce milligram quantities of hGH2 should facilitate the search for this protein in human tissues and sera and will allow us to test the biological activity of the variant protein by appropriate bioassays and animal tests. One approach for the identification of hGH2 in human tissues would be to generate monoclonal antibodies against the hGH2 molecule that do not react with hGH1.

V. Construction of Mutated hGH Genes

The expression system described above allows the rapid construction and assay of specifically mutated hGH genes. This permits analysis of various steps that affect the level of hGH production such as promoter function, mRNA processing and translation, as well as hGH processing and transport. The system should also be useful for producing recombinant proteins between hGH and related hormones, such as chorionic somatomammotropin or prolactin, thus facilitating the analysis of functional domains on these molecules.

We were particularly interested in the role of intervening sequences in the expression of hGH genes because results for the globin genes (Hamer and Leder, 1979) and the SV40 late genes (Gruss *et al.*, 1979) indicated that, in these cases, splicing is a prerequisite for the production of stable mRNA. We therefore constructed hGH mutants that contain either one or none of the four intervening sequences existing in the unaltered gene (Fig. 7). These mutant genes were inserted into viral SV40 vectors and introduced into cultured monkey cells. In all cases similar amounts of hGH were secreted from the infected cells. These results indicate that splicing is not required for hGH expression in the SV40–monkey cell system.

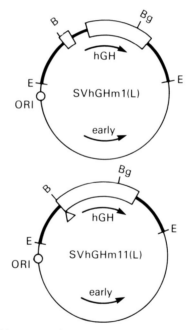

FIG. 7.   SV40 recombinants carrying mutated hGH genes. The top virus retains only one and the bottom recombinant none of the four intervening sequences present in the unaltered hGH1 gene. These molecules were constructed by replacing fragments of the genomic gene with corresponding sequences from an hGH cDNA clone. Boxes indicate hGH structural sequences, thick lines indicate hGH flanking and intervening sequences, and thin lines indicate SV40 vector sequences. ORI, origin of SV40 DNA replication: B, *Bam*HI; E, *Eco*RI; Bg, *Bgl*II.

VI. Attempts to Observe Hormonal Regulation Using SV40 Vectors

It has been shown that the production of growth hormone by the rat pituitary cell line GH3 is inducible by triiodothyronine (T3) and glucocorticoids (Dannies and Tashjian, 1973). We wished to examine whether the cloned hGH gene would be similarly regulated when introduced into monkey kidney cells on an SV40 vector.

We therefore cultured monkey kidney cells in T3- and glucocorticoid-depleted medium (Samuels et al., 1973; Wegnez et al., 1982) containing serum derived from a thyroidectomized animal (given to us by N. Eberhardt and J. Baxter). The cells were infected by the recombinant viruses and 10 to 24 hours postinfection were induced by T3 and dexamethasone for 12 to 20 hours. We did not observe a consistent induction in the amount of hGH produced, although some experiments gave a 1.2- to 2-fold increase in the secreted protein. It is not known if monkey kidney cells contain functional hormone receptors and/or other specific factors necessary for the induction of the hGH gene. We show below that the endogenous metallothionein genes cannot be induced by dexamethasone in these cells, but this result does not exclude the possibility that other genes might be responsive. Alternatively, we can hypothesize that additional flanking sequences and/or some sort of epigenetic information not present on the cloned hGH gene is required for induction.

Recently Robins et al. (1982) transfered the hGH1 gene into mouse Ltk⁻ cells and obtained clones that express the hGH gene. Some of these clones showed a 2- to 4-fold induction of hGH and presumptive hGH mRNA by dexamethasone whereas others exhibited constitutive expression. There are several differences between their experimental design and ours including the cell type, the status of the inserted DNA, and the gene dosage. It is not clear which of these factors is responsible for the difference in results nor is it known why their clones show such variability.

In an effort to eliminate some of the factors that confused the interpretation of the experiments, we decided to introduce a glucocorticoid-regulated gene into cells where it is naturally expressed and regulated. The mouse MT-I gene seemed a logical choice since this gene is inducible by both heavy metals and glucocorticoids in many different cell types (see Fig. 8). Moreover, it was shown recently that a cloned metallothionein-I gene retains its inducibility by cadmium when introduced into cells by microinjection (Brinster et al., 1982; Palmiter et al., 1982), co-transformation (Mayo et al., 1982), or transfection with SV40 recombinants (Hamer and Walling, 1982). We asked whether the transfered gene could be induced by glucocorticoids as well.

For this purpose we inserted the MT-I gene into a vector that contains

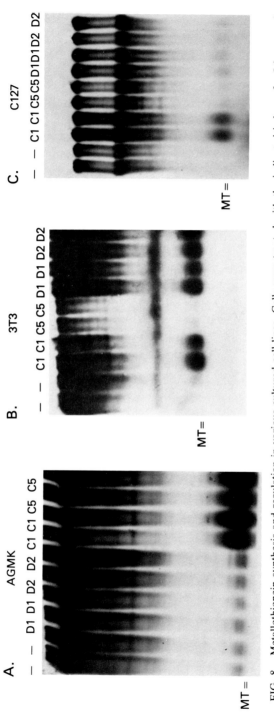

FIG. 8. Metallothionein synthesis and regulation in various cultured cell lines. Cells were treated with the indicated inducer for 8 hours and labeled with [^{35}S]cysteine for 2 hours. Total cellular proteins were carboxymethylated then analyzed on a 20% acrylamide gel. MT indicates the position of the metallothioneins on these gels. AGMK are primary African green monkey kidney cells whereas 3T3 and C127 are continuous mouse fibroblast lines. C1, 1 μM CdCl$_2$; C5, 5 μM CdCl$_2$; D1, 0.1 μM dexamethasone; D2, 1 μM dexamethasone.

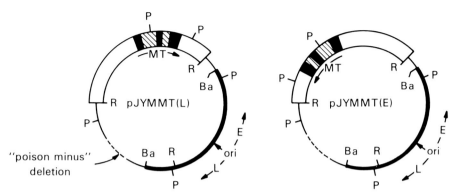

FIG. 9. SV40–MT-I plasmids used for acute transfection of HeLa cells. The 4000 bp *Eco*RI fragment containing the mouse MT-I gene was inserted into a "poison minus" pBR322 vector containing the complete SV40 genome. Solid boxes indicate MT-I structural sequences, cross-hatched boxes indicate MT-I intervening sequences, hollow boxes indicate MT-I flanking sequences, thick lines indicate SV40 sequences, and thin lines indicate pBR322 sequences. Ori, origin of SV40 DNA replication; E, direction of SV40 early transcription; L, direction of SV40 late transcription; P, *Pst*I; B, *Bam*HI. (From Hamer and Walling, 1982.)

the complete SV40 genome attached to a "poison minus" pBR322 derivative (Lusky and Botchan, 1981; Hamer and Walling, 1982) (Fig. 9). We then transfected the human HeLa cell line with these recombinants by either the DEAE-dextran or the Ca-phosphate technique and subsequently induced the transfected cells with Cd or dexamethasone. We chose HeLa cells as the host because they are inducible for metallothionein synthesis by both Cd and dexamethasone (Karin *et al.*, 1980) and because they are also permissive for SV40 replication. Total RNA was isolated from the transfected cells and the amount of mouse MT-I mRNA was determined by nuclease S1 mapping. The results of this experiment are shown in Fig. 10. It is clear that the cloned mouse MT-I gene is inducible by Cd but not by dexamethasone under these conditions.

VII. BPV Recombinants Carrying a MT–hGH Hybrid Gene

The failure to observe glucocorticoid regulation of the mouse MT-I gene in an SV40 vector led us to consider two additional possible difficulties. First, because we were introducing a mouse gene into human cells, it seemed conceivable that the factors required for induction might be species specific. Second, because SV40 replicates at very high copy numbers (up to 10^5 molecules per cell) it was possible that the cells simply did not contain sufficient quantities of regulatory factors. In an attempt to sur-

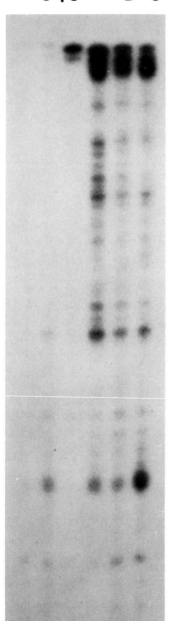

mount these objections we turned to vectors based on BPV, a virus that can transform cultured mouse fibroblasts and that replicates as a nuclear episome at relatively low copy numbers (about 10–100 copies per cell) (Lowy *et al.*, 1980; Law *et al.*, 1981).

Because we wished to reintroduce mouse MT-I sequences into mouse cells, it was necessary to devise a method for distinguishing between products derived from the cloned gene and its chromosomal counterparts. This was accomplished by fusing the MT-I promoter and presumptive control region to an hGH "minigene" that lacks all of the 5′ flanking sequences and three of the four introns found in the chromosomal hGH gene (Fig. 11). The resulting hybrid gene contains 1900 bp of MT-I 5′ flanking sequences, 68 bp of MT-I 5′ untranslated sequences, the 70 bp first exon of the hGH gene, a 250 bp hGH intron, the remaining 750 bp of hGH structural sequences, and 550 bp of hGH 3′ flanking sequences. This construct was inserted, in both possible orientations, into a pBR322-BPV vector containing the 69% transforming region of the viral genome (Sarver *et al.*, 1981). The two recombinant viruses, BPVMG6 and BPVMG7, were generated by excision of the plasmid sequences followed by recircularization (Fig. 12). The transcriptional orientations of the hybrid gene and BPV are in tandem in BPVMG7 and opposed in BPVMG6 (Heilman *et al.*, 1982; Chen *et al.*, 1982).

These molecules were transfected into mouse C127 cells and transformants were picked on the basis of their altered morphology. All of the first 25 clones isolated produced and secreted hGH as determined by radioimmunoassays of the media. Clones were named CBMG6-n (carrying the BPVMG6 recombinant) and CBMG7-n (carrying the BPVMG7 recombinant). To establish the status of the recombinant molecules in the transformed lines, we extracted their total DNA and analyzed it by gel transfer hybridization to a BPV probe. Figure 13 shows the results for 12 clones digested with *Bam*HI or *Sac*I, which cleave once, and with *Kpn*I, which cleaves twice. Ten of the 12 clones gave predominantly or exclusively a single, unit-length band with *Bam*HI and *Sac*I, and 2 bands of the appropriate lengths with *Kpn*I. Analysis of the low-molecular-weight Hirt supernatant DNA (Hirt, 1969) from clones that had been passaged for 10

FIG. 10. Expression of the mouse MT-I gene in transfected HeLa cells. HeLa cells were transfected with pJYMMT(E) (see Fig. 9) by the Ca-phosphate technique. At 36 hours posttransfection the cells were treated with 1 μM dexamethasone (D), 5 μM CdCl$_2$ (C), or no inducer (−). Total cell RNA was extracted 12 hours later and characterized by S1 mapping to a 5′ end-labeled mouse MT-I gene probe (Hamer and Walling, 1982). The band at 68 bases is indicative of appropriate transcription of the mouse MT-I gene. Also shown are samples from mouse L cells (L) treated with 5 μM CdCl$_2$ (C) or no inducer (−) and from HeLa cells mock-transfected with no DNA (O). Similar results were obtained with pJYMMT(L).

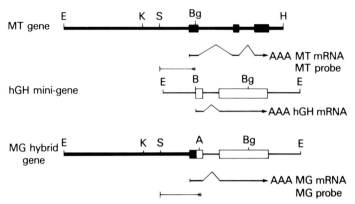

FIG. 11.   Structure of the MT–hGH hybrid gene. The *Eco*RI–*Bgl*II fragment containing the promoter of the mouse MT-I gene was fused to the *Bam*HI site of an hGH "minigene" that retains only the first of its four intervening sequences. This hGH "minigene" contains all the coding information for pre-hGH. The structures of the expected mRNAs and of the two 5′ end-labeled probes utilized for S1 mapping are shown: (i) a *Bgl*II–*Sac*I fragment of the MT gene 5′ end-labeled at the *Bgl*II site (MT probe). (ii) an *Ava*II–*Sac*I fragment of the hybrid gene 5′ end-labeled at the *Ava*II site (MG probe).

months showed no alterations in DNA structure and confirmed the presence of supercoiled episomal molecules (Fig. 14). This demonstrates, in agreement with previous results (Sarver *et al.*, 1981; Law *et al.*, 1981), that the recombinant molecules are maintained primarily or exclusively as episomes. By comparison with a plasmid DNA standard we estimate that

FIG. 12.   Construction of the MT–hGH hybrid gene and insertion into a BPV vector. A 4 kb *Eco*RI fragment containing the entire mouse MT-I gene (a) and a 2.1 kb *Eco*RI fragment containing an hGH minigene (b) were inserted into a pBR322-SV40 vector. The hGH minigene has three out of four intervening sequences of the hGH gene removed and is functional in monkey kidney cells (see Section V). A 2 kb *Bam*HI fragment, which extends from the cap site of the hGH gene to the *Bam*HI site of pBR322, was isolated from pSVGH3C2(L) and inserted into the *Bgl*II site in the first exon of the MT-I gene. A plasmid, pSVMTGH8, which has the hGH fragment in the same transcriptional orientation as the MT-I gene was isolated. Digestion of this plasmid with *Hin*dIII yielded a fragment that contained 2 kb of MT-I 5′ flanking sequences and part of the first exon of the MT gene fused to the cap site of the hGH minigene. This fragment was inserted into the *Hin*dIII-linearized plasmid pBPV69TD. This vector contains the 69% transforming *Bam*HI–*Hin*dIII fragment of bovine papilloma virus-1 cloned into pBR322 (P. Howley, unpublished). Note that the small *Hin*dIII–*Bam*HI fragment of pBR322 is duplicated in this vector in order to facilitate subsequent manipulations. After cloning in *E. coli* the four different orientations of recombinant plasmid were isolated. In two of these, designated pBPVMG6 and pBPVMG7, the pBR322 sequences can be excised by complete *Bam*HI digestion. This generated the two molecules designated BPVMG6 and BPVMG7 in which the hybrid gene is associated with the BPV vector in both possible orientations.

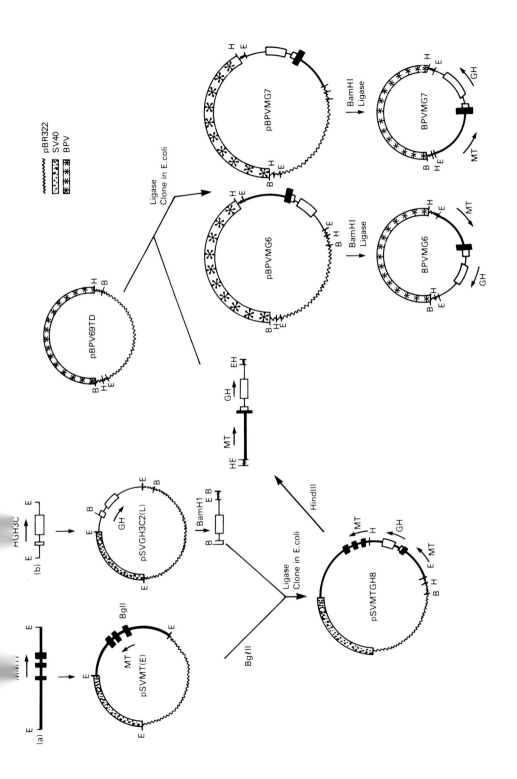

B   6-1 6-2 6-3 6-4 6-5 6-6 6-7 6-8 6-9 7-4 7-7 7-8

A.

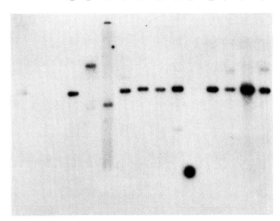

B.

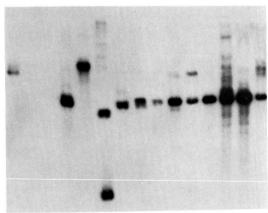

C.

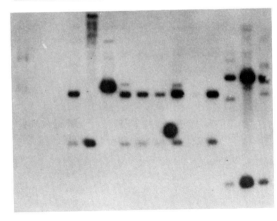

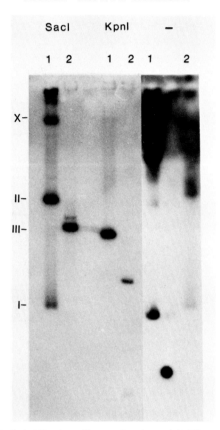

FIG. 14. Gel transfer hybridization of low-molecular-weight Hirt supernatant DNA from transformed cells. Line 1 is ID13 cells, a control line containing wild-type BPV. Line 2 is a clone of cells (CBMG6-9) that contains BPVMG6 (see Fig. 12) and produces hGH. The DNA was either undigested ($-$) or digested with nucleases *SacI* or *KpnI*. The approximate positions of supercoiled (I), nicked circular (II), and unit-length linear molecules (III) are indicated. Notice that BPV DNA is smaller than BPVMG6 DNA. The higher bands, indicated by X on the gel, are probably free multimers or concatenated molecules.

the transformants contain between 10 and 100 copies/cell of the recombinant molecules. The presence of faint bands in some of the digests may reflect minor rearrangements in the DNA or the presence of more than one cell type. Two of the clones (6-2 and 6-3) gave different restriction

FIG. 13. Gel transfer hybridization of total cell DNA from 12 clones containing the BPV recombinants and producing hGH. Total cell DNA was digested with (A) *Bam*HI, (B) *Sac*I, or (C) *Kpn*I, electrophoresed on 1% agarose gels, blotted on nitrocellulose filters, and hybridized to a nick-translated BPV probe. Lane B is pBPVMG6 DNA digested with the same enzymes.

patterns indicative of gross rearrangements. One of these lines (6-3) was unstable and stopped producing hGH after 5 months of culture. In contrast, all of the 10 clones with the expected DNA structure continued to produce hGH after 1 year of continuous passage.

We have also constructed pBR322-BPV recombinants retaining the intact mouse MT-I gene (Fig. 18). These recombinants, designated pBPVMT1 and pBPVMT5, can be partially digested with *Bgl*II for insertion of other sequences into the 5' untranslated region of the MT-I gene, bringing these sequences under the control of the inducible MT promoter. They can also be used as dominant selection vectors since they make C127 cells resistant to toxic concentrations of cadmium (see below).

VIII. Regulation of MT–hGH Hybrid mRNA

We expected the MT–hGH hybrid gene to encode a hybrid mRNA initiated at the MT-I gene promoter. To detect and map the 5' end of these transcripts we performed nuclease S1 protection experiments with a probe 5' end-labeled at the *Ava*II site in the hGH portion of the first exon of the hybrid gene (Fig. 11). Figure 15A shows that RNA from the transformed mouse cells protected a predominant fragment of 100 bases, corresponding to the distance between the end-label and the 5' end of the MT-I gene. Several larger bands were also protected in variable quantities, probably due to partial nuclease S1 digestion or secondary structure in the single-stranded DNA extending from the DNA–RNA hybrid. The specificity of this assay is shown by the fact that RNA from untransformed C127 cells gave no protected bands.

The regulation of hybrid mRNA synthesis was studied by S1 mapping the RNA from cells grown in media containing cadmium, dexamethasone, or no inducer. The RNA samples were hybridized to the hybrid gene-specific probe and the intensity of the protected bands was quantitated by densitometry of the autoradiograms. Typical results for four different clones are shown in Fig. 15A. We consistently observed increased levels of hybrid mRNA in the cadmium-treated cells. Induction ratios varied from 2-fold (clone 6-3) to 7-fold (clone 7-4). In contrast, induction by dexamethasone was not consistently observed. In the experiment shown in Fig. 15, in which we used RNA from approximately equal numbers of cells, the amount of hybrid RNA in the dexamethasone-induced cells is less than in the uninduced cells for clones 6-3 and 6-7. Dexamethasone inhibits total RNA and protein synthesis by 10–20% in our clones. If we normalize the S1 mapping results for equal amounts of RNA we find no significant difference at the levels of hybrid mRNA after dexamethasone

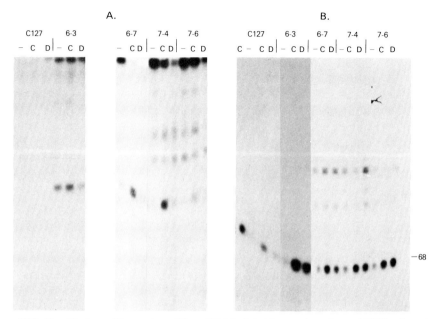

FIG. 15. Nuclease S1 mapping of the mRNA isolated from untransformed C127 cells and from four BPVMG-transformed lines. Total RNA was isolated from cells treated for 8 hours with 1 μM CdCl$_2$ (C), 50 nM dexamethasone (D), or no inducer (−). (A) Mapping with an AvaII–SacI MG gene probe 5′ end-labeled 100 bp downstream from the initiation site (see Fig. 11). This probe detects only hybrid gene transcripts. (B) Mapping with a BglII–SacI MT gene probe 5′ end-labeled 68 bp downstream from the initiation site. This probe detects transcripts from both the endogenous MT-I gene and from the cloned hybrid gene.

induction. In some experiments we found a slight induction (1.1- to 2-fold) by dexamethasone, but this result was not reproducible.

As a control for this experiment, the same RNA samples were hybridized to a MT-I gene probe (Figure 11) that will detect the RNAs encoded by the endogenous mouse MT-I gene as well as the cloned hybrid gene. As shown in Fig. 15B, regulation by both cadmium and dexamethasone was consistently observed with this probe. This demonstrates that the transformed cells have retained their ability to respond to both heavy metal and glucocorticoid induction.

The failure to observe regulation of the hybrid gene by dexamethasone cannot be due to a species difference because the cloned gene and host cells were both derived from the mouse. Furthermore, lack of sufficient glucocorticoid receptors or other regulatory factors seems unlikely since the chromosomal MT genes in the same cells remained responsive to dexamethasone. Recently, it has been shown that a MT–thymidine kinase hybrid gene loses glucocorticoid inducibility following introduction into mouse cells by direct DNA transformation (Mayo *et al.*, 1982) or microinjection into embryos (Brinster *et al.*, 1982). This suggests that our result is not due to an artifact of the BPV vector system. Glucocorticoid inducibility is also lost in cadmium-resistant cells containing amplified metallothionein genes (Mayo and Palmiter, 1981). However, sequence analysis has shown that our MT-I gene, which was cloned from cadmium-resistant L cells (Hamer and Walling, 1982), is identical to the gene cloned from cadmium-sensitive myeloma cells (Glanville *et al.*, 1981) for at least 300 bp of 5′ flanking sequences and all of the 5′ untranslated sequences (M. F. Jubier and D. H. Hamer, unpublished results). One possible explanation of our results is that the glucocorticoid regulatory sequences of the mouse MT-I gene lie outside of this region. Another possibility is that glucocorticoid regulation of the mouse MT-I gene requires a specific chromatin environment or other epigenetic information which is lost during the cloning procedures. The one clear conclusion that can be drawn from our data is that glucocorticoids and heavy metals regulate the mouse MT-I gene by independent mechanisms. Glucocorticoids cannot be simply increasing the concentration of available intracellular metal because this would have resulted in a induction of the hybrid gene.

IX. Efficient hGH Production by BPV Transformants

As shown in Section III, cultured monkey kidney cells infected with SV40–hGH recombinants are capable of both processing and secreting hGH (Pavlakis *et al.*, 1981). To determine if this was also true for the BPVMG transformants, cells were labeled with [^{35}S]cysteine and the secreted proteins in the media were analyzed by gel electrophoresis. Figure 16A shows a typical analysis of clone 7-4. A protein comigrating with authentic hGH was observed in the media from the BPVMG transformed cells but not from control ID13 cells. Furthermore, when cells were induced for 8 hours with Cd or dexamethasone the amount of this protein was increased 2-fold by cadmium but was unaffected by dexamethasone (Fig. 16B). We also observed variable quantities of a higher molecular weight band in the transformed cells. Although this protein has not been characterized, it is interesting to note that it migrates approximately at the position expected for prehGH. Parallel analysis of the labeled intracellular proteins from the same cells showed that metallothionein synthesis was induced by both cadmium and dexamethasone (Fig. 16C). This confirms that the endogenous metallothionein genes in the transformed cells have retained their responsiveness to both heavy metals and glucocorticoids. From scans of such gels we estimate that the transformed cells

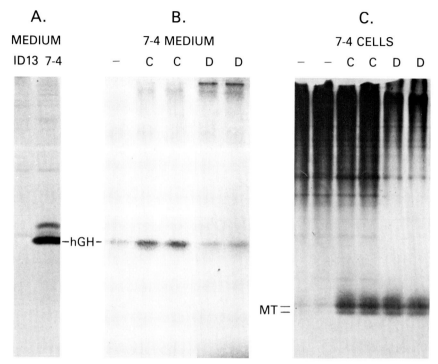

A.

MEDIUM

ID13 7-4

B.

7-4 MEDIUM

−   C   C   D   D

C.

7-4 CELLS

−   −   C   C   D   D

−hGH−

MT ═

FIG. 16. Induction of hGH and MT proteins. Induced and uninduced cells were labeled for 1 hour with [^{35}S]Cys after 7 hours of induction. Cellular and media proteins were analyzed by electrophoresis on 20% acrylamide gels and autoradiography. (A) Comparison of media proteins from the control line ID13 (transformed with BPV-I virus) and from clone 7-4 (transformed with BPVMG7). Only 7-4 medium contains a band comigrating with authentic pituitary hGH. (B) Total media proteins from cells that had been treated for 7 hours with 1 μM CdCl$_2$ (C), 50 nM dexamethasone (D), or no inducer (−). (C) Total cell proteins from the same cells analyzed in (B). Notice that dexamethasone treatment inhibits overall protein synthesis but nonetheless induces metallothionein production.

produce 20- to 60-fold more hGH than MT. (Note that MT contains 20 cysteine residues whereas hGH contains only 4.)

The amount of hGH secreted by the transformed mouse cells was quantitated by radioimmunoassay. Figure 17 shows results for nine clones 1 month after the initial transfection of C127 cells. Basal levels ranged from 0.2 to 2.5 μg/ml and these levels were increased 1.3- to 2.5-fold by treatment with cadmium but not by dexamethasone. The hGH production levels remained constant or actually increased as the cells were continuously passaged for 10 months (except for the unstable clone 6-3). Measurements of cell number and media levels of hGH for cells that had been in culture for 10 months showed basal levels of hGH production ranging

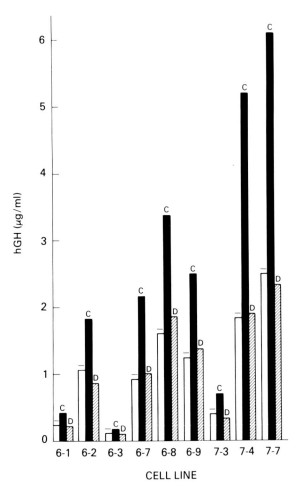

FIG. 17.   Production of hGH by the BPVMG transformed cell lines. Cells were grown in 24-well plates, induced by CdCl$_2$ or dexamethasone for 16 hours, and the hGH in the media was quantitated by radioimmunoassay. (−) Uninduced cells; (C) cells induced by 1 μM CdCl$_2$; (D) cells induced by 50 nM dexamethasone. Control lines (C127, ID13, NS8) gave values < 1 ng/ml in this assay.

from 2 to 6 × 10^8 molecules per cell per day in 4 different clones, or almost 10 times the amount of hGH produced in monkey kidney cells lytically infected with SV40 recombinants carrying the intact hGH gene. The high production levels and stability of the transformed clones suggest that BPVMT vectors might be useful for producing other eukaryotic gene products. In particular, the ability to regulate the expression of inserted structural sequences by cadmium should make it possible to overproduce toxic products and to study the physiological effects of proteins for which the genes are available but the functions are unknown.

X. Construction of New Dominant Selection Vectors

The activity of the MT promoter on BPV prompted us to construct BPV recombinants carrying the intact mouse MT-I gene and to attempt to utilize them as dominant selection vectors (Fig. 18). These BPV–MT recombinants were introduced into mouse C127 cells after the excision of the pBR322 sequences. Two days later the cells were treated with 20 μM CdCl$_2$, a concentration which normally kills C127 cells. Many transformed and cadmium-resistant colonies were isolated indicating that overproduction of MT from the BPV–MT recombinants can indeed be utilized as a dominant selection.

In order to demonstrate that these vectors can be used to introduce other, nonselectable genes into mouse cells, we constructed the BPV–MT–hGH recombinants shown in Fig. 19. These recombinants were introduced into mouse cells and transformants were selected on the basis of cadmium resistance. The majority of these clones produced and secreted large quantities of hGH. This simple dominant selection may allow the introduction of nonselectable genes into different cell types, thus expanding the utility of the BPV vectors. It should be especially interesting to see if this technique can be used to introduce cloned hGH genes into pituitary cells.

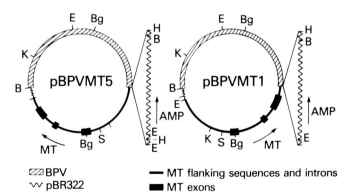

FIG. 18. Plasmid BPV recombinants containing the intact mouse MT-I gene in two different orientations. These molecules can be used to bring other structural sequences under the control of the MT-I promoter and to confer cadmium resistance to transformed cells. Hatched bars indicate BPV sequences, solid lines and boxes indicate MT-I sequences, and wavy lines indicate pBR322 sequences. Restriction enzyme symbols are E. *Eco*RI; B, *Bam*HI; H, *Hin*dIII; Bg, *Bgl*II; K, *Kpn*I; S, *Sac*I.

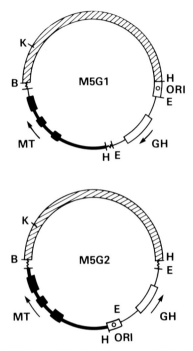

FIG. 19. BPV–MTI–hGH recombinants. These recombinants contain the 69% trans-forming fragment of BPV (hatched bars) and a complete mouse MT-I gene (solid bars). An hGH minigene with no intervening sequences (hollow bar) was ligated to this vector together with a DNA fragment containing the SV40 late promoter and origin of DNA replication (ORI). B, *Bam*HI; E, *Eco*RI; H, *Hind*III; K, *Kpn*I.

XI. Summary

DNA tumor virus vectors have been used to transfer hGH genes into cultured mammalian cells. SV40 recombinants were constructed carrying the normal hGH1 gene and the variant hGH2 gene which is expected to encode a protein with 13 amino acid substitutions. Monkey kidney cells infected with both types of recombinants synthesized hGH that was ap-propriately processed and secreted. The product of the normal gene was identical to pituitary hGH by several criteria. The variant gene product differed from pituitary hGH in its physicochemical properties and low immunoreactivity but bound efficiently to hGH cell surface receptors. This indicated that the variant gene has the potential to be expressed into a previously unrecognized form of hGH that could, conceivably, be active in some human cells or in certain developmental stages. By using artificially altered genes it was shown that hGH expression does not require the presence of any of the four introns present in the chromosomal gene.

The normal hGH gene was also introduced into mouse C127 cells by stable transformation with a BPV vector. In these experiments the hGH promoter region was replaced with the control region from the mouse MT-I gene, a sequence that is normally inducible by both heavy metals and glucocorticoids. The transformed cells secreted up to 5×10^8 molecules per cell per day of hGH. The expression of the MT–hGH gene was inducible by cadmium, but not by dexamethasone, even though the chromosomal MT genes in the same cells were regulated by both agents. This indicates that heavy metals and hormones induce the mouse MT-I gene by independent mechanisms.

The mouse MT-I gene inserted into BPV has also been used as a dominant selective marker for hGH gene transfer. This system allows transformed cells to be selected by cadmium resistance, rather than by altered morphology, and should be useful for introducing hormone-coding and hormone-responsive genes into a variety of cell types.

ACKNOWLEDGMENTS

We thank our many colleagues who collaborated on these experiments and Gail Taff for her critical and timely assistance with the manuscript.

REFERENCES

Bala, R. M., Ferguson, K. A., and Beck, J. C. (1973). In "Advances in Human Growth Hormone Research" (S. Raiti, ed.), pp. 494–516. HEW Publ. No. 74-612.

Blobel, G., Walter, P., Chang, C. N., Goldman, B., Erickson, A. H., and Lingappa, V. R. (1979). Symp. Soc. Exp. Biol. 33, 9–36.

Brinster, R. L., Chen, H. Y., Warren, R., Sarthy, A., and Palmiter, R. D. (1982). Nature (London) 296, 39–42.

Cheever, E. V., and Lewis, U. J. (1969). Endocrinology 85, 465–470.

Chen, E. Y., Howley, P. M., Levinson, A. D., and Seeburg, P. H. (1982). Nature (London) 299, 529–534.

Chow, J. Y., and Martin, R. G. (1974). J. Virol. 13, 1101–1109.

Chrambach, A., Yadley, R. A., Ben-David, M., and Rodbard, D. (1973). Endocrinology 93, 848–857.

Dannies, P. S., and Tashjian, A. H., Jr. (1973). In "Tissue Culture: Methods and Application" (P. F. Kruse, Jr. and M. K. Patterson, Jr., eds.), pp. 561–569. Academic Press, New York.

DeNoto, F. M., Moore, D. D., and Goodman, H. M. (1981). Nucleic Acids Res. 9, 3719–3730.

Durnam, D. M., and Palmiter, R. D. (1981). J. Biol. Chem. 256, 5712–5716.

Eastman, R. C., Lesniak, M. A., Roth, J., DeMeyts, P., and Gorden, P. J. (1979). J. Clin. Endocrinol. Metab. 49, 262–268.

Fiddes, J. C., Seeburg, P. H., DeNoto, F. M., Hallewell, R. A., Baxter, J. D., and Goodman, H. M. (1979). *Proc. Natl. Acad. Sci. U.S.A.* **76,** 4294–4298.

Given, B. D., Mako, M. E., Tager, H. S., Baldwin, D., Markese, J., Rubenstein, A. H., Olefsky, J., Kobayashi, M., Kolterman, O., and Poucher, R. (1980). *N. Engl. J. Med.* **302,** 129–135.

Glanville, N., Durnam, D. M., and Palmiter, R. D. (1981). *Nature (London)* **292,** 267–269.

Goodman, A. D., Tanenbaum, R., and Rabinowitz, D. (1972). *J. Clin. Endocrinol. Metab.* **35,** 868–878.

Gorden, P., Hendricks, C. M., and Roth, J. (1973). *J. Clin. Endocrinol. Metab.* **36,** 178–184.

Gorden, P., Lesniak, M. A., Eastman, R., Hendricks, C. M., and Roth, J. (1976). *J. Clin. Endocrinol. Metab.* **43,** 364–373.

Gruss, P., and Khoury, G. (1981). *Proc. Natl. Acad. Sci. U.S.A.* **78,** 133–137.

Gruss, P., Lai, C.-J., Dhar, R., and Khoury, G. (1979). *Proc. Natl. Acad. Sci. U.S.A.* **76,** 4317–4321.

Gumbiner, B., and Kelly, R. B. (1982). *Cell* **28,** 51–59.

Hager, J. H., and Palmiter, R. D. (1981). *Nature (London)* **291,** 340–342.

Hamer, D. H., and Leder, P. (1979). *Cell* **18,** 1299–1302.

Hamer, D. H., and Walling, M. J. (1982). *J. Mol. Appl. Genet.* **1,** 273–288.

Heilman, C. A., Engel, L. W., Lowy, D. R., and Howley, P. M. (1982). *Virology* **119,** 22–34.

Hirt, B. (1969). *J. Mol. Biol.* **40,** 141–144.

Hizuka, N., Hendricks, C. M., Pavlakis, G. N., Hamer, D. H., and Gorden, P. (1982). *J. Clin. Endocrinol. Metab.* **55,** 545–550.

Karin, M., Anderson, R. D., Slater, E., Smith, K., and Herschman, H. R. (1980). *Nature (London)* **286,** 295–297.

Law, M.-F., Lowy, D. R., Dvoretzky, I., and Howley, P. M. (1981). *Proc. Natl. Acad. Sci. U.S.A.* **78,** 2727–2731.

Lesniak, M. A., Gorden, P., Roth, J., and Gavin, J. R., III. (1974). *J. Biol. Chem.* **249,** 1661–1667.

Lewis, U. J., and Cheever, E. V. (1965). *J. Biol. Chem.* **240,** 247–250.

Lewis, U. J., Cheever, E. V., and Hopkins, W. C. (1970). *Biochim. Biophys. Acta* **214,** 498–508.

Lewis, U. J., Dunn, J. T., Bonewald, L. F., Seavey, B. K., and VanderLaan, W. P. (1978). *J. Biol. Chem.* **253,** 2679–2687.

Lewis, U. J., Bonewald, L. F., and Lewis, L. J. (1980). *Biochem. Biophys. Res. Commun.* **92,** 511–516.

Lowy, D. R., Dvoretzky, I., Shober, R., Law, M.-F., Engel, L., and Howley, P. M. (1980). *Nature (London)* **287,** 72–74.

Lusky, M., and Botchan, M. (1981). *Nature (London)* **293,** 79–81.

McCutchan, J. H., and Pagano, J. S. (1968). *J. Natl. Cancer Inst.* **41,** 351–357.

Martial, J. A., Hallewell, R. A., Baxter, J. D., and Goodman, H. M. (1979). *Science* **205,** 602–607.

Mayo, K. E., and Palmiter, R. D. (1981). *J. Biol. Chem.* **256,** 2621–2624.

Mayo, K. E., Warren, R., and Palmiter, R. D. (1982). *Cell* **29,** 99–108.

Moore, D. D., Walker, M. D., Diamond, D. J., Coukling, M. A., and Goodman, H. M. (1982). *Recent Prog. Horm. Res.* **38,** 197–225.

O'Farrell, P. H. (1975). *J. Biol. Chem.* **250,** 4007–4021.

O'Farrell, P. Z., Goodman, H. M., and O'Farrell, P. H. (1977). *Cell* **12,** 1133–1142.

Palmiter, R. D., Chen, H. Y., and Brinster, R. L. (1982). *Cell* **29,** 701–710.

Pavlakis, G. N., Hizuka, N., Gorden, P., Seeburg, P. H., and Hamer, D. H. (1981). *Proc. Natl. Acad. Sci. U.S.A.* **78,** 7398–7402.

Phillips, J. A., III, Hjelle, B. L., Seeburg, P. H., and Zachmann, M. (1981). *Proc. Natl. Acad. Sci. U.S.A.* **78**, 6372–6375.

Raiti, S., ed. (1973). "Advances in Human Growth Hormone Research." HEW Publ. No. 74-612.

Robins, D. M., Paek, I., Seeburg, P. H., and Axel, R. (1982). *Cell* **29**, 623–631.

Samuels, H. H., Tsai, J. S., and Cintron, R. (1973). *Science* **181**, 1253–1256.

Sarver, N., Gruss, P., Law, M.-F., Khoury, G., and Howley, P. M. (1981). *Mol. Cell. Biol.* **1**, 486–496.

Seeburg, P. H. (1982). *DNA* **1**, 239–249.

Tsushima, T., and Friesen, H. G. (1973). *J. Clin. Endocrinol. Metab.* **37**, 334–337.

Vale, W. Brazean, P., Rivier, C., Rivier, J., and Guillemin, R. (1973). In "Advances in Human Growth Hormone Research" (S. Raiti, ed.), pp. 159–181. HEW Publ. No. 74-612.

Wallis, M. (1980). *Nature (London)* **284**, 512.

Wegnez, M., Schachter, B. S., Baxter, J. D., and Martial, J. A. (1982). *DNA* **1**, 145–153.

DISCUSSION

D. V. Cohn: I was fascinated by your presentation. It represents terribly important work. I was interested in your statement that your mouse cells were secreting hGH without the apparent intervention of secretory granules. I wanted to comment that when one looks in the parathyroid cells of different species, one finds pretty much the same content of parathyroid hormone but the anatomist cannot always find a relationship to number secretory granules. In a mouse parathyroid gland as I recall there are relatively few secretory granules compared to a cow gland, yet the hormone content and secretory capacity of the cells are the same. A question I have in this regard is did you determine that secretion granules were not involved and do you think that the secretory granule may be the last stages in evolution for controlling hormone production and secretion.

G. Pavlakis: We have not really looked for secretory granules in these cells. All that I was trying to say before is that after listening to Dr. Cohn's talk it came to mind that maybe the secretory granules could exert some specific and additional levels of regulation which we fail to see in these gene transfer experiments because our current data show that more than 90% of the protein that we produce is immediately transported out of the cells.

L. S. Jacobs: I would like to speak to that last point. There are tumor models which secrete large quantities of hormone which leave little morphologic evidence of granule compartmentation of the secretory product but have very high secretory rates. In acromegaly, the concentration of growth hormone in the tumor tissue is considerably lower than that found in the normal pituitary; concomitantly, the number of visible morphologic secretory granules is far fewer. The same is true in the transplantable *in vivo* rat pituitary tumor cells and also in estrogen-induced prolactin-secreting pituitary tumors in the rat. There is also an inverse correlation which can be shown in rats bearing these transplantable tumors, and in acromegalics, between the serum level of growth hormone and the pituitary content. So it is entirely possible that the granule itself, via some signal from its storage compartment within the cell, helps to modulate the synthetic rate by some kind of an internal intracellular feedback signal and that speculation seems to me worthy of trying to approach experimentally in order to develop data.

G. Pavlakis: That was a very interesting comment, thank you very much.

Glucocorticoid Regulation of Gene Expression: Mouse Mammary Tumor Virus as a Model System

GORDON M. RINGOLD, DEBORAH E. DOBSON, J. RUSSELL GROVE, CAROL V. HALL,* FRANK LEE, AND JAMES L. VANNICE

Departments of Pharmacology and *Biology, Stanford University, Stanford, California

I. Introduction

Glucocorticoids, as well as other classes of steroid hormones, appear to function via the "two-step" model originally proposed by Jensen and his colleagues (Jensen *et al.*, 1968). It is generally accepted that steroids interact with a soluble receptor protein inducing a structural alteration that increases the receptor's affinity for DNA or chromatin. This so-called "activated" form of the steroid–receptor complex accumulates within the nucleus of the cell leading to increased (and perhaps in some cases, decreased) transcription of specific genes. The classes of new messenger RNAs produced in response to a given steroid are in large part cell or tissue specific and their utilization in production of new proteins leads to the characteristic hormonal response of the target cell. In this view, the primary role of the steroid is to act as an allosteric effector that unmasks a DNA-binding site on the receptor protein. The detailed molecular mechanisms by which the steroid–receptor complex stimulates transcription of specific genes are poorly understood and are in large part the focus of this article. For more extensive discussion of the basic "two-step" model and the evidence in support of it, the reader is directed to one or more of the many reviews on this subject (Gorski and Gannon, 1976; Yamamoto and Alberts, 1976; Higgins and Gehring, 1978).

In choosing a model system for studying gene regulation by steroid hormones, there are several criteria that one would like the system to meet. First, it is essential that the response under investigation be a primary hormone effect and second, that it be elicited by the appropriate intracellular receptor. Although these are difficult points to prove beyond a shadow of a doubt, the experimental evidence should include (1) rapid induction of RNA, (2) insensitivity of RNA induction to inhibitors of protein synthesis, (3) appropriate pharmacological relationships between receptor binding and induction, and (4) necessity of functional receptors.

387

Lastly, it is tremendously advantageous if the response can be measured in a homogeneous population of cells such as a continuous tissue culture cell line in which genetic approaches to steroid action could be employed. Many of these points are discussed in greater detail elsewhere (Yamamoto and Ringold, 1978).

We have previously documented that the glucocorticoid induction of mouse mammary tumor virus (MMTV) in a variety of cell lines fulfills these criteria (Ringold *et al.*, 1975, 1977a). In this article we briefly summarize some of these studies and present a detailed account of the use of MMTV in furthering our understanding of the mechanisms by which glucocorticoids regulate gene expression.

II. Mouse Mammary Tumor Virus

A. MMTV: STRUCTURE AND LIFE CYCLE

As is true of all retroviruses, MMTV is an enveloped virus containing a single-stranded RNA genome (Cardiff and Duesberg, 1968). Within each virus particle or virion there are two identical subunits of genomic RNA (9000 bases in length) and several associated small RNAs, including a hydrogen-bonded tRNA used as a primer for viral DNA synthesis. The virion itself is composed of a nucleoprotein core containing the RNA, several nonglycosylated structural proteins, and a polymerase, the so-called reverse transcriptase, capable of transcribing the RNA genome into double-standed DNA (for a recent review, see Bentvelzen and Hilgers, 1980). Surrounding this core is an envelope composed of cellular plasma membrane into which the major viral glycoproteins (gp52 and gp36) have been inserted.

During infection of a cell (Fig. 1), MMTV binds to a surface receptor, becomes internalized, and the nucleoprotein core becomes "activated." The mechanics of these processes are poorly understood. Within the cytoplasm of the infected cell, a linear double-stranded DNA copy of the viral RNA is synthesized by the viral reverse transcriptase (Vaidya *et al.*, 1976; Ringold *et al.*, 1977b,c, 1978). Later, MMTV DNA becomes covalently linked to the host DNA where it resides as a stable Mendelian locus in the progeny of the infected cell. There is some, although not incontrovertible, evidence that prior to integration, the viral DNA must be circularized (Guntaka *et al.*, 1975; Ringold *et al.*, 1977c). Once the DNA is integrated in the host cell's genome (in this state the DNA is refered to as a provirus) it is controlled in large part by the normal cellular machinery. Several species of RNA, including genomic-sized RNA for encapsidation

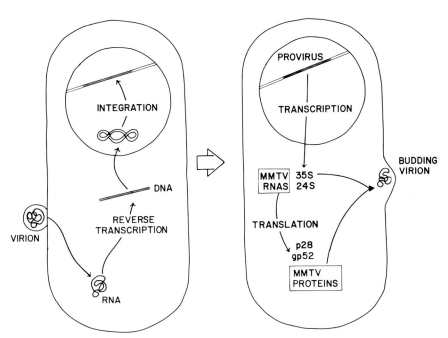

FIG. 1. Life cycle of mouse mammary tumor virus. After adsorption and uncoating of the virus particle, a linear double-stranded form of viral DNA is produced by reverse transcription in the cytoplasm, a portion of that DNA enters the nucleus where it becomes circularized, and finally one or a few molecules integrate into the chromosomal DNA to form MMTV proviruses (Ringold *et al.*, 1977c). The integrated DNA is transcribed by RNA polymerase II (Stallcup *et al.*, 1978) to yield full length viral RNA (35 S), as well as subgenomic messenger RNAs (e.g., 24 S). All of these RNAs are utilized to synthesize viral proteins (e.g., gp52 and p28). Virion cores are assembled within the cytoplasm and form new virus particles by budding from the plasma membrane.

into progeny virus and smaller RNAs for use as messenger RNAs, are synthesized by cellular RNA polymerase II (Stallcup *et al.*, 1978; Robertson and Varmus, 1979; Groner *et al.*, 1979). As has been alluded to earlier, and is the major focus of our work, it is the production of these RNAs that is under glucocorticoid control. The viral life cycle is completed by assembling the appropriate RNAs into a virion precursor which buds from the cell membrane, thereby releasing an intact virus particle; this occurs without killing or seriously damaging the host cell.

B. STRUCTURE OF MMTV DNA

Before proceeding with studies on glucocorticoid induction of MMTV RNA, a short digression is required to discuss a novel feature of MMTV

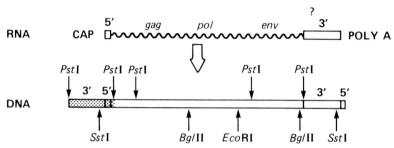

FIG. 2. The structure of the DNA and RNA forms of the MMTV genome. The RNA is approximately 9000 bases in length and encodes the genes for coat proteins or group-specific antigens (*gag*), envelope glycoproteins (*env*), reverse transcriptase (*pol*), and a postulated, but as yet unidentified, gene product (?). The linear form of MMTV DNA is the direct product of reverse transcription. At each end is a long terminal repeat (LTR) consisting of sequences derived from both the 5' and 3' ends of viral RNA; these are shown as the boxes denoted 3' (~1200 base pairs)/5' (~130 base pairs). The *Pst*I fragment (stippled) containing the left-hand LTR plus 135 base pairs coding for RNA beyond the 5' boxed region, was used in construction of the recombinant plasmids shown in Figs. 13 and 15. (From Lee *et al.*, 1981.)

DNA. The synthesis of retroviral DNA by reverse transcription is a fascinating and remarkably complex process (for reviews see Temin, 1981; Varmus, 1982). An important feature of such DNAs is that they are longer than the parental RNA; this extra length arises by duplication of sequences present at the extreme 5' and 3' ends of the viral RNA. These duplications exist at the ends of the linear viral DNA and are thus commonly referred to as the long terminal repeats or LTRs (Varmus, 1982). In the case of MMTV DNA, the LTRs are approximately 1350 base pairs (bp) in length, 130 of these arising from the 5' end (Ringold *et al.*, 1979; Majors and Varmus, 1981; Donehower *et al.*, 1981). The structure of MMTV RNA and DNA are depicted in Fig. 2. For the purposes of this discussion, it is only of primary importance to note that the beginning (5') end of the viral RNA resides within the left-hand LTR; indeed, as will be seen later, the promoter for transcription of the viral genome resides within the LTR.

III. Glucocorticoid Induction of MMTV RNA

Normal mouse cells in inbred strains of mice contain several MMTV proviruses (Varmus *et al.*, 1972; Michalides and Schlom, 1975); these represent endogenous viral genes, transmitted through the germ line as part of the normal gene complement. MMTV is probably a rather recent

DNA acquisition since some feral mice have been found to be devoid of such sequences (Cohen and Varmus, 1979). The expression of these endogenous proviruses is tightly regulated since viral RNA production varies widely depending on the tissue, the mouse strain, and the hormonal status of the animal (for review see Bentvelzen and Hilgers, 1980). The most striking production of virus particles (as well as viral proteins and RNA) occurs in lactating mammary gland, mammary tumors, or in continuous cell lines derived from such tumors.

Establishment of mammary tumor cell lines has provided a system for studying the mechanisms of glucocorticoid action, since the production of MMTV is increased 10- to 20-fold by addition of a glucocorticoid (e.g., dexamethasone) (McGrath, 1971; Fine *et al.*, 1974; Ringold *et al.*, 1975; Parks *et al.*, 1974). The ability to prepare radioactively labeled cDNA from the virus particle itself allowed us in early studies to directly measure the effects of dexamtheasone on MMTV RNA. As seen in Fig. 3, the addition of this hormone to the GR, mouse mammary tumor, cell line causes a dramatic and rapid accumulation of intracellular viral RNA (Ringold *et al.*, 1975). After a short lag of about 15 minutes, MMTV RNA increases 10- to 20-fold over uninduced levels with a half-time of approximately 2.5 hours.

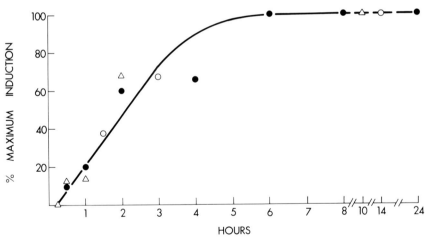

FIG. 3. Kinetics of accumulation of MMTV RNA in GR mouse mammary tumor cells after treatment with dexamethasone. The concentration of viral RNA at each time point was determined by hybridizing radioactively labeled MMTV cDNA with increasing amounts of cell RNA; hybrid formation was assessed by digestion with S1 nuclease. Different symbols refer to separate experiments; maximal induction in each was 15- to 20-fold. (From Ringold *et al.*, 1975.)

A. INDUCTION OF MMTV RNA IS A PRIMARY RESPONSE

As mentioned in Section I, it has been difficult to ascertain whether a particular steroid response represents a direct or primary action of the steroid–receptor complex at the genomic level. In the case of MMTV RNA induction, it seems likely that this is so. First, full induction of MMTV RNA occurs in cells whose protein synthesis has been completely inhibited with drugs, such as cycloheximide (Table I). As expected, inhibitors of RNA synthesis, such as actinomycin D, prevent the induction of MMTV RNA by dexamethasone (Ringold et al., 1975). Similar results have been obtained by other investigators using additional mammary cell lines with these and other metabolic inhibitors (Scolnick et al., 1976). From these studies, one would feel sanguine concluding that the induction of viral RNA does not require prior production of a protein intermediate; thus, the effect on MMTV RNA production is likely to be mediated directly by the glucocorticoid–receptor complex.

Further evidence that the effect of glucocorticoids on MMTV is direct is afforded by studies on the rate of synthesis of viral RNA. To perform these studies, GR cells were labeled with [^{3}H]uridine for 15-minute periods prior to and after addition of dexamethasone. The fraction of labeled RNA that was virus specific was determined by DNA excess hybridiza-

TABLE I

Effect of Metabolic Inhibitors on Induction of MMTV RNA by Dexamethasone

Drug	Percentage maximal induction[a]	Percentage inhibition of protein synthesis[b]	Percentage inhibition of RNA synthesis[c]
None	100	0	0
Cycloheximide (2 μg/ml)	100	90	<5
Actinomycin D (10 μg/ml)	0	<10	98

[a] Viral RNA concentrations were determined as shown in Fig. 5 and described previously (Ringold et al., 1975). RNA was prepared from cells pretreated for 1 hour with inhibitors and then in the continued presence of the inhibitor. Maximal inductions were 10- to 20-fold in all cases.

[b] Protein synthesis was measured by counting acid-precipitable material labeled with a ^{3}H-amino acid mixture 1 hour after addition of cychoheximide.

[c] RNA synthesis was determined by measuring the amount of acid precipitable material from cells labeled for 30 minutes with [^{3}H]uridine, 1 hour after addition of actinomycin D.

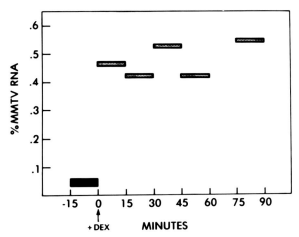

FIG. 4.   Kinetics of the effect of dexamethasone on the rate of synthesis of MMTV RNA. GR, mammary tumor cells, were incubated for 15 minutes with [³H]uridine at 500 μCi/ml. Total RNA was extracted and hybridized to excess MMTV DNA; hybrids were separated on columns of hydroxylapatite in 8 *M* urea/1% SDS/0.2 *M* Na-phosphate (Ringold *et al.,* 1977a) after treatment with pancreatic ribonuclease. ³²P-labeled MMTV RNA (~1000 cpm) was included in each reaction to control for the efficiency of hybridization; the percentage of the total ³H-labeled RNA that was MMTV specific is plotted. The bars represent the labeling periods; dexamethasone was added at time zero to a final concentration of 10^{-6} *M*. The control value −DEX (−15 to 0 minutes) was determined in duplicate. (From Ringold *et al.,* 1977a.)

tion (Ringold *et al.,* 1977a). The results of such a study are shown in Fig. 4 and reveal that dexamethasone stimulates viral RNA synthesis maximally at the earliest time measured, i.e., during the 15-minute period in which [³H]uridine and dexamethasone were added simultaneously. Furthermore, the absolute extent of this increase (10- to 15-fold) accounts completely for the increase in steady-state levels of MMTV RNA in GR cells. A more advanced nuclear run-off assay has recently been used to substantiate these findings (Ucker *et al.,* 1981); indications from such studies are that the increase in MMTV RNA synthesis occurs within 5 minutes after addition of hormone.

A large body of work, primarily in the chick oviduct system (for reviews see Schimke *et al.,* 1975; O'Malley *et al.,* 1979 in this series), led to the suggestion that steroid–receptor complexes act by altering the rate of transcription of specific genes. It is noteworthy, however, that the demonstration that dexamethasone stimulates the rate of synthesis of MMTV RNA (Ringold *et al.,* 1977a; Young *et al.,* 1977) provided the first definitive experimental evidence that steroid hormones may act via such a mechanism.

B. THE ROLE OF THE RECEPTOR IN MMTV INDUCTION

As summarized in Section I, the binding of a steroid hormone to its cognate receptor elicits an allosteric modification which promotes nuclear binding of the hormone–receptor complex. Several experimental observations suggest that this view of steroid hormone action is applicable to the induction of MMTV RNA. Extracts of mouse mammary tumor cells contain specific glucocorticoid receptors with a typical sedimentation coefficient of 4 S (Ringold *et al.*, 1975; Shyamala and Dickson, 1976). These receptors bind to DNA cellulose under appropriate conditions and migrate to the nucleus in a temperature-dependent fashion when bound to active hormones. The half-maximal induction of MMTV RNA in GR cells occurs at the same concentration of dexamethasone ($\sim 4 \times 10^{-8}\ M$) required to half-saturate receptors (Ringold *et al.*, 1975). Furthermore, an excess of progesterone, a competitive inhibitor of glucocorticoid receptor-mediated responses (Rousseau *et al.*, 1972), blocks the induction of viral RNA by dexamethasone (Ringold *et al.*, 1975). Similar results have been reported in other mammary tumor cell lines (Young *et al.*, 1975). Lastly, genetic evidence (to be described in detail below) suggests that loss of MMTV inducibility can be demonstrated in cells that lack functional glucocorticoid receptors (Grove *et al.*, 1980).

In sum, the results of studies related to induction of MMTV RNA indicate that (1) the major effect is on the rate of synthesis of viral RNA, (2) induction occurs in the absence of protein synthesis, and (3) the effect is receptor mediated. Thus, it seems tenable to propose that the glucocorticoid–receptor complex may interact directly with MMTV DNA.

IV. Infection of Rat Hepatoma Cells with MMTV

It was intriguing to consider the possibility that glucocorticoid regulation of MMTV could be transfered to heterologous cells by virus infection. Early attempts to infect tissue culture cells with MMTV were consistently negative; however, Vaidya reported in 1976 that some cells were susceptible to MMTV. Since the infected cells were unaltered in growth properties and/or morphology, biochemical tests were used to assess infection; thus, in the infected, but not the control cultures, one could detect the presence of MMTV DNA, RNA, or protein.

We chose to infect HTC, rat hepatoma, cells since they had been extensively characterized by Tomkins and his colleagues (Thompson *et al.*, 1966) as a model system for studying glucocorticoid action. In particular, these cells contain glucocorticoid receptors (Failla *et al.*, 1975) and contain several inducible gene products (Ivarie and O'Farrell, 1978), two of which are the easily measured enzymes, tyrosine aminotransferase (TAT) and glutamine synthetase (GS) (Thompson *et al.*, 1966; Kulka *et al.*, 1972). Thus, in infected HTC cells we could simultaneously measure the inducibility of normal cellular genes and MMTV in the same genetic background (the utility of such experiments will be discussed in the following section on selection of mutant cell lines).

From the point of view of steroid hormone action, the most striking result of infecting HTC and other heterologous cells (Vaidya *et al.*, 1976; Ringold *et al.*, 1977b) is that MMTV RNA remains highly glucocorticoid inducible (Fig. 5). Since these cells are ostensibly devoid of endogenous MMTV-specific sequences in their genomes, the viral RNA must be synthesized from newly acquired proviruses.

Thus, it seems likely that glucocorticoid responsiveness is an intrinsic property of the viral genome. One could, however, argue that hormonal sensitivity of MMTV is dependent on cellular DNA sequences flanking the proviral DNA. If so, MMTV DNA would have to integrate into specific sites or regions of the host cell genome.

The ability to purify small amounts of the unintegrated forms of MMTV DNA from infected HTC cells (Ringold *et al.*, 1977c, 1978) allowed us to construct a restriction endonuclease map of the viral DNA (Shank *et al.*, 1978). By extension of these studies we were also able to characterize the

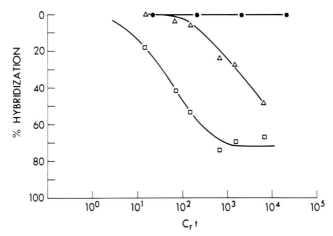

FIG. 5. MMTV RNA is inducible in infected HTC cells. RNA, prepared from HTC cells 4 weeks after infection with MMTV, was hybridized with [^{3}H]MMTV cDNA at 68°C in 0.6 *M* NaCl for 22 hours. The percentage hybridization was determined by treatment with S1 nuclease. $C_r t$ refers to the concentration of RNA multiplied by the time of hybridization (a lower $C_r t_{\frac{1}{2}}$ value is indicative of more viral RNA). Parallel cultures were grown in the presence (□) or absence (△) of 10^{-6} *M* dexamethasone. RNA from uninfected HTC cells is represented by the solid circles (●). (From Ringold *et al.*, 1977c.)

integration of MMTV DNA (Ringold *et al.,* 1979); to do so we analyzed DNAs from clones of infected HTC cells by the blotting and hybridization procedure of Southern (1975). The two major conclusions to be drawn from these studies are as follows: (1) a very large number of sites in cellular DNA can be used for proviral integration; indeed, integration may be completely random and (2) the integration event always utilizes the same sites on viral DNA, thereby preserving the structure containing both LTRs (Fig. 6). The implications of these observations for steroid responsiveness of MMTV are far reaching. First, it makes untenable the proposition that the glucocorticoid regulation of MMTV is imparted by flanking cellular sequences. Second, since proviral DNA maintains both copies of the terminal repeat and, by definition, the 5' end of viral RNA corresponds to a site within the lefthand LTR (see Fig. 2), it seems plausible to

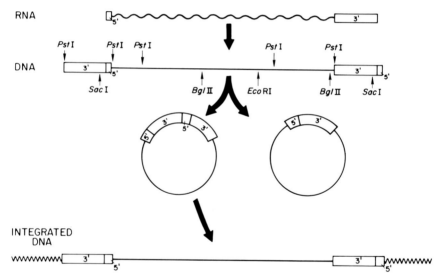

FIG. 6.   Integration of MMTV DNA maintains the LTR structure of unintegrated viral DNA. Data accumulated from restriction endonuclease mapping (Shank *et al.,* 1978; Ringold *et al.,* 1979) and recent sequencing (Donehower *et al.,* 1981; Majors and Varmus, 1981) have led to the model depicted here. As in Figs. 1 and 2, reverse transcription leads to synthesis of a linear molecule with LTRs derived from both the 3' and 5' ends of MMTV RNA. In the nucleus, some of the DNA becomes circularized; however, in many of the molecules one copy of the LTR is deleted, presumably by homologous recombination. The circular form containing both copies of the LTR is shown as the precursor to the integrated (proviral) form; this remains to be proven. The provirus is colinear with the unintegrated linear DNA (with very minor alterations of two nucleotides at the extreme ends (Majors and Varmus, 1981)). Transcription initiates within the upstream LTR (Lee *et al.,* 1981; Ucker *et al.,* 1981). (From Ringold, 1979.)

suggest that the LTR itself contains a hormone-regulated promoter. This issue will be raised again in a following section.

EXPRESSION OF MMTV RNA IN CLONES OF INFECTED HTC CELLS

In the process of generating clones of infected HTC cells and characterizing the integrated MMTV DNA, it became clear that not only were the sites of integration different from clone to clone, but the absolute number of proviruses also varied widely (Ringold *et al.*, 1979). Although never rigorously documented, it appears that cells infected at a higher multiplicity of infection (i.e., a higher virus-to-cell ratio) acquired more copies of MMTV DNA. Characterization of MMTV RNA levels in clones containing from 1 to 30 or more copies of viral DNA (Table II) has revealed some interesting facts: (1) there is generally more viral RNA in cells containing multiple copies; this correlation holds both in the absence and presence of dexamethasone; (2) the extent of induction by the hormone varies substantially and appears not to be related in any particular fashion to DNA copy number; (3) some clones that harbor only one or two proviruses make no RNA either in the presence or absence of dexamethasone; this could be accounted for by random integration of proviruses into chromosomal sites that are transcriptionally quiescent. Recent data from Yamamoto's lab would support this interpretation (Feinstein *et al.*, 1981); and (4) the ability to respond to hormone seems to be dependent on basal expression of the MMTV DNA, even if that level is low (e.g., less than one viral RNA molecule per cell in the steady state). These last two points suggest the possibility that at least in the case of MMTV, the glucocorticoid–receptor complex is unable to "turn-on" the production of a completely silent gene. We point out that this is consistent with the tissue-specific expression of most steroid-responsive genes. For example, the glucocorticoid inducible enzyme TAT is not expressed in most non-liver tissues or cells, even though other genes in the same cells are highly glucocorticoid inducible.

These studies of MMTV RNA production in clones of HTC cells provide a rather compelling case for a role of chromatin structure or chromosomal position in controlling the expression of a hormone-responsive gene. The factors influencing the absolute level of expression of an integrated provirus remain obscure and may provide a fruitful, yet difficult, avenue of investigation. Nevertheless, it is clear that the ability of MMTV to respond to glucocorticoids is intimately associated with the viral genome itself.

TABLE II

MMTV RNA and DNA in Infected HTC Cells[a]

Clone	MMTV DNA (copies/cell)	MMTV RNA (molecules/cell)	
		−DEX	+DEX
HTC	0	0	0
J2-14	2	0	0
J2-15	1	0	0
J2-31	1	0	0
J2-17	1	0.1	70
J0-1	1–2	0.1	100
J1-3	2	0.1	1
M1-7	5–10	1	300
M1-54	5–10	15	1800
M1-19	5–10	2	1300
M1-20	10–20	5	800
M1-60	10–20	15	650
M1-49	20–30	2	360
M1-9	N.T.	6	800
M1-46	N.T.	8	1300
M1-62	N.T.	25	1300

[a] MMTV-infected HTC cells were cloned in soft agar; no more than six clones were selected from any one plate. The number of copies of MMTV DNA was determined by solution hybridization with [^{3}H]MMTV cDNA or by the Southern blotting procedure (Southern, 1975). Intracellular viral RNA was quantitated by hybridization with [^{3}H]cDNA, as described by Ringold *et al.* (1975); the numbers of molecules per cell are based on a $C_r t_{\frac{1}{2}}$ of 10^{-2} mol sec liter^{-1} for pure viral RNA and the fact that HTC cells are pseudotetraploid. These data are compiled from Ringold *et al.* (1979) and Yamamoto and Ringold (1978).

A last point to be made regarding glucocorticoid inducibility of MMTV RNA in heterologous cells pertains to the evolutionary conservation of glucocorticoid receptors. If the glucocorticoid–receptor complex interacts specifically with MMTV DNA, it is of interest that the receptor present in a variety of mammalian species (e.g., mouse, rat, hamster, cat, mink, and human) is capable of eliciting induction of viral RNA. Thus, not only must the steroid binding site be highly conserved, but the business end of the molecule (i.e., the DNA binding site) must be conserved as well.

V. Genetic Approach to Glucocorticoid Action

The ability to select mutants in a complex biochemical pathway is often useful in delineating the components involved in a given reaction. In the study of hormone action, the most fruitful use of genetics has been in characterization of adenyl cyclase activation and elucidation of the role of the GTP-binding protein that couples receptors to the catalytic subunit (Bourne *et al.*, 1975; Ross and Gilman, 1977). Selection of cells with altered responses to glucocorticoids was first accomplished by Tomkins and his colleagues (Baxter *et al.*, 1971; Rosenau *et al.*, 1972) using the S49 mouse lymphoma cell line (for a review see Yamamoto *et al.*, 1976 in this series). The normal responses of these cells to glucocorticoids are pyknosis and death. Thus, by simply selecting cells capable of continued growth in dexamethasone, Sibley and Tomkins (1974a,b) isolated a large number of glucocorticoid-resistant variants of S49. This approach has also been exploited by Bourgeois and colleagues using other lines of mouse lymphoma cells (Pfahl *et al.*, 1978). To date, all of the reported lymphoma variants (>1000 independent isolates) either lack glucocorticoid receptors or contain receptors with altered physical properties. Furthermore, the biochemical events that lead to killing of S49 cells have not been identified; in fact, no obvious changes in gene expression have been observed in glucocorticoid-treated lymphoma cells. For these reasons, we have felt that another system in which specific gene products could be measured,

TABLE III

Possible Phenotypes of Glucocorticoid Unresponsive Cells Selected for Lack of MMTV gp52 Induction[a]

	M1-19 5–10 MMTV proviruses	J2-17 1 MMTV provirus
1. Glucocorticoid receptor defect	+	+
2. Undefined coordinate lesion affecting all inducible genes	+	+
3. Structural mutation in gp52	−	+
4. MMTV promoter defect	−	+
5. MMTV glucocorticoid regulatory region defect	−	+

[a] Since there are multiple copies of the MMTV provirus in M1-19, the probability of interfering with induction in these cells by mechanisms 3, 4, and 5 is miniscule. However, in J2-17, the single provirus could be altered to produce less gp52 by any of the mechanisms listed.

and in which nonreceptor defects could be isolated, might be more fruit-ful.

Our approach to selecting glucocorticoid unresponsive cells is depicted in Fig. 7. In brief, since the major MMTV glycoprotein (gp52) is ex-pressed on the surface of infected HTC cells in a glucocorticoid-depen-dent manner (Ringold et al., 1977b), it seemed likely that we could sepa-rate induced from uninduced cells in a fluorescence-activated cell sorter (FACS). For these studies we chose two clones of MMTV-infected HTC cells, M1-19, which contains approximately 10 proviruses and J2-17, which contains a single provirus (see Table III). Our expectations were

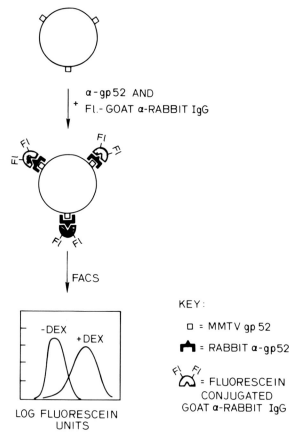

FIG. 7. Protocol for fluorescent staining of cells for gp52 and separation in a fluores-cence-activated cell sorter (FACS). MMTV-infected HTC cells are grown in the presence or absence of dexamethasone (10^{-6} M), collected, and incubated with rabbit antibody directed against gp52 followed by fluorescein conjugated goat anti-rabbit IgG. Stained cells are then analyzed in a FACS and a histogram is produced describing the fluorescence intensity distribution of the cell population. (From Grove et al., 1980.)

that if we could select cells in the FACS that no longer induce gp52, these two cell lines would give rise to hormone unresponsive variants of different types (Table III). For example, since M1-19 has multiple-expressed copies of MMTV DNA, as evidenced by the high levels of MMTV RNA in these cells (Table II), a defect resulting in lack of gp52 induction would have to reside in a cellular component required for hormone responsiveness of all of the proviruses; the most likely candidate would be the glucocorticoid receptor itself. In contrast, J2-17-derived mutants could be defective in gp52 induction as a result of mutations in the promoter or putative glucocorticoid regulatory region of its single MMTV provirus.

A selection of unresponsive cells derived from M1-19 is shown in Fig. 8. Cells were induced for 48 hours in dexamethasone (10^{-6} M), stained with rabbit antibody against gp52, followed by fluorescein-conjugated

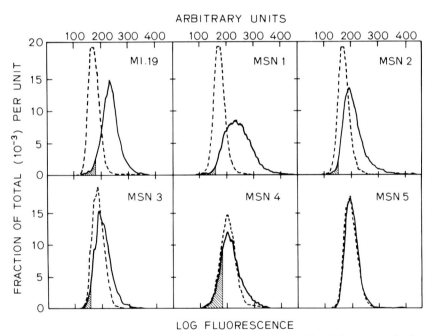

FIG. 8. Selection of glucocorticoid unresponsive M1-19 cells. Cells were stained as described in Fig. 7 and passed through a FACS. That portion of the population (+DEX) displaying the lowest fluorescence was collected under sterile conditions; this represented approximately 1–4% of the population or 5000–30,000 cells. The sorted population (MSN1) was propagated in the absence of dexamethasone for 2 weeks to accumulate sufficient numbers of cells for another sorting cycle. This procedure was repeated until we obtained a population (MSN5) which failed to induce gp52. The hatched area represents the population collected from the induced cells at each sort. The analyses indicate the fluorescence intensity distributions of cells grown in the presence (——) or absence (- - -) of dexamethasone. (From Grove *et al.*, 1980.)

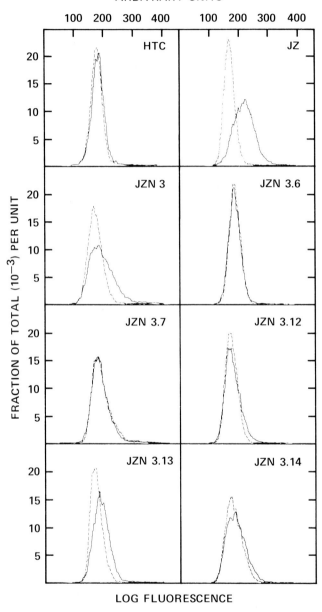

ARBITRARY UNITS

LOG FLUORESCENCE

goat anti-rabbit IgG, and analyzed in the FACS. Those cells displaying the lowest fluorescence in the presence of hormone (typically 1–3% of the cells) were collected under sterile conditions and grown for 2–3 weeks in the absence of hormone prior to another sorting cycle. This process was repeated until no detectable induction of gp52 could be observed in the FACS. After five rounds of enrichment in the FACS such a population, designated MSN5, was obtained; MSN6 was produced as a subpopulation sorted from MSN5 (Grove et al., 1980). These populations were then cloned either in soft agar or by sorting single cells into microtiter wells.

In the case of J2-17, cells were first mutagenized with ethyl methanesulfonate to yield a population designated JZ. These cells retain hormonal responsiveness, as evidenced by their ability to induce both MMTV gp52 and the enzyme tyrosine aminotransferase in response to dexamethasone (Grove and Ringold, 1981). A similar protocol to that for MSN was used to isolate glucocorticoid response variants of JZ cells in the FACS; in this case, three cycles of enrichment produced a population, JZN3, that displays markedly reduced levels of hormone-induced gp52 (Fig. 9). Fourteen single cell clones derived from JZN3 were isolated and characterized. A few examples are shown in Fig. 9 and demonstrate that these cells exhibit a range of glucocorticoid responsiveness; some clones (e.g., JZN3.6) shown no gp52 induction, whereas others (e.g , JZN3.13) show partial induction.

ANALYSIS OF GLUCOCORTICOID UNRESPONSIVE CELLS: RECEPTOR VERSUS NONRECEPTOR DEFECTS

As described above, unresponsive cells derived from M1-19 should contain a defect in a component involved in the response mechanism of all active proviruses, whereas this need not be the case in J2-17-derived nonresponders. To determine whether the defects reside in the glucocorticoid receptor, cells were screened using an assay described by Baxter and Tomkins (1970). Intact cells were incubated with varying concentrations of [^{3}H]dexamethasone in the absence and presence of excess unlabeled hormone to determine total and nonspecific binding, respectively. The

---

FIG. 9.   Analysis of J2-17 and glucocorticoid-response variants derived from J2-17 in the FACS. The MMTV-infected HTC cell line J2-17, containing a single MMTV provirus (Table II), was mutagenized with ethyl methanesulfonate to yield a population designated JZ. Cells unable to induce gp52 normally were enriched by three rounds of sorting, as described in Fig. 8. This population, JZN3, displays markedly reduced levels of dexamethasone-induced gp52; several clones derived from JZN3 also show reduced induction of gp52. Analyses were performed using cells grown in the presence (——) or absence (---) of 10^{-6} M dexamethasone.

results, summarized in Table IV, demonstrate that there are markedly reduced levels of glucocorticoid receptors in MSN5 and its subclones; indeed, all unresponsive cells derived from M1-19 appear to have defects in glucocorticoid binding activity (Grove *et al.*, 1980). In contrast, both noninducers and partial inducers derived from J2-17 contain a full complement of glucocorticoid receptors.

One of the advantages to using HTC cells for our genetic studies is the availability of cellular glucocorticoid inducible genes that can be easily measured. It is, therefore, possible to approach issues related to the coordinate regulation of gene expression by glucocorticoids and to ascertain whether the defects in MSN and JZN cells are global or restricted to MMTV induction. The three cellular markers we have used are tyrosine aminotransferase (TAT), glutamine synthetase (GS), and the secreted glycoprotein known as Belt I (Ivarie and O'Farrell, 1978). Figure 10 shows dose–response curves for induction of TAT and GS in a subclone of wild-

TABLE IV

Glucocorticoid Receptors in Glucocorticoid Unresponsive Variants[a]

Cell line	Receptors/cell
M1.19	7.3×10^4
MSN5	$<1 \times 10^4$
MSN5.3	$<1 \times 10^4$
MSN5.4	$<1 \times 10^4$
MSN6	$<1 \times 10^4$
MSN6.3	2×10^4
MSN6.7	2×10^4
MSN6.10	$<1 \times 10^4$
JZ	1.2×10^5
JZN3.4	1.1×10^5
JZN3.5	1.3×10^5
JZN3.6	6×10^4
JZN3.7	1.2×10^5
JZN3.14	1.2×10^5

[a] The content of glucocorticoid receptors in wild-type M1.19 and JZ, as well as in the noninducible variants derived from each, was determined using the whole cell binding assay described by Baxter and Tomkins (1970). The number of receptors/cell represents the average of at least three separate determinations. The data are compiled from Grove *et al.* (1980) and Grove and Ringold (1981).

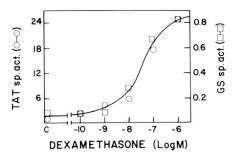

FIG. 10. Dexamethasone dose–response curves of tyrosine aminotransferase (TAT) and glutamine synthetase (GS) in MMTV-infected HTC cells. JZ.1 cells were grown in the presence of the indicated concentrations of hormone for 48 hours; cell extracts were prepared and enzyme activities were determined according to the procedure of Diamondstone (1966) for TAT and Kulka *et al.* (1972) for GS. TAT specific activity is expressed as moles of *p*-hydroxybenzaldehyde formed per minute per milligram protein. GS specific activity is expressed as micromoles γ-glutamyl-hydroxamic acid formed per hour per milligram protein.

type JZ cells indicating that both are induced by the same concentrations of dexamethasone.

Belt I is a glycoprotein that sticks tightly to plastic tissue culture dishes; this has allowed us to develop a simple procedure to monitor its production. Briefly, cells (grown for 48 hours in the presence or absence of dexamethasone) are incubated in medium containing [^{35}S]methionine and then the medium and cells are removed from the dish. After washing extensively to remove as much free label and cell debris as possible, the protein remaining on the dish is solubilized in SDS-containing buffer and aliquots are electrophoresed on a 10% denaturing polyacrylamide gel as described by Laemmli (1970). The results of such an experiment using wild-type JZ.1 cells are shown in Fig. 11; the band appearing in the 50–55 kd region migrates at the position expected for known Belt I and as is apparent is highly glucocorticoid inducible. Dose–response studies of Belt I, TAT, GS, and MMTV with dexamethasone, cortisol, and the suboptimal inducer, dimethylprogesterone, indicate that all four of these genes respond in a coordinate fashion to glucocorticoids (Vannice and Ringold, unpublished).

We have used inducibility of cellular genes to analyze the defects in our variant cells in greater detail. As seen in Table VA, MSN5.3 cells (representative of all MSN cells) are incapable of inducing any glucocorticoid inducible functions, whereas the parental cells MSC-1 (a subfraction of the original M1-19 cells) induce all four markers. These results corroborate our previous conclusion that the unresponsiveness of MSN cells is a result of a receptor defect; an ancillary point of interest is that all four of

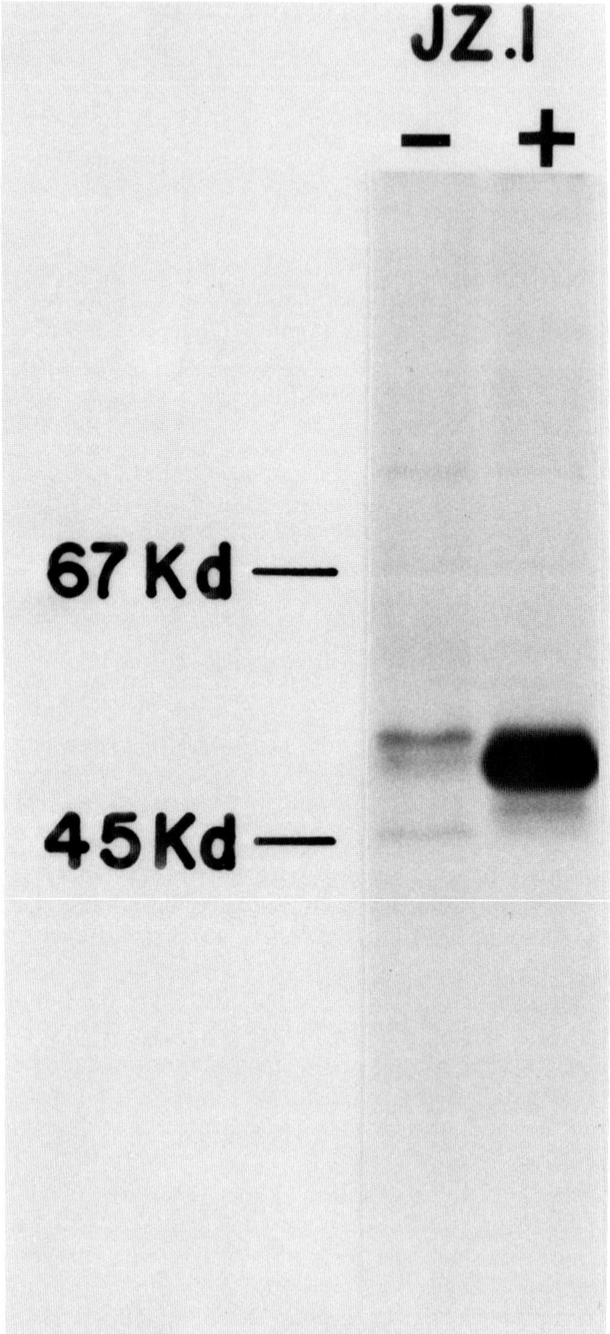
JZ.1
–
+
67 Kd
45 Kd

TABLE V

Inductions of gp52, TAT, GS, and Belt I in Parental and Nonresponsive Cells[a]

		TAT fold-ind. (n)	gp52 Δ(n)	GS fold-ind. (n)	Belt I fold-ind. (n)
(A)	MSC1[b]	4.8(5)	105(7)	3.1(2)	7.9(3)
	MSN5.3	1.0(4)	8.8(5)	1.0(2)	1.3(3)
(B)	JZ	10.6(16)	32.7(15)	7.0(2)	8.7(4)
	JZN3.7	8.3(9)	6.4(15)	6.4(4)	7.6(3)

[a] TAT, GS, and Belt I assays and inductions were performed as described in the legends to Figs. 10 and 11. MMTV gp52 was analyzed in the FACS where Δ represents the change in arbitrary logarithmic units of fluorescence (see Figs. 8, 9, and 12) and does not reflect a fold-induction; the difference between 8.8 and 105 log fluorescence units represents at least a 20-fold change in gp52 expression. The fold-induction of Belt I was determined by optical densitometry of several autoradiograms such as the one shown in Fig. 11. The data are presented as means, with the number of independent experiments shown in parentheses.

[b] (A) MSC1 is a population of cells derived from M1-19 that maintains all of its normal glucocorticoid responsive properties.

the glucocorticoid inducible gene products in HTC cells thus appear to be regulated by a single receptor pathway.

In contrast, JZN cells, which do not induce MMTV yet contain normal levels of receptor, retain the ability to induce GS, TAT, and Belt I (Table VB). Thus, in this case, the defect appears to be specific to the MMTV genome (one is reminded that there is a single MMTV provirus in these cells). The results of these studies strongly suggest that the defect in JZN3.7 (as well as the other JZN clones) resides in the MMTV DNA itself, or possibly in a cellular factor, e.g., a chromosomal acceptor pro-

---

FIG. 11. Induction of Belt I by dexamethasone. JZ.1 cells, a subclone of wild-type JZ cells, were grown in the absence or presence of dexamethasone (10^{-6} M, 48 hours). Cells were incubated for 1 hour in medium containing [^{35}S]methionine at 250 μCi/ml. The labeling medium was removed, cells were washed with phosphate-buffered saline (PBS), and then removed from the plate using PBS/EDTA (2.5 mM). The plates were washed vigorously and air dried for 15–20 minutes. The proteins that remained on the plate were removed by scraping with a rubber policeman in SDS-containing buffer. An equivalent aliquot from the control and hormone-treated samples was electrophoresed on a 10% acrylamide gel as described by Laemmli (1970). Molecular weight markers (BSA, 67 kd and ovalbumin, 45 kd) were visualized by staining with Coomassie Blue; after destaining, the gel was dried and autoradiographed. The major inducible band represents the secreted glycoprotein identified as Belt I by Ivarie and O'Farrell (1978).

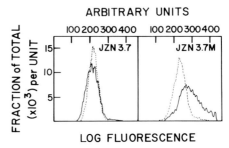

FIG. 12.   Induction of MMTV gp52 in superinfected JZN3.7 cells. Cell surface gp52 was measured in the FACS using the indirect immunofluorescent staining procedure diagrammed in Fig. 7. JZN3.7 cells were infected with MMTV purified from the culture fluid of GR mammary tumor cells, as described by Ringold *et al.* (1977b). The control level of fluorescence (---) and the dexamethasone-induced level (——) are depicted for JZN3.7 and its superinfected counterpart, JZN3.7M.

tein (Spelsberg *et al.*, this volume) that is specifically required for the glucocorticoid induction of the viral genes. One method for distinguishing between these alternatives is to superinfect JZN cells with MMTV; this is accomplished by the same procedure used originally to infect HTC cells (Ringold *et al.*, 1977b). As described earlier, infection with MMTV results in random insertion of one or more copies of viral DNA into the recipient cell's genome. If the defect in the unresponsive cells resides in a cellular protein that acts upon MMTV DNA (i.e., is trans acting), the newly acquired proviruses will also be unresponsive to hormone. However, if it is the original provirus that is defective (i.e., a cis acting defect), then the newly introduced viral DNA should be inducible. The experiment shown in Fig. 12 clearly demonstrates that superinfected JZN3.7 cells exhibit glucocorticoid inducible gp52. Similar results have been obtained with other completely unresponsive clones such as JZN3.6 and with partially inducible clones such as JZN3.9 and JZN3.13 (data not shown). Thus, the incorporation of new copies of MMTV DNA into these cells leads to restoration of gp52 induction and one must therefore conclude that a defect exists in the original MMTV provirus.

VI. Mapping a Glucocorticoid Regulatory Region on MMTV DNA

A. MMTV–dhfr FUSIONS

The results of our previous studies on integration and transcription of MMTV (Section IV) and our genetic studies (Section V) provide strong circumstantial evidence that MMTV encodes its own glucocorticoid regulatory region. To test this directly, we have constructed hybrid genes containing the putative promoter and regulatory region from MMTV fused to the coding region of genes whose activity can be assayed conveniently and/or whose function can be selected for *in vivo* (Lee *et al.*, 1981). Our initial constructions (Fig. 13) utilized a cDNA containing the coding region for mouse dihydrofolate reductase (dhfr) (Chang *et al.*, 1978; Subramani *et al.*, 1981) fused to the *Pst*I fragment encompassing the left hand LTR of MMTV (see Fig. 2). The plasmids we have constructed are derivatives of the SV40 eukaryotic expression vectors developed by Berg and his colleagues (Mulligan and Berg, 1980, 1981; Subramani and Berg, 1981).

A cell line derived from Chinese hamster ovary (CHO) provides a suitable recipient for the *dhfr* vectors in DNA transfection experiments. These cells are defective in *dhfr* and are thus unable to grow in medium lacking thymidine, glycine, or hypoxanthine (Urlaub and Chasin, 1980). Plasmid DNA was introduced into CHO dhfr⁻ cells using the calcium phosphate precipitation technique of Graham and van der Eb (1973). Cells were grown in nonselective medium for 3 days and then passaged into dhfr-selective medium (i.e., lacking thymidine, glycine, and hypoxanthine). Colonies of cells expressing *dhfr* from the plasmid appeared with frequencies ranging from 10^{-4} to 10^{-6}, depending on the exact construction of the plasmid, and could be visualized within 7–10 days.

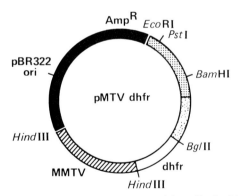

FIG. 13. Structure of the fusion plasmid containing dihydrofolate reductase (dhfr) cDNA linked to the MMTV LTR. The solid black segment is a 2.3 kb fragment of the plasmid pBR322 (from the *Eco*RI site to the *Pvu*II site) containing the ampicillin-resistance gene and the origin of replication. The stippled regions are derived from SV40 virus and provide signals for processing of mRNA transcripts (Mulligan and Berg, 1980, 1981; Subramani *et al.*, 1981). The hatched region represents the MMTV LTR, derived from the *Pst*I fragment shown in Fig. 2. The open region is the dhfr cDNA (Chang *et al.*, 1978). Transcription from the MMTV promoter is in the counterclockwise direction as is the coding region for dhfr. (See Lee *et al.*, 1981, for further description of the construction of this plasmid.)

Our major interest in these experiments was to determine whether the expression of *dhfr* in the transformants had become glucocorticoid sensitive. We have used the folate analog and inhibitor of *dhfr*, methotrexate, to estimate levels of the enzyme. Cells were plated in various concentrations of methotrexate, either in the presence or absence of dexamethasone, and cell growth was monitored. As seen in Fig. 14a, approximately 10^{-7} *M* methotrexate is sufficient to inhibit the growth of wild-type CHO-K1 cells and dexamethasone has no effect on the cells' sensitivity to the drug. Similar results are obtained when transformants derived from a fusion between the SV40 promoter and *dhfr* are tested (Fig. 14b). In contrast, in cells transformed with the MMTV LTR-containing plasmids (Fig. 14c, d, and e), the concentration of methotrexate required to inhibit cell growth was considerably higher in cells grown with dexamethasone. An additional experiment was performed in which the MMTV LTR was inserted in the orientation opposite to normal MMTV transcription; in this case (Fig. 14f), the expression of *dhfr* was not hormonally regulated.

To obtain a more quantitative estimate of the levels of *dhfr* in the transformed cells, we have measured [³H]methotrexate binding to cell extracts. Table VI summarizes these results and corroborates the fact that pMTVdhfr-transformed cells contain 3- to 5-fold more enzyme, when grown in the presence of dexamethasone than in its absence. The absolute extent of induction in these CHO cells is lower than the 10- to 20-fold

TABLE VI

Induction of dhfr in pMTVdhfr Transformants[a]

Cell line	cpm [³H]methotrexate bound		Fold induction
	−DEX	+DEX	
pSV2dhfr.1	9882	8745	0
pMTVdhfr.1	116	571	5
pMTVdhfr.2	444	1148	3
pMTVdhfr.3	972	5111	5

[a] Cells of individual transformants derived from infection with pSV2dhfr or pMTVdhfr (SV40 and MMTV promoter plasmids, respectively) were grown in the presence or absence of dexamethasone (10^{-6}) for 2 days. Cell extracts were prepared by freeze-thawing in phosphate-buffered saline and centrifuging 15 minutes in a microfuge. [³H]methotrexate was added to equal quantities of extract (30 μg of protein) from each cell line. After binding for 10 minutes at 25°C in the dark, the mixture was chromatographed on Sephadex G-50. The excluded volume containing bound methotrexate was counted in a scintillation spectrometer. Additional detail is provided in Lee *et al.* (1981).

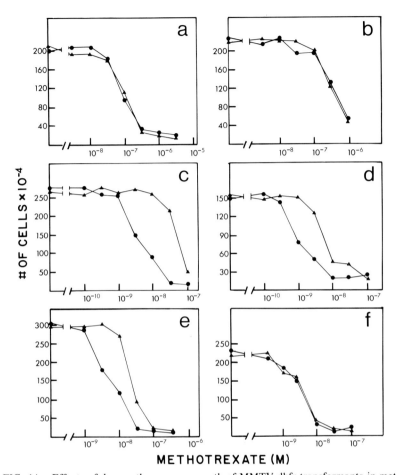

FIG. 14. Effects of dexamethasone on growth of MMTV-dhfr transformants in metho-trexate. Individual clones of CHO dhfr⁻ cells arising from transformation with pMTVdhfr (and related plasmids) (Lee *et al.*, 1981) were grown in dhfr selective medium (i.e., lacking glycine, hypoxanthine, and thymidine). Approximately 10⁵ cells were plated either in the presence (●) or absence (▲) of 10⁻⁶ M dexamethasone. Methotrexate was added to each dish at the indicated concentrations 24 hours later. Fresh medium containing methotrexate was added after 2 days and the surviving cells were counted after 2 more days. (a) Wild-type CHO-K1 cells; (b) transformant #1 derived from a fusion between the SV40 promoter and dhfr cDNA, pSV2dhfr (Subramani *et al.*, 1981); (c) transformant #2 derived from pMTVdhfr; (d) transformant #8 derived from pMDSG, a plasmid that is, for the purpose of this assay, identical with pMTVdhfr; (e) transformant #4 from pSVMdhfr, again a nearly identical plasmid; (f) transformant #6 derived from pSVM dhfr in which the MMTV LTR sequence is pointed in the wrong direction, i.e., transcription from the MMTV promoter is in the clockwise direction. (From Lee *et al.*, 1981.)

induction of MMTV RNA in mouse mammary tumor cells and may be attributable to the fact that the CHO cells contain relatively low levels of glucocorticoid receptors (Lee and Ringold, unpublished).

B. MMTV–XGPRT FUSIONS

Similar experiments have recently been performed using an analogous plasmid (Fig. 15) containing the *E. coli* gene encoding xanthine guanine phosphoribosyltransferase (XGPRT). This plasmid designated pSVMgpt was used to transform mouse 3T6 cells using the dominant selection scheme described by Mulligan and Berg (1980, 1981). In this case, the expression of the bacterial gene is increased approximately 10- to 15-fold by addition of dexamethasone. We have quantitated the amount of XGPRT RNA and determined that the message initiates at the known start site of MMTV transcription using the procedure of Berk and Sharp (1977). The *Bgl*II–*Eco*RI fragment encompassing the MMTV LTR and part of the XGPRT sequence (see Fig. 15) was labeled with ^{32}P at the *Bgl*II site. Hybrids between this plasmid and RNA from the pSVMgpt transformed 3T6 cells were treated with S1 nuclease and analyzed by electrophoresis on 6% polyacrylamide gels. The hybrid band detected by autoradiography is 400 bp in length (Fig. 16) indicating that the predominant 5' end of the XGPRT RNA maps to a site within the MMTV LTR, 275 bases upstream of the XGPRT insert; this corresponds to the 3'–5' border of the

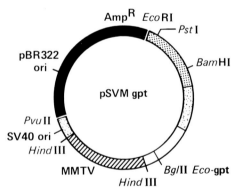

FIG. 15. Structure of a plasmid containing the *E. coli gpt* gene encoding xanthine-guanine phosphoribosyltransferase fused to the MMTV promoter. Except for the *gpt* fragment and an SV40 origin of replication (upstream of the MMTV LTR), this plasmid is identical to the pMTVdhfr described in Fig. 13. Selection of cells expressing *gpt* was performed using the mycophenolic acid + xanthine procedure described by Mulligan and Berg (1981).

LTR (i.e., the start site for MMTV transcription). Moreover, the production of this RNA is increased in dexamethasone-treated cells.

C. MMTV–β-GALACTOSIDASE FUSIONS

As described in the dhfr and XGPRT experiments, expression of foreign genes encoded on plasmids has generally been studied in stable transformants arising either from direct selection for the functional gene or from cotransfection with another selectable marker (Perucho *et al.*, 1980). A general shortcoming of this approach is the length of time required to grow sufficient numbers of cells from individual clones for analysis. A very useful alternative is provided by experiments in which expression of plasmid genes is assayed within the first few days following DNA infection. These so-called "transient-expression assays" offer not only a time advantage, but since the average level of gene expression from the transfected population is measured, the considerable variability typically observed among individual clones can be avoided. Clonal differences in gene expression may be due in large part to the site of integration of the transfected plasmid, as was seen in clones of MMTV-infected HTC cells (Section IV). This potential source of variability is eliminated by analyzing transient expression from unintegrated plasmid molecules.

The gene we have utilized for this series of experiments is the *E. coli lac* Z gene, which encodes the enzyme β-galactosidase. A long history of its use in the study of bacterial gene regulation and its recent successful expression in yeast cells (Rose *et al.*, 1981) indicated that this gene would be a useful marker in mammalian cells. Moreover, quantitation of the enzyme is performed by a very simple, reproducible, and extremely sensitive colorimetric assay (Miller, 1972). The plasmid we have constructed, pCH105 (Hall *et al.*, 1982), is again a derivative of the pSVMgpt plasmid (Fig. 15) in which the XGPRT gene has been replaced by the *E. coli lac* Z gene obtained originally as a fusion gene product (Casadaban and Cohen, 1980). A similar plasmid, pCH110, containing the SV40 promoter, rather than the MMTV promoter, was also constructed (Hall, *et al.*, 1982).

We have utilized several cell lines to analyze the transient expression of β-galactosidase from pCH105 and found that the mouse L tk⁻ cell was the most efficient. As shown in Table VII, when this plasmid is introduced using the DEAE-dextran procedure (Sompayrac and Danna, 1981), the levels of β-galactosidase detected in cell extracts 3 days after DNA infection were approximately the same as mock-infected cells. However, when dexamethasone ($10^{-6} M$) was added to the transfected cells 24 hours prior to assaying the enzyme, the levels were at least 25 times above back-

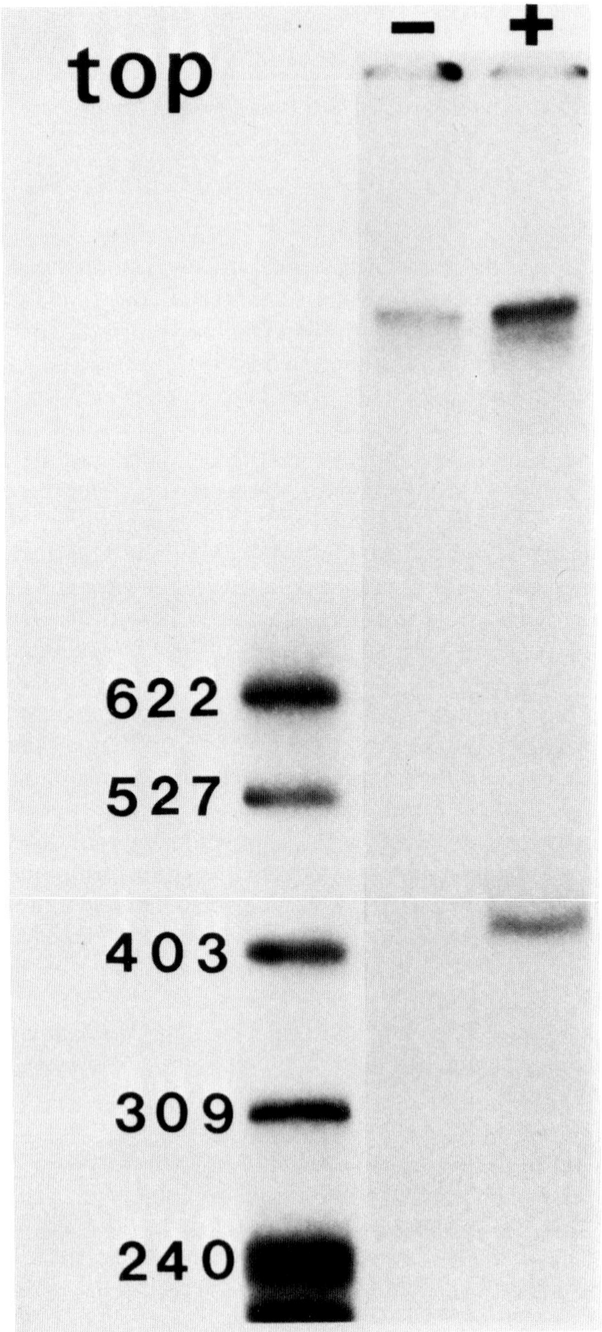
top
–
+
622
527
403
309
240

TABLE VII

Glucocorticoid Induction of β-Galactosidase in Transient Expression Experiments[a]

Plasmid	β-Galactosidase specific activity		
	−DEX	+DEX	Fold induction
Mock	0.67 (4)	0.95 (4)	1.4
pCH110 (SV40–β-gal)	11.8 (2)	8.6 (2)	0
pCH105 (MMTV–β-gal)	0.7 (4)	18.3 (4)	26

[a] Infections with DNA were performed by incubating mouse L tk⁻ cells with 10–20 μg plasmid in the presence of 200 μg/ml DEAE-dextran (Samparyac and Danna, 1981) for 4 hours. Cells were washed and then incubated for 2 days in growth medium. Dexamethasone (10^{-6} M) was added for 1 day and cells were collected, pelleted, and resuspended in 0.25 M sucrose, 10 mM Tris–HCl, pH 7.4, and 10 mM EDTA. Cells were lysed by freeze-thawing and debris was removed by a 5 minute centrifugation in a microfuge. β-Galactosidase activity is expressed as nanomoles ONPG cleaved per minute per milligram protein as described by Miller (1972).

ground. In contrast, β-galactosidase production from the SV40 promoter is not glucocorticoid inducible.

These results demonstrate that transient expression from pCH105 is a very convenient way to measure hormonal regulation of the MMTV promoter. Moreover, one can surmise that glucocorticoid-regulated transcription from the MMTV promoter is not dependent on integration of the DNA into chromosomal sequences.

FIG. 16. Glucocorticoid induction and mapping of *gpt* RNA in 3T6 cells transformed with pSVM gpt. Mouse 3T6 cells were transfected with plasmid DNA using $CaPO_4$ (Graham and van der Eb, 1973); transformants expressing *gpt* were selected by their ability to grow in the presence of mycophenolic acid and xanthine (Mulligan and Berg, 1981). One such transformant was grown in the presence (48 hours) or absence of dexamethasone (10^{-6} M) and cytoplasmic RNA was isolated. Poly(A)-containing RNA was prepared by chromatography on oligo(dT)-cellulose and approximately 1 μg was hybridized with a probe end labeled with [³²P]ATP at the *Bgl*II site within the *gpt* gene (see Fig. 15). Hybridization was performed at 50°C for ~16 hours in 80% formamide according to the procedure of Berk and Sharp (1977). RNA–DNA hybrids were treated with S1 nuclease and run on a 6% acrylamide gel which was autoradiographed for 4 days. Left lane: size marker of ³²P-labeled pBR322 DNA digested with *Hin*fI. RNA from cells grown in the absence (−) or presence (+) of dexamethasone. The band migrating at a size of ~410 base pairs corresponds to a *gpt* RNA that is initiated at the proper MMTV promoter. The band appearing further up in the gel corresponds to a full length probe renealed during the hybridization; inducibility of this material is likely to be an artifact of the nuclease digestion; however, we have not yet proven this.

D. DELETION MAPPING STUDIES OF THE MMTV LTR

The results of our gene fusion experiments clearly demonstrate that the MMTV LTR contains a region that confers glucocorticoid responsiveness on the expression of any linked gene. Similar studies using the Herpes virus thymidine kinase gene and the Harvey sarcoma virus transforming protein have been reported (Huang *et al.*, 1981; Groner *et al.*, 1982). To further delineate the sequences of importance for hormonal regulation, we have constructed deletion mutants that remove portions of the LTR in either the XGPRT plasmid (pSVMgpt) or the β-galactosidase plasmid (pCH 105). Data from the XGPRT deletions were obtained by RNA mapping studies in transformed 3T6 cells as described in Section VI,B; from the β-gal plasmids, data were obtained using the transient expression assay (Section VI,C). A summary of a large set of such studies is presented in Fig. 17; positive basal activity indicates that the promoter function (i.e., the uninduced level of expression) remains intact. Positive induced activity indicates that the level of XGPRT RNA and/or β-galactosidase activity, in the presence and absence of hormone, is equivalent to that with plasmids containing the entire LTR (Fig. 17a).

These experiments with deletion mutants allow three major conclusions to be made. The first is that one can eliminate inducible expression without interfering with basal promoter function (Fig. 17b); moreover, the sequences important for regulation must reside (at least in part) upstream of nucleotide −109, since deletion of such sequences abolished hormonal responsiveness. Second, the left-hand (upstream) border of the glucocorticoid regulatory region must be downstream of nucleotide −240, since plasmids in which the entire left end of the LTR up to −240 respond normally to hormone (Fig. 17c). Third, the right-hand boundary of the regulatory region must be upstream of nucleotide −141, since plasmids in which the sequence between −109 and −141 is deleted retain inducibility (Fig. 17e). The deletion shown in Fig. 17f corroborates these points, since deletion of the nucleotides between −210 and −109 eliminates glucocorticoid responsiveness. In the aggregate, these studies strongly suggest that the major region of the MMTV LTR responsible for glucocorticoid sensitivity resides between nucleotides −210 and −141 relative to the start of transcription. Sequence analysis of the LTR (Donehower *et al.*, 1981) indicates that the promoter region itself encompasses the so-called "CAT" and "TATA" boxes at nucleotides −70 and −30, respectively.

A further, and perhaps subtle, point that can be made from analysis of some of the internal deletions (Fig. 17d and e) is that the absolute spacing between the promoter and regulatory region need not be constant. In fact, we have also found that insertion of four nucleotides at position −109

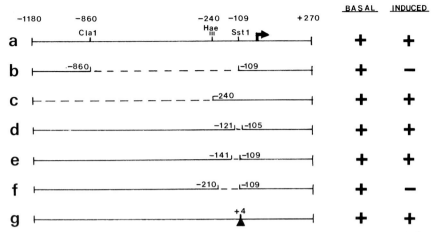

FIG. 17.   Mapping the glucocorticoid regulatory region of the MMTV LTR by deletion analysis. Deletion mutants in the LTR were constructed as follows: (a) wild-type LTR, (b) deletion of the fragment between the *Cla*I and *Sst*I sites, (c) deletion of all sequences up to the *Hae*III site at −240, (d) DNA was digested with *Sst*I, treated briefly with the exonuclease Bal 31, and then religated, (e and f) DNA was treated with Bal 31 as in (d), linkers containing *Xho*I sites were added, and then the region from −109 to +270 was replaced with the corresponding wild-type fragment, and (g) DNA was digested with *Sst*I, the ends were trimmed, and *Xho*I linkers were added, resulting in a net insertion of four nucleotides. The exact positions of the deletions have been determined for d, e, and f by sequence analysis. The wild-type molecules (a) were pSVMgpt and pCH105 (β-gal). Deletions b, d, e, and f were constructed in both *gpt* and β-gal plasmids. Analyses of *gpt* basal and induced RNAs were performed as described in Fig. 16. Analysis of β-gal activity was performed as described in Table VII. In all cases shown, (+) indicates normal levels, whereas (−) indicates no detectable induction; we have not seen intermediate values with any of these deletions. In the case of deletion (b), the RNA produced in *gpt* transformants (+ or − DEX) starts at the same site in the MMTV LTR and is made in the same quantities as from the wild-type LTR (Dobson, Lee, and Ringold, unpublished).

does not interfere with induction by dexamethasone (Fig. 17g). Since this is a minor alteration, we are currently determining the maximum distance by which the promoter and regulatory region can be separated by inserting larger fragments at position −109.

VII. Speculations on the Role of the Glucocorticoid Regulatory Region

The most straightforward model one could envision, depicted in Fig. 18, is that the regulatory region contains one or more high-affinity binding sites for the glucocorticoid–receptor complex and that the promoter region contains a binding site for RNA polymerase. Recent data from several laboratories have, indeed, shown that both extensively purified and crude preparations of glucocorticoid–receptor complexes do, in fact, bind specifically to MMTV DNA (Payvar *et al.*, 1981; Govindan *et al.*, 1982; Pfahl, 1982). Although there is some disagreement as to the exact sites of binding, at least two of these reports contain evidence for high-affinity interactions with the MMTV LTR. Major questions remain, however, not the least of which is what the function of binding at such a site could be.

Several types of models could be envisioned to explain the mechanism(s) by which steroid–receptor complexes stimulate transcription. The first, and perhaps most widely discussed, is that binding of the receptor induces a local unwinding of the DNA that somehow permits increased transcription; this model could accommodate either increased polymerase binding or increased initiation complexes. A second model would invoke a requirement for direct protein–protein interactions between receptor and polymerase; again, in this model the details must remain fuzzy, since so little is known about polymerase function. Both of these models have been widely discussed in the context of positive regulation of transcription in bacterial systems (see McKay and Steitz, 1981, for discussion). A third model for describing steroid–receptor action would involve alterations in chromatin structure that would, again in some rather mysterious way, stimulate transcription; in such a scheme, one could envision that the effects of the receptor might be exerted over a long distance (Yamamoto and Alberts, 1976). An alternative, but perhaps similar notion, is that the glucocorticoid regulatory region (in association with

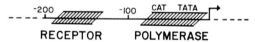

FIG. 18. A schematic model indicating the regions of the MMTV LTR important in basal and glucocorticoid-inducible gene expression. The exact sequences to which the receptor binds have not been established, however, we presume that the region that is functionally required will contain one or more such binding site. The model is presented primarily to indicate that the regulatory and promoter regions are truly distinct entities. We make no implications as to the subunit structure of the receptor or the polymerase, nor do we wish to imply that there could not be direct interaction between these two DNA sites or the receptor and polymerase proteins themselves. The utility of this sketch is that it allows visualization of the spatial arrangement of a hormone regulated promoter. The questions that arise from such a picture include (1) Can any promoter (i.e., the region from -100 to $+1$) substitute for the MMTV promoter and retain hormonal sensitivity? (2) Is there a required spacing between the regulatory and promoter regions? (3) Is hormonal induction of transcription due to direct interaction of the glucocorticoid–receptor complex with the RNA polymerase? These and other questions are amenable to experimental study using the systems we have described here.

receptor) serves as an efficient site of entry on the DNA for RNA polymerase; the polymerase would then be free to scan the DNA (perhaps bidirectionally) for an appropriate promoter site. This model would ascribe to the hormonal regulatory sequences properties akin to the recently described "enhancer" sequences of SV40 and other viral genomes (Banerji *et al.*, 1981; Fromm and Berg, 1982); these sequences have the amazing ability to exert their effect at distances of several thousand base pairs from the promoter.

Whatever the detailed mechanisms involved in glucocorticoid regulation of gene expression may be, it is clear that the MMTV system will continue to play an active role in deciphering the answers. Additional development of genetic approaches, gene-fusion studies, and direct measurement of steroid receptor binding to DNA will be required to compile a coherent picture of the details of steroid hormone action at a molecular level. It is indeed exciting to realize that the next 7 years will provide as much entertainment as have the past seven.

ACKNOWLEDGMENTS

The early phase of the work summarized here was initiated in the laboratory of Drs. H. Varmus and J. M. Bishop and continued in the laboratory of Dr. K. Yamamoto. G. M. R. is most appreciative for their support and continued encouragement. We would also like to thank P. Berg, A. Chapman, M. Costello, B. Dieckmann, E. Jacob, R. Mulligan, and T. Schroer for their many valuable contributions. This work was supported by a grant (GM25821) from the National Institute of General Medical Science and by a Basil O'Connor Grant from the National Foundation March of Dimes. The patient assistance provided by F. Lindsay-Fink in typing this manuscript is greatly appreciated.

REFERENCES

Banerji, J., Rusconi, S., and Schaffner, W. (1981). *Cell* **27,** 299–308.
Baxter, J., and Tomkins, G. (1970). *Proc. Natl. Acad. Sci. U.S.A.* **65,** 709–715.
Baxter, J., Harris, A., Tomkins, G., and Cohn, M. (1971). *Science* **171,** 189–191.
Bentvelzen, P., and Hilgers, J. (1980). *In* "Viral Oncology" (G. Klein, ed.), pp. 311–355. Raven, New York.
Berk, A., and Sharp, P. (1977). *Cell* **12,** 721–732.
Bourne, H., Coffino, P., and Tomkins, G. (1975). *Science* **187,** 750–752.
Cardiff, R., and Duesberg, P. (1968). *Virology* **36,** 696–700.
Casabadan, M., and Cohen, S. (1980). *J. Mol. Biol.* **138,** 179–207.
Chang, A., Nunberg, J. Kaufman, R., Erlich, H., Schimke, R., and Cohen, S. (1978). *Nature (London)* **275,** 617–624.
Cohen, J. C., and Varmus, H. E. (1979).*Nature (London)* **278,** 418–423.
Donehower, L., Huang, A., and Hager, G. (1981). *J. Virol.* **37,** 226–238.
Failla, D., Tomkins, G., and Santi, D. (1975). *Proc. Natl. Acad. Sci. U.S.A.* **72,** 3849–3852.
Feinstein, S., Ross, S., and Yamamoto, K. (1981). *J. Mol. Biol.* **156,** 549–565.

420   GORDON M. RINGOLD ET AL.

Fine, D., Plowman, J., Kelley, S., Arthur, L., and Hillman, E. (1974). *J. Natl. Cancer Inst.* **52,** 1881–1886.

Fromm, M., and Berg, P. (1982). *J. Mol. Appl. Genet.* **1,** 457–481.

Gorski, J., and Gannon, F. (1976). *Annu. Re. Physiol.* **38,** 425–450.

Govindan, M., Spiess, E., and Majors, J. (1982). *Proc. Natl. Acad. Sci. U.S.A.* **79,** 5157–5162.

Graham, F., and van der Eb, A. (1973). *Virology* **52,** 456–467.

Groner, B., Hynes, N., and Diggelman, H. (1979). *J. Virol.* **30,** 417–420.

Groner, B., Kennedy, N., Rahmsdorf, U., Herrlich, P., van Ooyen, A., and Hynes, N. (1982). *In* "Hormones and Cell Regulation" (J. Damont, J. Nunez, and G. Schutz, eds.), pp. 217–228. Elsevier, Amsterdam.

Grove, J. R., and Ringold, G. M. (1981). *Proc. Natl. Acad. Sci. U.S.A.* **78,** 4349–4353.

Grove, J. R., Dieckmann, B., Schroer, T., and Ringold, G. M. (1980). *Cell* **21,** 47–56.

Guntaka, R., Mahy, B., Bishop, J. M., and Varmus, H. (1975). *Nature (London)* **253,** 507–511.

Higgins, S. J., and Gehring, U. (1978). *Ad. Cancer Res.* **28,** 313–397.

Huang, A., Ostrowski, M., Berard, D., and Hager, G. (1981). *Cell* **27,** 245–255.

Ivarie, R., and O'Farrell, P. (1978). *Cell* **13,** 41–55.

Jensen, E. V., Suzuki, T., Kawashima, T., Strumpf, W. E., Jungblut, P. W., and DeSombre, E. R. (1968). *Proc. Natl. Acad. Sci. U.S.A.* **59,** 632–638.

Kulka, R., Tomkins, G., and Crook, R. (1972). *J. Cell Biol.* **54,** 175–179.

Laemmli, U. (1970). *Nature (London)* **227,** 680–685.

Lee, F., Mulligan, R., Berg, P., and Ringold, G. (1981). *Nature (London)* **294,** 228–232.

McGrath, C. (1971). *J. Natl. Cancer Inst.* **47,** 455–467.

McKay, D., and Steitz, T. (1981). *Nature (London)* **290,** 744–749.

Majors, J., and Varmus, H. (1981). *Nature (London)* **289,** 253–258.

Michalides, R., and Schlom, J. (1975). *Proc. Natl. Acad. Sci. U.S.A.* **72,** 4635–4639.

Miller, J. (1972). "Experiments in Molecular Genetics." Cold Spring Harbor Laboratories, Cold Spring Harbor, New York.

Mulligan, R., and Berg, P. (1980). *Science* **209,** 1423–1427.

Mulligan, R., and Berg, P. (1981). *Proc. Natl. Acad. Sci. U.S.A.* **78,** 2072–2076.

O'Malley, B., Roop, D., Lai, E., Nordstrom, J., Catterall, J., Swaneck, D., Colbert, D., Tsai, M. J., Dugaiczyk, A., and Woo, S. (1979). *Recent Prog. Horm. Res.* **35,** 1–46.

Parks, W., Scolnick, E., and Kozikowski, E. (1974). *Science* **184,** 158–160.

Payvar, F., Wrange, O., Carlstedt-Duke, J., Orket, S., Gustafsson, J., and Yamamoto, K. (1981). *Proc. Natl. Acad. Sci. U.S.A.* **78,** 6628–6632.

Perucho, M., Hanahan, D., and Wigler, M. (1980). *Cell* **22,** 309–317.

Pfahl, M. (1982). *Cell* **31,** 475–482.

Pfahl, M., Kelleher, R., and Bourgeois, S. (1978). *Mol. Cell. Endocrinol.* **10,** 193–207.

Ringold, G. (1979). *Biochim. Biophys. Acta* **560,** 487–508.

Ringold, G., Yamamoto, K., Tomkins, G., Bishop, J. M., and Barmus, H. (1975). *Cell* **6,** 299–305.

Ringold, G., Yamamoto, K., Bishop, J. M., and Varmus, H. (1977a). *Proc. Natl. Acad. Sci. U.S.A.* **74,** 2879–2883.

Ringold, G., Cardiff, R., Varmus, H., and Yamamoto, K. (1977b). *Cell* **10,** 11–18.

Ringold, G., Yamamoto, K., Shank, P., and Varmus, H. (1977c). *Cell* **10,** 19–26.

Ringold, G., Shank, P., and Yamamoto, K. (1978). *J. Virol.* **26,** 93–101.

Ringold, G., Shank, P., Varmus, H., Ring, J., and Yamamoto, K. (1979). *Proc. Natl. Acad. Sci. U.S.A.* **76,** 665–669.

Robertson, D., and Varmus, H. (1979). *J. Virol.* **30**, 576–589.

Rose, M., Casadaban, M., and Botstein, D. (1981). *Proc. Natl. Acad. Sci. U.S.A.* **78**, 2460–2464.

Rosenau, W., Baxter, J., Rousseau, G., and Tomkins, G. (1972). *Nature (London) New Biol.* **237**, 20–22.

Ross, E., and Gilman, A. (1977). *J. Biol. Chem.* **252**, 6966–6970.

Rousseau, G., Higgins, S., Baxter, J., Gelfand, D., and Tomkins, G. (1975). *J. Biol. Chem.* **250**, 6015–6021.

Schimke, R., McKnight, G. S., Shapiro, D., Sullivan, D., and Palacios, R. (1975). *Recent Prog. Horm. Res.* **32**, 175–209.

Scolnick, E., Young, H., and Parks, W. (1976). *Virology* **69**, 148–156.

Shank, P., Cohen, J. C., Varmus, H., Yamamoto, K., and Ringold, G. (1978). *Proc. Natl. Acad. Sci. U.S.A.* **75**, 2112–2116.

Shyamala, G., and Dickson, C. (1976). *Nature (London)* **262**, 107–112.

Sibley, C., and Tomkins, G. (1974a). *Cell* **2**, 213–220.

Sibley, C., and Tomkins, G. (1974b). *Cell* **2**, 221–227.

Sompayrac, L., and Danna, K. (1981). *Proc. Natl. Acad. Sci. U.S.A.* **78**, 7575–7578.

Southern, E. (1975). *J. Mol. Biol.* **98**, 503–517.

Stallcup, M., Ring, J., and Yamamoto, K. (1978). *Biochemistry* **17**, 1515–1521.

Subramani, S., Mulligan, R., and Berg, P. (1981). *Mol. Cell. Biol.* **1**, 854–864.

Temin, H. (1981). *Cell* **27**, 1–3.

Thompson, E. B., Tomkins, G., and Curran, J. (1966). *Proc. Natl. Acad. Sci. U.S.A.* **56**, 296–303.

Ucker, D., Ross, S., and Yamamoto, K. (1981). *Cell* **27**, 257–266.

Urlaub, G., and Chasin, L. (1980). *Proc. Natl. Acad. Sci. U.S.A.* **77**, 4216–4220.

Vaidya, A., Lasfargues, E., Henkel, G., Lasfargues, J., and Moore, D. (1976). *J. Virol.* **18**, 911–917.

Varmus, H. (1982). *Science* **216**, 812–820.

Varmus, H., Bishop, J. M., Nowinski, R., and Sarkar, N. (1972). *Nature (London) New Biol.* **238**, 189–191.

Yamamoto, K., and Alberts, B. (1976). *Annu. Re. Biochem.* **45**, 721–746.

Yamamoto, K., and Ringold, G. (1978). *In* "Receptors and Hormone Action: (B. O'Malley and L. Birnbaumer, eds.), pp. 297–322. Academic Press, New York.

Yamamoto, K., Gehring, U., Stampfer, M., and Sibley, C. (1976). *Recent Prog. Horm. Res.* **32**, 3–32.

Young, H. Scolnick, E., and Parks, W. (1975). *J. Biol. Chem.* **250**, 3337–3343.

Young, H., Shih, E., Scolnick, E., and Parks, W. (1977). *J. Virol.* **21**, 139–146.

DISCUSSION

U. Zor: I would like to suggest another explanation which may partially be responsible for the induction of MMTV virus by glucocorticoid steroids. If one can infect the cell with the virus, stimulation of prostaglandin (PG) and interferon production, both have an antiviral action. Glucocorticoid steroids are best inhibitors of interferon production at least in fibroblasts. So maybe the stimulatory effect of glucocorticoid steroids on a mammary tumor viral infection, as well as on other viral multiplications, is due to the inhibition of interferon and prostaglandin production. By the way, the prostaglandin inhibitor, aspirin, also increased the viral multiplication.

G. Ringold: That is certainly a possible suggestion; however, there are two types of experiments which rule out that possibility. The first is that we can inhibit protein synthesis completely and still see perfectly normal induction of viral RNA. We do not need to induce something like macrocortin or lipomodulin by glucocorticoids which in turn affect viral replication. The second is that when we just use the LTR fused to some normal cellular gene product like dihydrofolate reductase we still see induction. We have no virus production or replication in that situation. Although there may well be effects of interferon or prostaglandins on some aspects of viral replication per se, I think that the inducibility of viral RNA synthesis by glucocorticoids is independent of those mechanisms.

U. Zor: Still, if you use the antibiotics, cycloheximide and actinomycin D you get superinduction of interferon production; therefore this does not mean that in the presence of the antibiotics the glucocorticoid is still active on MMTV. The suggestion that I just made could not still be correct.

G. Ringold: If I could comment again, a portion of what you have said is true. That is if you add cycloheximide and then remove it, one observes superinduction of interferon. We have in fact been studying interferon genes and the superinduction phenomenon. If one just adds cycloheximide and leaves it there, no interferon is made. However, the interferon message is induced by poly(I · C). Analogously, in the presence of inhibitors of protein synthesis such as puromycin and cycloheximide, induction of viral RNA occurs normally. To sum up, I think those are all good ideas; at least in this case it seems likely that interferon is not involved in the induction process.

I. A. Kourides: The theme of your talk has been glucocorticoid induction of MMTV; I am interested in knowing what the possible effects of other hormones on MMTV might be, particularly hormones such as thyroid hormone, estrogen, progesterone, prolactin, and insulin, all hormones that have been implicated in some fashion or another in mammary carcinogenesis.

G. Ringold: Both we and Ed Scolnick's group, working independently, analyzed a series of hormones that might affect MMTV production. Estrogen clearly does not stimulate MMTV production. Progesterone by itself does not do anything, but will block the induction by glucocorticoids; this is consistent with progesterone's ability to act as a competitive inhibitor of glucocorticoid binding to its receptor. I do not know whether anyone has ever tested thyroid hormone. Insulin does, in fact, under certain conditions, seem to have a permissive effect on viral replication in some cell types. However this appears to be an effect independent of viral RNA production itself. Rather, it seems to be an effect on the ability of the cell to make virus. Those are the only studies of which I am aware.

I. A. Kourides: Prolactin has not been looked at then?

G. Ringold: If it has I am unaware of it.

P. Robel: Normal cells contain genes that are induced by glucocorticoids and you have shown the mechanism of induction of MMTV. Is there any homology between the glucocorticoid regulatory region of the LTR and the flanking regions of those mammalian genes?

G. Ringold: That is a very interesting question and something that we have tried to look for. The genes that have been sequenced and analyzed as being glucocorticoid responsive include growth hormone, α_{2u}-globulin, and MMTV. Comparing those sequences we have found nothing apparent. We now have in hand clones for a couple of other rat hepatoma, glucocorticoid inducible, genes and as soon as we sequence them, we will go through the same process. For the moment, however, there is nothing striking that comes out from the sequences available. I think the first thing to do should be to localize the region that is responsible for the responsiveness to glucocorticoids functionally. When such a region is much better defined, it will be easier to start looking. If, for example, in growth hormone that region resides between −250 and −290 we might not pick it up as well as if we are looking in a region similar to the one in MMTV (−140 to −190). Thank you for the question; it is something that we will be pursuing.

T. Spelsberg: This was a fantastic presentation of excellent data. Just for the record, even if you insert expanding sequences between the two regions (i.e., the initiation sites of transcription and the sites where there is possible binding of the receptor) and interfere with induction, that does not rule out the possibility of a more distant binding site for receptor with a following mediator coming over into that region. Do you follow what I am saying?

G. Ringold: No.

T. Spelsberg: Okay, if you put in expanding DNAs at the site between the promoter and regulatory regions and they were to expand for the possible receptor interaction or needed function versus the initiation region, and that stops the induction, that does not rule out that receptor is binding elsewhere with a mediator coming into that region for induction.

G. Ringold: That is a possibility, however, I am really not sure what you mean by a mediator though?

T. Spelsberg: Well, if it is at a distance of 2000 bases away it cannot reach over itself and do something. One would have to envision the transcription of a product of the Britten–Davidson type.

J. D. Baxter: Yes, or for instance the steroid receptor could bind 1000 bases away, affect the chromatin in the region upstream from the promoter, and that would have an effect on the promoter.

T. Spelsberg: Yes.

G. Ringold: If you are willing to call a mediator a transmissible alteration in chromatin structure or an RNA product, then I certainly would agree with you. That is in fact what we are trying to test since there may be some suggestion for such a model. In the case of the metallothionein gene, for instance, the glucocorticoid regulatory region may well be very far away and be affecting inducibility by some other mechanism.

S. L. Cohen: Do you know whether estrogen has a permissive effect in inducing these tumors? In other words, can they be induced in ovariectomized animals?

G. Ringold: There is a large body of phenomenological data in the mouse mammary tumor virus and mouse mammary tumor literature from about 1920 to 1960, in which every kind of hormone in every kind of ablated mouse has been tested. Estrogens per se do stimulate mammary tumorogenesis in a variety of mouse strains; however, that seems to be independent of mouse mammary tumor virus production. It seems to be a stimulatory effect on growth of the mammary gland. I am not sure if that answers your question, but yes, a variety of other hormones including estrogen can stimulate mammary tumor formation.

S. L. Cohen: Can mammary tumors be induced in ovariectomized animals?

G. Ringold: By estrogen, yes.

S. L. Cohen: By mammary tumor virus?

G. Ringold: Yes, in those mammary tumors as well as most naturally occurring mammary tumors in inbred strains of mice, the mouse mammary tumor virus is being produced and is probably responsible for the initiating oncogenic effect. As you suggest, however, the other hormones must play some permissive role in either the growth of the developing mammary gland or growth of the tumor itself.

J. E. Rall: As a general comment it is interesting to me how much virology has played a role in teaching us something about genetic mechanisms in higher eukaryotes. I'm thinking of split genes which I guess were first found in adenovirus, multiple switching in SV40 with big and little T, and now with MMTV you may find out how it is that steroids turn on genes. One question is that in your matrix in which you had your mutant cell lines, there did not seem to be any entry for an inducible gp52 and a noninducible TAT. Is there any reason for that, or is it just bad luck?

G. Ringold: The reason is that we were selecting for lack of gp52 induction, so that everything that we obtained was either gp52 noninducible or partially inducible. If one goes through the mutagenized starting population, however, and just does a random screen, one can pick up a very rare cell which has retained gp52 inducibility but lost TAT inducibility. The figure however reflected the phenotypes of the cells that were selected to be gp52 noninducible.

Hormone and Age-Dependent Regulation of α_{2u}-Globulin Gene Expression

ARUN K. ROY, BANDANA CHATTERJEE, WILLIAM F. DEMYAN,
BRUCE S. MILIN, NALINI M. MOTWANI, T. SUREND NATH, AND
MICHAEL J. SCHIOP

*Hormone Research Laboratory, Departments of Biological Sciences and Chemistry,
Oakland University, Rochester, Michigan*

I. Introduction

In recent years studies of various animal models contributed considerably to our overall understanding of the mechanism of hormonal regulation of gene expression. Estrogen and progesterone-mediated synthesis of ovalbumin and other egg white proteins in the chicken oviduct has been greatly exploited for exploration of the molecular mechanism of steroid hormone action (Schimke *et al.*, 1975; Palmiter *et al.*, 1976; Tsai *et al.*, 1978; O'Malley *et al.*, 1979). Parallel studies of estrogenic induction of vitellogenin, the precursor of egg yolk protein, in the chicken and frog liver have provided additional and complementary information on steroidal regulation of gene expression (Gruber *et al.*, 1976; Tata and Smith, 1979; Goldberger and Deeley, 1980; Wahli *et al.*, 1981; Shapiro *et al.*, 1983). Studies using two mammalian model systems have also contributed significantly to an understanding of the mechanism of hormone action. One of these systems involves hormonal regulation of development, differentiation and milk protein synthesis in the mammary gland (Lyons *et al.*, 1958; Topper, 1970; Turkington *et al.*, 1973; Rosen *et al.*, 1980). In this system several hormones including estrogen, progesterone, glucocorticoid, prolactin, growth hormone, insulin, and thyroxine seem to act in concert for mammogenesis and lactation. Although experimental analysis of the mammary model has made a substantial impact on clinical medicine and offers a valuable resource for the study of development and differentiation, complex cytological features of the mammary gland and hormonal stimulation of cell proliferation complicate investigation of specific gene expression. However, the multihormonal regulation of α_{2u}-globulin synthesis in rat liver as developed in our laboratory is free from most of the complications of the mammary system (Roy, 1979). Since 60–70% of the liver is comprised of hepatocytes whose functional integrity is indepen-

425

dent of sex steroids, the androgen-dependent synthesis of α_{2u}-globulin provides a useful model for the study of hormonal regulation of specific gene expression in a mammalian system. Additional advantages of this model system include the multiple endocrine interactions and the age-dependent changes in androgen action. The multihormonal regulation of α_{2u}-globulin synthesis can be exploited for studying the mode of action of steroid, peptide, and thyroid hormones on the expression of a single gene in the context of changing endocrine responses during aging.

II. α_{2u}-Globulin and Its Hepatic Origin

α_{2u}-Globulin is the major urinary protein of the mature male rat. Rats and other rodents show an unusually high degree of proteinuria. During our studies on the identification and characterization of various protein in the male rat urine we found that about 50% of the total urinary proteins can be accounted for by one immunochemically distinct protein moiety with the same electrophoretic mobility as α_2-globulins of rat serum. This urinary α_2-globulin was different from the serum α_2-globulin and thus we named this protein α_{2u}-globulin with the subscript "u" to signify its abundance in the urine (Roy and Neuhaus, 1966a). Subsequent studies showed that α_{2u}-globulin is synthesized and secreted by the hepatic parenchymal cells and because of its relatively low molecular weight (M_r, 18,000) it is rapidly filtered through the kidneys where in one pass only about 15% is recycled into the plasma and the rest is excreted into the urine (Roy and Neuhaus, 1966b; Roy and Raber, 1972). Because of its rapid filtration through the kidneys into the urine, the plasma concentration of α_{2u}-globulin remains very low.

The messenger RNA for α_{2u}-globulin constitutes about 1–2% of the total hepatic mRNA and it contains approximately 1200 nucleotide residues with 300–400 noncoding sequences and about 175 poly(A) residues at the 3' end (Deshpande et al., 1979; Chatterjee and Roy, 1980). The cDNA corresponding to α_{2u}-globulin mRNA has been cloned in Escherichia coli (Kurtz and Nicodemus, 1981; Unterman et al., 1981; Roy et al., 1982). α_{2u}-Globulin actually consists of a family of proteins with minor variations in molecular weights and isoelectric points. Two molecular weight variants (differing in about five amino acid residues) and five major and two minor isoelectric variants of α_{2u}-globulin within the total hepatic proteins have recently been identified in our laboratory. In addition, a small amount (~3%) is posttranslationally modified to contain a 2500-dalton carbohydrate residue (Chatterjee et al., 1982). As documented in a later section of this article, all of these variant forms of α_{2u}-globulin can be resolved by two-dimensional gel electrophoresis.

In addition to liver and kidney, immunochemical analyses of various other tissues have shown the presence of α_{2u}-globulin in the salivary gland (Roy and Byrd, 1976). Results of our studies suggest that similar to kidneys, the salivary glands concentrate α_{2u}-globulin from the circulation and secrete it into the saliva. However, a recent report has indicated that salivary glands may also be capable of synthesizing this protein (Laperche *et al.*, 1982). With the help of a specific cDNA probe Hastie *et al.* (1979) have examined the tissue distribution of the male mouse urinary protein, MUP (a protein analogous to rat α_{2u}-globulin) and have found that the hepatic tissue of the male mouse contains 30,000 copies of the MUP mRNA per cell, while the salivary gland and spleen contain 130 and 13 copies per cell, respectively. Studies on serum accumulation as well as urinary output of α_{2u}-globulin after partial hepatectomy have shown a

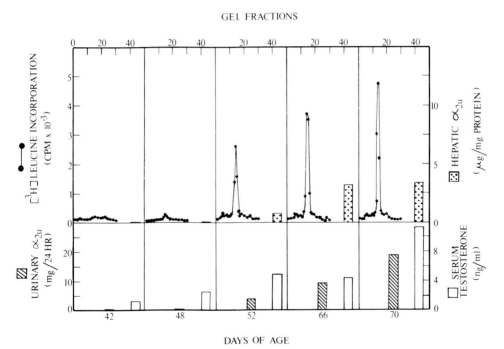

GEL FRACTIONS

DAYS OF AGE

FIG. 1. Relationship between the levels of serum testosterone and hepatic messenger RNA for α_{2u}-globulin in maturing male rats. The messenger RNA activity of α_{2u}-globulin (●——●) is represented as the pattern of radioactivity of SDS–polyacrylamide gel electrophoresis of α_{2u}–anti-α_{2u} immunoprecipitate obtained from 2×10^6 cpm of released peptide chains synthesized *in vitro* under the direction of hepatic mRNA. Dotted bars, hepatic concentration of α_{2u}-globulin; hatched bars, 24 hour urinary output of α_{2u}-globulin; open bars, serum testosterone. (From Roy *et al.*, 1976b.)

close correlation between the levels of this protein in serum and urine and the extent of liver remnants (Roy and Neuhaus, 1966b; Roy, 1973a). Thus regardless of the limited expression of α_{2u}-globulin gene by the salivary gland or other secretory organs, the liver remains the only major site of α_{2u}-globulin synthesis.

α_{2u}-Globulin is normally found only in trace amounts in the liver of prepubertal male rats and female rats of all ages (Roy and Neuhaus, 1967; Roy, 1973a). In the male animal the hepatic synthesis of α_{2u}-globulin begins to increase near puberty which is associated with a corresponding increase in the hepatic level of α_{2u}-globulin mRNA (Fig. 1). In the normal male rat the maximum level of hepatic synthesis of α_{2u}-globulin is achieved at about 100 days of age.

III. Androgenic and Estrogenic Regulation of α_{2u}-Globulin

A. EFFECT OF ANDROGEN AND ESTROGEN ON FEMALE AND MALE RATS

Although α_{2u}-globulin is virtually absent in female rats, treatment of ovariectomized females with androgenic steroid results in the induction of this protein (Roy and Neuhaus, 1967). The effects of various androgenic steroids on the induction of α_{2u}-globulin, as shown in Fig. 2, indicate that 5α-dihydrotestosterone is the most potent inducer of this protein. Castration of the male rat results in a decreased synthesis of α_{2u}-globulin. Since the adrenal cortex provides about 10% of the total androgen output, castration alone fails to completely abolish the hepatic synthesis of this protein. The decreased synthesis of α_{2u}-globulin in the castrated male rat can be reversed by androgen supplementation (Roy and Neuhaus, 1967). Androgenic induction of α_{2u}-globulin in the ovariectomized rat has been shown to be associated with a corresponding increase in the hepatic concentration of α_{2u}-globulin mRNA (Sippel et al., 1975).

Hepatic synthesis of α_{2u}-globulin can be strongly inhibited by daily treatment with both steroidal and nonsteroidal estrogens. Within 5 to 7 days of the initiation of estrogen treatment almost a complete inhibition of the synthesis of α_{2u}-globulin is observed (Roy et al., 1975). Simultaneous administration of estradiol along with 5α-dihydrotestosterone in the ovariectomized female rats blocks the androgenic induction of α_{2u}-globulin in these animals. This indicates that the effect of estrogen is not mediated through inhibition of testicular androgen output. Similar to androgenic induction, estrogenic inhibition of α_{2u}-globulin is also associated with a

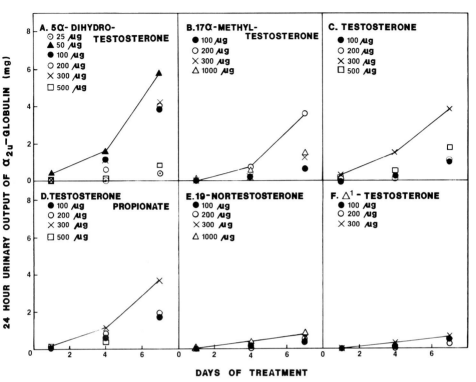

FIG. 2.   Comparative effects of testosterone and testosterone derivatives on the induction of α_{2u}-globulin. Various doses of testosterone and testosterone derivatives (μg/100 g body wt) were administered daily as subcutaneous injections to ovariectomized female rats and the daily urinary output of α_{2u}-globulin was determined by specific immunoassay. Each point is an average of values from four experimental animals. The points representing the optimum doses are joined together. Based on this assay, the potencies of various androgenic steroids are as follows: 5α-dihydrotestosterone > 17α-methyl testosterone > testosterone > testosterone propionate > 19-nortestosterone > Δ^1-testosterone (A–F).

corresponding change in the hepatic concentration of its mRNA (Roy *et al.*, 1977).

A total inhibition of α_{2u}-globulin synthesis by estrogen is followed by a quiescent period during which androgenic hormones are completely ineffective in the induction of this protein. The extent of the refractory period is a dose-dependent phenomenon, and with seven daily treatments of estradiol-17β at a dose of 0.5 μg/g/day it takes about 3 weeks before the animal recovers from the androgen refractory state. Parabiotic joining of an estrogen-treated male rat with its normal male littermate failed to change the preparabiotic pattern of α_{2u} synthesis in the respective partners. Thus, the estrogen-mediated androgen insensitivity does not appear to be due to changes in circulatory endocrine factors but rather to an effect of the estrogen on the liver itself (Roy *et al.*, 1975).

B. ANDROGENIC AND ESTROGENIC INDUCTION AT THE EARLY STAGE OF HORMONE ACTION

Investigation of the early events of estrogen action showed a paradoxical effect of the estrogenic hormones on the hepatic synthesis of α_{2u}-globulin. A single intraperitoneal injection of either DHT or estradiol-17β caused a maximum induction of this protein at about 6 hours after hormone administration (Fig. 3). The optimum dose for this effect was found to be 5 μg/100 g for estradiol and 25 μg/100 g for DHT. This induction can be effectively blocked by the translational inhibitor cycloheximide. The most interesting aspect of this early response of the androgenic and estrogenic induction of α_{2u}-globulin, however, is the effect of pretreatment with either one of these steroids on the subsequent inductive response

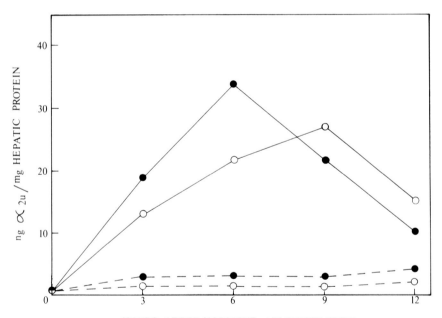

HOURS AFTER HORMONE ADMINISTRATION

FIG. 3. Hepatic induction of α_{2u}-globulin after a single injection of either 5α-dihydrotestosterone or estradiol. Ovariectomized female rats were given intraperitoneal injections of either DHT (30 μg/100 g) or estradiol-17β (5 μg/100 g) at time 0 and sacrificed at 3-hour intervals. Cycloheximide (0.6 mg/100 g) was administered 15 minutes before hormone administration. ($\bullet$——$\bullet$) Estradiol; ($\bigcirc$——$\bigcirc$) dihydrotestosterone; ($\bullet$---$\bullet$) cycloheximide + estradiol; ($\bigcirc$---$\bigcirc$) cycloheximide + dihydrotestosterone. (From Roy, 1977.)

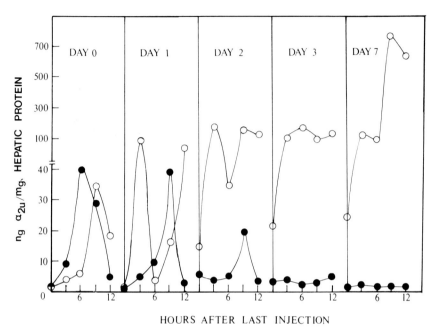

FIG. 4.   Effect of daily pretreatments with estradiol or 5α-dihydrotestosterone on the hepatic levels of α_{2u}-globulin in ovariectomized female rats after a single final injection of the same hormone. The animals in day 0 did not receive any pretreatment and received only a single injection of either estradiol (●——●) or DHT (○——○). Animals in days 1, 2, 3, and 7 received 1, 2, 3, and 7 daily pretreatments with either estradiol (●——●) or DHT (○——○) followed 24 hours later by a single injection of the same hormone. Amounts per injection were 5 μg estradiol/100 g body wt and 30 μg DHT/100 g body wt. (From Roy, 1977.).

(Roy, 1977). Results presented in Fig. 4 show that a single injection of either DHT or estradiol causes a similar degree of induction of α_{2u}-globulin in ovariectomized female rats that did not receive pretreatment with either hormone. Continued exposure of these animals to estradiol, however, caused a gradual decrease in the estrogenic induction. After seven daily pretreatments, estradiol became an ineffective inducer of α_{2u}-globulin. On the other hand, daily pretreatment with DHT greatly enhanced the subsequent inductive response of the androgen. The response of a single final injection of DHT in ovariectomized female rats that had received seven daily pretreatments was about 18-fold higher than that did not receive any previous injection of the androgen. These results can be best explained by postulating the mediation of the response through the cytoplasmic androgen–estrogen binding protein that binds both DHT and estradiol and whose intracellular concentration is inversely regulated by these two hormones.

C. CYTOPLASMIC ANDROGEN BINDING PROTEIN OF RAT LIVER AND ITS POSSIBLE ROLE IN THE REGULATION OF α_{2u}-GLOBULIN

A 3.5 S cytoplasmic androgen binding protein has been identified in the liver of mature male rats (Roy *et al.*, 1974). This cytoplasmic androgen binder (CAB) also binds estradiol-17β (Fig. 5). *In vitro* nuclear uptake studies have shown that CAB does not translocate into the nucleus. Therefore, it is unlikely that it functions as a classical steroid hormone receptor. The existence of this cytoplasmic androgen binder in the rat liver has been confirmed by several other investigators (Smirnov *et al.*, 1977; Dickson *et al.*, 1978; Thompson *et al.*, 1981). The dissociation constants (K_d) for binding of DHT and estradiol-17β to CAB are 1×10^{-8} and 1×10^{-7} M, respectively. The hepatic tissue of the adult (150 days) male rat contains about 10 pmole of CAB per mg protein. The two potent antiandrogens, cyproterone acetate and flutamide, do not bind to CAB nor do they inhibit the androgen-dependent synthesis of α_{2u}-globulin in the male rat. Similar cytoplasmic steroid hormone binding proteins that do not translocate into the nucleus have been identified in frog and fish liver and in the chicken oviduct (LeMenn *et al.*, 1980; Hayward and Shapiro, 1981; Taylor and Smith, 1982). Moreover, there appears to be a strict correlation between the hepatic level of CAB and the ability of the liver to respond to androgenic induction of α_{2u}-globulin. For example, androgen-insensitive Tfm rats do not contain this androgen binder, and these animals fail to synthesize α_{2u}-globulin after androgen treatment (Milin and Roy, 1973). Even a 50-fold higher dose of DHT (2.5 mg/100 g) fails to induce α_{2u}-globulin in these animals. Prepubertal, senescent, and estrogenized male rats that show androgen insensitivity with respect to α_{2u}-synthesis also lack this hepatic androgen binding protein (Roy *et al.*, 1974). As indicated earlier, in mature animals, the hepatic concentration of CAB is regulated by its own ligands. Continued exposure of ovariectomized female rats to androgen results in a gradual rise in the hepatic level of the CAB, while similar exposure to estrogen causes a gradual decline and ultimate loss of the CAB (Fig. 6). Assuming that CAB has a physiological role in the mediation of androgenic induction, the above observations may explain the "anamnestic" type of secondary response in ovariectomized female rats that received androgen pretreatments. Similarly, the gradual decline of the estrogenic induction after estrogen pretreatment (as shown in Fig. 4) also correlates with the decreased hepatic level of the

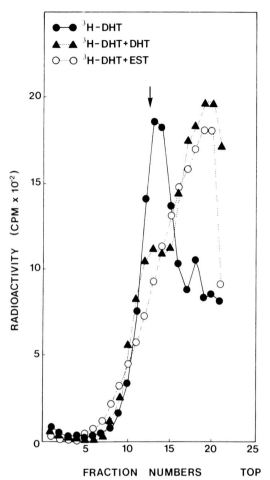

FIG. 5. Binding of 5α-dihydrotestosterone and estradiol-17β by the cytoplasmic andro-gen binding protein of rat liver. Cytosol from the liver of male rats ($\sim$300 g) was prelabeled with [^{3}H]DHT and competition experiments were carried out with a 30-fold excess of unla-beled DHT or estradiol-17β (EST). The arrow shows the position of the marker protein (ovalbumin, 3.55 S). (From Roy *et al.*, 1974).

CAB. The pattern of androgenic response as presented in this figure shows an initial rise in the hepatic level of α_{2u}-globulin, followed by a decline and a secondary rise which is evident 6 hours later. The second peak may be the result of the cytoplasmic appearance of the newly syn-thesized CAB induced by the initial effect of the androgen.

Although the biochemical role of CAB in the hepatic synthesis of α_{2u}-globulin remains to be established, our working hypothesis is that CAB

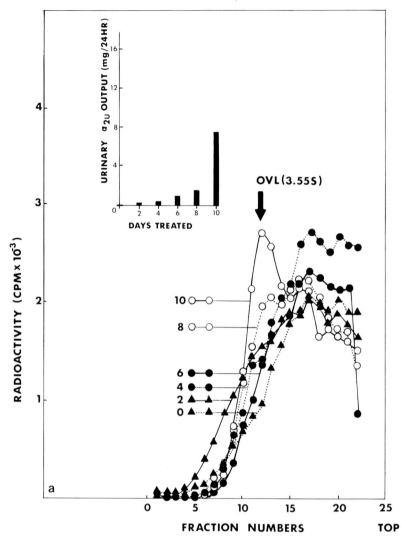

FIG. 6. (a) Androgen-dependent appearance of the hepatic androgen binder and induction of α_{2u}-globulin in the ovariectomized female rat. Sucrose density gradient patterns of [³H]DHT binding to the hepatic cytosol obtained from animals treated with DHT (50 μg/100 g/day) for 0 (▲---▲), 2 (▲——▲), 4 (●---●), 6 (●——●), 8 (○----○), and 10 (○——○) days are presented at the bottom. The inset on the upper left shows the 24-hour urinary output of α_{2u}-globulin of these animals immediately prior to their sacrifice for the androgen binding assay. (From Roy et al., 1974). (b) Estradiol-mediated suppression of the hepatic androgen binder and α_{2u}-globulin in the adult male rat. Male rats (~100 days of age) were treated with estradiol-17β (50 μg/100 g/day) for periods of up to 8 days. Cytosol androgen

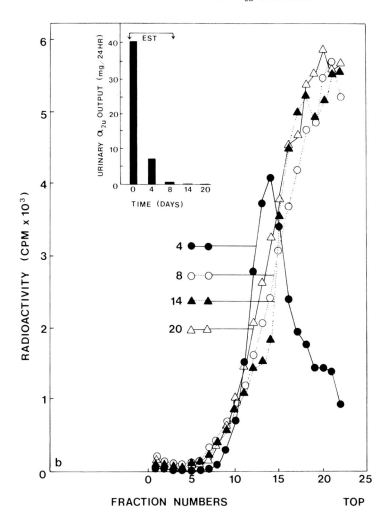

binding activities were assayed on sucrose density gradients both within the above periods of treatment as well as after the withdrawal of the estradiol treatment. Time periods indicated in the figure are expressed as days from the initiation of estradiol treatment. The gradient patterns marked 14 (▲----▲) and 20 (△——△) were obtained from animals which received 8 days of treatment followed by 6 and 12 days of rest, respectively. The inset shows the daily urinary output of α_{2u}-globulin in these animals immediately prior to their sacrifice. The period of estradiol treatment is marked with arrows (EST). (From Roy *et al.*, 1974.)

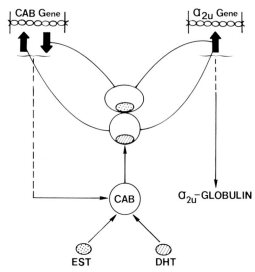

FIG. 7. A proposed model illustrating the effect of androgenic and estrogenic steroids on the regulation of α_{2u}-globulin through the cytoplasmic androgen binder of rat liver. The cytoplasmic androgen binder (CAB) can bind to either estradiol (EST) or 5α-dihydrotestosterone (DHT). Binding to DHT results in increased synthesis of both α_{2u}-globulin and CAB itself. However, binding to estradiol may initially cause increased synthesis of α_{2u}-globulin but because of its repressive effect on CAB synthesis it will eventually lead to the inhibition of the synthesis of α_{2u}-globulin.

may protect both androgenic and estrogenic steroids from hepatic metabolism and make them available for gene regulation. A tentative scheme for androgenic and estrogenic regulation of α_{2u}-globulin via CAB is presented in Fig. 7.

IV. Age-Dependent Changes in the Hepatic Androgen Responsiveness

A. AGE-DEPENDENT CHANGES IN THE HEPATIC SYNTHESIS OF α_{2u}-GLOBULIN AND OTHER ANDROGEN-SENSITIVE PROTEINS

Translational analysis of the total hepatic mRNA obtained from rats of various ages shows that in addition to α_{2u}-globulin, the mRNAs for two other major hepatic proteins undergo marked changes with aging (Fig. 8). One of these codes for a 28.5 kilodalton protein, which like α_{2u}-globulin can be induced by the androgen. The mRNA for this 28.5 kd protein is present at a low concentration in the liver of immature male rats, appears

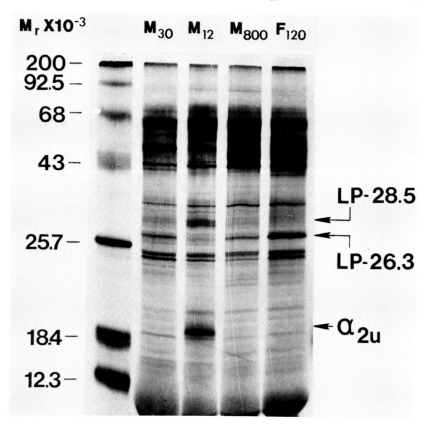

FIG. 8. Age-dependent changes in the messenger RNA for α_{2u}-globulin and two other major hepatic proteins. The picture shows an autoradiogram of the electrophoretically separated *in itro* translation products of hepatic mRNA obtained from 30-, 120-, and 800-day-old male rats and a 120-day-old-female rat. The electrophoretic mobilities of proteins of known molecular weights are shown on the left. The arrows point to α_{2u}-globulin and two other liver proteins (LP) with M_r 26,300 and 28,500.

in the adult, and disappears in senescent rats. On the other hand, the mRNA for a 26.3 kd protein that is present in the liver of prepubertal male rats shows a marked decrease associated with puberty. It is present in very low amounts in adult male rats and its synthesis is enhanced again at senescence (Chatterjee *et al.*, 1981). The 26.3 kd protein is an androgen-repressible protein, and the hepatic tissue of the normal female rat contains a high amount of the corresponding mRNA. The coordinate decrease in the hepatic synthesis of α_{2u}-globulin and its mRNA with the increase in the synthesis of the 26.3 kd protein shows that the decline of α_{2u} synthesis in senescent rats is not due to any nonspecific degenerative changes associated with aging, but to a programmed loss of androgen responsiveness.

The hepatic concentration of the androgen binder begins to drop as senescence sets in, and it disappears from the liver of rats that are older than 750 days. The gradual decrease and ultimate disappearance of CAB in the aging male rat are shown in Fig. 9. Similar to senescent rats, the hepatic tissue of prepubertal animals does not contain CAB. In the maturing male rat CAB begins to appear at about 40 days of age (Roy *et al.*, 1974). It should be noted that prepubertal and senescent rats with no hepatic androgen binding activity fail to synthesize α_{2u}-globulin even after androgen supplementation. The inverse correlation between hepatic synthesis of α_{2u}-globulin, an androgen-inducible protein, and the 26.3 kd liver

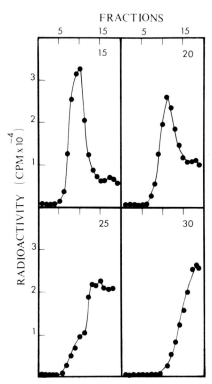

FIG. 9.   Age-dependent loss of the cytoplasmic androgen binding protein in the male rat. The patterns show the distribution of radioactivity of the hepatic cytosol prelabeled with [³H]DHT and separated on a sucrose density gradient. The cytosols were obtained from 15-, 20-, 25-, and 30-month-old male rats as indicated on each frame. The direction of centrifugation is from right to left. Very little and no binding of DHT by the liver cytosol obtained from 25- and 30-month-old male rats are evident.

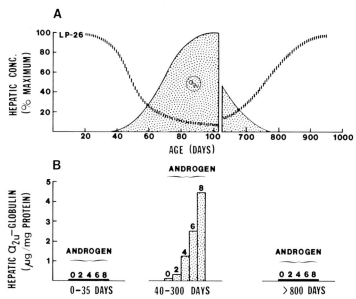

FIG. 10. Changes in the hepatic androgen responsiveness during maturation and aging. Age-dependent changes in the hepatic concentration of α_{2u}-globulin and the 26.3 kilodalton liver protein (LP-26) in the male rat are shown in (A). (B) illustrates the effect of eight daily DHT treatment on the hepatic level of α_{2u}-globulin in the prepubertal male and ovariectomized female (0–35 days), young adult ovariectomized female (40–300 days), and senescent male rats (>800 days).

protein (LP-26), an androgen-repressible protein, during age-dependent changes in androgen sensitivity of the hepatic tissue is illustrated in Fig. 10.

In addition to the three major hepatic proteins as described, sexual dimorphism of several other hepatic proteins has also been observed. Differential patterns of hepatic protein synthesis in male and female rats have been investigated by two-dimensional gel electrophoresis of the hepatic proteins after pulse labeling of cultured hepatocytes. Figure 11 shows the hepatic protein patterns of young intact male and female and ovariectomized female rats with and without androgen treatment. When a comparison is made between intact male and intact female rats, it is found that four protein spots with molecular weights between the 68,000 and 28,000 range are present in the female liver that are virtually absent in male liver. Two clusters of proteins are found almost exclusively in the male rat. One of the clusters is comprised of the various molecular forms of α_{2u}-globulin and falls within the range of 18 to 22 kd. Five major isoelectric variants of α_{2u}-globulin have been identified and designated as

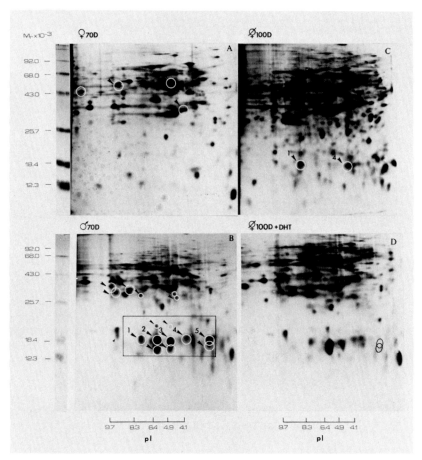

FIG. 11. Sex-difference in specific protein synthesis by primary cultures of rat hepatocytes. Hepatocytes were labeled *in vitro* for 2 hours with [^{35}S]methionine and the cell lysates were separated by two-dimensional electrophoresis. Comparison of the autoradiographic patterns between 70-day-old male and female rats shows several sex-specific protein spots which are marked with white circles. The multiple forms of α_{2u}-globulin are distributed within 18 to 22 kilodalton range and are specified within the rectangular box. The five major isoelectric forms of α_{2u}-globulin are numbered from left (basic) to right (acidic). The circled spots immediately underneath forms 2, 3, and 5 represent the molecular weight variants of α_{2u}-globulin differing in five amino acid residues. The small circle immediately above form 2 represents the glycosylated form of α_{2u}-globulin. Two other minor isoelectric variants of α_{2u}-globulin are overshadowed by the two major forms (2 and 3) and these minor forms are located immediately to the left of these two major spots. Comparison of the patterns presented in A (normal female) and C (female ovariectomized 30 days prior to sacrifice) shows that ovariectomy alone results in the appearance of the variants 1 and 4. Treatment of the ovariectomized females for 10 days with DHT results in the appearance of all other isoelectric variants of α_{2u}-globulin except the most acidic one (form 5). Sex and age of the animals in days are given on the upper left of each panel.

variants 1, 2, 3, 4, and 5 (apparent p*I* 7.8, 6.1, 4.9, 4.1, and 3.7, respectively). In addition, two minor isoelectric variants migrating immediately before the second and third forms have also been noted. The other cluster is comprised of six protein spots within the 28 to 35 kd range. Ovariectomy alone causes the appearance of two isoelectric variants (1 and 4) of α_{2u}-globulin. Treatment of ovariectomized female with androgen results in the appearance of all of the male-specific proteins except the most acidic isoelectric variant (variant 5).

Figure 12 summarizes changes in the androgen responsiveness of the variant forms of α_{2u}-globulin during maturation and aging. It is of interest to note that out of five different isoelectric variants, the process of aging initially causes the disappearance of the most basic form of α_{2u}-globulin (p*I* 7.8), followed by the disappearance of the two more acidic ones (p*I* 3.7 and 4.9). Androgen treatment of the ovariectomized females results in the induction of the three isoelectric variants of α_{2u}-globulin. However, androgenization of the female rats fails to induce the most acidic form (variant 5) of this protein. In the case of globin gene family sequential expression of the genes for β-type globins during development has been clearly established (Fritsch *et al.*, 1980). The differential expression of multiple isoelectric forms of α_{2u}-globulin may be comparable to the developmental switching of the various forms of the globin gene. Noninduction of the most acidic form of α_{2u}-globulin after androgen treatment of the ovariectomized female rat can explain our earlier observation which showed that androgenization of ovariectomized female animals fails to bring α_{2u}-globulin synthesis to the level of the normal male (Roy and Neuhaus, 1967). A rearrangement of chromatin conformation within and around the α_{2u}-globulin gene via pre- and neonatal "imprinting" by androgenic steroids may be responsible for endowing the differential androgen responsiveness in the male and female rats (Roy and Chatterjee, 1983).

B. PROBING OF α_{2u}-GLOBULIN SYNTHESIZING HEPATOCYTES WITH MONOCLONAL ANTIBODY

Age-dependent changes in the amount of α_{2u}-globulin production can be explained on the basis of two alternative possibilities: (1) changes in the rate of synthesis of α_{2u}-globulin by all competent hepatocytes and (2) changes in the number of competent cells capable of synthesizing α_{2u}-globulin. This has been an outstanding issue not only for age-dependent changes in the output of α_{2u}-globulin by the liver but also for hormonal induction of other hepatic proteins such as vitellogenin (Jailkhani and

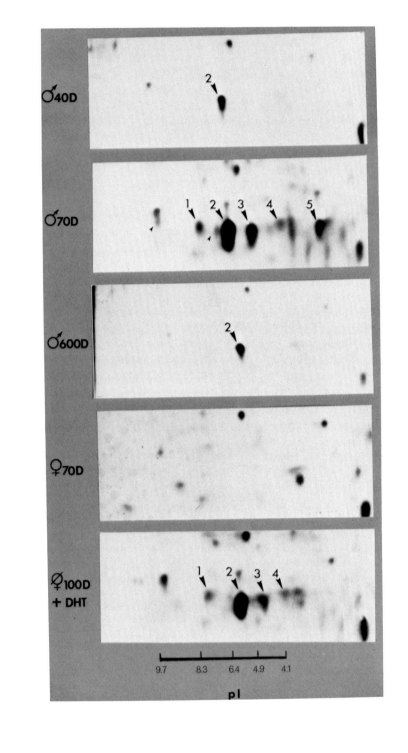

Talwar, 1972). We have approached this problem by immunofluorescent labeling of isolated hepatocytes with monoclonal antibody and quantitation of the specific cellular fluorescence with fluorescence-activated cell sorter (FACS). For the FACS analysis hepatocytes isolated from rats of various ages were allowed to react with the monoclonal antibody, and subsequently the cells were labeled with fluorescein-tagged goat anti-mouse IgG. Comparison of the FACS pattern generated by liver cells derived from male rats of different ages is shown in Fig. 13. The FACS pattern revealed two distinct populations of hepatocytes with one showing much stronger fluorescence than the other. The highly fluorescing population comprised about 50% of the total cells, and the degree of antigenic concentration (as revealed by the fluorescent intensity) within this group of hepatocytes varied considerably with aging. The hepatocytes from a 50-day-old rat and 540-day-old rat showed only less than half of the fluorescent intensity as compared with a 150-day-old animal. No specific fluorescence could be detected in the liver cells obtained from either female or 885-day-old male rats. Thus the primary mechanism of the age-dependent increase in α_{2u}-globulin synthesis in maturing male rats and its age-dependent decrease in senescent male rats is due to changes in the rate of synthesis of this protein by the competent hepatocytes and not to changes in selective cell recruitment or cell proliferation.

C. AGE-DEPENDENT CHANGES IN CHROMATIN CONFORMATION WITHIN AND AROUND THE GENE FOR α_{2u}-GLOBULIN

Hybridization data of both rat and mouse DNA with cloned probes indicate that α_{2u}-globulin is coded by a gene family consisting of at least 16–20 copies within the haploid genome (Hastie et al., 1979; Kurtz, 1981). Translational analysis of the mRNA has indicated that multiple forms of α_{2u}-globulin may be coded by different members of this gene family (Chatterjee et al., 1982). Hormonal and developmental changes in the conformation of specific areas of dipteral polytene chromosomes containing DNA sequences coding for specific proteins have provided concrete evidence that relaxation of chromatin structure within and around specific genes or gene families plays an important role in the transcriptional regulation of gene expression (Pelling, 1964). Weintraub and Groudine (1976)

FIG. 12. Differential regulation of the variant forms of α_{2u}-globulin. Segments of autoradiograms showing only the area containing the various forms of α_{2u}-globulin are presented in this figure. Age, sex, and endocrine status of the animals from which the hepatocytes were obtained are labeled on the left of each frame.

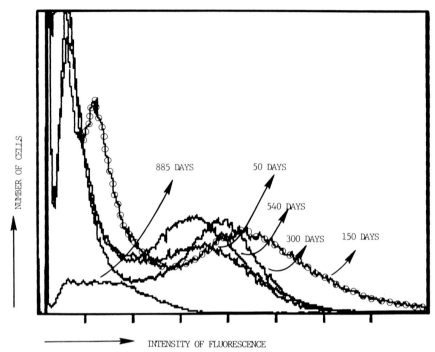

FIG. 13. Age-dependent changes in α_{2u}-globulin synthesis by male rat hepatocytes. Hepatocytes isolated from rats of various ages were treated with a monoclonal mouse antibody to α_{2u}-globulin and subsequently tagged with fluorescent-labeled antimouse goat IgG. The hepatocytes were then analyzed through a fluorescent-activated cell sorter. The fluorescence intensity of the hepatocytes from a 150-day-old rat (O——O) was too high to be accommodated within the normal scale and the intensity scale for this sample is reduced by half.

have shown that pancreatic DNase I can selectively digest the DNA regions in the chromatin whose conformation is suitable for transcription. Preferential digestion of the transcriptionally active genes by DNase I has been extensively used to study changes in chromatin organization under different developmental and endocrine conditions (Anderson *et al.*, 1983). We have used the selectivity of DNase I as a probe to investigate possible changes in the organization of the chromatin area containing the genes for α_{2u}-globulin. The principle and design of the experiment are schematically presented in Fig. 14. Liver nuclei isolated from rats of different ages were digested with three different concentrations of DNase I. DNA isolated from these nuclear preparations was fragmented with restriction endonuclease *Eco*RI, and the DNA fragments were transferred from the gel to

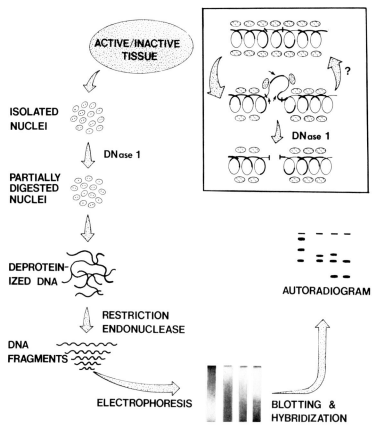

FIG. 14.   Scheme showing the principle and design of the experiment to determine transcriptionally favorable conformation of a specific gene. The assay is based on the ability of the pancreatic DNase I for preferential degradation of the DNA sequences containing the genes that are present in a relaxed or "open" conformation as indicated in the middle segment of the boxed area. Specific nuclear proteins and degree of DNA methylation may be responsible for maintaining these transcriptionally accessible "loops" of the chromatin.

the nitrocellulose filter and hybridized with a moderate excess of ^{32}P-labeled α_{2u}-globulin cDNA probe cloned in *E. coli*. Results of such an experiment are presented in Fig. 15. Site-specific fragmentation with the endonuclease *Eco*RI resulted in several DNA fragments that hybridized with the α_{2u}-globulin cDNA probe. A 1.5 kilobase pair fragment showed the highest degree of hybridization. The relative concentration of this 1.5 kb fragment when compared in samples that were derived from nuclei digested with increasing concentrations of DNase I provided a rough

0, 0.2, 0.6, 1.2 µg DNase I

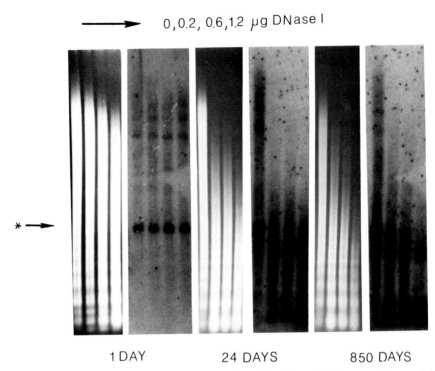

1 DAY   24 DAYS   850 DAYS

FIG. 15. Age-dependent changes in the conformation of α_{2u}-globulin gene. Liver nuclei from male rats of various ages, as indicated, were digested with increasing concentrations (from left to right lanes) of DNase I (0, 0.2, 0.6, and 1.2 µg/mg DNA). DNA extracted from the nuclei were treated with restriction endonuclease EcoRI and separated by agarose gel electrophoresis. The left panel on each age group shows the electrophoretic distribution of the total DNA, and the right panel shows the autoradiogram of the Southern blot after hybridization with a ^{32}P-labeled α_{2u}-globulin cDNA probe cloned in E. coli. The major (1.5 kilobase pair) DNA fragment containing α_{2u}-globulin gene is marked with an asterisk. Only the α_{2u}-globulin gene present in the nuclei of the liver of 1-day-old rat is protected from DNase I digestion.

estimate of the accessibility of the α_{2u}-globulin gene to this DNase probe. Immediately after birth α_{2u}-globulin genes seem to be located within a chromatin structure that is unaccessible to DNase I. This is indicated by the nondigestibility of the 1.5 kb band even at the highest concentration of the DNase I (1.2 µg/mg DNA). However, beginning from 24 days of age the chromatin area containing the α_{2u}-globulin DNA shows increased sensitivity to DNase I and this sensitivity is maintained up to 850 days of age. Although 850 days is the oldest animal which we have used for such experiments—it seems reasonable that once the region of DNA containing α_{2u}-globulin genes is opened up, this "open" conformation is maintained for the rest of the animal's life. However, it should be noted that mRNA for α_{2u}-globulin in the male rat begins to be synthesized at an appreciable amount only after 35 days of age and that senescent rats older than 750 days cease to synthesize the protein. Thus, in addition to changes in chromatin conformation, other regulatory factors such as availability of the hormone receptors may play a major role in the age-dependent changes in the expression of the genes of α_{2u}-globulin.

V. Multiple Endocrine Interactions in the Regulation of α_{2u}-Globulin and Its mRNA

A. MULTIPLE HORMONE REQUIREMENT FOR THE SYNTHESIS OF α_{2u}-GLOBULIN IN THE HYPOPHYSECTOMIZED RAT

Hypophysectomy in the male rat causes a rapid decline in and within 3 days a total inhibition of the hepatic synthesis of α_{2u}-globulin. It cannot be reversed with androgen administration. A complete reversal of the effect of hypophysectomy, however, requires a hormone combination containing androgen, glucocorticoid, thyroxine, and growth hormone (Roy, 1973b). A three-hormone combination containing androgen, glucocorticoid, and growth hormone is more than 50% effective in reversing the effect of hypophysectomy (Fig. 16). Drastic reductions in the hepatic synthesis of α_{2u}-globulin after adrenalectomy (Irwin *et al.*, 1971) or thyroidectomy (Roy, 1973b) have also been recorded. Studies with these endocrine ablations and *in vitro* cell culture studies have clearly established that the hepatic synthesis of α_{2u}-globulin is under multihormonal regulation (Motwani *et al.*, 1980). The effect of glucocorticoid on the hepatic synthesis of α_{2u}-globulin is found to be mediated through changes in the hepatic concentration of α_{2u}-globulin mRNA (Sippel *et al.*, 1975) and the mechanism of the permissive effect of other hormones on the androgen-dependent synthesis of this protein is discussed below.

B. INTERACTING INFLUENCE OF THYROXINE AND GROWTH HORMONE ON THE SYNTHESIS OF α_{2u}-GLOBULIN

Results presented in Fig. 17 show that thyroidectomy causes a reduction of approximately 90% in the urinary output of α_{2u}-globulin which can be reversed with thyroxine administration (Roy, 1973b). Thyroxine treatment to these hypothyroid rats for the first 2 days causes a rather slow increase in the synthesis of α_{2u}-globulin, followed by a rapid rise in the

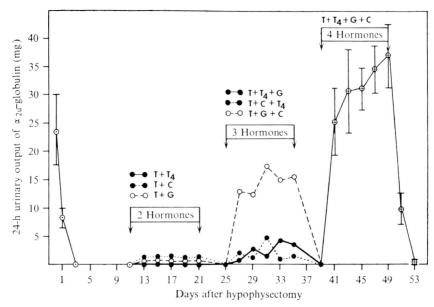

FIG. 16. Multiple hormone requirement for the induction of α_{2u}-globulin in the hypophysectomized rat. Male rats were hypophysectomized at day 0 and received daily injections of various hormone combinations for 10 days as indicated in the figure (T, testosterone; T_4, thyroxine; C, corticosterone; G, growth hormone). The periods of hormone treatments are marked with arrows. (From Roy, 1973b.)

synthesis of this protein. The decreased synthesis of α_{2u}-globulin after thyroidectomy and its reversal after thyroxine treatment are associated with corresponding changes in the hepatic concentration of the mRNA for this protein (Roy et al., 1976a; Kurtz et al., 1976).

   Treatment of hypophysectomized rats with androgen, glucocorticoid, thyroxine, and growth hormone was highly effective in increasing the hepatic content of both α_{2u}-globulin and its mRNA. When growth hormone was omitted from this combination, hepatic synthesis of α_{2u}-globulin did not increase significantly. As shown in Fig. 18, in the absence of growth hormone the hepatic content of α_{2u}-globulin and its mRNA as assayed by both translational analysis and by hybridization with a cloned cDNA probe remained low (about 5% of the control). These results clearly demonstrate that growth hormone acts at a pretranslational level to regulate the hepatic synthesis of α_{2u}-globulin (Roy and Dowbenko, 1977; Roy et al., 1982). An earlier claim for the evidence of translational regulations of α_{2u}-globulin by growth hormone has been withdrawn (Lynch et al., 1982).

   Initial studies by Peake et al. (1973) and Hervas et al. (1975) have

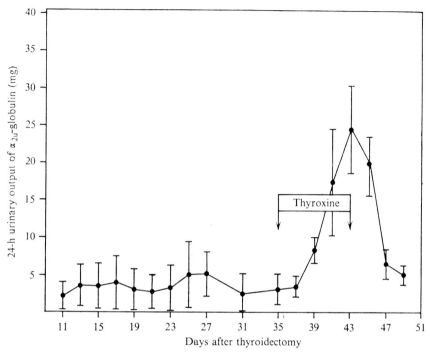

FIG. 17.   The effect of thyroxine on the daily urinary output of α_{2u}-globulin in thyroidectomized adult male rats. The duration of daily thyroxine treatment is indicated with arrows. (From Roy, 1973b.)

shown that the synthesis and secretion of growth hormone in the pituitary gland are regulated by thyroid hormone. Thus a hypothyroid rat is in fact almost devoid of growth hormone. These results have been confirmed at the molecular level by Martial *et al.* (1977) and by Samuels *et al.* (1979). In addition Duran-Garcia *et al.* (1979) have reported more than a 50% reduction in the hepatic growth hormone receptor activity in the hypothyroid rat. Since studies with hypophysectomized rats have shown that growth hormone plays an important role in the hepatic synthesis of α_{2u}-globulin, we have investigated the interacting influence of growth hormone and thyroxine on the synthesis of this protein. As shown in Fig. 19, treatment of hypothyroid rats with either growth hormone or thyroxine can raise the hepatic concentration of the mRNA for this protein. However, despite the fact that growth hormone is as effective as thyroxine in increasing the hepatic level of α_{2u}-globulin mRNA to almost normal, the hepatic synthesis of this protein remained about 50% of the control (Fig. 20). These results show that (1) growth hormone plays a predominant role in the

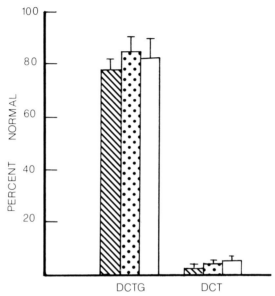

FIG. 18.   Growth hormone-dependent increase in the hepatic level of α_{2u}-globulin and its mRNA in hypophysectomized rats. Hatched bars, α_{2u}-globulin mRNA sequences as determined by liquid hybridization with a cloned α_{2u}-globulin cDNA probe; dotted bars, translatable α_{2u}-globulin mRNA as determined by *in vitro* translation followed by specific immunoprecipitation and SDS–polyacrylamide gel electrophoresis; open bars, cytoplasmic α_{2u}-globulin determined by radioimmunoassay. Animals received eight daily treatments of either DHT, corticosterone, thyroxine, and growth hormone (DCTG) or DHT, corticosterone, and thyroxine (DCT). (From Roy *et al.*, 1982.)

regulation of the hepatic concentration of α_{2u}-globulin mRNA; (2) the effect of the thyroid hormone on the hepatic concentration of α_{2u}-globulin mRNA may be mediated indirectly through the pituitary growth hormone; and (3) in addition to its indirect effect through growth hormone, thyroid hormone may also play a direct role in regulating the efficient utilization of α_{2u}-globulin mRNA. It is of interest to note that an almost 50% reduction in the synthesis of serum albumin without any corresponding decrease in the albumin mRNA has been noted in the liver of hypothyroid rats (Peavy *et al.*, 1981). Thus thyroid hormone may somehow promote efficient utilization of mRNAs for α_{2u}-globulin, serum albumin, and possibly other hepatic secretory proteins. Earlier studies in the laboratory of Tata have shown that forced metamorphosis of the bullfrog (*Rana catesbeiana*) tadpole with thyroxine causes a sequential rise in the hepatic synthesis of RNA, membrane phospholipid, and finally serum albumin (Tata, 1967). A marked increase in the proliferation of the rough endoplas-

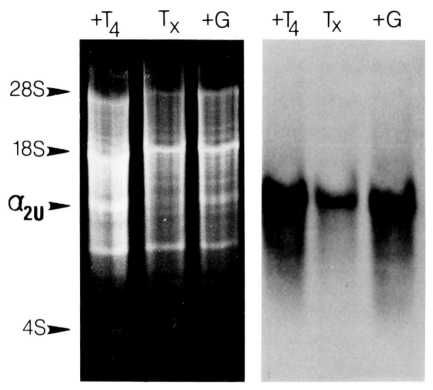

FIG. 19. Elevation of the hepatic concentration of α_{2u}-globulin mRNA in hypothyroid rats with either thyroxine or growth hormone. RNA samples (20 μg) from thyroidectomized male rats without any hormone supplementation (T_x) and after thyroxine ($+T_4$) or growth hormone ($+G$) treatment were subjected to electrophoresis on agarose gel containing methyl-mercury. The left panel shows the banding pattern of the RNA after electrophoresis and staining with ethidium bromide. The corresponding autoradiogram of the "Northern blot-ted" RNA after hybridization to ^{32}P-labeled cloned α_{2u}-globulin cDNA probe is presented on the right. The arrow heads point to 28 S, 18 S, and 4 S RNAs which serve as internal markers. In addition to its autoradiographic detection after hybridization with the labeled probe, the α_{2u}-globulin mRNA band can also be visualized in the stained gel.

mic reticulum was also noted. Studies in our laboratory have shown that hypothyroidism in the rat causes a very significant reduction in the level of rough endoplasmic reticulum of the hepatocytes that can be reversed to normal with thyroxine but not with growth hormone (Roy, 1983). Thus it is possible that the direct effect of the thyroid hormone on the hepatic synthesis of α_{2u}-globulin is mediated through proliferation of the rough endoplasmic reticulum.

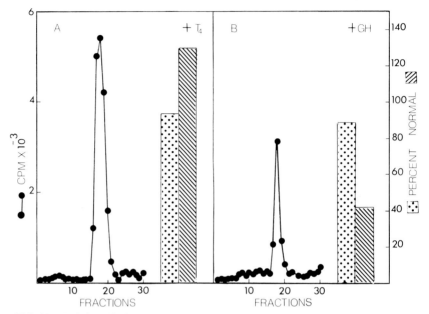

FIG. 20. Relationship between the hepatic content of α_{2u}-globulin mRNA and synthesis of this protein in hypothyroid male rats receiving either thyroxine or growth hormone. Thyroidectomized rats were treated with either thyroxine (A) or growth hormone (B) as indicated. The histograms on the right of either frame show the hepatic content of α_{2u}-globulin (hatched bars) and α_{2u}-globulin mRNA sequences (dotted bars) as percentage of the normal male. The distribution of the *in vivo* pulse-labeled α_{2u}-globulin radioactivity after SDS–polyacrylamide gel electrophoresis is shown on the left (●). (From Chatterjee *et al.*, 1983.)

C. α_{2u}-GLOBULIN SYNTHESIS IN THE DIABETIC RAT

Experimental diabetes induced by either alloxan or streptozotocin causes a marked reduction in the hepatic synthesis of α_{2u}-globulin that can be reversed with insulin supplementation. Studies in our laboratory have shown that infliction of a mild diabetic condition (blood glucose level 250–350 mg/dl) with a moderate dose of streptozotocin (4.5 mg/100 g body w) causes only a small decrease in the overall protein synthesizing capacity of the hepatic tissue as indicated by minor changes in the polysomal profiles and ultrastructural characteristics of the rough endoplasmic reticulum. Even this mild degree of diabetes causes more than an 80% reduction in the hepatic synthesis of α_{2u}-globulin (Roy *et al.*, 1980). The depressed synthesis of α_{2u}-globulin in diabetic rats can be stimulated 3-fold after 4 days of continuous infusion of insulin through osmotic minipumps. *In vitro* translation of the total poly(A) containing hepatic mRNA ob-

tained from normal and diabetic rats does not show any significant difference in their translational efficiency, and mRNAs from both animals are
found to be equally effective in stimulating the incorporation of labeled
amino acids into proteins. However, both translational and hybridizational analyses of specific α_{2u}-globulin mRNA within the total hepatic
mRNA show that decreased synthesis of α_{2u}-globulin in diabetic rats and
its reversal with insulin are associated with corresponding changes in the
hepatic concentration of α_{2u}-globulin mRNA (Fig. 21). These results indicate that similar to growth hormone, insulin is capable of regulating the
hepatic synthesis of specific proteins through selective changes in the
concentration of specific mRNA. The molecular basis of the action of

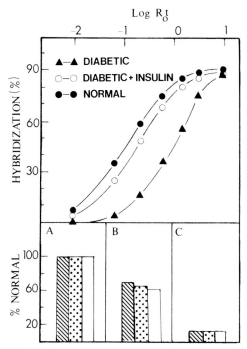

FIG. 21. α_{2u}-Globulin and its mRNA in normal and diabetic rats with and without insulin
supplementation. The upper frame shows the kinetics of hybridization of a ^{32}P-labeled
cDNA fragment complementary to α_{2u}-globulin mRNA in the presence of a vast excess of
poly(A)$^+$ hepatic RNA from normal (●——●), diabetic with insulin supplementation for 4
days (○——○), and diabetic without insulin supplementation (▲——▲). The lower frame
shows composite data expressed as percentage normal of hepatic concentration of α_{2u}-
globulin (hatched bar), translatable mRNA for α_{2u}-globulin (dotted bar), and the open bar
showing hybridizable α_{2u}-sequence derived from the relative $R_0 t_{\frac{1}{2}}$ values of the $R_0 t$ curves
shown in the upper frame. (A) Normal; (B) diabetic with insulin treatment for 4 days; (C)
diabetic without insulin supplementation. (From Roy et al., 1980.)

protein hormones on the regulation of specific gene expression is presently unclear. Mediation of the nuclear effect of these hormones through changes in other endocrine or nonendocrine regulatory factors remains a distinct possibility (Roy *et al.*, 1983).

VI. Summary

α_{2u}-Globulin is a low-molecular-weight (162 $\pm$ 5 amino acid residues), androgen-dependent rat urinary protein, synthesized and secreted by hepatic parenchymal cells. On two-dimensional gel electrophoresis, α_{2u}-globulin can be resolved into several variant forms, some of which are generated by posttranslational modification while others are produced from different mRNA species and coded by different genes. This protein and its cognate mRNA are either absent or present only in trace amounts in the female, immature, Tfm, and senescent male rats. α_{2u}-Globulin normally begins to be synthesized in maturing male rats at the time of puberty, and it can be induced in mature female rats after ovariectomy followed by androgen treatment. Estrogen administration to normal male rats causes complete inhibition of α_{2u}-globulin synthesis. Androgen-dependent synthesis of α_{2u}-globulin requires the permissive influence of several growth and developmental hormones including glucocorticoid, thyroxine, growth hormone, and insulin. Requirement of these permissive hormones for *in vitro* synthesis of α_{2u}-globulin by cultured hepatocytes has also been established. Translational analysis in the heterologous cell-free system and in *Xenopus* oocytes and hybridizational assay with a cloned cDNA probe have shown that steroid hormones, insulin, and growth hormone regulate hepatic synthesis of α_{2u}-globulin through changes in the hepatic concentration of the mRNA for this protein. The effects of thyroidectomy and thyroxine supplementation on α_{2u}-globulin synthesis are also reflected by corresponding changes in the hepatic concentration of α_{2u}-globulin mRNA. However, this effect of thyroid hormone on α_{2u}-globulin mRNA is indirectly mediated through pituitary growth hormone. In addition to its indirect effect via growth hormone, thyroid hormone seems to directly influence efficient utilization of α_{2u}-globulin mRNA for the synthesis of this protein. The latter effect may be mediated through thyroid hormone dependent proliferation of rough endoplasmic reticulum.

Androgen-dependent synthesis of α_{2u}-globulin by the rat liver seems to be dependent on the presence of a 3.5 S cytoplasmic androgen-binding protein. This cytoplasmic androgen binder (CAB) also binds estradiol-17β and does not seem to translocate into the nucleus. Thus, CAB does not function as a classical steroid receptor and may provide protection of the bound steriods from hepatic metabolism. Immature and senescent rats whose hepatocytes do not possess CAB show complete androgen insensitivity with regard to the induction of α_{2u}-globulin. Examination of the DNase I sensitivity of the α_{2u}-globulin genes in the hepatic nuclei obtained from rats of different ages shows how these genes undergo a conformational rearrangement within the first 24 days that makes them accessible to regulatory proteins and enzymes. This relaxed conformation is maintained for the rest of the life of the animal, yet senescent rats fail to synthesize α_{2u}-globulin under androgenic stimulation. Therefore, in addition to changes in chromatin conformation, developmental and age-dependent changes in other regulatory factors, such as CAB and hormone receptors, are involved in coordinating the changing androgen response during aging. Cytofluorometric analysis of isolated hepatocytes tagged with the monoclonal antibody against α_{2u}-globulin shows that the age-dependent changes in α_{2u}-globulin synthesis is primarily due to an altered rate of synthesis of this protein by the competent hepatocytes rather than to changes in the population of α_{2u}-globulin producing cells. It is of considerable interest to note that the age-dependent changes in α_{2u}-globulin synthesis involve differential regulation of the variant forms of this protein. Further exploration into the molecular mechanism of this observation may provide an important clue to preprogrammed age-dependent alterations in specific gene expression and their relationship to hormone action.

ACKNOWLEDGMENTS

This work was supported by a Research Grant (AM-14744) and a Research Career Development Award (AM-00141) from the National Institutes of Health.

REFERENCES

Anderson, J. N., Vanderbilt, J. N., Bloom, K. S., and Germain, B. J. (1983). *In* "Gene Regulation by Steroid Hormones—II" (A. K. Roy and J. H. Clark, eds.), p. 17. Springer-Verlag, Berlin and New York.

Chatterjee, B., and Roy, A. K. (1980). *J. Biol. Chem.* **255**, 11607.

Chatterjee, B., Nath, T. S., and Roy, A. K. (1981). *J. Biol. Chem.* **256**, 5939.

Chatterjee, B., Motwani, N. M., and Roy, A. K. (1982). *Biochim. Biophys. Acta.* **698**, 22.

Chatterjee, B., Demyan, W. F., and Roy, A. K. (1983). *J. Biol. Chem.* **258**, 688.

Deshpande, A. K., Chatterjee, B., and Roy, A. K. (1979). *J. Biol. Chem.* **254**, 8937.

Dickson, R. B., Aten, R. F., and Eisenfeld, A. J. (1978). *Endocrinology* **103**, 1636.

Duran-Garcia, S., Gomez-Nieto, J., Fouchereau-Peron, M., Padron, V. F., Obregon, M. J., DeEscobar, M. G., and Escobar del Rey, F. (1979). *Clin. Endocrinol.* **11**, 275.

Fritsch, E. F., Lawn, R. M., and Maniatis, T. (1980). *Cell* **19**, 959.

Goldberger, R., and Deeley, R. J. (1980). *In* "Gene Regulation by Steroid Hormones (A. K. Roy and J. H. Clark, eds.), p. 32. Springer-Verlag, Berlin and New York.

Gruber, M., Bos., E. S., and AB., G. (1976). *Mol. Cell. Endocrinol.* **5**, 41.

Hastie, N. D., Held, W. A., and Toole, J. J. (1979). *Cell* **17**, 449.

Hayward, M. A., and Shapiro, D. J. (1981). *Dev. Biol.* **88**, 333.

Hervas, F., Morreale de Escobar, G., and Escobar del Rey, F. (1975). *Endocrinology* **97**, 91.

Irwin, J. F., Lane, S. E., and Neuhaus, O. W. (1971). *Biochim. Biophys. Acta* **252**, 328.

Jailkhani, B. L., and Talwar, G. P. (1972). *Nature (London) New Biol.* **239**, 240.

Kurtz, D. T. (1981). *J. Mol. Appl. Genet.* **1**, 29.

Kurtz, D. T., and Nicodemus, C. F. (1981). *Gene* **13**, 145.

Kurtz, D. T., Sippel, A. E., and Feigelson, P. (1976). *Biochemistry* **15**, 1031.

Laperche, Y., Lynch, K. R., Dolan, K. P., and Feigelson, P. (1982). *Fed. Proc. Fed. Am. Soc. Exp. Biol.* **41**, 678.

Lemenn, F., Rochefort, H., and Garcia, M. (1980). *Steroids* **35**, 315.

Lynch, K. R., Dolan, K. P., Nakhasi, H. L., Unterman, R., and Feigelson, P. (1982). *Cell* **28**, 185.

Lyons, W. R., Li, C. H., and Johnson, R. E. (1958). *Recent Prog. Horm. Res.* **14**, 219.

Martial, J. A., Baxter, J. D., Goodman, H. M., and Seeburg, P. H. (1977). *Proc. Natl. Acad. Sci. U.S.A.* **74**, 1816.

Milin, B., and Roy, A. K. (1973). *Nature (London) New Biol.* **242**, 248.

Motwani, N. M., Unakar, N. J., and Roy, A. K. (1980). *Endocrinology* **107**, 1606.

O'Malley, B. W., Roop, D. R., Lai, E. C., Nordstrom, J. L., Catterall, J. F., Swaneck, G. E., Colbert, D. A., Tsai, M. J., Dugaiczyk, A., and Woo, S. L. C. (1979). *Recent Prog. Horm. Res.* **35**, 1.

Palmiter, R. D., Moore, P. B., and Mulvihill, E. R. (1976). *Cell* **8**, 557.

Peake, G. T., Birge, C. A., and Daughaday, W. H. (1973). *Endocrinology* **92**, 487.

Peavy, D. E., Taylor, J. M., and Jefferson, L. S. (1981). *Biochem. J.* **198**, 289.

Pelling, C. (1964). *Chromosoma* **15**, 71.

Rosen, J. M. Matusik, R. J., Richards, D. A., Gupta, P., and Rodgers, J. R. (1980). *Recent Prog. Horm. Res.* **36**, 147.

Roy, A. K. (1973a). *Endocrinology* **92**, 957.

Roy, A. K. (1973b). *J. Endocrinol.* **56**, 295.

Roy, A. K. (1977). *Eur. J. Biochem.* **73**, 537.

Roy, A. K. (1979). *In* "Biochemical Actions of Hormones" (G. Litwack, ed.), Vol. 6, p. 481. Academic Press, New York.

Roy, A. K. (1983). *In* "Molecular Basis of Thyroid Hormone Action" (J. H. Oppenheimer and H. H. Samuels, eds.), p. 213. Academic Press, New York.

Roy, A. K., and Byrd, J. G. (1976). *J. Endocrinol.* **71**, 265.

Roy, A. K., and Chatterjee, B. (1983). *Annu. Rev. Physiol.* **45**, 37.

Roy, A. K., and Dowbenko, D. J. (1977). *Biochemistry* **16**, 3918.

Roy, A. K., and Neuhaus, O. W. (1966a). *Proc. Soc. Exp. Biol. Med.* **121**, 894.

Roy, A. K., and Neuhaus, O. W. (1966b). *Biochim. Biophys. Acta* **127**, 82.

Roy, A. K., and Neuhaus, O. W. (1967). *Nature (London)* **214**, 618.

Roy, A. K., and Raber, D. L. (1972). *J. Histochem. Cytochem.* **20**, 89.

Roy, A. K., Milin, B. S., and McMinn, D. M. (1974). *Biochim. Biophys. Acta* **354**, 213.

Roy, A. K., McMinn, D. M., and Biswas, N. M. (1975). *Endocrinology* **97**, 1505.

Roy, A. K., Schiop, M. J., and Dowbenko, D. J. (1976a). *FEBS Lett.* **64**, 393.

Roy, A. K., Schiop, M. J., and Dowbenko, D. J. (1976b). *FEBS Lett.* **70**, 137.

Roy, A. K., Dowbenko, D. J., and Schiop, M. J. (1977). *Biochem. J.* **164**, 91.

Roy, A. K., Chatterjee, B., Prasad, M. S. K., and Unakar, N. J. (1980). *J. Biol. Chem.* **255**, 11613.

Roy, A. K., Chatterjee, B., Demyan, W. F., Nath, T. S., and Motwani, N. M. (1982). *J. Biol. Chem.* **257,** 7834.

Roy, A. K., Chatterjee, B., Demyan, W. F., Nath, T. S., and Motwani, N. M. (1983). *In* "Gene Regulation by Steroid Hormones—II" (A. K. Roy and J. H. Clark, eds.), p. 299. Springer-Verlag, Berlin and New York.

Samuels, H. H., Stanley, F., and Shapiro, L. E. (1979). *Biochemistry* **18,** 715.

Schimke, R. T., McKnight, G. S., Shapiro, D. J., Sullivan, D., and Palacios, R. (1975). *Recent Prog. Horm. Res.* **31,** 175.

Shapiro, D. J., Brok, M. L., and Hayward, M. A. (1983). *In* "Gene Regulation by Steroid Hormones—II" (A. K. Roy and J. H. Clark, eds.), p. 61. Springer-Verlag, Berlin and New York.

Sippel, A. E., Feigelson, P., and Roy, A. K., (1975). *Biochemistry* **14,** 825.

Smirnov, A. N., Smirnova, O. V., and Rozen,V. B. (1977). *Biokhimiia* **42,** 560.

Tata, J. R., (1967). *Biochem. J.* **104,** 1.

Tata, J. R., and Smith, D. F. (1979). *Recent Prog. Horm. Res.* **35,** 47.

Taylor, R. N., and Smith, R. G. (1982). *Proc. Natl. Acad. Sci. U.S.A.* **79,** 1742.

Thompson, C., Powell-Jones, W., and Lucier, G. W. (1981). *Biochem. J.* **194,** 1.

Topper, Y. J. (1970). *Recent Prog. Horm. Res.* **26,** 287.

Tsai, S. Y., Roop, D. R., Tsai, M.-J., Stein, J. P., Means, A. R., and O'Malley, B. W. (1978). *Biochemistry* **17,** 5773.

Turkington, R. W., Majumdar, G. C., Kadohama, N., Macindoe, J. H., and Frantz, W. L. (1973). *Recent Prog. Horm. Res.* **29,** 417.

Unterman, R. D., Lynch, K. R., Nakhasi, H. L., Dolan, K. P., Hamilton, J. W., Cohn, D. V., and Feigelson, P. (1981). *Proc. Natl. Acad. Sci. U.S.A.* **78,** 3478.

Wahli, W., Dawid, I. B., Ryffel, G. U., and Weber, R. (1981). *Science* **212,** 298.

Weintraub, H., and Groudine, M. (1976). *Science* **193,** 848.

DISCUSSION

I. Kourides: You mentioned that there were multiple genes for α_{2u}-globulin but you didn't discuss this point in your talk. When I looked at the figure on DNase I treatment of *Eco*RI fragments of the genomic DNA, it seemed equally possible that there might either be one gene or multiple identical genes since there was one dominant *Eco*RI fragment hybridizable to your cDNA probe. There are certainly different forms of α_{2u}-globulin as shown by isoelectric focusing. Could you explain this point a little further?

A. K. Roy: Yes, you are right. Hybridization of the Southern blot of *Eco* RI digested genomic DNA with our probe showed one major band which is about 1.5 kilobase pair in size. We have used this major band to follow the DNase I sensitivity of α_{2u}-globulin gene. In samples where α_{2u}-globulin genes were not digested with DNase I, at least ten additional faint bands, above the dominant (1.5 kb) fragment could be seen. The observation of multiple bands of α_{2u}-globulin gene fragments and unequal distribution of these bands would suggest multiple genes coding for this protein. Dr. David Kurtz (*J. Mol. Appl. Genet.* **1,** 29, 1981) has performed a comparative analysis of hybridization kinetics of albumin gene (a single copy gene) and α_{2u}-globulin gene within the *Eco*RI fragments of the genomic DNA. From these liquid hybridization data he concludes that the haploid rat genome contains 18–20 genes that code for α_{2u}-globulin which is close to what Dr. Hastie and his colleagues found for the number of genes for the analogous mouse urinary protein (N. D. Hastie, W. Held, and J. J. Toole, *Cell* **17,** 449, 1979).

I. Kourides: So you are saying that there was more than one hybridizable band because it looked as though you were pointing out one dominant *Eco*RI fragment?

A. K. Roy: Right, while describing the changes in DNase I sensitivity during aging I was only emphasizing the disappearance of the most intensely hybridizable *Eco*RI fragment on the Southern blot of the genomic DNA.

V. C. Jordan: I would like to ask a series of questions about the pharmacological control of your system. You showed in one of the figures that the nonsteroidal antiandrogen flutamide did not inhibit the binding of DHT to your particular binding protein. Have you done any experiments *in vivo* to load the animals with flutamide and then administer the androgen?

A. K. Roy: Yes, we have done those experiments. Flutamide does not inhibit the androgen-dependent synthesis of α_{2u}-globulin.

V. C. Jordan: In most of your inhibitory experiments with estrogens, you appear to have used estradiol. Have you tried any nonsteroidal estrogens or nonsteroidal antiestrogens? The reason for my question is because the nonsteroidal antiestrogens have different pharmacological effects in different species. Dr. Catherine Lazier has shown that nonsteroidal antiestrogens are completely antiestrogenic, with no estrogenic properties, in chick liver [C. Lazier *et al.* (1981). *In* "Nonsteroidal Antioestrogens" (R. L. Sutherland and V. C. Jordan, eds.), pp. 215–230. Academic Press, New York], but there is a body of evidence to suggest that nonsteroidal antiestrogens show full estrogenic properties in the rat liver. Have you undertaken any studies in your model system?

A. K. Roy: Yes, we have also done those experiments. The nonsteroidal estrogen DES does not bind to the hepatic androgen binding protein. However, it is a potent inhibitor of α_{2u}-globulin synthesis in the rat. Of the various nonsteroidal antiestrogens that we have examined, U-11 (100 A) and CI-628 were certainly estrogenic in the male rat.

V. C. Jordan: So they were weakly estrogenic?

A. K. Roy: That is correct.

T. Spelsberg: I was very intrigued by your DNase sensitivity of your gene during development. Other people have seen this course with target or nontarget tissues (i.e., nonexpressing tissues). Have you ever performed an experiment wherein one takes the chromatins that have genes protected from the DNase, strips off the proteins gently from these chromatins, and then the partially deproteinized chromatins at different stages with the DNase to see which group of proteins is involved in protecting the genes?

A. K. Roy: That is a very interesting suggestion and we plan to do those experiments. However, before we get into that we would like to perform some simpler ones such as looking for age-dependent changes in the degree of methylation of the α_{2u}-globulin gene.

C. Lazier: I am interested in your cytoplasmic binding protein and it reminds me of a similar protein in chicken liver, which was described by Dower and Ryan. The chicken protein binds estrogen and progesterone with intermediate affinity and is not translocated into the nucleus. It is present in very high concentrations and it confounds assays of the classical high-affinity estrogen receptor, unless it is removed by a technique such as ammonium sulfate precipitation. Have you looked for small amounts of high-affinity binding with strict androgen specificity by fractionation of your cytosols?

A. K. Roy: So far we have not been able to show any high-affinity classical androgen binder in the rat liver that can translocate into the nucleus. Although this does not mean that it does not exist. However, as you may know since our original report in 1973, several other cases of middle affinity androgen and estrogen binding proteins in the liver of various species have been described. Let me add that this type of sex hormone binding protein may not be unique for the hepatic tissue. Only recently Taylor and Smith have reported the existence of a cytoplasmic estrogen–progesterone binder in the chicken oviduct with strikingly similar properties to those of the rat liver androgen binding protein (R. N. Taylor and R. G. Smith, *Proc. Natl. Acad. Sci. U.S.A.* **79**, 1743, 1982).

C. Lazier: What is the concentration of your cytosol binding protein?

A. K. Roy: In the liver of young adult male its concentration is about 10 pmole/mg protein. This is a rather high concentration when one compares it to the amount of classical estrogen receptor in the rat liver cytosol, which is about 0.2 pmole/mg protein (R. B. Dickson and A. J. Eisenfeld, *Biol. Reprod.* **21**, 1105, 1979).

P. Robel: There is some similarity between this binder and the androgen receptor. The major points are (1) the high affinity for the androgen hormones testosterone and dihydrotestosterone, (2) 10 times less affinity for estradiol, (3) very low amounts in prepubertal animals, (4) large induction by testosterone, and (5) disappearance in very old animals. All these characteristics have been well documented in the rat ventral prostate. Of course there are general discrepancies, such as the absence of binding of antiandrogens. Finally, the sizes of the molecule are quite different; your binder is 3.5 whereas the androgen receptor is 8–10 S. Nonetheless I wonder if you could explain those differences by proteolytic cleavage of the androgen receptor, so that you get a form that has undergone changes in its binding specificity and whose DNA binding capacity has been lost. Such differences have been described for the so-called meroreceptors of several steroid hormone receptors. Can you completely dismiss the possibility that your binder is a degraded androgen receptor?

A. K. Roy: It is a difficult question to answer. Even with all of the available inhibitors of proteolytic enzymes one can always argue that this particular cleavage may be catalyzed by a specific enzyme that is not inhibited by any one of these inhibitors. Dr. Gerald Litwack of Temple University has been fighting this issue for the glucocorticoid receptor of rat liver for many years, and has yet to convince all of the skeptics that the different molecular forms are not generated by the protease action. Initially when we first discovered this androgen binding protein in the rat liver, we thought that this was a classical androgen receptor. However, inability to show its translocation into the nucleus has subsequently modified our thinking. Thus, I cannot completely dismiss your ideas, but presently I will not bet on it. The reason, I say so, is based primarily on our observation that neither cyproterone acetate nor flutamide binds to this protein and none of these antiandrogens is capable of inhibiting the hepatic synthesis of α_{2u}-globulin in the male rate. At least in this case we can see that the apparent anomaly observed *in vitro* is also reflected *in vivo*.

K. Sterling: This was a very interesting presentation. I just want to ask you about the work by Phil Fiegelsons's group which, as I recall it, showed that in the normal adult male or androgen-treated castrate male, thyroid hormone increased the amount of mRNA directing the synthesis of this protein. I have regarded rightly or wrongly this particular work to be the first demonstration of a thyroid hormone effect in increasing the mRNA of an inducible protein. Could you help me orient that paper in the history of this protein.

A. K. Roy: I will be happy to do that. I discovered the role of thyroid hormones on the hepatic synthesis of α_{2u}-globulin in the early 1970s and published it in 1973 (A. K. Roy, *J. Endocrinol.* **56**, 295, 1973). In this paper I also described the multiple hormone requirements for the synthesis of this protein. In 1974, I was able to set up a collaboration with Dr. Albrecht Sippel, who was then a postdoctoral fellow in Dr. Philip Feigelson's laboratory, to study the hepatic changes of the messenger RNA for α_{2u}-globulin under different endocrine conditions. Our first collaborative paper describing the effects of DHT and corticosterone on the hepatic concentration of α_{2u}-globulin mRNA appeared in 1975 (A. E. Sippel, P. Feigelson, and A. K. Roy, *Biochemistry* **14**, 825, 1975). I hoped to continue this collaboration to examine the question of pre- or posttranscriptional effect of other hormones which were known to influence α_{2u}-globulin synthesis. However, after our first joint paper came out, Dr. Feigelson switched his primary interest from tryptophan oxygenase to α_{2u}-globulin and decided to discontinue our collaboration. The effect of thyroxine on the hepatic concentration of the mRNA for α_{2u}-globulin was published by our group and independently by Dr. Feigelson's group in 1976 (A. K. Roy, M. J. Schiop, and D. J. Dowbenko, *FEBS Lett.* **64**, 393, 1976; D. T. Kurtz, A. E. Sippel, and P. Feigelson, *Biochemistry* **15**, 1031, 1976). So much for the history of the thyroid hormone and α_{2u}-globulin. Concerning the other part of your question, I believe you are referring to the effect of glucocorticoid, and not thyroxine on the synthesis of α_{2u}-globulin in the castrated rat. After we discontinued our collaboration, Dr. Feigelson and his associates raised their own antiserum against α_{2u}-globulin by following a different procedure for the isolation of this protein. With their antiserum they reported two novel observations; (1) existence of two high-molecular-weight (M_r 74,000 and 45,000) glycosylated forms of α_{2u}-globulin (C. C. Chen and P. Feigelson, *J. Biol. Chem.* **253**, 7880, 1978), and (2) induction of α_{2u}-globulin in the castrated rat with glucocorticoid alone (D. T. Kurtz, K. M. Chan, and P. Feigelson, *J. Biol. Chem.* **253**, 7886, 1978). The so-called "high-molecular-weight glycosylated forms of α_{2u}-globulin" are present in female and prepubertal male rats, and the hepatic concentration of this protein is inversely related to the level of circulating androgen (L. J. Haars and H. C. Pitot, *Arch. Biochem. Biophys.* **201**, 556, 1980). With our antibody (both polyclonal and monoclonal) we have not been able to detect any one of those high molecular forms of α_{2u}-globulin. It is possible that their antiserum is not monospecific and possibly contaminated with anti-orosomucoid. Orosomucoid (also known as α_1 acid glycoprotein) is synthesized and secreted by the hepatocytes and is known to be highly inducible by glucocorticoids.

S. Plymate: Do you think the mechanism by which thyroid hormone stimulates α_{2u}-globulin had any relation to the stimulation of sex hormone binding globulin, a protein produced in the liver of man and other primates regulated by sex steroids but not found in the rat?

A. K. Roy: In addition to our observation concerning the role of thyroid hormone on the synthesis of α_{2u}-globulin, Peavy *et al.* (*Biochem. J.* **198**, 289, 1981) have reported that hypothyroid rats produce only about half the amount of serum albumin as compared to euthyroid rats without any corresponding decrease in the hepatic concentration of albumin mRNA. Thus, it is possible that the hepatic synthesis of other secretory proteins can also be reduced under hypothyroid state.

K. L. Barker: I have two brief questions. Have you examined the medium after *in vitro* incubation of hepatocytes for the presence of a secreted form of the intracellular steroid binding protein to see if it may be a secreted form of something analogous to the sex steroid binding globulin which is seen in the blood of other species and have you any idea regarding the biological function of your α_{2u}-globulin?

A. K. Roy: The hepatic androgen binder which we have described is a nonsecretory cytoplasmic protein. In collaboration with Dr. C. Wayne Bardin of Rockefeller University, we have examined the possible antigenic relationship of the hepatic androgen binder with the testicular androgen binding protein (ABP) and could not find any cross-reactivity. Concerning the biological function of α_{2u}-globulin, several years ago we performed some collaborative experiments with Dr. Ajit Chowdhury of the University of Texas at Houston. Preliminary results have indicated that α_{2u}-globulin can protect estrogenic inhibition of spermatid maturation. Further investigation of this and possible pheromonal activity of this protein may provide the clue to its biological function.

R. O. Greep: I am somewhat reluctant to introduce a pragmatic note into such a beautiful piece of basic science as you have just presented, and I do not mean to imply that I am not interested in what happens in rats. While you were talking, however, I kept wondering whether these findings have implications for the human species. Would you please comment about what the implications for mankind are? Does this substance exist in the human species?

A. K. Roy: When we first found this protein in the rat urine, by using the paper electrophoretic technique of those days, I looked for male specific urinary proteins in the human but could not find any. However, with the modern technology of two-dimensional gel electrophoresis and highly sensitive silver staining, it will be interesting to look into the sex difference of urinary proteins in the human, and I am quite sure that one will be able to identify some minor sex-specific proteins. Unlike humans, rodents show a rather massive proteinuria. An adult male rat in its prime of youth excretes daily as much protein in its urine as a full-grown man. α_{2u}-Globulin accounts for about half of the total urinary protein in the rat. Thus, α_{2u}-globulin and analogous proteins are unique to rodents. Our primary interest, however, is to exploit the multihormonal control of this protein and its age-dependent regulation to study the mechanism of hormone action and its alteration during development and aging. Certain types of endocrinological experiments are not obviously feasible in the human. Therefore, we always will need good animal models and, to my knowledge, this is the only well-characterized mammalian model where one could explore the interacting influence of so many hormones, and in addition, study the dramatic change in hormone responsiveness during aging. I surely hope that results of our studies on the interacting influences of thyroxine, growth hormone, insulin, and so on will soon find their way into clinical medicine and be helpful in the management of such affliction as diabetes and hypothyroidism which have been agonizing mankind for millenniums. Similarly, our results on the changing endocrine response during aging will hopefully some day have its impact on geriatric endocrinology which is an expanding area of concern both in this country and abroad.

J. E. Rall: I wonder if you could say a little bit more about the different α_{2u}-globulin that you see in urine. Are these products of different genes or are they posttranscriptional modifications of the product of the same gene? I gather you and Kurtz both showed that they are between 10 and 18 genes for α_{2u}-globulins. Does anyone have genomic clones, and, if so, are these identical genes coding for different proteins, or are they the same protein that has undergone different posttranslational modifications?

A. K. Roy: The two molecular weight variants, which differ by 700, and the five major isoelectric variants are both present within the *in vitro* translation products of the hepatic mRNA. In addition, distribution of these variant forms shows genetic differences. Thus it seems that these proteins are coded by different genes. Furthermore, we have sequenced two cDNA clones of α_{2u}-globulin and have found minor differences in nucleotide sequences. The different forms of this protein to some extent undergo posttranslation modification where a carbohydrate side chain of about 2500 daltons is added to the peptide backbone. However, in order to establish the precise number of genes and their structural peculiarities, we will have to sequence the genomic clones.

I Kourides: So what do you think about the other putative genes for α_{2u}-globulin?

A. K. Roy: Others, which cannot be accounted for, may represent pseudogenes.

D. V. Cohn: I was under the impression that there is a relationship between the α_{2u}-globulin and the milk protein β-lactalbumin—is that true?

A. K. Roy: Yes, there is some sequence homology with bovine lactoglobulin.

D. V. Cohn: I thought that there was a high degree of sequence homology?

A. K. Roy: The significance of this observation is presently unknown.

Role of Specific Chromosomal Proteins and DNA Sequences in the Nuclear Binding Sites for Steroid Receptors

Thomas C. Spelsberg,* Bruce A. Littlefield,† Ralph Seelke,*
Ginger Martin Dani,† Hiroo Toyoda,‡ Patricia Boyd-Leinen,§
Cary Thrall,** and Oi Lian Kon††

*Cell Biology, Section of Biochemistry, Mayo Clinic and Graduate School of Medicine,
Rochester, Minnesota; †Department of Biology, Fredrick Hutchinson Cancer Center,
Seattle, Washington; ‡Department of Molecular Genetics, City of Hope Medical Center,
Duarte, California; §Chemical Abstracts, Columbus, Ohio; **Department of
Neurological Research, Mayo Clinic and Graduate School of Medicine, Rochester,
Minnesota; ††Faculty of Medicine, Health Science Center, Memorial University of
Newfoundland, St. Johns, Newfoundland, Canada

I. Introduction

The chemical nature of the nuclear binding sites for steroid receptors [termed nuclear acceptor sites (1)] is a very important but very obscure aspect of the processes of steroid hormone action and gene regulation. The steroid receptor complexes themselves represent the first intracellular gene regulator ever discovered in eukaryotes. The receptors are bound with high affinity and steroid specificity by steroid hormones. The complex in turn migrates and binds to the acceptor sites on the genome and alters the gene expression in a quantitative and qualitative fashion (1–6). The steroid–receptor complex then dissociates from the nuclear acceptor sites, the steroid is probably metabolized and secreted from the cell, and the free receptor is probably recycled back into the receptor–acceptor site pathway, to await another steroid. Thus, the nuclear acceptor sites represent the first intranuclear sites through which steroid receptors initiate regulation of gene expression. Their importance is obvious. This laboratory has investigated the properties and composition of the nuclear acceptor sites for the avian oviduct progesterone receptor complex for almost a decade. Much of this work has previously been reviewed (see 6–8).

Presented in this chapter are (a) properties of the cell-free binding assay in brief, (b) evidence for masking of acceptor sites and properties of the masking proteins, (c) novel regulations of the chick oviduct progesterone receptor and how these data are used to support and assess the nativeness

463

of our cell-free binding assay and reconstituted nuclear acceptor sites, (d) the isolation and characterization of specific chromatin proteins (termed acceptor proteins) which are involved in the nuclear acceptor sites for the progesterone receptor (P-R), (e) evidence that specific DNA sequences are also involved in the nuclear acceptor sites, and (f) possible models for the nuclear acceptor site organization in the genome.

II. The General Scheme of the Mechanism of Steroid Hormone Action

The same general theme for the mechanism of action of steroids has been identified in all steroid–target tissue systems in all animals. This is outlined in Fig. 1. For more comprehensive reviews, the readers are referred elsewhere (2–6). Briefly, systemic steroids are found to be

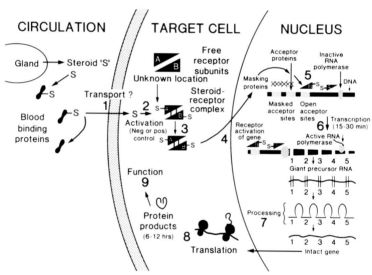

FIG. 1. Basic pathway for the action of steroid hormones in target cells. This pathway is described in the text. It represents the general mechanism of action of all steroids. Briefly, beginning on the left side of the model, the steroid (H) passes through the cell membrane and binds to its specific receptor. The receptor, represented as two subunits, is then "activated" and the complex of steroid–receptor translocates and binds to the nuclear acceptor sites. This results in changes (quantitative and qualitative) in DNA-dependent RNA synthesis. The giant precursor mRNA molecules are "processed" to small mRNA molecules which are transported out of the nucleus to the ribosomes where they code for specific steroid-induced proteins. These proteins carry out the various steroid-induced physiological responses of the target cell. In essence, the first major intracellular process which responds to the steroids is the alteration in gene transcription (RNA synthesis). This is preceded by the binding of the steroid receptor to the nuclear acceptor sites. Data for this schema were taken in part from Thrall et al. (6) and in part from O'Malley and Means (4).

mostly bound to serum carrier proteins. Those that are unbound enter target cells. Whether the transfer involves active transport or passive diffusion remains in question (9–12). Whether a steroid enters nontarget tissues is also open to question. Radiolabeled steroids are found in the cytosols of nontarget cells (13,14); however, these results may be explained by an artificial transfer of the steroids from the blood compartments of organs to the "cytosol" during tissue homogenization. In any event, the steroids are retained in their target cells but not in nontarget cells for extended periods (13–15). This retention is due to specific steroid binding proteins termed receptors which are found only in target cells (16–20). Although the exact intracellular compartment in which unbound receptors reside remains obscure, there is some evidence that they are associated with microsomes (21,22) while others claim they might reside in the nucleus (23,24).

Once bound by the steroid, the receptor becomes "activated," a process which invests in the complex the capacity to "migrate" into the nucleus (or at least to the nuclear acceptor sites) and bind to these acceptor sites. These processes of activation and translocation of a steroid receptor complex into the nucleus are not well understood. For instance, exactly from what site the migration occurs is unknown. Cytosolic factors have been reported which can induce (enhance) activation (26–29) and others which suppress activation or translocation (30–36). Still others have presented evidence that the native form of at least one receptor (the chick oviduct progesterone receptor) is composed of two molecular species which they speculate act as individual subunits of a dimer (37–42). The latter represents the active form of the receptor (41–45). It is further speculated that this dimer then migrates to the nucleus where the two different subunits (termed A and B) perform distinct functions. The B subunit binds the complex to specific acceptor sites on the chromatin, while A alters transcription by binding the adjacent DNA sequence. This active subunit model, however, requires further study. For instance, two forms of the native-like large complexes of the oviduct P-R have been isolated using molybdate to stabilize them. These large complexes were each found to contain only one of the species (46), i.e., one large complex contained multiples of one of the subunit species, the other large complex contained the other species.

Once bound to nuclear acceptor sites, the steroid–receptor complex markedly alters RNA synthesis (47–49) and the transcription of specific genes (50–54). The subsequent effects of steroids on RNA processing and protein synthesis, if any, are poorly understood due to the few studies undertaken (55).

On a chronological basis, the above events occur rapidly. Within 1 to 2 minutes after injection of labeled progesterone into the chicks, which have been primed with estrogen, the steroid is located in the cytosol bound to its receptor. By 10 minutes postinjection, the steroid accumulates in the nucleus, followed closely by changes in RNA synthesis and chromatin template capacity. After 1 to 2 hours specific messenger RNAs appear whose coded proteins begin to accumulate within 3 to 6 hours (2–6). If only a single injection of the steroid is used, the steroid-induced changes rapidly return to control values. At 12 hours postinjection, the radiolabeled steroids in the cytoplasm and nucleus are markedly reduced as are the alterations in RNA synthesis. The fate of the steroids is unclear but it is probable they are not reutilized but are metabolized and excreted from the cells. Whether or not all of the receptor is reutilized to some degree in the steroid action pathway is unknown. At least some of the receptor is thought to be recycled (56,57).

Thus, the binding of the steroid–receptor complex to acceptor sites on the chromatin represents the first nuclear event which occurs before the steroid-induced changes in transcription occur. The receptor, when bound by a specific steroid, is triggered to migrate into the nucleus, binds to chromatin acceptor sites, and alters transcription. The whole process is rapidly reversible to allow immediate control of the target tissue by the steroid. It is the authors' opinion that the steroid receptors may well represent one of the first, if not the first, intracellular gene regulators discovered in eukaryotes.

III. Chemical Properties of Nuclear Acceptor Sites for Steroid Receptors

A. GENERAL

The exact biological components comprising the nuclear acceptor sites for steroid receptors remain elusive. The following have been implicated as being involved in the nuclear acceptor sites for various steroid receptors: the nuclear envelope (58,59), histones (60–63), nonhistone basic proteins (64–66), nonhistones and nonhistone–DNA complexes (1,6,39,61,62,67–88), pure DNA (32,34,76,77,89–117), ribonucleoproteins (118), and finally the nuclear matrix (119,120). Since candidates for acceptor sites have been reviewed extensively in recent reviews (6–8), they will only be briefly outlined here. Of the many components suggested, the DNA and DNA–nonhistone protein complexes have received the most attention. A few studies of the nuclear components whose role in nuclear acceptor sites is still regarded as potential are described in more detail in the following section.

B. SPECIFIC NUCLEAR COMPONENTS ANALYZED AS NUCLEAR ACCEPTOR SITES

It is undisputed that in cell-free conditions, steroid receptors bind to DNA. Many laboratories have reported that a variety of steroid–receptor complexes bind to DNA (1,28,32,34,70–74,76,77,85,89,91–95,101–117). The binding of the receptor to DNA appears to be in part electrostatic interaction, decreasing with increasing ionic strength (2,3,77,93,100,109–111,122). Many facts point to a nonspecific interaction of steroid receptors with pure DNA. The affinity of the progesterone receptor for the DNA of the chick oviduct is significantly lower than that of the receptor for nuclei and chromatin (121). Furthermore, the differences in binding of the steroid receptors to different DNA sequences are relatively small. In fact, many laboratories have found no differences in the binding of steroid–receptor complexes to the native DNAs of a variety of sources (93,101,103,104,108). In most instances, the binding to pure DNA is not saturable (32,34,85,93,98,100,101,106,121,122). It is possible that the lack of DNA specificity for steroid receptors could be due to the inability to detect a few specific sites among an overwhelming number of slightly lower affinity, nonspecific sites. Recently, several groups, working with purified rat liver glucocorticoid receptor and murine mouse mammary tumor virus genomes (114,115) or the purified chick oviduct progesterone receptor and chick oviduct ovalbumin gene (116,117), have identified a marked preference of binding *in vitro* of each receptor for certain sequences in the 5′ region preceding the respective gene. The oviduct progesterone receptor bound to a similar region of several different genes that the steroid regulates *in vivo,* but did not bind in a similar region of β-globin which is a nonprogesterone regulated gene. Saturation in both the glucocorticoid–MMTV and the progesterone–chick oviduct systems has not been achieved. Thus, quantitative or affinity analysis cannot be estimated. As pointed out in these papers, the actual function of this "preference of binding" by these steroid–receptor complexes for certain sequences remains to be determined. In each instance, the sequence involved in this preferred binding is A-T rich (up to 80%). These A-T-rich regions are subject to nonspecific, nonsaturable enhanced binding of steroid receptors as discussed in the following paragraph.

Recent studies in our laboratory indicate that the binding of the chick oviduct progesterone receptor to whole genomic DNA does not correlate with the native (*in vitro*) binding and is subject to many artifacts (108). The chick oviduct progesterone receptor displays a variable, nonsaturable binding to pure DNA in cell-free binding assays whereas a saturable binding is observed with whole chromatin or a specific protein–DNA complex (see 6–8 for a review). Three factors are identified which affect the binding of P-R to the DNA. These are (a) the conditions of the binding assay, (b) the particular receptor preparation, and (c) the state of the DNA (7,8,108). The conditions in the binding assay which affect the extent of DNA binding are the choice of the blanks, the salt concentration, and the pH of the assay. Concerning the second class of factors controlling DNA binding, various preparations of the receptor display their own characteristic levels of binding to native DNA, the basis of which is unknown. Lastly, the composition purity and integrity of the DNA also determines the level of binding of the P-R. Protein impurities, moderate degradation of the DNA by enzymatic or physical fragmentation, and ultraviolet (UV) light treatment greatly enhance the receptor binding to the DNA. This binding remains unsaturable. Interestingly, totally denatured (single-stranded) DNA displays little or no binding of the P-R (108). Thus, the extent of binding of the steroid receptor depends on the degree of damage to the DNA. Further, A-T-rich DNA appears to bind P-R to a greater extent than the G-C-rich or whole genomic DNA (8). Furthermore, A-T-rich regions of the DNA are much more unstable than G-C-rich regions and thus would be more susceptible to the artificially enhanced binding by steroid receptors. This indeed has been found to be the case for poly(dA-T) with the avian oviduct progesterone receptor (174). Lastly, as will be discussed later, seasonal differences which are observed for the binding of P-R to chromatin *in vivo* and *in vitro* do not occur with pure DNA. Thrall and Spelsberg (108) concluded from their studies that under controlled conditions and by using DNA preparations as undamaged as possible, minimal binding of P-R to pure DNA occurs. They further concluded that native, or partially degraded, pure DNA alone does not appear to represent the native nuclear acceptor sites for the P-R in the chick oviduct (108). In contrast, the DNA–nonhistone protein (acceptor protein) complexes do show characteristics of the native-like acceptor sites. Thus, it is possible that the numerous reports in the literature describing marked binding of the steroid–receptor complex to DNA, especially A-T-rich DNA, may be due to one of the conditions listed above and that DNA alone does not have the properties characteristic of the binding *in vivo*.

Barrack, Coffey, and co-workers (119,120) have reported that as much as 67% of the total nuclear bound dihydrotestosterone binding sites with properties of the receptor and 100% of the salt resistant nuclear receptors are localized in the nuclear matrix of the rat ventral prostate. Similar results were obtained with estrogen in the chicken liver. Structurally, this nuclear matrix is composed of a residual nuclear envelope with pore complexes, remnants of an internal fibrogranular network, and the residual nucleoli. Chemically, it contains 7% of the total nuclear protein and

2% of the total cellular DNA. Thus, it still consists of huge amounts of different proteins and DNA sequences. These sites appear to be destroyed by a combination of DNase treatments, RNase, and dithiothreitol. These sites displayed expected quantitative changes [in steroid binding (exchange)] under different endocrine states of the animals. Unfortunately, these analyses of the steroid "receptors" bound to the nuclear matrix involves an indirect binding assay, i.e., the binding is only achieved using free steroid in an exchange assay and not the steroid–receptor complex. These sites (receptors) are not extracted by 2 M NaCl extractions in contrast to the bulk of the natively bound nuclear steroid receptor which is extracted. As indicated by these authors, the chemical nature of these binding sites remains obscure.

As mentioned at the beginning of this section, many laboratories have reported evidence supporting a combination of DNA and protein as a complex in chromatin serves as the nuclear acceptor sites for a variety of steroid receptors (1,6,40,41,64,65,68,69,70–86,122–125). Most of these nucleoprotein complexes contain specific fractions of nonhistone chromatin proteins bound to DNA and display high-affinity, saturable nuclear binding sites for steroid receptors (i.e., acceptor activity). Several lines of evidence support these nonhistone protein–DNA complexes (nucleoacidic protein or NAP) as the nuclear acceptor sites for the progesterone receptor in the avian oviduct (1,6–10,41,42,68,69,70–74,85,122–124). These are the subject of the remaining portions of this article.

IV. Development of a Cell-Free Nuclear Binding for the Chick Oviduct Progesterone Receptor

A. THE BASIC METHOD

The basic procedure for performing cell-free nuclear binding studies is to incubate a labeled steroid receptor preparation with isolated nuclei or nuclear component, and then measure bound versus free steroid receptor. The numerous reports involving such studies utilize some variation of this approach. These variations include the level of purification of the receptor, the method of "activation" of the steroid–receptor complex (e.g., salt treatment, dilution, partial purification, or heat activation, etc.), the experimental design used in analyzing nuclear uptake (e.g., varying the receptor levels, varying the nuclear levels, etc.), the conditions of the cell-free assay (e.g., temperature of incubation, ionic strength, etc.), and the method of separating unbound steroid–receptor complex from the nuclear components.

Using these considerations, a cell-free nuclear binding assay for the progesterone receptor in the chick oviduct was developed. This is outlined in Fig. 2 for both whole nuclei/chromatin as well as for various soluble nuclear components which require special handling. Since the free steroid–receptor complexes are soluble but the nuclei and chromatin are not, it is easy to separate the chromatin bound from unbound steroid receptors by using short-term centrifugation. The partially deproteinized chromatins, however, are soluble and thus are more difficult to separate

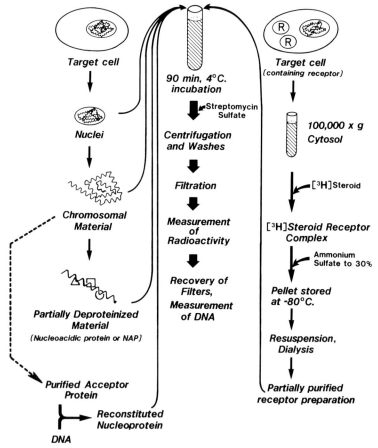

FIG. 2. Outline of basic procedure for the cell-free assay of [³H]P-R binding to nuclear acceptor sites. These methods are described in detail elsewhere (71–74,85,123,124,128). The methods were selected on the basis of achieving saturable binding to the highest affinity class of sites and for maintaining the integrity of the steroid–receptor complex, the chromatin protein, and its DNA (see text). Reproduced with permission from Thrall *et al.* (6).

from the soluble receptors. Long periods of centrifugation were initially used to separate these two soluble entities, but low recovery, degradation, and limited sample numbers presented problems (1,68). A better approach is to rapidly render the soluble nucleoproteins insoluble without damaging the steroid receptor or its binding to the acceptor sites. This is accomplished in either one of two ways as shown in Fig. 2. First, the chromatin can be attached to an insoluble resin such as cellulose or acrylamide and the various protein fractions removed, leaving residual DNA or DNA–protein complex attached to the resins in an insoluble state. These resins can then be used in the binding assays (69,72,85). Alternately, one can perform the binding using free nucleoproteins. After the hormone binding, the soluble chromatin fractions can be rendered insoluble using streptomycin sulfate to precipitate the nucleoprotein with bound steroid receptors (126). In each method, the complexes of DNA and steroid receptor are washed several times to remove traces of the unbound steroid receptor. The washed complexes are then transfered to Millipore filters and the bound radioactivity counted. The DNA per filter is quantitated and the cpm per milligram DNA or molecules of bound P-R per cell are calculated as described elsewhere (85,125). These methods as well as their problems and limitations are detailed elsewhere (6–8).

The assay conditions utilized in the studies described in this article involve a partially purified receptor (20-fold purification) which is preactivated (125,127), a low temperature (4°C), a 90-minute incubation period, and varying ratios of receptor/nuclear DNA with 30 to 100 μg DNA (as nuclei or nuclear components) per assay. The time of incubation was selected to allow equilibrium between bound (to acceptor sites) and free progesterone receptor complex using an acceptable receptor and chromatin concentrations. As shown in Fig. 3, these conditions allow a saturable binding in a short period of time using increasing amounts of the nuclear components with constant amounts of receptor. The same pattern of binding can be achieved using constant nuclear components with variable receptor levels (6,70–74,85,125). The affinity of this cell-free nuclear binding has been determined by Scatchard analysis with a K_d of approximately 10^{-9} M (85,125). We have found that 90% of the progesterone receptor remains intact throughout the assay (6,125,128), the chromatin proteins and DNA show relatively little damage (6,128), and about 60 to 80% of the chromatin DNA is recovered on the filters after the binding, washings, and transfer. Further, when [^{14}C]ovalbumin is added to the binding assays and then assayed by SDS–polyacrylamide gel electrophoresis, less than 10% of the ovalbumin is damaged (T. C. Spelsberg, unpublished results). This is routinely achieved when mild protease inhibitors such as phenylmethylsulfonyl fluoride are included in the binding assays. We have

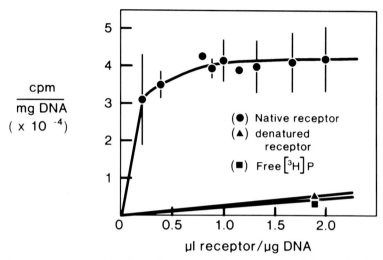

FIG. 3. Titration of P-R binding to hen oviduct chromatin. The cell-free nuclear binding of (●) native P-R, (▲) P-R denatured by heating at 50°C for 1 hour, and (■) free steroid to oviduct chromatin, was performed as described elsewhere (125) except that the levels of chromatin were varied and the P-R concentration per assay kept constant. The mean and standard deviation of four replicate binding assays to the native receptor are presented. Reproduced with permission from Spelsberg (7).

found that the more potent protease inhibitors often damage the receptors and prevent nuclear binding (T. C. Spelsberg, unpublished). In contrast when the cell-free binding assays are performed without protease inhibitors or under conditions of higher temperature (25°C) or for longer periods or with crude cytosol, significant proteolytic damage to the [^{14}C]ovalbumin can occur. Mild proteolytic activity is accompanied by increases in binding of the progesterone receptor to nuclear acceptor sites, as discussed in the following section on masking proteins. Extensive proteolytic activity results in a loss of nuclear binding by the P-R since both the receptor and the acceptor protein are degraded.

B. SOME FACTORS AFFECTING THE CELL-FREE NUCLEAR BINDING ASSAYS

Many problems confront the establishment of cell-free nuclear binding assays. The cell-free binding assays eliminate many of the obstacles involved in the *in vivo* assays, such as need of expensive amounts of the radiolabeled steroid, difficulty in saturating the nuclear acceptor sites, achieving an equilibrium in binding, and the loss of nuclear bound steroid–receptor complexes during isolation and manipulation of the chromatin. The latter is observed due to the noncovalent binding of the ste-

TABLE I

Some Factors Affecting the Cell-Free Nuclear Binding of Steroid Receptor Complexes

Protease and nuclease activities in the chromatin and receptor preparations: Protease action on receptors will lower nuclear binding while such action on chromatin initially causes rise and then a rapid loss in nuclear binding (7,8,128). Nuclease action on chromatin will also cause an initial rise in nuclear binding and then a decrease with extensive action (7,8,128). Lower temperatures, more purified receptor preparations, and protease inhibitors in the binding assays will reduce these activities

Ionic strength in the binding assays: Low ionic strength causes a nonspecific, nonsaturable high level of adsorption of steroid–receptor complexes to the nuclei or chromatin or DNA (85,108,122,125)

Variations in the stability and biological activities of receptors: Certain steroid receptors in certain tissues and animal species display marked instability making it difficult to perform the cell-free nuclear binding assays. The progesterone receptor in the avian oviduct is particularly stable while the estrogen receptor in this same tissue and the androgen receptors from about all tissues are extremely unstable. Steps must be taken to stabilize the more unstable receptors during the cell-free binding assays. Further, it has been found that the avian oviduct progesterone receptor can vary significantly in its capacity to bind to nuclear acceptor sites *in vivo* or *in vitro*, depending on the endocrine state of the animal when the receptor is isolated. Mature oviducts in the winter (7,8,41,124), undeveloped oviducts (7,8), estrogen withdrawn chick oviducts (7,8,42), and aged or moulting hen oviducts (7,8,42) contain progesterone receptors which are nonfunctional, i.e., cannot bind to nuclear acceptor sites

Steroid-specific properties: For example, free estrogens display 5- to 10-fold greater nonspecific adsorption to nuclear fractions than does free progesterone. Such specific problems may occur with other steroids (androgens, glucocorticoids, etc.)

roid–receptor complex to nuclear sites. This noncovalent binding prevents the fractionation of chromatin (bound with the steroid–receptor complex) to identify the chemical nature of the nuclear acceptor sites for a particular steroid receptor. The cell-free binding approach on the other hand allows the chemical characterization of the acceptor sites by the selective dissociation of certain chromatin components followed by the binding of the steroid–receptor complex to the residual nucleoprotein. It must be stated, however, that the cell-free assay does include variables and artifacts, some intrinsic to the assay and some to the particular receptor and nuclei/chromatin preparations used. Since these problems have been reviewed previously (6–8), they are only listed in Table I.

C. BIOLOGICAL RELEVANCE OF THE CELL-FREE NUCLEAR BINDING OF THE AVIAN OVIDUCT PROGESTERONE RECEPTOR USED IN OUR LABORATORY

Before discussing the isolation and characterization of the nuclear acceptors, a brief discussion of the biological relevance of the cell-free assays should be made. Table II summarizes the similarities of cell-free

TABLE II

Comparison of the Cell-Free Nuclear Binding Assays with That in Vivo[a]

The receptor binds the steroid under cell-free conditions with the same affinity and apparent specificity as measured under whole cell conditions (2–5,37,38,95,125,132,140–144)

The steroid–receptor complex formed under cell-free conditions has the same physicochemical properties (molecular weight, hydrodynamic properties, etc.) as the complex formed in intact cells (2–5,37,38,95,132,140–144)

Requirements for nuclear uptake and binding in cell-free assays (e.g., steroid bound to a receptor, receptor activation, etc.) are the same as those for the whole cell (2–5,34, 37,85,95–98,125,132,140–144)

The conditions required to activate the receptor, a prerequisite for nuclear uptake and binding, are the same for both cell-free and whole cell systems (2–5,37,39,85,95,125, 132,140,142–144)

Under proper conditions, the cell-free binding results in a similar pattern and the level of nuclear binding as does the whole cell binding (6–8,11–16,18–23,25,26). The levels of both cell-free and whole cell nuclear bound steroid correlate with those levels needed for physiological responses (71–74,137,145,146)

The properties of the triplex of steroid–receptor–chromatin formed under cell-free conditions closely resemble that formed under whole cell conditions with respect to dissociation by salt, by certain divalent ions, and detergents, etc. The dissociated radioactive steroids from both in vivo and in vitro bindings are still complexed to the receptor (85,95–98,125,132,140–144)

The interaction of an isolated steroid–receptor complex with isolated nuclei has been reported to alter RNA polymerase activity and transcription of selected genes in a pattern similar to that which occurs in the intact cell (44,126–131,135,136)

The receptor isolated from periods in vivo in which the steroid receptor fails to translocate and bind to nuclear acceptor sites and alter transcription also show no nuclear binding in the cell-free assay. This includes the annual rhythms in receptor function in the mature avian oviduct, as well as the lack of progesterone function in the immature oviduct and the oviduct of estrogen withdrawn chicks or aged or molting hens (7,8,41,42)

Nuclear acceptor sites are distinct for estrogen and progesterone receptors have been demonstrated in vivo as well as in the cell-free assays (139)

---

[a] Taken from Thrall, C. L., Webster, R. A., and Spelsberg, T. C. (1978). In "The Cell Nucleus" (H. Busch, ed.), Vol. 6, p. 461. Academic Press, New York.

nuclear binding assays, which have been reported by many laboratories for many steroid receptor–target tissue systems, to the nuclear binding that occurs in vivo.

1. Alteration of Transcription in Cell-Free Binding Assays for Steroid Receptors

Many laboratories have reported that the cell-free nuclear binding assays alter transcription of the DNA similar to the in vivo conditions (44,129–136). These studies do support the nativeness of the cell-free nuclear binding assays. Unfortunately, none have included proper controls in their assays. Most of these studies have not been pursued, so whether these responses *in vitro* occur by the same mechanism(s) as occurs *in vivo* remains dubious.

2. Quantitative Correlation between in Vitro and in Vivo Nuclear Binding Sites

Several lines of evidence support the view that the cell-free nuclear binding in the progesterone receptor (P-R) avian oviduct system represents the native (endogenous) binding sites. It has been reported using whole cell and cell-free studies that multiple classes of nuclear binding sites exist for P-R (69,71–73,85,125,137). In these studies, the binding to the highest affinity class of sites occurred when physiological levels of the steroid in the plasma are achieved (72,73,137). These high-affinity sites, but not the low-affinity sites, survive conditions of physiological ionic strengths in the cell-free binding assay (69–73,125). The high-affinity nuclear binding sites measured in the cell-free binding assays have been shown to quantitatively resemble those measured in the nuclei with *in vivo* studies.

3. Qualitative Correlations between the in Vitro and in Vivo Nuclear Binding

a. Receptor Dependency of the Steroid Binding.   As shown in Figure 4A, the high-affinity sites measured in the cell-free assays also resemble those measured *in vivo* with regard to a dependency on an intact steroid–receptor complex and to the dissociation of the steroid–receptor complex from the chromatin binding sites by 0.3 M KCl (85,125).

b. Receptor Specificity of the Nuclear Binding of Steroid Receptors. A receptor specificity is observed for nuclear binding sites measured in the *in vivo* and *in vitro* assays. In these studies the estrogen receptor from the chick/hen oviduct was isolated, partially purified, and sufficiently stabilized for use in a cell-free binding assay (138), Figure 5 shows that using competitive binding studies in the cell-free assay described here for P-R, the unlabeled estrogen receptor effectively competes with the radiolabeled estrogen receptor but not with the radiolabeled P-R (139). Studies *in vivo* support the cell-free binding assays in that the progesterone does not compete with [^{3}H]estrogen for nuclear binding and vice versa (139). These studies support those of Higgens *et al.* (98) who reported receptor specific nuclear binding for estrogen and dexamethasone in the rat uerus and HTC cells. The observation that the cell-free assay demonstrates receptor-specific acceptor sites, a specificity observed *in vivo,* provides yet further support for the nativeness of these assays.

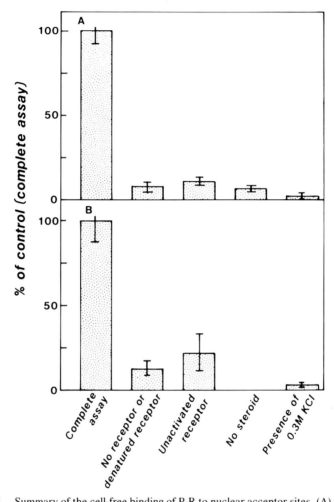

FIG. 4.   Summary of the cell-free binding of P-R to nuclear acceptor sites. (A) shows the level of P-R binding to oviduct nuclei or chromatin under the varying conditions listed. (B) shows the levels of P-R binding to oviduct NAP under similar conditions. The cell-free P-R nuclear binding was performed as described elsewhere (85). Reproduced with permission from Spelsberg (8).

c. Correlations in the Patterns of Binding of Steroid Receptors between in Vitro and in Vivo Nuclear Binding.   Finally, recent studies in the authors' laboratory has revealed a marked correlation between the endogenous nuclear binding and the cell-free binding. In one instance, a marked correlation between the cell-free and endogenous nuclear bindings was observed at different periods of the year. Every winter for a 4-

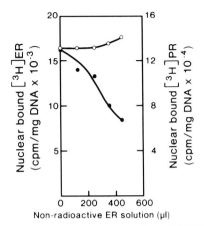

FIG. 5.   Competition of nonradioactive ER for binding of [³H]ER and [³H]P-R to isolated oviduct nuclei. A constant volume (400 μl) of [³H]P-R prepared as previously described (125) or of [³H]ER prepared as previously described (138) (with an additional heparin agarose chromatography) was added to the cell-free nuclear binding assays. Increasing amounts of unlabeled ER were then added. In order to maintain constant protein concentration in all incubations, the volume of each incubation was brought to 1 ml with redissolved ammonium sulfate precipitate (35% saturation) of spleen cytosol prepared in a similar manner as ER. The ratio of [³H]receptor complex to nuclei employed in this experiment was saturating, as previously determined. Nuclear bound [³H]ER in the presence of nonradioactive ER is represented by (●); nuclear bound [³H]P-R in the presence of nonradioactive ER is represented by (○). Each value is the mean of triplicate determinations. Reproduced with permission from Kon and Spelsberg (139).

year period a loss of nuclear binding capacity of P-R to whole oviduct chromatin and NAP was demonstrated (41,124) Figure 6A shows the binding of P-R to oviduct chromatin *in vitro* and *in vivo*. Clearly, a seasonal variation in the pattern of binding is observed with a decrease or loss in binding occurring in the winter. Such a pattern is not observed when using pure DNA (Fig. 6B). As shown in Fig. 6C a similar seasonal pattern in the effects of progesterone on RNA polymerase II activity (transcription) is observed (41,124). This activity represents the first nuclear response to the binding of the steroid–receptor complex to nuclear acceptor sites. These circannual rhythms were also accompanied by similar rhythms in the oviduct weights and cytosol protein. The rhythm in the nuclear binding was subsequently found to be due to functional changes in the progesterone receptor as is discussed in Section IV (41,124).

Similar correlations between the *in vivo* and *in vitro* nuclear binding have also been shown in the aged hen (42), withdrawn chick (42), and developing oviduct (7,8). In the aged hen, or estrogen withdrawn chick or immature oviduct, the progesterone receptor is not capable of translocat-

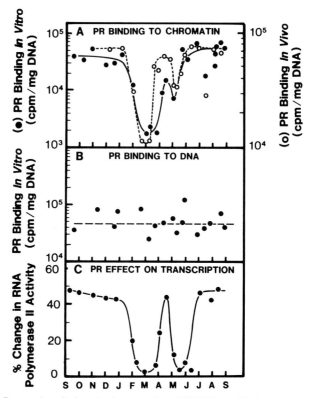

FIG. 6. Seasonal variations in the capacity of [³H]P-R to bind to chromatin acceptor sites *in vivo* and *in vitro*. (A) represents the *in vitro* binding to whole chromatin. The solid line represents the *in vitro* binding performed within 1 week in June, using [³H]P-R isolated at various periods of the year. The receptor preparations and the nuclear binding assays were conducted as described elsewhere (41,42,71,125). Saturating levels of [³H]P-R (300 μl/assay) for 60 μg/DNA assay were used in the binding assays. Each point represents the mean of four replicate analyses of the binding of [³H]P-R to chromatin. The receptor preparations were isolated at specific times during the year, stored at −80°C as ammonium sulfate precipitates, and resuspended on the day of the binding assay. The chromatin represented two preparations which were stored similarly and used upon demand. The broken line represents the *in vivo* binding of [³H]P-R to nuclear chromatin in fully developed oviducts of immature chicks conducted at various periods of the year. DES-treated chicks were injected with 200 μCi of [³H]P in 50 μl of ethanol–H₂O (1 : 1) into the wing vein. Evans Blue dye was included as a marker for the accuracy of the injection. One-half hour after injection, the birds were sacrificed and the oviducts quickly excised. The nuclear chromatin was immediately isolated and quantitated for DNA and assayed for nuclear binding. The nuclear bound [³H]P was extracted with 0.3 *M* KCl and quantitated by charcoal analysis. The extracted radioactivity was found to be bound to a 4 S sedimenting macromolecule in sucrose. The blood was collected and the radioactivity per 50 ml did not change. The data are plotted as cpm bound per mg DNA for the nuclear binding versus the date on which [³H]P was injected. (B) represents binding *in vitro* of P-R to pure DNA. The basic procedure followed

ing and binding to nuclear acceptor sites and altering transcription. In the case of the oviduct development system, as it progresses, this nuclear binding capacity gradually appears. The cell-free binding assays similarly show that the progesterone receptor from the immature oviduct displays no nuclear binding while the receptor from the more developed stages does show nuclear binding.

In summary, the cell-free nuclear bindings mimic the endogenous nuclear binding which in turn correlate with the subsequent transcriptional response to the steroid. Reciprocally when the steroid–receptor complex fails to translocate and bind to nuclear acceptor sites *in vivo*, the receptor fails to bind to isolated nuclei in the cell-free assays. In the active stage when the complex does bind to nuclear acceptor sites *in vivo*, the receptor in the cell-free assay shows marked nuclear binding in the cell-free assay.

V. Masking of Nuclear Acceptor Sites for the Avian Oviduct Progesterone Receptor

Initial studies on the effects of protein dissociation from the chromatin on the acceptor activity met with unexpected results. In the procedure of selectively removing proteins beginning with whole chromatin and ending with pure DNA, the extent of steroid receptor binding first markedly increases followed by an even greater decrease to a level of almost no binding. This rise in binding was later termed an "unmasking" of acceptor sites while the subsequent loss in binding has been termed the dissociation of nuclear acceptor components from the DNA. This is described below.

A. ROLE OF A SPECIFIC CHROMATIN NONHISTONE PROTEIN(S) IN THE MASKING OF NUCLEAR ACCEPTOR SITES

In the early studies, crude fractions of the chromosomal proteins were removed from chromatin followed by an analysis of the acceptor activity on the residual protein–DNA complexes (7,8,70,85). These studies were performed on free chromatin or chromatin attached to cellulose. Figure 7 presents an outline of the fractionation procedure, how they were dissociated from chromatin, and the proportion of total chromatin protein they

---

that for *in vitro* binding to chromatin as described in (A). (C) represents the effect of unlabeled P (0.5 mg) injected into estrogen-treated chicks at various times of the year. After 1 hour of the injections, the oviduct nuclei were isolated and assayed for RNA polymerase II activity as described elsewhere (41,124,137). Data reproduced with permission from Boyd and Spelsberg (41).

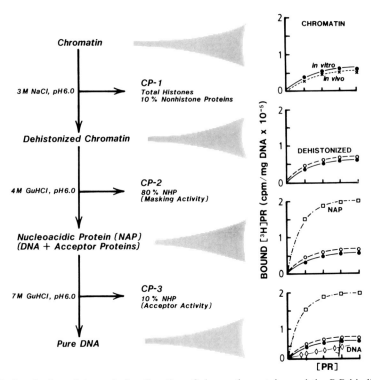

FIG. 7.   Outline of the early fractionation of chromatin proteins and the P-R binding *in vitro* to the residual treated chromatins. The left side of this figure outlines the crude fractionation procedure for isolating the chromatin protein fractions CP-1, CP-2, and CP-3. This method is described in detail elsewhere (6–8,72–74,85). The residual treated chromatins are obtained either by centrifugation of the chromatin stepwise in the designated solvents or by filtration of the solvents through chromatin-cellulose or chromatin acrylamide resins as described elsewhere (6,85). The right side of this figure shows a series of cell-free P-R binding assay using the residual treated chromatins (either free or attached to the resins) and a titration with increasing P-R levels. These data are taken from previously published articles (72–74, 85). Reproduced with permission from Webster *et al.* (85).

represent. The terminology of the residual deoxyribonucleoprotein after removal of each of the protein fractions from the chromatin is also given. The figure also shows on the right side the acceptor activity (i.e., the P-R binding) in the residual deoxyribonucleoprotein after the removal of the histones (CP-1), then the bulk of the nonhistone proteins (CP-2), and finally the remainder of the nonhistone protein tightly bound to the DNA (CP-3) to yield pure DNA (70,85). As can be seen, the removal of the CP-1 fraction (histones) from oviduct chromatin yielding dehistonized chromatin causes little change in the binding of P-R to the residual nucleoprotein (dehistonized chromatin). However, when fraction CP-2 (representing the bulk of the nonhistone protein) is removed, yielding nucleoacidic proteins (NAP), the binding by the P-R is markedly increased (1,7,8,70,72,73,85). Finally, the removal of the CP-3 fraction yielding pure DNA results in a marked loss in P-R binding. The DNA displays a low level, nonsaturable binding. Table III shows the extent of masking in oviduct chromatin with regard to the number of molecules of the P-R bound to nuclear acceptor sites per cell.

Following lengthy studies of this phenomenon (discussed further in the following sections), the increase in binding was termed an "unmasking" of acceptor sites with the CP-2 fraction assumed to contain the masking factor(s). As shown in Table III, the residual DNA–CP-3 complex,

TABLE III
Extent of Masking of High-Affinity Sites[a]

Source	Level of binding at saturation (molecules/cell)	Percentage of total sites masked
1. Oviduct nuclei *in vivo*	10,600	58
2. Oviduct nuclei *in vitro*	5,951	76
3. Oviduct chromatin *in vitro*	7,441	71
4. Oviduct chromatin minus histone (CP-1) (dehistonized chromatin)	9,278	58
5. Oviduct chromatin minus histone (CP-1) and CP-2 (nucleoacidic protein or NAP)	25,290	0
6. DNA	2,055	—
1. Spleen nuclei	60	100
2. Spleen chromatin	48	100
3. Spleen chromatin minus histone (CP-1) and CP-2 (NAP)	24,106	0
1. Erythrocyte nuclei	357	100
2. Erythrocyte chromatin	416	100
3. Erythrocyte chromatin minus histone (CP-1) and CP-2 (NAP)	15,018	0

[a] The number of binding sites measured in each of the chromatin minus histone (CP-1) and CP-2 preparations was assumed to represent the total sites in the respective chromatin, and thus each of these preparations was assigned 0% masking. The values at saturation for each preparation were taken at 100 μg of injected hormone for the *in vivo* binding and 200 μl labeled receptor preparation for the *in vitro* binding. The preparations of the nuclear components as well as the hormone binding assays were performed as described elsewhere (85). Reproduced with permission from Spelsberg *et al.* (71).

termed "nucleoacidic protein" or NAP, contains the high capacity binding. The significant decrease in binding of the progesterone receptor with the removal of the CP-3 fraction suggests that this fraction contains the acceptor component(s) (i.e., those needed for P-R binding). This CP-3 fraction is discussed in detail later in this article.

Interestingly, the nontarget tissue chromatins such as spleen and erythrocyte show little or no binding by the P-R (Table III) (1,7,8,69,70,72,73,85). When the CP-1 and CP-2 fractions are removed from these chromatins, the resulting NAPs display marked binding, equivalent to the NAP obtained from the target tissue chromatin. Thus, the acceptor sites in nontarget tissue chromatin appear to be totally masked, i.e., are not expressed. When the NAPs from these chromatins are completely deproteinized, the resulting pure DNAs show the same low level of binding as the DNA from oviduct. Table III shows the extent of masking to these nontarget tissue chromatins based on the number of steroid–receptor complexes bound to nuclear acceptor sites per cell. Thus, the chromosomal material of many tissues of the bird appears to contain the same number of acceptor sites for the progesterone receptor but the majority in the oviduct and all in nontarget tissues are "masked." Similar findings have subsequently been reported in the estrogen receptor–calf uterine chromatin system (88), the estrogens and progesterone receptor–sheep brain chromatin system (86), and the androgen receptor–rat prostate chromatin system (84). It should be mentioned that Chytil and Spelsberg (147,148) successfully prepared rabbit antisera to the chick oviduct CP-3 protein fraction. Using a complement fixation assay, these investigators demonstrated that the majority of the antigenic sites of the CP-3 fraction were "masked" in whole oviduct chromatin. Removal of the CP-2 fraction unmasked approximately 80% of the antigenic sites. These results using the complement fixation assays with antisera to CP-3 closely mimic those obtained with the cell-free nuclear binding assays of P-R with regard to the "masking" of the CP-3 proteins.

The CP-2 proteins have been reannealed to the NAP (the DNA–CP-3 complex) using a regressing concave gradient from 6 M GuHCl to 0 M GuHCl in specially designed chambers (175). Interestingly, a remasking of a similar quantity of sites as measured in the original intact chromatin is achieved. The CP-2 fraction has been subfractionated into three fractions, CP-2a, CP-2b, and CP-2c. As shown in Fig. 8, when a variety of different protein fractions are reannealed to NAP, only one fraction, the CP-2b, representing only 10% of the CP-2 fraction, displays the masking activity by markedly lowering the extent of binding of the P-R. The CP-2a fraction, ovalbumin, and histones display no masking activity. The CP-2c fraction remained insoluble and could not be analyzed. The increase in

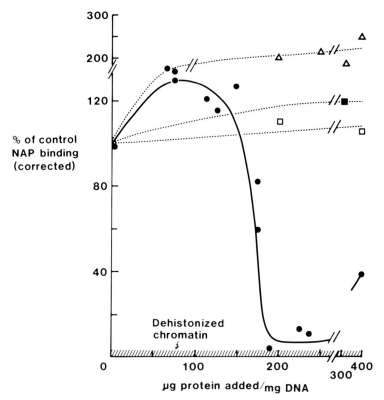

FIG. 8.   Reconstitution of chromatin components which mask nuclear acceptor sites for progesterone. The CP-2 fraction of the chromatin proteins was subfractionated into several groups: CP-2a, CP-2b, and CP-2c, representing 10, 6, and 33% of the total chromatin protein, respectively. Two of these fractions, as well as standard ovalbumin and total histone, were reannealed to the NAP at increasing ratios of protein to DNA using methods described previously (6,71,73). After reconstitution, the DNA bound protein was separated from the unbound protein and the former assayed for P-R binding using the streptomycin assay (85). The values are corrected for DNA binding. (●) CP-2b, (□) CP-2a, (△) ovalbumin, and (■) histone. The hatched area on the abscissa represents values for P-R binding to the dehistonized chromatin. From Martin-Dani and Spelsberg (175).

binding observed with the ovalbumin was observed occasionally and found to be caused by a protection of the acceptor sites from proteolytic activity occurring toward the end of the reconstitution. Since proteolytic but not nucleolytic action on chromatin causes an unmasking of sites, protein(s) are believed to represent the masking factors (175). Since the CP-2b fraction dissociates from chromatin long after the histones and since the histones do not mask the acceptor sites in the reconstitution assays, it is speculated that the masking activity is a specific class of nonhistone proteins. Preliminary analysis by molecular sieve chromatography using CL-Sepharose 6B in 6 M GuHCl containing mercaptoethanol (pH 6.0) suggests a very heterogeneous population of masking "proteins" with monomer molecular weights ranging from 60,000 to 130,000 and possibly larger (175).

B. COMPARISON OF THE MASKED ACCEPTOR SITES WITH THE UNMASKED ACCEPTOR SITES FOR THE PROGESTERONE RECEPTOR

In order to examine the significance of these findings, the biological relevance of these masked sites was examined. Comparisons between the binding of the progesterone receptor to the oviduct NAP (in which all acceptor sites are exposed) and the binding to whole chromatin (in which only a fraction of the sites are exposed) were performed.

Figure 4B shows that the binding of the progesterone receptor to acceptor sites on the oviduct NAP (with all acceptor sites available for binding including many which normally are masked in whole chromatin) requires an intact, activated receptor as found with the unmasked sites in whole chromatin. Further, the receptor is dissociated from the NAP with 0.3 M KCl as is the case for the binding to unmasked sites. The binding to these sites on the NAP is saturable. Previous studies showed similar affinities of binding of the P-R to both the masked and unmasked sites with a K_d approximately 10^{-8} to 10^{-9} M (85). Thus, a marked similarity between the acceptor sites expressed in intact chromatin (representing unmasked sites) and the sites on NAP (representing both masked and unmasked sites) is found.

The receptor preparations showing seasonal rhythms in nuclear binding as described earlier (see Fig. 6) were then used to analyze these unmasked sites. Figure 9A shows that cell-free binding of the progesterone receptor to the NAP (with all binding sites expressed) reflects the same seasonal rhythm as does the *in vivo* binding to whole chromatin displayed by the dashed line (with 80% of the binding sites masked). As shown in Fig. 6, the binding to pure DNA shows no fluctuation during the year using these receptors. Similar studies were performed using the estrogen-induced oviduct development system. As shown in Fig. 10 (upper graph), in the early stages of the oviduct development, the P-R is incapable of translocating and binding to nuclear acceptor sites *in vivo* and altering transcription. As development progresses, the receptor acquires the capacity for nuclear binding and inducing changes in transcription (176). Interestingly, the P-R isolated from the undeveloped oviduct also shows little or no cell-free binding to NAP. As development progresses, the receptors isolated from

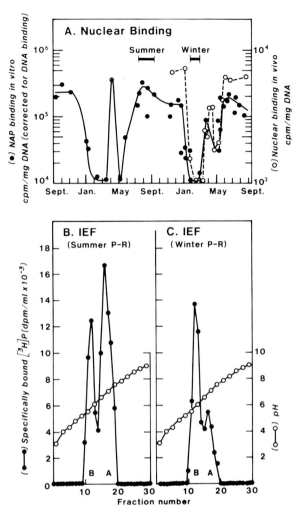

FIG. 9. Seasonal changes in P-R binding to nuclear acceptor sites in the chick oviduct. The binding of P-R to isolated NPA *in vitro* and chromatin *in vivo* using receptors isolated at various times of the year has been described in the legend of Fig. 6 and elsewhere. In (A) the solid line shows the seasonal binding by P-R to NAP (representing the total acceptor sites) *in vitro;* the broken line shows the seasonal binding to whole oviduct chromatin in vivo. In (B and C) the P-R isolated from the summer and winter period, respectively (see periods of isolation in A), were analyzed for the molecular species by isoelectric focusing as described elsewhere (40,41). Reproduced with permission from Boyd and Spelsberg (41).

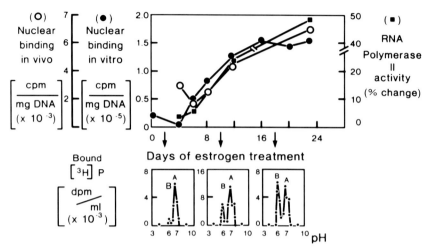

FIG. 10. Composite of functions of the progesterone receptor during oviduct development. The undeveloped oviducts of immature chicks were induced to full development with
daily injections of estrogens. In the upper large panel, changes in the (●) cell-free NAP
binding by the isolated P-R, (○) nuclear binding *in vivo*, and (■) RNA polymerase II
responses to injected progesterone are displayed. The methods are described elsewhere
(41). It can be seen that a nonfunctioning P-R (i.e., incapable of nuclear binding and alteration of transcription) occurs in the immature oviduct, explaining the nonresponsiveness of
the organ to progesterone. In the lower panels, the isolated P-R from different stages of
oviduct development (see arrows) were analyzed for the molecular species by isoelectric
focusing as described elsewhere (40,41). From Boyd and Spelsberg (176).

these developing tissue gain the capacity for binding to NAP in the cell-
free assays. These changes in the cell-free binding are not observed when
pure DNA or DNA–CP-1 fractions are used in place of NAP. Since the
NAP used in these studies was the same preparation from mature oviducts, the pattern of binding was not due to the nuclear acceptor sites.
Thus, the cell-free binding to NAP mimics the binding to chromatin *in
vivo*.

In conclusion, it can be seen that the normally masked sites in chromatin which are unmasked by the removal of the CP-2 fraction (to yield
NAP) appear to have many properties in common with the unmasked
sites on the whole chromatin. The similarities include dependency on an
intact, activated receptor, the affinity of binding, the concentration of salt
required to dissociate the steroid–receptor complex, and the patterns of
binding observed during oviduct development and during the year in the
mature oviduct. Absolute proof of identical sites will require purification
of the acceptor proteins, preparation of antisera, and comparison of antigenic properties between the masked and unmasked sites.

C. ROLE OF MASKING PROTEINS IN THE SELECTION OF STEROID-INDUCED GENE EXPRESSION

The question arises as to the biological role of the masking phenomenon. One possible function may be that the masking regulates which genes will respond to the P-R. The regulation of which genes will respond to a steroid would explain a heretofore unexplained but important dilemma in endocrinology: "why different target tissues of the same organism with presumably the same type of receptor display markedly different responses to the same steroid with regard to gene expression." In short, different genes seem to be regulated by the same steroid–receptor complex in different tissues. Recent evidence indicating that the steroid receptors are antigenically similar in different tissues of different animals minimizes the tissue specificity of the receptors themselves (149–151).

In short, those genes which are masked in the oviduct chromatin may represent either genes which are currently expressed (unmasked) in other progesterone target tissues or genes which were expressed at an earlier stage of development of the organism. In nontarget tissues which do not possess steroid receptors and thus do not require genes that respond to steroids, all such steroid-regulated genes (or at least their acceptor sites) would be masked. this is supported in Table III wherein all acceptor sites appear to be masked in the chromatin of a nontarget tissue. This concept is further supported by studies on the developing oviduct. During the development of a target organ such as the chick oviduct, quantitative and qualitative changes in the masking activity might be expected as different cell types appear or change in proportions. During oviduct development, different genes are found to respond to the same steroid such as estrogen (152). Figure 11 shows that quantitative changes in the extent of masking of a constant amount of acceptor sites occur during oviduct development (175). The number of available acceptor sites (chromatin binding) but not the total number of sites (NAP binding) changes throughout the estrogen-induced development. Thus, the extent of masking changes considerably.

Indications that the masking during organ development may be qualitatively changing was suggested by antigenic analysis of the CP-3 fraction during rat liver and oviduct development. Using the complement fixation assay with antisera prepared against the CP-3 fraction of the adult rat liver or mature oviduct chromatin, as discussed earlier with the chick oviduct (148), an indication of qualitative changes in masking during the development of the rat liver and chick oviduct was observed (148,153). One explanation of these results is that the masking of different fractions of the CP-3 proteins (i.e., different regions of the genome) is occurring on the chromatin during organ development.

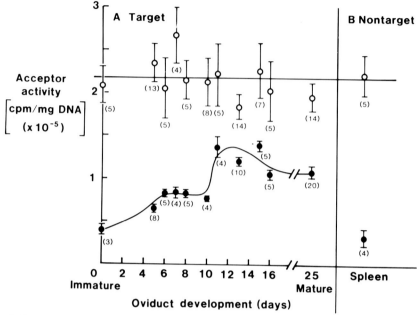

FIG. 11. Differential masking of progesterone acceptor sites during oviduct cytodifferentiation. (A) shows the acceptor levels for P-R (at saturation) in (●) whole chromatin or (○) NAP during oviduct development using a cell-free binding of P-R as described elsewhere (41,85). (B) shows the same values for spleen, a nontarget tissue for progesterone removed at day 25 of estrogen treatment. The mean and standard deviation of multiple replicate analyses of the binding (the number shown in parentheses) are presented. These experiments are described in greater detail in the text. From Martin-Dani and Spelsberg (175).

Further, several other laboratories have reported similar masking of nuclear acceptor sites of other steroid receptor systems using methods developed in this laboratory (69,85). These are androgens in the rat prostate (84), estrogens and progesterone in the sheep brain (86), glucocorticoids in the rat liver (87), estrogens in the rat and bovine uterus (88), and estrogens in the chick oviduct (177). The basic results of these studies in general confirmed those described in this article for the avian oviduct progesterone receptor.

Therefore, the masking phenomenon may well represent the means by which steroid-regulated genes are differentially expressed in different target tissues. Figure 12 shows a model which outlines a scheme for regulating different steroid inducible genes during oviduct development. At different stages of cytodifferentiation, the masking proteins establish different patterns of masked and unmasked acceptor sites, thereby determining

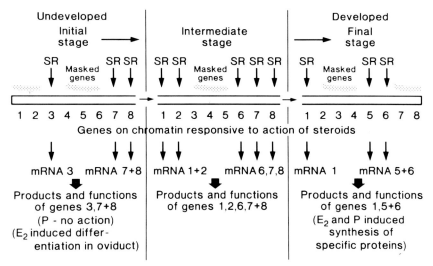

FIG. 12.   Hypothetical model of the regulation of steroid-induced gene expression by the masking proteins during oviduct development.

which genes will and which ones will not respond to the incoming steroid receptor. At present this model of masking remains to be verified. Evidence that masking exists in other steroid target tissue systems lends support to its existence. The evidence of total masking of the steroid receptor binding sites in nontarget tissues is interesting but the rationale for it is obscure since these tissues do not contain receptors anyway.

D. A HYPOTHETICAL MODEL OF CHROMATIN STRUCTURE WITH MASKING PROTEINS

Figure 13 shows a model of chromatin with its nucleosomes containing the bulk of the histones, a suggested position for the H-1 histone, and expressed (unmasked) acceptor sites (the square blocks) as well as the masked acceptor sites (square blocks overlaid with cylinders). The acceptor sites (denoted as blocks) are bound to specific DNA sequences (discussed later). The removal of the CP-1 fraction (or histones) by 3 M NaCl does not remove the masking proteins. The removal of the CP-2 fraction with 4 M GuHCl to yield the NAP does remove the masking proteins represented by the cylinders and causes a marked enhancement in binding of the P-R by exposing many additional acceptor sites. During cytodifferentiation, the masking components (the cylinders) would be shifted from one acceptor site to another, thereby preventing some while allow-

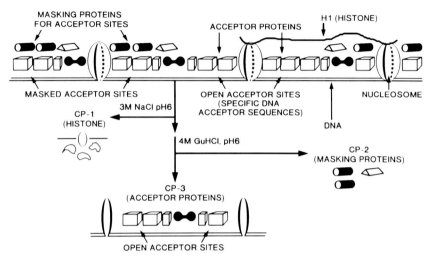

FIG. 13. Model of the oviduct chromatin with regard to unmasking of acceptor sites in avian oviduct chromatin. This model depicts the DNA wrapping in and around the nucleosomes (Nu bodies) which contain all of the histones, termed the CP-1 fraction, except the H1 histone species. The multitude of different nonhistone species are represented in large groups as symbols, i.e., one symbol represents many species. The cylinders represent masking proteins which are a part of the CP-2 fraction which in turn masks the acceptor proteins, represented by the square. The squares which represent the acceptor proteins are a part of the CP-3 fraction. These acceptor proteins in turn sit on specific DNA sequences. Positions on the intact chromatin where the cylinders do not cover the squares represent the "open acceptor" sites for P-R; those with cylinders covering them represent masked sites. The model also depicts the removal of the CP-1 fraction with 3 M NaCl and the CP-2 fraction with 4 M GuHCl. The latter causes an unmasking of all acceptor sites, as depicted in the figure. Reproduced with permission from Spelsberg (7).

ing others to bind incoming steroid receptors and respond to the steroid stimulus.

VI. Discovery of Novel Regulations in the Avian Oviduct Progesterone Receptor during These Studies

The identification of inactive progesterone–receptor complexes in the avian oviduct (i.e., incapable of translocating and binding to nuclear acceptor sites) during the winter (Figs. 6 and 9) (7,8,41,74,108,123,124,154) in the undeveloped oviduct (Fig. 10) (7,8,154,176), after estrogen withdrawal, or in aged hens (42) and in moulting hens (178), represents the first instances of such "inactivation" of receptors in "normal" tissue. The interesting fact is that, except for the aged hen, the inactivations are reversible. Thus, the P-R in these instances can bind the steroid but cannot bind to nuclear acceptor sites and alter transcription (Figs. 6, 9, and 10). This incapacity is also found in the cell-free system where cell compartmentalization is removed. Analysis of the inactive and active receptors in each instance revealed similar molecular sizes by molecular sieve chromatography, similar 8 S to 4 S transitions on high salt sucrose gradients, and similar affinities of binding the steroid (41,42,154). However, in every instance, one of the two molecular species of the avian oviduct P-R [the A and B species as characterized previously (37–39,43–45)] disappear as the receptor becomes inactive (see Figs. 9 and 10 and Refs. 7,41,42,154). In the winter, the A species is missing (Fig. 9) and in

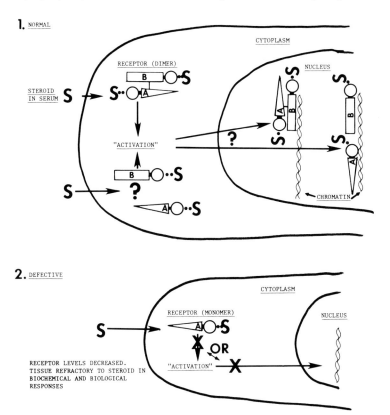

FIG. 14.   Hypothetical models of the regulation of steroid receptor activity via one of the two molecular species. In Model 1, the P-R contains both molecular species and is functional, i.e., it can translocate and bind to nuclear acceptor sites and alter gene expression. The molecular species act either individually or as a dimer as depicted. In either case, both species are required for full activity. In Model 2, one of the two species is missing (in this case, B is depicted as missing), i.e., incapable of translocating and binding to nuclear acceptor sites. Reproduced with permission from Boyd *et al.* (42).

the undeveloped oviduct (Fig. 10) the B species is missing. The cause of the species' disappearance and its exact relationship to the inactivation of the P-R remain unknown. Mixing experiments of oviduct cytosol containing inactive receptor with those of active receptor show no effect on either receptor state, suggesting that inhibitors are not present (or available) or activators missing which would cause the receptor inactivation (124).

It was previously speculated that the two receptor species (A and B) may function as a dimer since both species were found to be translocated to the nucleus (37–39,43–45). The results presented above support but do not prove this theory. As shown in a model in Fig. 14-1, when both species of the P-R are observed, the receptor is functional and translocates to the nucleus, binds to the nuclear acceptor sites, and alters transcription. The two subunits or species do not have to function as a dimer. However, as shown in Fig. 14-2, when one of these species is missing, the receptor is inactivated. It should be stated that the loss of one of the two species of P-R during inactivation may be a secondary event to the inactivation process.

The identification of inactive steroid receptors in these tissues may explain why many human tumors of steroid target tissues do not respond to steroid therapy even though the receptors are present (see Ref. 154 for further discussion).

VII. Chemical Characterization of the Nuclear Acceptor Sites for the Avian Oviduct Progesterone Receptor

A. SPECIFIC CHROMATIN NONHISTONE PROTEINS AND DNA IN THE NUCLEAR ACCEPTOR SITES

1. Analysis of the Acceptor Activity Dissociated from Chromatin: Reconstitution of the CP-3 Fraction to DNA

The free proteins in CP-3 were found not to bind P-R. However, when the proteins containing the acceptor activity were reannealed to DNA, P-R binding was observed. This reconstituted NAP is a soluble complex which contains acceptor activity.

The procedure for reannealling the isolated acceptor proteins (contained in the CP-3 protein fraction) to pure DNA was developed in part empirically and in part from the literature published over the past 20 years. Many methods have been published which allow the refolding of denatured enzymes and proteins to their biologically active forms (155–162), as well as to recombine proteins to DNA for the reconstruction of native-like deoxyribonucleoproteins (1,6,68,71,74,123,163–172). The methods and conditions used to reconstruct nucleoproteins are similar to those used to renature proteins. Since NaCl-urea and GuHCl were used to dissociate the acceptor activity from the DNA, a method to reconstitute the activity on the DNA was developed using a reverse gradient of these solvents (6,68,71–73,123,163–172). The method was modified for achieving optimal amounts of active acceptor sites and several conditions were found to be critical. The method is outlined in Fig. 15. Details of the method are described elsewhere (174). This reconstitution approach is necessary to monitor the acceptor activity for P-R after it is dissociated from the chromatin and during its purification. During the reannealing of the CP-3 fraction to pure DNA, the acceptor activity was found to reconstitute to the DNA when the GuHCl concentration reached 2.0 M GuHCl from 6 M GuHCl.

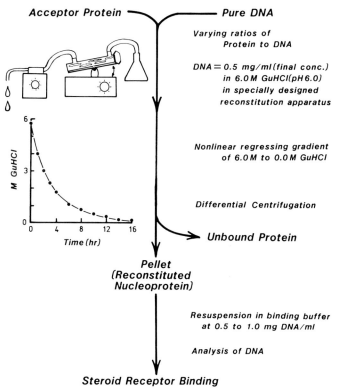

FIG. 15. Outline of the method for reconstituting the progesterone receptor acceptor activity using isolated CP-3 protein fraction and pure DNA. From T. C. Spelsberg, (unpublished).

2. Identification of the Acceptor Activity with a Specific Protein Fraction

Figure 16 shows the acceptor activity remaining on the protein–DNA complexes after the oviduct chromatin was treated with various concentrations GuHCl. In Panel A the chromatin was attached to cellulose while it was unattached in Panel B. After each extraction of the chromatin–cellulose resin in Panel A, the resin is washed with dilute buffers to remove traces of guanidine. The free chromatin (Panel B) is first sedimented by ultracentrifugation to separate it from the dissociated protein. The residual nucleoprotein is resuspended in dilute buffer and dialyzed against the same buffer to remove traces of GuHCl. In each method, there is an unmasking of acceptor sites on the residual deoxyribonucleoprotein with extractions of 2 to 4 M GuHCl. The level of unmasking achieved with

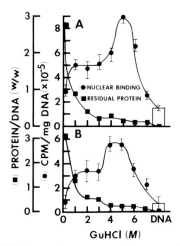

FIG. 16.   Binding of [³H]P-R to nuclear acceptor sites on residual deoxyribonucleoprotein after extractions with sequential increases in GuHCl concentration of chromatin. (A) represents binding of [³H]P-R to hen oviduct chromatin-cellulose treated with GuHCl; (B) represents P-R binding to unattached hen oviduct chromatin resuspended in GuHCl and centrifuged. In these experiments, portions of chromatin-cellulose or unattached chromatin were washed twice in 20 volumes of solutions containing various concentrations of GuHCl buffered at pH 6.0. The cellulose resins were then washed in dilute Tris–EDTA buffer several times, frozen, and lyophilized. The free chromatin samples in various concentrations of GuHCl were centrifuged at 10^5 g for 36 hours. The pellets of residual deoxyribonucleoproteins were resuspended in dilute Tris buffer at 1 mg DNA/ml and dialyzed versus the buffer. The residual material was tested for (■) protein and (●) acceptor activity using saturating levels of the P-R. The binding assays were performed essentially as described by Webster *et al*. The average and range of three replicate analyses for each assay of the hormone binding are shown. (A) is reproduced with permission of Spelsberg *et al*. (69). (B) is reproduced with permission of Thrall *et al*. (6).

the 4 M GuHCl (pH 6.0) is identical with that achieved using the 2 M NaCl–5 M urea (pH 6.0) shown in Fig. 7. As shown in Fig. 16, when the chromatin is extracted with 7 M GuHCl (or treated with phenol-chloroform or pronase as seen in Fig. 3B), the acceptor activity markedly decreases to levels found with pure DNA. The 7 M GuHCl treatment thus dissociates the CP-3 from DNA and thus removes the "acceptor activity" from the DNA.

The proteins dissociated from the chromatin DNA by the chromatin-cellulose and similarly by the chromatin-hydroxylapatite methods were

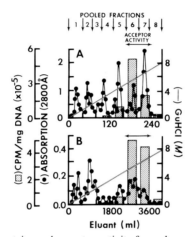

FIG. 17.   Elution of proteins and acceptor activity from chromatin-cellulose and chromatin-hydroxylapatite resins. In (A) hen oviduct chromatin-cellulose resin was prepared as described elsewhere (69,85). Briefly, 20 g of this resin containing approximately 60 mg DNA as chromatin was resuspended in 100 ml cold phosphate buffer (pH 6.0) and allowed to hydrate for 2–6 hours with gentle stirring at 4°C. The resin was collected in a column and a gradient of 0–8 M GuHCl in phosphate buffer (pH 6.0) passed through the column within a 4-hour period. In (B) resins of chromatin-hydroxylapatite were prepared in the presence of 0.05 M KPO_4, pH 6.0. The resin containing 100 mg chromatin DNA and 100 g hydroxylapatite was placed on the column and 4 ml fractions were collected under a 0–7 M GuHCl gradient. Tubes were monitored by absorption at 280 nm. Fractions were also monitored for conductivity as well as refractive index, and the gradient level of GuHCl plotted. Fractions from both resins were pooled according to their elution with each unit of concentration of GuHCl (1, 2, 3 M, etc.). Pooled samples were then dialyzed thoroughly against water and lyophilized. The lyophilized materials were resuspended in a small volume of water, homogenized in a Teflon pestle glass homogenizer, assayed for protein, and reannealed to pure hen DNA using a reverse gradient of 6 M GuHCl to 0 M GuHCl as described in the text. The reconstituted nucleoproteins were analyzed for acceptor activity by the streptomycin method (85), subtracting the values obtained with pure DNA. The acceptor activity is presented as bar graphs. Total recoverable protein after dialysis and lyophilization was estimated to be 50% of the total protein placed on the column as chromatin-cellulose or chromatin-hydroxylapatite. Reproduced with permission from Spelsberg et al. (73).

then examined for acceptor activity. As depicted in Fig. 17, the fractions eluting from these resins were pooled according to unit molarities of GuHCl in the eluants. These pooled samples were reconstituted to DNA and assayed for acceptor activity, i.e., P-R binding. Figure 17 shows that in two different methods of fractionating the chromosomal proteins, the fractions dissociating from DNA between 4 and 6 M GuHCl contained the acceptor activity. Thus, as the acceptor activity disappears from the chromatin (Fig. 16), it appears in the eluant (Fig. 17).

3. Biological Relevance of the Reconstituted Acceptor Sites

The binding of the P-R to the reconstituted NAP displays the same requirements as was determined for the native (undissociated) NAP and chromatin with regard to intact, activated receptor (see Fig. 4). Further, as shown in Fig. 18, the receptor preparations isolated at various periods of the year display a seasonal rhythm in binding to a common preparation of reconstituted NAP as is observed for the native NAP and whole chromatin (shown in Fig. 6). These results indicate that the reconstituted NAP is very similar to the native NAP which in turn displays the same seasonal pattern of nuclear binding as found *in vivo* (see Figs. 6 and 9). Section VI,B describing the quantitative titration of the acceptor activity on the DNA gives further support to the reconstitution of native acceptor sites.

4. Problems and Artifacts in Analyzing the Nuclear Acceptor Sites

The isolation and handling of the acceptor activity in the CP-3 fraction and the reconstitution of the activity by reannealling the CP-3 proteins to the DNA involve many obstacles and artifacts. The proteolytic degradation of the acceptor proteins, the conditions required for optimal reconstitution (e.g., proper pH, DNA and CP-3 concentrations and proportions, period of the reverse gradient, proper mixing, etc.), the separation of DNA bound from unbound proteins and so on, had to be resolved. One major problem was the effect of damage to pure DNA on the P-R binding. Figure 19 shows a summary of the effects of various treatments of pure DNA on this P-R binding. Practically every treatment or agent which partially damages the native DNA double helix causes a marked enhancement of the P-R binding (see Ref. 108 for details). Thus, by slightly damaging the DNA, we can create marked binding of a steroid receptor. This binding, however, has been shown to be nonsaturable and to not follow the seasonal pattern of binding as the native chromatin (Fig. 6), NAP (Fig. 9), or reconstituted NAP (Fig. 18) (108). In any case, great care must be taken in performing these above described methods to eliminate the artifacts which artificially decrease or increase the P-R binding.

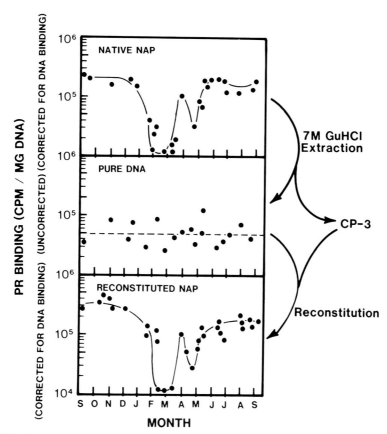

FIG. 18. Comparison of acceptor activities in native (undissociated) and reconstituted NPA using P-R isolated at different periods of the year. The binding of P-R isolated at various periods of the year to native (undissociated) NAP, pure DNA, and reconstituted NPA was performed essentially as described in the legends of Figs. 6 and 9. The right side of the figure shows the removal of the CP-3 protein fraction from native NAP using 7.0 M GuHCl (pH 6.0) to obtain pure DNA. Also shown is the reannealling of the CP-3 to the DNA to obtain reconstituted NAP. Reproduced in part with permission from Spelsberg and Halberg (124).

B. SPECIFIC REPETITIVE DNA SEQUENCES ASSOCIATED WITH THE ACCEPTOR SITES

The 7 M GuHCl extract from the chromatin hydroxylapatite resin was subsequently used as a source of the acceptor activity and subjected to a series of analyses, first in the reconstitution assays for analysis of the involvement of specific DNA sequences and second as the starting point in the purification and chemical characterization of the acceptor activity.

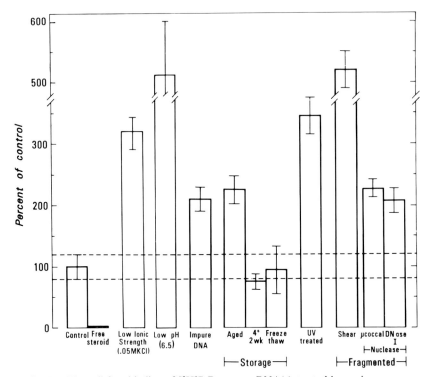

FIG. 19.   The cell-free binding of [³H]P-R to pure DNA(s) treated by various means as depicted in the abscissa. Pure hen DNA were subjected to a variety of treatments and conditions for damaging DNA structure as described in detail elsewhere (108). These preparations were analyzed for the cell-free P-R binding using levels of the receptor which would saturate all sites on the same amount of DNA as NAP. Reproduced with permission from Thrall and Spelsberg (108).

Figure 20 shows the reconstitution of the acceptor activity (P-R binding capacity) as a function of the ratio of the CP-3 protein to whole hen DNA. Two interesting aspects arise from these studies. First, the reconstitution of the acceptor sites on the DNA is saturable. Second, the level of progesterone receptor binding at this saturation is approximately the same level measured in native (undissociated) NAP (see broken line in Fig. 20). These results suggest a DNA sequence specificity for the acceptor protein since not all sequences on the whole hen DNA appear to generate the P-R binding sites.

To further analyze this possibility, the CP-3 fraction was reannealed to DNA from different sources containing different sequences. As shown in Fig. 21A, little differences in P-R binding are detected in P-R binding to the pure DNA(s) from bacterial, Salmon sperm, and hen DNA. The bind-

ings are nonsaturable and low capacity. However, when the CP-3 is reannealed to these DNAs, only the reconstituted NAP containing hen DNA
displays the high level of P-R binding as is found with native NAP (Fig.
21B). The CP-3 bound to Salmon sperm or bacterial DNA show little
change in P-R binding compared to the respective pure DNA. Thus, not
only does DNA seem to be required for acceptor activity but specific
sequences of DNA appear to be required.

Preliminary studies to characterize the DNA sequences involved in the
nuclear acceptor sites for the oviduct progesterone receptor have been
initiated. As described in Fig. 7, only 10 to 20% of the total nonhistone
chromosomal proteins in chromatin remains in the NAP as a complex
with DNA. It was found that these proteins protect about 10–15% of the
total DNA from deoxyribonuclease digestion (DNase I). Thus, an enriched fraction of the protein–DNA complexes can be achieved by digestion of the NAP with deoxyribonuclease (DNase I). Interestingly, the
acceptor sites are maintained in this enriched protein DNA complex. The
DNA in the protein–DNA complexes of the NAP which contain the ac-

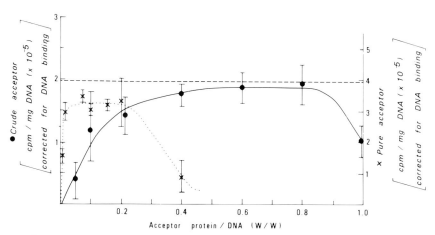

FIG. 20.   Effects of varying quantities of the acceptor protein added to DNA on the
acceptor activity of the reconstituted NAP. The acceptor proteins were obtained from the 4–
7 M GuHCl extract from hydroxylapatite–hen oviduct chromatin resin. These were reannealed to the hen DNA in varying quantities using a reverse gradient of 6 M GuHCl to 0 M
GuHCl, as described in the text. The DNA concentration was 0.2 mg/ml. After reconstitution the pelleted DNA–protein was resuspended in the dilute Tris buffer (0.5 mg DNA/ml)
and analyzed for (●) P-R binding. Pure DNA was also analyzed for hormone binding and the
values subtracted from those obtained from the protein–DNA. The (×) represent reconstitution of acceptor proteins purified further by molecular sieve chromatography (using agarose
1.5M). (---) represents the average binding levels of P-R to native NAP. Reproduced with
permission from Spelsberg et al. (73).

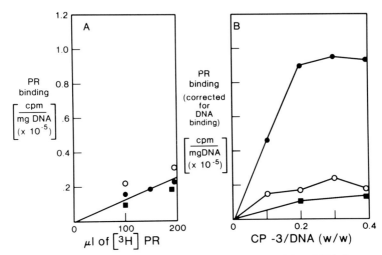

FIG. 21. Binding of [³H]P-R to reconstituted NAP containing DNA from several sources. (A) represents the binding of P-R to the pure DNA isolated from different species. The *E. coli* and Salmon sperm DNAs were purchased from PL Biochemicals (Milwaukee, WI) and further purified to less than 1% (w/w) protein and RNA. (●), Hen DNA; (○), *E. coli* DNA; (■), Salmon sperm DNA. The mean of four replicate analyses of each receptor level for each DNA is presented in each panel. (B) represents the binding of [³H]P-R is reconstituted NAP containing the different DNAs. The NAPS were reconstituted using the various DNAs and increasing levels of hen oviduct acceptor protein (CP-3 fraction) as described in the legend of Fig. 23. The binding assays were performed at the saturating receptor level. The various reconstituted NAPs contained (●), hen DNA; (■), Salmon sperm DNA; (○), *E. coli* DNA. The binding values to the various pure DNA preparations were subtracted from the corresponding DNA reconstituted as NAP to give the "corrected for DNA binding." Reproduced with permission from Spelsberg (7,8).

ceptor activity and which are resistant to the DNAse were isolated, labeled with ³²P or ³H by nick translation methods, and used for sequence complexity analysis by DNA–DNA hybridization. Based on the low c_0t values from these hybridization studies, these DNase-resistant DNA fragments appear to contain little to no unique sequences but only intermediate to highly repetitive sequences. The exact class of sequences representing those involved in the acceptor sites for the P-R in the avian oviduct is being investigated.

VIII. Characterization of the Acceptor Protein

Two early studies were performed to determine whether or not the acceptor activity was due to protein(s). When the NAP was treated with pronase, most of the acceptor activity was lost. It was further found that, when isolated, CP-3 was subjected to increasing degrees of proteolysis (as determined by degradation of the [^{14}C]ovalbumin) and then reannealed to DNA, a loss in the acceptor function occurred. No such loss in acceptor function was observed when the CP-3 protein was subjected to ribonuclease action (T. C. Spelsberg, unpublished data).

A more physical chemical approach was used to show the proteinaceous property of the acceptor activity. Figure 22 shows the patterns of isopycnic centrifugation of the DNA-free acceptor "activity" in the CP-3 fraction. Standards for protein, RNA, and DNA were also applied to similar gradients. The gradients consisted of 6 M GuHCl with increasing concentrations of metrizamide and run at 5°C for 72 hours. This method was developed for application to hydrophobic proteins (T. C. Spelsberg, unpublished results). Fractions from the gradient were collected, pooled as shown in the figure, reannealed to the DNA at varying protein to DNA ratios, and the reconstituted NAP assayed for acceptor activity. All acceptor activity banded in the density region of simple (nonconjugated) proteins. Thus, the acceptor factor behaves as a protein with regard to protease substrates and density. The acceptor appears to be a protein(s).

The acceptor activity in the CP-3 fraction is presently being purified. The CP-3 is isolated by chromatin-hydroxylapatite chromatography.

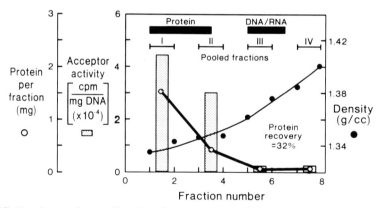

FIG. 22.   Isopycnic centrifugation of acceptor proteins in metrizamide gradients containing 6 M GuHCl. The CP-3 protein fraction was placed in 6 M GuHCl buffered at pH 6.0 and the solution layered over a gradient of 10 to 50% CsCl$_2$ in 6 M GuHCl in SW 50.1 rotor tubes. The tubes were centrifuged for 72 hours at 100,000 g_{ave}. Some tubes contained standard DNA, RNA, or protein. Fractions of the gradients were collected and the (●) density determined. The fractions were then pooled as depicted in the figure, and the (○) protein content quantitated. These fractions were reannealed to pure DNA and the reconstituted NAP assessed for P-R binding (acceptor activity) as illustrated by the bars. Values for P-R binding to pure DNA were subtracted from the respective NAP binding values. Reproduced with permission from Spelsberg (7).

First, histones (CP-1) are removed by 3 M NaCl (pH 6.0). The CP-2 fraction (containing the masking activity) is removed with 4 M GuHCl (pH 6.0). The CP-3 fraction (containing the acceptor activity) is then removed with 7 M GuHCl (pH 6.0). The CP-3 fraction is then concentrated in an Amicon hollow fiber dialyzer/concentrator, dialyzed against water, lyophilized, and stored as a lyophilized powder. It is this stock CP-3 fraction that was used in the following analysis and those in Figs. 20 through 22.

Figure 23 shows the elution of total protein and the acceptor activity from a 5 × 100-cm column of CL-Sepharose 6B using 6 M GuHCl buffered at pH 6.0 as the solute. The fractions were pooled into six large groups (as shown in the figure) and each fraction reannealed to DNA and assayed for P-R binding. Although some of the activity elutes near the void volume, the bulk of the acceptor elutes near the inclusion volume of the column in the molecular weight range of 14,000 and 18,000. When resins with exclusion sizes, e.g., Sephadex G-200 or agarose 0.5 M were used with 6 M GuHCl, the activity elutes near or at the void volumes. Isoelectric focusing patterns of the acceptor activity using the LKB flat bed gel apparatus with Superfine G-60 Sephadex in 6 M urea and ampho-

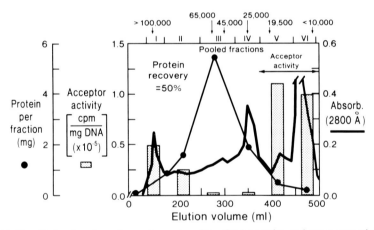

FIG. 23.   Molecular sieve chromatography of the CP-3 proteins and acceptor activity in CL-Sepharose 6-B. The CP-3 protein fraction was resuspended in a 6 M GuHCl solution at 2 mg protein/ml. This protein solution was clarified by centrifugation at 20,000 g for 10 minutes and then applied to a 2.6 × 94-cm column of the resin. The eluted fractions were pooled according to the absorbing peaks (——) as shown in the figure. The pooled fractions were quantitated for (●) protein and then reannealed to DNA and assayed for "acceptor" activity (as illustrated by the bars) using the streptomycin assay (85). Values for P-R binding to pure DNA were subtracted from respective values obtained with nucleoprotein. The average of four replicates of the binding analysis are shown. Reproduced with permission from Spelsberg (7).

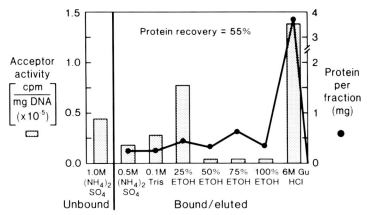

FIG. 24. Hydrophobic chromatography of the acceptor activity on octyl Sepharose. The lyophilized CP-3 fraction of chromatin was resuspended in 6 M GuHCl (pH 6.0) for several hours. The solution was dialyzed against 1 M $(NH_2)_2SO_4$ and the retentate clarified by centrifugation. The supernatant was applied to the octyl Sepharose column. Two to three column volumes of each of the solvents listed in the figure were passed through the resin and collected. Each fraction was (●) quantitated for protein and portions of each fraction reconstituted to DNA. The reconstituted NAPs were then tested for P-R binding (acceptor activity), as depicted by the bars (T. C. Spelsberg, unpublished results).

lines for a 3 to 10 pH range, displayed two primary peaks of acceptor activity, one focusing around a pH range of 5.0 to 5.5 and the other over a broader range of pH 6 to 7.0. These proteins clearly are not histones since they dissociate from the DNA at much higher GuHCl concentrations than histones and they focus in acidic pH range while histones focus at the extreme basic pH range (off the scale of the isoelectric focusing plates). Using hydrophobic chromatography, and eluting the acceptor activity from octyl Sepharose with various concentrations of methanol and then 6 M GuHCl also revealed two major peaks of activity (Fig. 24). Two peaks of activity are also detected when other eluting solvents such as ethylene glycol and chaotropic salts (Na perchlorate or acetonitrile, etc.) are used. The major peak of activity consistently elutes only at the higher concentrations of the GuHCl or the chaotropic salts suggesting the acceptor protein(s) are very hydrophobic. This in turn suggests that the proteins might lie in one of the two grooves of the DNA to interact with the hydrophobic regions (base pairs) in the center of the helix. Alternatively, the proteins might interact with the hydrophobic regions of each other in clusters on the DNA.

In any event, the acceptor activity appears to be a nonhistone protein(s) bound to specific sequences of the DNA. To summarize the studies to date, the properties of the acceptor (protein) activity are presented. As

TABLE IV
General Properties of Acceptor Proteins for Progesterone Receptor in Aian Oviduct

Property	Value	Evidence
Proteinaceous	Yes	1. Activity destroyed by proteases but not RNase, DNase, or phosphatase
Simple or conjugated	If so, only minor	2. Purified activity contains no RNA or DNA
		3. Isopycnic centrifugation
Side chain modification	Unknown	
Molecular weight	13,000–18,000	1. Molecular sieve
		2. SDS–PAGE
Isoelectric point	pH 6; pH 7.0 possibly more	1. Isoelectric focusing
		2. Chromatofocusing
Density	1.24 g/cm³	Isopycnic centrifugation
Molecular species	One major, one minor, possibly more	1. Isoelectric focusing/chromatofocusing
		2. Hydrophobic chromatography
Steroid receptor specificity	Yes	Does not bind Estrogen receptor
DNA sequence specificity	Yes	Activity reconstituted with most animal DNA; not bacteria, viral, fish, or plant DNA
Tissue specificity	Tentative no	Activity masked and protein present in nontarget tissue chromatins
Species specificity	Unknown	

shown in Table IV the acceptor activity appears to be a small molecular sized, slightly acidic protein, two species (or more), a simple protein with little or no conjugated lipids, nucleic acids, or sugars, and appears to have a DNA sequence specificity and a steroid receptor specificity. Attempts are now in progress to further purify these proteins to homogeneity from bulk quantities of chromatin.

IX. Potential Function(s) of the Acceptor Proteins and the Acceptor DNA Sequences

Figure 25 represents a hypothetical model for the distribution of acceptor sites in the oviduct genome for the hen oviduct progesterone receptor or any steroid–target tissue system. In Model A (direct action), the steroid receptor (SR) binds to acceptor sites neighboring the steroid regulated structural genes. Each binding would directly regulate that particular gene's transcription. In Model B (indirect action), the SR binds to regulatory gene regions, which transcribe RNA and possibly protein which in turn regulate structural gene expression. Acceptor sites with different affinities for the SR would be differentially regulated depending on the concentration of the SR. How many SR molecules bound per acceptor site or the exact location of acceptor sites is unknown.

Figure 26 presents a hypothetical model of the binding of the steroid receptor to the acceptor sites containing specific acceptor protein(s) and specific DNA sequence(s). In Fig. 26, Model A shows the acceptor proteins inducing a particular ultrastructure of the DNA to serve as a recognition site for the SR which binds directly to the protein (AP)–DNA complex. In Model B, the SR binds directly to the DNA adjacent to the protein (AP)–DNA complex whose structure is perturbed by the protein–DNA interaction. In both of these models the SR binding somehow induces gene transcription. Model C combined both Models A and B. This model shows one of the two known species of the steroid receptor (the B species) binding to the acceptor protein in the chromatin acceptor sites with the A species binding to the adjacent DNA region to somehow acti-

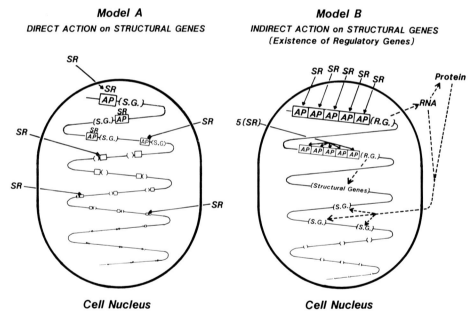

FIG. 25. Models for the distribution of acceptor sites for steroid receptors in the oviduct nucleus. In Model A, the steroid receptor complexes (SR) enter the nucleus and bind to many acceptor sites, each located near a structural gene(s) (SG) which is regulated by that steroid. One or a few SR would bind to each acceptor site which is composed of a specific acceptor protein and a specific DNA sequence. In Model B the SR binds next to regulatory genes (RG) which code for RNA. The RNA (or its coded protein) in turn regulate the structural genes. In this instance, the acceptor sites would be distant from the structural genes. In both Models A and B, the acceptor sites would be composed of specific proteins (AP) and a specific subclass of intermediate repetitive sequences.

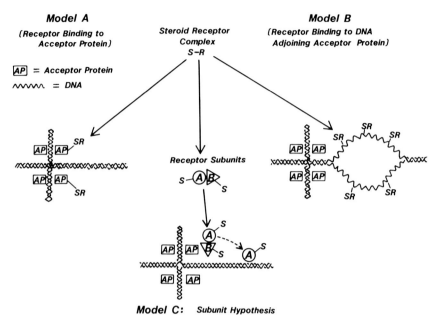

Model A

(Receptor Binding to Acceptor Protein)

Steroid Receptor Complex
S–R

Model B

(Receptor Binding to DNA Adjoining Acceptor Protein)

AP = Acceptor Protein

⋀⋀⋀⋀ = DNA

Receptor Subunits

Model C: Subunit Hypothesis

FIG. 26.   Model of possible mechanism of action of steroid receptor complexes on transcription. In this scheme, the steroid–receptor complex enters the nucleus and binds to the acceptor sites, either directly to the acceptor proteins (Model A) or to the adjacent DNA (Model B) or both (Model C). The receptor would then activate transcription by modulating the DNA structure or affecting the polymerase itself. The acceptor proteins in this instance would serve either as a direct binding site for the steroid receptor (Model A) or would perturb the DNA structure to allow the steroid–receptor complex to bind to the DNA. In Model B, examples of the perturbation of the DNA structure could be hairpin loops of pallindromic regions or induction of left-handed helices or single-stranded regions. In Model C, one of the two subunits of the P-R (the B species) binds to the protein, the A species then binds to the adjacent DNA to activate transcription. This model was first described by Schrader *et al.* (39,43,173).

vate transcription. This two subunit receptor theory was devised somewhat empirically based on the nuclear binding properties of the two receptor species (39,44,45,173). It should be mentioned, however, that the exact mechanism of binding of the receptors to the nuclear acceptor sites remains to be determined. The biological function of the A and B subunits of the chick oviduct progesterone receptor is also not totally clear.

It is this author's opinion that steroid receptors represent one class (of a multitude) of intracellular gene regulators in eukaryotes. The nuclear acceptor sites may reside in or near structural genes or at a distance at regulatory gene regions. The acceptor proteins and their specific DNA sequences may function indirectly only as recognition (binding) sites or may be directly involved in the regulation of transcription of DNA. Since there may be thousands of nuclear acceptor sites, the DNA component may be a class of repetitive sequences (probably intermediate, repetitive class), residing at a few or many locations throughout the genome as depicted in Fig. 24.

X. Conclusions

This article has dealt with the problems and progress in the chemical characterization of the nuclear acceptor sites for steroid receptors with major emphasis on the progesterone receptor of the avian oviduct. These nuclear acceptor sites and their components are important for the understanding of the mechanism of steroid-induced changes in gene transcription and for understanding how genes are regulated. As mentioned earlier, the high-affinity binding to chromatin in cell-free assays, the masking phenomenon, and the high-affinity saturable binding to the unmasked sites on NAP have been reported for other steroid target tissue systems (84–88). It is not known whether the steroid–receptor complex binds directly to the acceptor protein(s) or to the DNA in the vicinity of the acceptor protein–DNA sequence. The stoichiometric relationship between the number of receptors and the number of acceptor proteins or acceptor DNA sequences is also not known. Lastly, if the receptor binds directly to the DNA, the mechanism by which the acceptor proteins function to enhance this binding is unknown. These and many other questions must first await the elucidation of the exact chemical nature of the acceptor sites, the isolation of the components, and the reconstruction of the acceptor sites with these components. Major effort is presently underway to purify to homogeneity the acceptor proteins for the progesterone receptor of the avian oviduct. It is planned to prepare antisera (polyclonal and monoclonal) against these proteins, and to use these antibodies to examine the masked and unmasked acceptor sites, the tissue and species specificity of the acceptor proteins, and to assist in the isolation of the specific DNA sequences bound by acceptor proteins.

Most studies on the quantitative nuclear binding of steroids estimate between 1,000 and 10,000 biologically important nuclear acceptor sites per cell for a variety of steroid–target tissue systems (2–6). If the masked sites are the same as the unmasked sites in the hen oviduct chromatin, then about 25,000 acceptor sites per cell are estimated. Assuming that there is one P-R per one acceptor protein, that the acceptor proteins average about 15,000 in molecular weight, and using the facts that avian DNA contains 2.5×10^{-12} g DNA per diploid cell and that 1 mg chromatin DNA can be isolated from 1 g of oviduct, it can be calculated that 10 kg of oviduct should yield 2.5 mg acceptor protein at 100% recovery. If the above assumptions are close to the actual state, the purification of the acceptor protein(s) to homogeneity is feasible.

ACKNOWLEDGMENTS

Funds for these studies were provided by the NIH HD 9140B and NIH HD 16705 and the Mayo Foundation.

REFERENCES

1. Spelsberg, T. C., Steggles, A. W., and O'Malley, B. W. (1971). *J. Biol. Chem.* **246,** 4188.
2. Gorski, J., and Gannon, F. (1976). *Annu. Rev. Physiol.* **39,** 425.
3. Jensen, E. V., and DeSombre, E. R. (1972). *Annu. Rev. Biochem.* **41,** 203.
4. O'Malley, B. W., and Means, A. R. (1974). *Science* **183,** 610.
5. Spelsberg, T. C., and Toft, D. O. (1976). *In* "Receptors and the Mechanism of Action of Steroid Hormones" (J. R. Pasqualini, ed.), Pt. 1, p. 261. Dekker, New York.
6. Thrall, C., Webster, R. A., and Spelsberg, T. C. (1978). *In* "The Cell Nucleus" (H. Busch, ed.), Vol. 6, Pt. 1, p. 461. Academic Press, New York.
7. Spelsberg, T. C. (1982). *In* "Biochemical Actions of Hormones" (G. Litwack, ed.), Vol. 9, p. 141. Academic Press, New York.
8. Spelsberg, T. C. (1983). *In* "Chromosomal Nonhistone Proteins—Biochemistry and Biology" (L. S. Hnilica, ed.). CRC Press, Cleveland, Ohio, in press.
9. Harrison, R. W., Fairfield, S., and Orth, D. N. (1974). *Biochem. Biophys. Res. Commun.* **61,** 1262.
10. Milgrom, E., Atger, M., Baulieu, E.-E. (1970). *Steroids* **167,** 741.
11. Peck, E. J., Burgner, J., Clark, J. H. (1973). *Biochemistry* **12,** 4596.
12. Williams, D., and Gorski, J. (1974). *Biochemistry* **13,** 5537.
13. Jensen, E. V., and Jacobson, H. I. (1962). *Recent Prog. Horm. Res.* **18,** 387.
14. Jensen, E. V., Suzuki, T., Kawashima, T., Stumpf, W. E., Jungblut, P. W., and DeSombre, E. R. (1968). *Proc. Natl. Acad. Sci. U.S.A.* **59,** 632.
15. Stumpf, W. E., and Sar, M. (1976). *In* "Receptors and Mechanisms of Action of Steroid Hormones" (J. R. Pasqualini, ed.), Pt. 1, p. 41. Dekker, New York.
16. Talwar, G. P., Segal, J. J., Evans, A., and Davidson, O. W. (1964). *Proc. Natl. Acad. Sci. U.S.A.* **52,** 1059.
17. Toft, D. O., and Gorski, J. (1966). *Proc. Natl. Acad. Sci. U.S.A.* **55,** 1574.
18. Beato, M., Biesewig, D., Braendle, W., and Sekeris, C. E. (1969). *Biochim. Biophys. Acta* **192,** 494.
19. Baulieu, E.-E., Alberga, A., and Jung, I. (1967). *C. R. Acad. Sci. Ser. D* **265,** 501.
20. Gorski, J., Toft, D. O., Shyamala, D., Smith, A., and Notides, A. (1968). *Recent Prog. Horm. Res.* **24,** 45.
21. Little, M., Rosenfeld, G. C., and Jungblut, P. W. (1972). *Hoppe-Seylers Z. Physiol. Chem.* **53,** 231.
22. Little, M., Szendro, P. I., and Jungblut, P. W. (1973). *Hoppe-Seylers Z. Physiol. Chem.* **354,** 1599.
23. Sheridan, P. J., Buchannon, J. M., Anselmo, V. C., and Martin, P. M. (1979). *Nature (London)* **282,** 579.

24. Martin, P. M., and Sheridan, P. J. (1980). *Experientia* **36**, 620.
25. Yamamoto, K. R. (1974). *J. Biol. Chem.* **249**, 7068.
26. Notides, A. C., and Nielsen, S. (1974). *J. Biol. Chem.* **249**, 1866.
27. Cake, M. H., Goidl, J. A., Parchman, L. G., and Litwack, G. (1976). *Biochem. Biophys. Res. Commun.* **71**, 45.
28. Thrower, S., Hall, C., Lim, L., and Davidson, A. N. (1976). *Biochem. J.* **160**, 271.
29. Puca, G. A., Nola, E., Sica, V., and Bresciani, F. (1977). *J. Biol. Chem.* **252**, 1358.
30. Milgrom, E., Atger, M., and Baulieu, E.-E. (1973). *Biochemistry* **12**, 5198.
31. Chamness, G. C., Jennings, A. W., and McGuire, W. L. (1974). *Biochemistry* **13**, 327.
32. Andre, J., and Rochefort, H. (1975). *FEBS Lett.* **50**, 319.
33. Nishigori, H., and Toft, D. (1979). *J. Biol. Chem.* **254**, 9155.
34. Simons, S. S., Martinez, H. M., Gracea, R. L., Baxter, J. D., and Tomkins, G. M. (1976). *J. Biol. Chem.* **251**, 334.
35. Goidl, J. A., Cake, M. H., Dolan, K. P., Parchman, L. G., and Litwack, G. (1977). *Biochemistry* **16**, 2125.
36. Bailly, A., Sallas, N., and Milgrom, E. (1977). *J. Biol. Chem.* **252**, 858.
37. Sherman, M. R., Corvol, P. L., and O'Malley, B. W. (1970). *J. Biol. Chem.* **245**, 6085.
38. Schrader, W. T., and O'Malley, B. W. (1972). *J. Biol. Chem.* **247**, 51.
39. Schrader, W. T., Toft, D. O., and O'Malley, B. W. (1972). *J. Biol. Chem.* **247**, 2401.
40. Boyd, P. A., and Spelsberg, T. C. (1979). *Biochemistry* **18**, 3679.
41. Boyd, P. A., and Spelsberg, T. C. (1979). *Biochemistry* **18**, 3685.
42. Boyd-Leinen, P. A., Fournier, D., and Spelsberg, T. C. (1982). *Endocrinology* **111**, 30.
43. Schrader, W. T., Heuer, S. S., and O'Malley, B. W. (1975). *Biol. Reprod.* **12**, 134.
44. Buller, R. E., Schwartz, R. J., Schrader, W. T., and O'Malley, B. W. (1976). *J. Biol. Chem.* **251**, 5178.
45. Vedeckis, W. V., Schrader, W. T., and O'Malley, B. W. (1978). *In* "Biochemical Actions of Hormones" (G. Litwack, ed.), Vol. 5, p. 321. Academic Press, New York.
46. Dougherty, J. J., and Toft, D. O. (1982). *J. Biol. Chem.* **257**, 3113–3119.
47. Mueller, G. C., Herranen, A. M., and Jervell, K. J. (1958). *Recent Prog. Horm. Res.* **14**, 95.
48. Hamilton, T. H., Teng, C. S., and Means, A. R. (1968). *Proc. Natl. Acad. Sci. U.S.A.* **59**, 1265.
49. Knowler, J. T., and Smellie, R. M. S. (1971). *Biochem. J.* **125**, 605.
50. Chan, L., Means, A. R., and O'Malley, B. W. (1973). *Proc. Natl. Acad. Sci. U.S.A.* **70**, 1870.
51. Chan, L., Jackson, R. L., O'Malley, B. W., and Means, A. R. (1976). *J. Clin. Invest.* **58**, 368.
52. Harris, S. E., Rosen, J. M., Means, A. R., and O'Malley, B. W. (1975). *Biochemistry* **14**, 2072.
53. Palmiter, R. D., Moore, P. B., Mulvihil, E. R., and Emtage, S. (1976). *Cell* **8**, 557.
54. Spelberg, T. C., and Cox, R. F. (1976). *Biochim. Biophys. Acta* **435**, 376.
55. Church, R. B., and McCarthy, B. J. (1970). *Biochim. Biophys. Acta* **199**, 103.
56. Clark, J. H., Peck, E. J., and Anderson, J. N. (1974). *Nature (London)* **251**, 446.
57. Capony, F., and Rochefort, H. (1975). *Mol. Cell. Endocrinol.* **3**, 233.
58. Jackson, V., and Chalkley, R. (1974). *J. Biol. Chem.* **249**, **1615.**
59. Jackson, V., and Chalkley, R. (1974). *J. Biol. Chem.* **249**, **59.**
60. Sekeris, C. E., and Lang, N. (1965). *Hoppe-Seylers Z. Physiol. Chem.* **340**, 92.
61. Sluyser, M. (1966). *J. Mol. Biol.* **19**, 591.
62. Sluyser, M. (1969). *Biochim. Biophys. Acta* **182**, 235.
63. King, R. J. B., and Gordon, J. (1967). *J. Endocrinol.* **39**, 533.

64. Puca, G. A., Sica, V., and Nola, E. (1974). *Proc. Natl. Acad. Sci. U.S.A.* **71**, 979.
65. Puca, G. A., Nola, E., Hibner, U., Cicala, G., and Sica, V. (1975). *J. Biol. Chem.* **250**, 6452.
66. Mainwaring, W. I. P., Symes, E. K., and Higgins, S. J. (1976). *Biochem. J.* **156**, 129.
67. Alberga, A., Jung, I., Massol, N., Raynaud, J.-P., Raynaud-Jammet, C., Rochefort, H., Truong, H., and Baulieu, E.-E. (1971). *In* "Advances in the Biosciences" (G. Raspe, ed.), Schering Workshop on Steroid Hormone Receptors, Vol. 7, p. 45. Pergamon, Oxford.
68. Spelsberg, T. C., Steggles, A. W., Chytil, F., and O'Malley, B. W. (1972). *J. Biol. Chem.* **247**, 1368.
69. Spelsberg, T. C., Webster, R. A., and Pikler, G. M. (1975). *In* "Chromosomal Proteins and Their Role in Gene Expression" (G. Stein and E. Kleinsmith, eds.), p. 153. Academic Press, New York.
70. Spelsberg, T. C., Webster, R. A., and Pikler, G. M. (1976). *Nature (London)* **262**, 65.
71. Spelsberg, T. C., Webster, R., Pikler, G., Thrall, C., and Wells, D. (1976). *J. Steroid Biochem.* **7**, 1091.
72. Spelsberg, T. C., Webster, R., Pikler, G., Thrall, C., and Wells, D. (1977). *Ann. N.Y. Acad. Sci.* **286**, 43.
73. Spelsberg, T. C., Thrall, C. L., Webster, R. A., and Pikler, G. M. (1977). *J. Toxicol. Environ. Health* **3**, 309.
74. Spelsberg, T. C., Knowler, J., Boyd, P. A., Thrall, C. L., and Martin-Dani, G. (1979). *J. Steroid Biochem.* **11**, 373.
75. Tymoczko, J. L., and Kiao, S. (1971). *Biochim. Biophys. Acta* **252**, 607.
76. Baxter, J. D., Rousseau, G. G., Bensen, M. C., Garcea, R. L., Ito, J., and Tomkins, G. M. (1972). *Proc. Natl. Acad. Sci. U.S.A.* **69**, 1892.
77. King, R. J. B., and Gordon, J. (1972). *Nature (London) New Biol.* **240**, 185.
78. Liang, T., and Liao, S. (1972). *Biochim. Biophys. Acta* **277**, 590.
79. Liao, S., Liang, T., and Tymoczko, J. L. (1972). *J. Steroid Biochem.* **3**, 401.
80. O'Malley, B. W., Spelsberg, T. C., Schrader, W. T., Chytil, F., and Steggles, A. W. (1972). *Nature (London)* **235**, 141.
81. Lebeau, M. C., Maisol, N., and Baulieu, E.-E. (1973). *Eur. J. Biochem.* **36**, 294.
82. Defer, N., Dastugue, B., and Kruh, J. (1974). *Biochimie* **56**, 559.
83. Gschwendt, M. (1976). *Eur. J. Biochem.* **67**, 411.
84. Klyzsejko-Stefanowicz, L., Chui, J. F., Tsai, Y. H., and Hnilica, L. S. (1976). *Proc. Natl. Acad. Sci. U.S.A.* **73**, 1954.
85. Webster, R. A., Pikler, G. M., and Spelsberg, T. C. (1976). *Biochem. J.* **156**, 409.
86. Perry, B. N. and Lopez, A. (1978). *Biochem. J.* **176**, 873.
87. Hamana, K., and Iwai, K. (1978). *J. Biochem. (Jpn.)* **83**, 279.
88. Ruh, T. S., Ross, P., Wood, P. M., and Keene, J. L. (1981). *Biochem. J.* **200**, 133.
89. Clemens, L. E., and Kleinsmith, L. J. (1972). *Nature (London) New Biol.* **237**, 204.
90. Musliner, T. A., and Chader, G. J. (1972). *Biochim. Biophys. Acta* **262**, 256.
91. Toft, D. O. (1972). *J. Steroid Biochem.* **3**, 515.
92. Yamamoto, K. R., and Alberts, B. M. (1972). *Proc. Natl. Acad. Sci. U.S.A.* **69**, 2105.
93. Yamamoto, K. R., and Alberts, B. M. (1974). *J. Biol. Chem.* **249**, 7076.
94. Yamamoto, K. R., and Alberts, B. M. (1975). *Cell* **4**, 301.
95. Yamamoto, K. R., and Alberts, B. M. (1976). *Annu. Rev. Biochem.* **45**, 722.
96. Higgins, S. J., Rousseau, G. G., Baxter, J. D., and Tomkins, G. M. (1973). *Proc. Natl. Acad. Sci. U.S.A.* **70**, 3415.
97. Higgins, S. J., Rousseau, G. G., Baxter, J. D., and Tomkins, G. M. (1973). *J. Biol. Chem.* **248**, 5866.

98. Higgins, S. J., Rousseau, G. G., Baxter, D. D., and Tomkins, G. M. (1973). *J. Biol. Chem.* **248,** 5873.
99. Yamamoto, K. R., Stampfer, M. R., and Tomkins, G. M. (1974). *Proc. Natl. Acad. Sci. U.S.A.* **71,** 3901.
100. Rousseau, G. G., Higgins, S., Baxter, J. D., Gelfand, D., and Tomkins, G. M. (1975). *J. Biol. Chem.* **250,** 6015.
101. Alberta, A., Ferrez, M., and Baulieu, E.-E. (1976). *FEBS Lett.* **61,** 223.
102. Bugany, H., and Beato, M. (1977). *Mol. Cell. Endocrinol.* **7,** 49.
103. Simons, S. S. (1977). *Biochim. Biophys. Acta* **496,** 349.
104. Kallos, J., and Hollander, V. (1978). *Nature (London)* **272,** 177.
105. Cidlowski, J. A., and Munck, A. (1978). *Biochim. Biophys. Acta* **543,** 545.
106. Thanki, K., Beach, T., and Dickerman, H. (1978). *J. Biol. Chem.* **253,** 7744.
107. Kallos, J., Fasy, T., Hollander, V., and Beck, M. (1978). *Proc. Natl. Acad. Sci. U.S.A.* **75,** 4896.
108. Thrall, T. C., and Spelsberg, T. C. (1980). *Biochemistry* **19,** 4130.
109. Toft, D. O. (1973). *Adv. Exp. Med. Biol.* **36,** 85–96.
110. Socher, S. H., Krall, J. F., Jaffe, R. C., and O'Malley, B. W. (1976), *Endocrinology* **99,** 891.
111. Yamamoto, K. R., Gehring, U., Stampfer, M. R., and Sibley, C. H. (1976). *Recent Prog. Horm. Res.* **32,** 3.
112. Andre, J., Pfeiffer, A., and Rochefort, H. (1976). *Biochemistry* **15,** 2964.
113. Carlstedt-Duke, J., Okret, S., Wrange, O., and Gustafsson, J. A. (1982). *Proc. Natl. Acad. Sci. U.S.A.* **79,** 4260.
114. Payvar, F., Wrange, O., Carlstedt-Duke, J., Okret, S., Gustafsson, J. A., and Yamamoto, K. (1981). *Proc. Natl. Acad. Sci. U.S.A.* **78,** 6628.
115. Govindan, M. V., Speiss, E., Majors, J. (1982). *Proc. Natl. Acad. Sci. U.S.A.* **79,** 5157.
116. Mulvihill, E. R., LePennec, J. P., and Chambon, P. (1982). *Cell* **24,** 621.
117. Compton, J. G., Schrader, W. T., and O'Malley, B. W. (1982). *Biochem. Biophys. Res. Commun.* **105,** 96.
118. Liao, S., Liang, T., and Tymoczko, J. L. (1973). *Nature (London) New Biol.* **241,** 211.
119. Barrack, E. R., and Coffey, D. S. (1980). *J. Biol. Chem.* **255,** 7265.
120. Barrack, E. R., Hawkins, E. F., Allen, S. L., Hicks, L. L., and Coffey, D. S. (1977). *Biochem. Biophys. Res. Commun.* **79,** 829.
121. Buller, R. E., and O'Malley, B. W. (1976). *Biochem. Pharmacol.* **25,** 1.
122. Spelsberg, T. C., Pikler, G. M., and Webster, R. A. (1976). *Science* **194,** 197.
123. Spelsberg, T. C., Thrall, C. L., Martin-Dani, G., Webster, R. A., and Boyd, P. A. (1979). *In* "Ontogeny of Receptor and Reproductive Hormone Action" (T. H. Hamilton, J. H. Clark, and W. A. Sadler, eds.), p. 31. Raven, New York.
124. Spelsberg, T. C., and Halberg, F. (1980). *Endocrinology* **107,** 1234.
125. Pikler, G. M., Webster, R. A., and Spelsberg, T. C. (1976). *Biochem. J.* **156,** 399.
126. Spelsberg, T. C. (1983). *Biochemistry.*
127. Lohmar, P. H., and Toft, D. O. (1975). *Biochem. Biophys. Res. Commun.* **67,** 8.
128. Webster, R. A., and Spelsberg, T. C. (1979). *J. Steroid Biochem.* **10,** 343.
129. Beziat, Y., Guilleux, J. C., and Mousseron-Canet, M. (1970). *C. R. Acad. Sci. Ser. D* **270,** 1620.
130. Mohla, S., DeSombre, E. R., and Jensen, E. V. (1972). *Biochem. Biophys. Res. Commun.* **46,** 661.
131. Jensen, E. V., Brecher, P. I., Numata, M., Mohla, S., and DeSombre, E. R. (1973). *Adv. Enzyme Regul.* **11,** 1.

132. Jensen, E. V., Mohla, S., Gorell, T. A., and DeSombre, E. R. (1974). *Vitam. Horm.* **32**, 89.
133. Buller, R. E., Schwartz, R. J., and O'Malley, B. W. (1976). *Biochem. Biophys. Res. Commun.* **69**, 106.
134. Schwartz, R. J., Tsai, M. J., Tsai, S. Y., and O'Malley, B. W. (1975). *J. Biol. Chem.* **250**, 5175.
135. Schwartz, R. J., Kuhn, R. W., Buller, R. E., Schrader, W. T., and O'Malley, B. W. (1976). *J. Biol. Chem.* **251**, 5166.
136. Schwartz, R. J., Schrader, W. T., and O'Malley, B. W. (1976). *In* "Juvenile Hormones" (L. Gilbert, ed.), p. 530. Plenum, New York.
137. Spelsberg, T. C. (1976). *Biochem. J.* **156**, 391–398.
138. Kon, O. L., Webster, R. A., and Spelsberg, T. C. (1980). *Endocrinology* **107**, 1182.
139. Kon, O. L., and Spelsberg, T. C. (1982). *Endocrinology*.
140. Spelsberg, T. C. (1974). *In* "Acidic Proteins of the Nucleus" (I. L. Cameron and J. R. Jeter, Jr., eds.), p. 249. Academic Press, New York.
141. O'Malley, B. W., Toft, D. O., and Sherman, M. R. (1971). *J. Biol. Chem.* **246**, 1117.
142. Raspe, G., ed. (1971). "Advances in Biosciences," Vol. 7. Pergamon, Oxford.
143. King, R. J. B., and Mainwaring, W. I. P., eds. (1974). "Steroid Cell Interactions." Univ. Park Press, Baltimore, Maryland.
144. Pasqualini, J. R., ed. (1976). "Receptors and Mechanism of Action of Steroid Hormones," Pts. 1 and 2. Dekker, New York.
145. Tomkins, G. M. (1970). *Cold Spring Harbor Symp. Quant. Biol.* **35**, 635.
146. Clark, J. H., Anderson, J. N., and Peck, E. J. (1973). *Adv. Exp. Biol. Med.* **36**, 15.
147. Chytil, F., and Spelsberg, T. C. (1971). *Nature (London) New Biol.* **233**, 215.
148. Chytil, F. (1975). *Methods Enzymol.* **40**, 191.
149. Greene, G. L., Closs, D. E., Fleming, H., DeSombre, E. R., and Jensen, E. V. (1977). *Proc. Natl. Acad. Sci. U.S.A.* **74**, 3681.
150. Greene, G. L., Nolan, C., Engler, J. P., and Jensen, E. V. (1980). *Proc. Natl. Acad. Sci. U.S.A.* **77**, 5115.
151. Eisen, H. J. (1980). *Proc. Natl. Acad. Sci. U.S.A.* **77**, 3893.
152. O'Malley, B. W., McGuire, W. L., Kohler, P. O., and Korenman, S. G. (1969). *Recent Prog. Horm. Res.* **25**, 105.
153. Chytil, F., Glasser, S. R., and Spelsberg, T. C. (1974). *Dev. Biol.* **37**, 295.
154. Spelsberg, T. C., Boyd-Leinen, P. A., Martin-Dani, G., and Kon, O. L. (1981). *In* "Drug Receptors and Their Effectors" (N. J. M. Birdsell, ed.), p. 133. Macmillan, New York.
155. Tanford, C. (1968). *Adv. Protein Chem.* **23**, 122.
156. Teipel, J. W., and Kochland, D. E. (1971). *Biochemistry* **10**, 792.
157. Weber, K., and Kuter, D. J. (1971). *J. Biol. Chem.* **246**, 4504.
158. Teipel, J. W. (1972). *Biochemistry* **11**, 4100.
159. Yazgan, A., and Henkens, R. W. (1972). *Biochemistry* **11**, 1314.
160. Carlsson, U., Henderson, L. E., and Lindskog, S. (1973). *Biochim. Biophys. Acta* **310**, 367.
161. Ahmad, F., and Salahuddin, A. (1976). *Biochemistry* **15**, 5168.
162. Lykins, L. F., Akey, C. W., Christian, E. G., Duval, G. E., and Topham, R. W. (1977). *Biochemistry* **16**, 693.
163. Spelsberg, T. C., Hnilica, L. S., and Ansevin, A. T. (1971). *Biochim. Biophys. Acta* **228**, 550.
164. Spelsberg, T. C., and Hnilica, L. S. (1970). *Biochem. J.* **120**, 435.
165. Paul, J., Gilmour, R. S., Affara, N., Birnie, G. D., Harrison, B. P., Hell, A., Humphe-

ries, S., Windass, J., and Young, B. (1973). *Cold Spring Harbor Symp. Quant. Biol.* **38**, 885.

166. Axel, R., Melchior, W., Sollner-Webb, B., and Felsenfeld, G. (1974). *Proc. Natl. Acad. Sci. U.S.A.* **71**, 4101.
167. Barrett, T., Maryanka, D., Hamlyn, P. H., and Gould, H. J. (1974). *Proc. Natl. Acad. Sci. U.S.A.* **71**, 5057.
168. Stein, G. S., Spelsberg, T. C., and Kleinsmith, L. J. (1974). *Science* **183**, 817.
169. Stein, G. S., Mans, R. J., Gabbay, E. J., Stein, J. L., Davis, J., and Adawadkar, P. D. (1975). *Biochemistry* **14**, 1859.
170. Chae, C. B. (1975). *Biochemistry* **14**, 900.
171. Gadski, R. A., and Chae, C. B. (1976). *Biochemistry* **15**, 3812.
172. Woodcock, C. L. F. (1977). *Science* **195**, 1350.
173. Schrader, W. T., Kuhn, R. W., and O'Malley, B. W. (1977). *J. Biol. Chem.* **252**, 299.
174. Toyoda, H., Seelke, R., and Spelsberg, T. C. (1983). In preparation.
175. Martin-Dani, G., and Spelsberg, T. C. (1983). In preparation.
176. Boyd, P. A., and Spelsberg, T. C. (1983). In preparation.
177. Ruh, T., and Spelsberg, T. C. (1983). In preparation.
178. Kon, O. L., and Spelsberg, T. C. (1983). In preparation.

DISCUSSION

I. A. Kourides: Your data show that there are repetitive sequences of DNA rather than unique sequences in the chicken genome that are involved in the interaction of the progesterone nuclear receptor with the chromatin. Earlier this year, Chambon's laboratory had published a paper in which they showed that there was a unique area of nucleotides, 5'-ward or upstream from the transcription initiation site of the ovalbumin gene, that was involved in receptor binding to chromatin. How would your data and their data fit together?

T. C. Spelsberg: Not mutually exclusive and I'll comment on that. Our data strongly suggest that we're dealing with repetitive sequences but it may look that way because of the crude preparation that we have right now. We have to enrich these sequences to be sure. In Chambon's studies, the binding was performed with a fairly purified receptor, wherein he has separated the A and B subunits. When we do that (i.e., when we separate the A and B) and we have done this, we don't see any binding to our NAP over that of DNA. This is supported by the bindings *in vivo*. That is, through our seasonal or developmental studies, when one of the two species is absent, we see no binding to chromatin *in vivo* or *in vitro*. If we take a native receptor with two subunits (A and B) and separate them on ion exchange chromatography, we see no binding to acceptor sites with either subunit alone. In any case, I think the differences between Dr. Chambon's laboratories, and Drs. Schrader's and O'Malley's for that matter, are not mutually exclusive in that they may be looking at secondary interaction of the A subunit of the receptor with specific sequences of DNA. I feel that our conditions are probably measuring the initial interaction of the receptor with chromatin acceptor sites and I think our biological relationships (to the binding *in vivo*) support this position.

I. A. Kourides: Do you think the Chambon laboratory is looking at a second level of interaction conceivably?

T. C. Spelsberg: I think that's possible. Let me add a point to that. It's interesting that Chambon's group reported in their recent paper that when they use the partially purified receptor preparation containing both subunits as we use, they see no DNA sequence-specific binding to their 5' end of the ovalbumin gene.

M. G. Rosenfeld: With regards to the idea of the importance of repetitive sequences I would request some clarification with respect to the restriction digests used. Given the frequency of repetitive sequences in DNA, could there be a statistical probability of their presence in such digests; hence unique sequences rather than repeat sequences could be the critical determinants.

T. C. Spelsberg: What we did was to digest these NAP preparations to about 200 base pairs. We still have plenty of acceptor activity. If we digest further, we start losing our binding activity. About 8–10% of DNA appears to be protected by these proteins. When we perform hybridization (c_0t) analysis of this DNA, we observe only repetitive sequences and cannot (within 10–15% sensitivity) see any unique sequences. We realize that this does not represent all of the repetitive sequences since the chick genome has about 20–30% repetitive sequences and we have only 8% of the DNA protected from nuclease digestion. So we lose a lot of the repetitive sequences. However, what we had left over appears to be only repetitive DNA sequences. In collaboration with Dr. Mike Gety, we have found that some of these sequences contain some of the Alu-like family of sequences. We're now doing three things: In collaboration with Bert O'Malley, we're analyzing the sequences in the 5' region of the ovalbumin gene (i.e., in the area of x and y genes) for acceptor sequences which will bind our acceptor protein and create the acceptor sites for binding the progesterone receptor. Second, we are reannealling our acceptor protein to the DNA fragments in the chicken library screens which hybridize to the protected sequences in the nuclease digested NAP. Lastly, we are enriching the intact acceptor sites (containing the native acceptor protein–DNA sequence complexes) by digesting the native NAP with nuclease and fractionating these protein–DNA complexes by molecular sieve chromatography, isoelectric focusing, etc. When we achieve approximately 100-fold enrichment of the intact acceptor sites, we will deproteinize it, isolate the sequences, and use them to screen the chicken library or directly sequence this fragment(s).

M. G. Rosenfeld: I wonder if you could bring us up to date on the characteristics of the protein as thus far purified; I would like to know if there is any reason to believe that there is more than a single protein.

T. C. Spelsberg: This acceptor protein appears to be relatively homogeneous. We do see several different species during purification which can "function" alone. Whether these are different proteins, modifications of the same protein, or proteolytic fragments which still maintain function is unknown. We are presently attempting to make monoclonal antibodies against the protein with activity that we have purified. We plan to use these to test for heterogeneity of protein species, for tissue and species specitivity, examining whether the masked sites are the same as those that are normally unmasked in chromatin and finally to use the antibodies to help isolate the intact acceptor sites (protein–DNA complexes) from nuclease digested NAP.

P. Robel: I see another point of controversy because not everybody agrees on the A and B structure of the progesterone receptors. As you know, David Toft has indeed shown two forms of progesterone receptors with different behavior on ion exchange columns but they do not have the difference in sedimentation coefficient, molecular weight, and subunit structure reported by Schrader and co-workers. In our laboratory we have also purified the progesterone receptor from chick oviduct to apparent homogeneity and we are unable to observe the A and B forms. I'm reluctant to accept at least one of the three hypotheses you have raised concerning the initial interaction of the complex that can direct the A form to the regulatory region of genes; however, the general idea of having an acceptor protein on the chromatin that can facilitate the access of the receptor to the regulatory region of the genes is a very interesting idea; in fact, I think it is worth going on along those lines.

T. C. Spelsberg: I'm glad you brought that point up. The point is very well taken. The question is: How do A and B work? All we really can say is that when we see one of these two species missing, nuclear binding shuts down. The missing species could be the cause or simply the secondary result of the receptor inactivation. The model I presented is readily explained by the Schrader–O'Malley hypothesis but doesn't prove the theory unequivocally.

In addition, I want to say that as one purifies the progesterone receptor, the two species are readily separated. The A is more unstable than B and is often lost. Dr. Schrader's studies have shown this. Dr. Sherman of Sloan-Kettering thoroughly examined the species of the chick oviduct progesterone receptor and concluded that the A and B species, which she and O'Malley first discovered, did actually exist and are not artifacts of the preparation. So I feel the two species (or subunits) of the receptor are present and can be quantitated. Their exact functions are yet to be clarified.

K. Sterling: That was a very impressive presentation, Dr. Spelsberg. My question is a technical one. Toward the latter part of your talk you mentioned you found chromatofocusing to be more useful than isoelectric focusing, and I asked the person next to me what is chromatofocusing. Neither of us knew. Can you give me a 1 minute dissertation and tell me where to learn about it?

T. C. Spelsberg: Thank you for your kind comments. Chromatofocusing material (kits) can be purchased from Pharmacia Fine Chemicals. They also publish a booklet on the technique. The method allows the fractionation of proteins by their isoelectric point. Special high capacity exchangers attached to CL-Sepharose 6B resin are used. Starting at a high pH condition with the resin, the protein fraction is added, allowed to bind to the resin, and a buffer then passed through at another (lower) pH. The resin and buffer will exchange ions and a pH gradient on the column occurs. The proteins bind and dissociate, then bind again, and so on based on their pI, and finally each elutes at its pI.

S. L. Cohen: I have two questions. First, I would like to thank you for a very lucid discussion of a subject which I have long been interested in. I was particularly interested in your masking proteins. My first question concerns the fact that it seems to me that I read somewhere that somebody claimed that the diphasic form of the receptor did not exist for estrogen. Are you familiar with that?

T. C. Spelsberg: Yes, however, using conditions which we feel better stabilize the estrogen receptor, we have found two subunits similar to those found for the progesterone receptor. We have found and quantitated these using ion exchange chromatography and isoelectric focusing. The instability of one of the two subunits might explain the previous observation that only one subunit exists.

S. L. Cohen: My second question concerns the fact that if an estrogen has a dual action, such as in the pregnant myometrium where it can stimulate growth, or stimulates contraction, how does the receptor know which receptor protein to combine with?

T. C. Spelsberg: We feel that since the steroid and the receptor are the same in different tissues, the differential response at the genome is due to differential binding of the steroid–receptor complex to the chromatin acceptor sites. This may be determined by the "masking proteins" which alter the extent of expressed acceptor sites in the chick oviduct during development.

J. M. Hutson: I have one comment and one question. First, the comment relates to what Dr. Donahoe described last year that we found that Müllerian inhibiting substance was present in the chick ovary right through adult life (*Recent Prog. Horm. Res.* **38,** 279). I was wondering whether it is possible that the Müllerian inhibiting substance may be responsible for the oviduct "regression" which occurs seasonally with molting.

T. C. Spelsberg: It may be, at present, we *do not* know what causes the loss in the biological activity (i.e., nuclear binding) of the chick oviduct progesterone receptor during the winter, in the undeveloped oviduct or during estrogen withdrawal or during molting.

J. M. Hutson: I have a question as well. In the same presentation last year Dr. Donahoe described some recent data we have from our laboratory showing that there are low-affinity, high-capacity (Type II) estrogen receptors in the nuclei of cells of the left chick Müllerian duct (which is preserved), while on the other side (which regresses) there are few Type II estrogen receptors. Have you any hypothesis to explain what estrogen Type II nuclear receptors are doing in the nucleus?

T. C. Spelsberg: I have none; it has interesting possibilities but I have no hypothesis worth pursuing.

C. Lazier: I would like to ask you about the possible interaction of receptor with the nuclear matrix. A number of people have been suggesting that this is important in steroid action.

T. C. Spelsberg: The nuclear matrix is quite a complex entity in its own right. Binding by steroids can only be achieved by exchange assays—that is, no receptor addition is needed. Our acceptor sites require intact steroid–receptor complexes. So we differ in that respect. The nuclear matrix besides containing hundreds of different protein species, also contains a few percent of the total cell DNA—still a large number of genes. We do not rule out that our acceptor proteins bound to specific acceptor DNA sequences may reside in the matrix. Frankly, we are interested in but don't care where our acceptor sites reside.

P. Robel: Marie-Claire Lebeau and Nelly Massol in our laboratory have made an interesting observation concerning estrogen receptor complexes in chick oviduct chromatin. Upon DNase I digestion, they find a significant peak of receptor bound to an ^{14}S region of the sucrose gradients that is a slightly heavier than the mononucleosome peak. When the estrogen is replaced by an antiestrogen this localization of receptor is no longer observed. They are in the process of analyzing the DNA and protein associated with estrogen receptor complexes. My question is: Have you had the opportunity to investigate if binding of receptor is still observed when you use antihormone instead of hormone? You may know that a very efficient antiprogesterone is available that is completely devoid of progestational activity; it might be interesting to see what is going on when this antagonist is substituted to the progesterone.

T. C. Spelsberg: Yes, I would very much like to try that. That is what Dr. Baulieu was talking to me about at the recent Gordon Conferences. You all have the only antiprogestin that is sufficiently potent to make such studies worthwhile.

P. Robel: I wanted to know if you had the ability to use an antiprogestin for binding to the receptor and see whether the acceptor activity is still observable.

T. C. Spelsberg: No, we have not. We would like to do those studies.

P. Robel: Do you find such an acceptor protein for estrogen receptors?

T. C. Spelsberg: Yes, with the chick oviduct or cow uterine estrogen receptor it is in the same group of CP-3 protein fraction from chromatin that contains the acceptor proteins. Dr. Tom Ruh spent a sabbatical in my lab and was able to extract the CP-3 fraction from the DNA and to reconstitute this fraction back to DNA. As I described in my talk, this same fraction contains the progesterone receptor acceptor activity. He found the acceptor activity for the estrogen receptor in this same fraction. The anti-estrogen receptor complex I believe also binds similarly in the cow system. I might add that after extensive purification of the acceptor protein for the progesterone receptor, we have been able to separate the estrogen from the progesterone acceptor site. We have about 100 g of the CP-2 protein (to purify the masking activity in the future). We also now have pooled fractions (from repeat runs) of 45 different subfractions of the oviduct chromatin. We saved these fractions so we can go after the estrogen acceptor proteins soon. I am hoping that there will be two distinct acceptor proteins—one for estrogen receptor and one for progesterone receptors, each in turn bound to their own class of repetitive sequences.

H. Papkoff: With respect to the seasonal variation that you see in receptor concentration, are you able to take a group of chickens and manipulate various conditions (i.e., photoperiod, temperature, hormone levels, etc.) and so effect changes artificially?

T. C. Spelsberg: We haven't examined that very well with the chicks; the A species only disappears in the winter. However, we can manipulate the B species of the progesterone receptor by estrogen treatment. By withdrawing estrogen, one can cause the B species to disappear. By secondary injection, the B species returns. Also, in the adult hen, one can manipulate the environment and induce moulting. In this situation the oviducts atrophy and both the estrogen and progesterone receptors lose one of their two species (subunits) and become inactivated.

J. Larner: I really enjoyed your presentation very much. I have two questions: What is the explanation for the inhibition that occurs at high protein concentrations, and then second, it has recently been reported, in fact at the Gordon Conference, that one of the two subunits, I can't remember which one, is phosphorylated by the progesterone receptor. Do you have any thoughts or ideas about this covarient phosphorylation?

T. C. Spelsberg: Thank you for your kind comments. I thought you would ask that first question. Let me refer to the second question first. There is evidence that phosphorylation does occur on steroid receptors. It is possible that phosphorylation may be involved in the regulation of receptor function and explain the biologically inactive receptors I described here. We don't know the answer to that at present.

Concerning your first question on the inhibition that occurs at the higher protein/DNA ratios. The observations are very intriguing and we really don't know the answer. As we purify the acceptor protein, we still see the inhibition. This inhibition appears to be highly specific since the addition of other proteins to the reconstitution has no effect. To further analyze the inhibition, we reconstituted several different ratios of acceptor protein to DNA, at low, medium, and high ratios. The high ratio was strongly inhibitory in terms of acceptor activity. We then removed the proteins from these reconstituted NAPs, separating each into two groups, those that were loosely bound to the DNA (extractable in 4.0 M GuHCl) and those that were tightly bound to the DNA (extractable at 7.0 M GuHCl) as is the native activity. We then assayed each of these fractions for acceptor activity by reconstituting them back to hen DNA for a second time at an optimal ratio. We found that when the acceptor protein/DNA ratio is too high in the original reconstitution (whereby an inhibition of acceptor activity is observed), there appears to be less of the acceptor protein bound to the "native-like" high-affinity sites. Most of it is loosely bound. Thus, the acceptor protein (acceptor activity) appears to be prevented from reconstituting to the DNA properly (tightly) when its ratio (protein/DNA) is excessive. I feel the whole problem of inhibition of acceptor activity with higher ratios of acceptor protein/DNA occurs at the level of the acceptor protein interacting at the specific DNA sequences. Too much of this protein somehow reverses or blocks this specific (high-affinity) interaction. An aggregation of the free protein may be involved but this is plagued by the fact that protein concentration does not appear to be a problem since different dilutions of the reconstitution assay or the use of more purified preparations does not prevent the inhibition. Maybe an aggregation occurs after protein binds to the DNA sites. We don't know the mechanism.

Actions of Insulin on Glucose Transport and cAMP Phosphodiesterase in Fat Cells: Involvement of Two Distinct Molecular Mechanisms

Tetsuro Kono

Department of Physiology, School of Medicine, Vanderbilt Medical School, Nashville, Tennessee

I. Introduction

Since the metabolic effects of insulin are rather diverse and complicated, I would like to make a quick review at the beginning. In this article, I shall concentrate only on the acute insulin actions that are involved in the regulation of energy metabolism. Since this subject has been extensively reviewed in the past (Fritz, 1972; Pilkis and Park, 1974; Czech, 1977), I shall present here only the outline without citing any individual references except for recent papers that are not included in the above review articles.

As is well documented, insulin is secreted from the pancreas under fed conditions and facilitates the uptake and conversion of blood glucose into fat in fat cells and into glycogen in muscle and liver (Fig. 1). Thus, in adipocytes, insulin stimulates glucose transport and pyruvate dehydrogenase (Reactions 7 and 1) and inhibits lipase (Reaction 3); in muscle, the hormone stimulates glucose transport and glycogen synthase (Reactions 7 and 2) and inhibits phosphorylase (Reaction 4); and in liver, it stimulates glycogen synthase (Reaction 2) and inhibits phosphorylase (Reaction 4). In addition, the hormone lowers the cAMP concentration in liver and fat cells by stimulating phosphodiesterase (Reaction 6) and blocks gluconeogenesis in liver at least in part by inhibiting pyruvate kinase (Reaction 5, Claus *et al.*, 1979).

When the secretion of insulin is minimized under starved conditions, the above insulin effects are reversed either for lack of any continued insulin actions or by antagonistic effects of other hormones. As a result, fat in adipocytes and glycogen in liver and muscle are degraded (Reactions 3 and 4) and utilized. At the same time, glucose is synthesized from

519

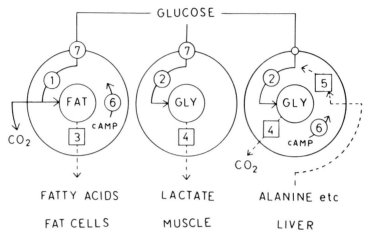

FIG. 1. Effects of insulin on metabolic activities in muscle, liver, and fat cells. The hormone stimulates (○) certain enzyme activities while inhibiting (□) certain others. The names of the enzymes are shown in Table I (Kono, unpublished).

the three carbon precursors in liver (Reaction 5), as well as in certain other cell types. The newly synthesized glucose is readily secreted into the blood stream since the glucose transport activity in the plasma membrane of liver (and other cell types that are involved in gluconeogenesis) is always active regardless of the presence or absence of insulin. On the other hand, the blood glucose (which is essential for the normal function of certain cell types) is not rapidly consumed by muscle and adipocytes under starved conditions since the glucose transport activity in these latter two cell types is insulin dependent (Reaction 7).

Our problem is to delineate the mechanism or mechanisms by which insulin regulates the above mentioned enzyme activities in such a coordinated manner as shown in Fig. 1. Fortunately, the characteristics of the enzymes involved in this system are not entirely different, and at least some of the enzyme activities appear to be regulated by a common mechanism. Thus, among the enzymes shown in Fig. 1 and also listed in Table I, the first five enzymes designated as Type A in Table I are known to be either activated or deactivated according to their state of phosphorylation (Greengard, 1978; Krebs and Beavo, 1979). The effects of insulin on these enzymes are consistent with the view (1) that the hormone either stimulates dephosphorylation or inhibits phosphorylation, and (2) that the effects of the hormone are reversed by phosphorylation (Pilkis and Park, 1974; Czech, 1977). Since insulin decreases the cAMP concentration in liver and fat cells (at least in part) by stimulating phosphodiesterase (Re-

TABLE I
Classification of Insulin-Sensitive Enzymes

Number	Enzyme	Insulin effect	Type
1	Pyruvate dehydrogenase	Stimulation	A
2	Glycogen synthase	Stimulation	A
3	Lipase	Inhibition	A
4	Phosphorylase	Inhibition	A
5	Pyruvate kinase	Inhibition	A
6	Phosphodiesterase	Stimulation	B
7	Glucose transport	Stimulation	C

action 6), it can be argued that insulin regulates Type A enzyme activities by lowering the cAMP concentration. In fact, this may be the mechanism by which insulin inhibits lipase (Reaction 3) in fat cells and deactivates pyruvate kinase (Reaction 5) in liver (Claus *et al.,* 1979). However, this may not be the only mechanism since insulin does not significantly change the cAMP concentration in muscle, and it was recently reported from several laboratories that insulin generates a substance that stimulates dephosphorylation. Thus, Larner *et al.* (1979) obtained a heat-stable substance from rat skeletal muscle perfused with insulin. This factor, which is referred to as the insulin mediator substance, reportedly stimulates glycogen synthase by activating a specific phosphatase. Jarett and Seals (1979) noted that this mediator substance from muscle stimulates pyruvate dehydrogenase from adipocytes in a cell-free system. Popp *et al.* (1980) also reported that insulin stimulates mitochondrial pyruvate dehydrogenase in a cell-free system (in the absence of ATP) provided that the system contains fragments of the plasma membrane. They suggested that the interaction of insulin with the cellular receptor generates a chemical mediator which then activates pyruvate dehydrogenase. Larner *et al.* (1979) reported that the mediator substance from muscle is a mucopeptide with a molecular weight of approximately 1500; on the other hand, Seals and Czech (1981) noted that the molecular weight of the adipocyte mediator is 2000–4000.

In contrast to the mechanism of regulation of the Type A enzymes mentioned above, those of phosphodiesterase (Type B) and the glucose transport mechanism (Type C) apparently require either ATP or metabolic energy for the hormone-dependent stimulation, and while the effect of insulin on phosphodiesterase (Type B) is reversed in the absence of ATP, the effect on the glucose transport mechanism (Type C) is not, as described in detail in the following sections.

II. Effects of Cellular ATP Concentration on the Development and Reversal of Insulin Effects on Glucose Transport and Phosphodiesterase

Our understanding on this subject has greatly changed during the last 10 years. Earlier, Randle and Smith (1958) discovered that the effect of insulin on glucose uptake in rat diaphragm is mimicked by anoxia or 2,4-dinitrophenol, and they suggested that insulin may stimulate glucose transport by decreasing the ATP concentration. Their empirical observation was confirmed by others in experiments with diaphragm and cardiac muscles, and their suggestion was widely accepted, particularly because their view was consistent with the Type A effect discovered later (see Park *et al.*, 1961; Pilkis and Park, 1974, for review). However, when we attempted to examine whether the effects of insulin and dinitrophenol on sugar transport are additive, it was found that the effect of insulin is entirely abolished by 0.1 m*M* dinitrophenol (Fig. 2; Kono and Colowick, 1961) although the basal transport activity is indeed stimulated, albeit small, as reported by Randle and Smith (1958). In addition, the data in Fig. 2 clearly indicate that even the stimulatory effect of dinitrophenol itself is suppressed when its concentration is increased to 1 m*M*. In other

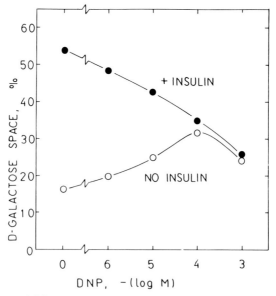

FIG. 2. Effects of different concentrations of 2,4-dinitrophenol on the D-galactose uptake by rat intact hemidiaphragms in the presence or absence of insulin. Dinitrophenol inhibited the insulin action on sugar uptake although it partially stimulated the basal transport activity (Kono and Colowick, 1961).

words, these old data strongly suggested that either ATP or metabolic energy is involved in the hormone-dependent stimulation of glucose transport. Nevertheless, in 1961, we simply interpreted these data as indicating that (1) a low ATP level mimics the effect of insulin, and (2) dinitrophenol (an uncoupler of oxidative phosphorylation) appears to have a certain injurious effect on the system (Kono and Colowick, 1961). Then, Zinman and Hollenberg (1974) reported that stimulation of phosphodiesterase by either catecholamines or insulin is inhibited by oligomycin (an inhibitor of oxidative phosphorylation). In the next year, Reeves (1975) noted that while uptake of 3-O-methyl-D-glucose by rat thymocytes is partially stimulated by anoxia or dinitrophenol, the maximum stimulation is induced either when the anoxia-treated cells are briefly exposed to oxygen or when dinitrophenol-treated cells are washed and suspended in fresh buffer free of the inhibitor. He suggested that while glucose transport is partially stimulated by a decrease in the ATP concentration, a certain minimum level of the nucleotide is required for the maximum stimulation of the transport activity. At about the same time, it was noted in our laboratory that dinitrophenol inhibits the translocation of cell-bound iodoinsulin from the plasma membrane to an unknown fraction (a process which was later identified to be the internalization of insulin, as discussed in Section V) (Kono *et al.*, 1975, 1977a). Furthermore, it became generally known by that time (I am not certain who did the first experiment) that the glucose transport activity in fat cells is scarcely stimulated by anoxia or dinitrophenol, although this activity in adipocytes is stimulated by insulin to a greater extent than that in muscle (usually 5- to 10-fold vs 2- to 3-fold).

With these old and new data in the background, we reexamined how the metabolic effects of insulin are affected by the cellular level of ATP. As shown in Fig. 3, the ATP concentration in fat cells is rapidly and considerably decreased upon exposure of cells to 1 mM 2,4-dinitrophenol. This dinitrophenol effect is reversible; when cells treated with the agent for 10 minutes are washed and suspended in fresh buffer containing 2 mM glucose or pyruvate, the cellular level of the nucleotide is increased almost to the normal level in 10 minutes. Apparently, only a small fraction of adipocytes are "destroyed" by this low-ATP treatment. Although the data are not presented, similar results are also obtained when 1 mM dicumarol, 1-2 mM KCN, or 10 mM sodium azide is substituted for dinitrophenol (Kono *et al.*, 1977a). As is well documented, dinitrophenol and dicumarol are lipophilic agents that decrease the ATP concentration by uncoupling oxidative phosphorylation. In contrast, KCN and sodium azide are hydrophilic compounds that lower the nucleotide level by inhibiting cellular respiration at the cytochrome level.

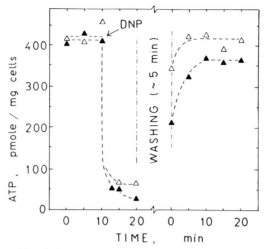

FIG. 3.   Effects of 2,4-dinitrophenol on the ATP level in fat cells. Dinitrophenol added to cells rapidly depressed the ATP concentration. This effect of dinitrophenol was largely reversed when treated cells were washed and incubated with fresh buffer containing 2 mM D-glucose or pyruvate. The ATP concentration was determined by the luciferin–luciferase method. Results of two sets of experiments are reported (Kono *et al.*, 1977a).

As shown in Table II, 1 mM dinitrophenol almost completely blocks the actions of insulin on both glucose transport and phosphodiesterase without significantly affecting their basal activities. The effects of dinitrophenol on these two hormone actions are reversible; when dinitrophenol-treated cells are washed and incubated for 10 minutes with 2 mM glucose or pyruvate, both glucose transport and phosphodiesterase activities are

TABLE II

*Reversibility of the 2,4-Dinitrophenol Effects on the Actions of
Insulin on Glucose Transport and Phosphodiesterase[a]*

	3-*O*-Me-D-glucose uptake (μl/g cells)		Phosphodiesterase activity (pmol/mg protein)	
	Basal	+Insulin	Basal	+Insulin
Control	14 ± 1	35 ± 0	65 ± 4	197 ± 3
DNP treated	12 ± 1	15 ± 2	72 ± 2	64 ± 2
Recovered	17 ± 1	37 ± 2	70 ± 3	189 ± 7

[a] Cells were treated with 1 mM dinitrophenol (DNP) and then washed as in Fig. 3 (Kono *et al.*, 1977a).

rendered insulin sensitive and are stimulated almost normally (Kono *et al.*, 1977a). This indicates that dinitrophenol treatment under the given conditions does not inflict any irreversible damage on the insulin-sensitive system of fat cells. Although the data are not presented, results similar to these (Table II) are also obtained when 1 mM dicumarol, 2 mM KCN, or 10 mM sodium azide is substituted for 1 mM dinitrophenol (Kono *et al.* 1977a; Vega *et al.*, 1980). Significantly, at one-tenth of these indicated concentrations, none of the above four agents exhibits any detectable effect on the ATP concentration or on the insulin effects on glucose transport and phosphodiesterase (Kono *et al.*, 1977a). In summary, our newly obtained data indicated that (1) 2,4-dinitrophenol, dicumarol, KCN, and sodium azide rapidly and greatly lower the ATP concentration in adipocytes and concomitantly block the actions of insulin on both glucose transport and phosphodiesterase without significantly affecting their basal activities, (2) the effective concentrations of each of the above agents on the ATP level and the insulin actions are similar, and (3) the effects of the agents on the ATP level and the insulin effects are both reversible (Kono *et al.*, 1977a). From these observations, we concluded that either ATP or metabolic energy is involved in the actions of insulin on both glucose transport and phosphodiesterase (Kono *et al.*, 1977a).

In agreement with the above conclusion, it was independently discovered by Chandramouli *et al.* (1977) that the effect of insulin on the glucose transport activity in adipocytes is blocked by dinitrophenol or KCN. In addition, Korbl *et al.* (1977) and Yu and Gould (1978) reported that the effect of insulin on glucose transport in soleus muscle is blocked by prolonged incubation with dinitrophenol or in the absence of oxygen.

We next examined whether dinitrophenol can rapidly terminate the ongoing hormone actions. As is well known, it is difficult to arrest insulin actions since the rate of dissociation of the cell-bound hormone is not very rapid (Gliemann *et al.*, 1975; Vega and Kono, 1979), anti-insulin serum does not facilitate dissociation of the hormone from the cellular receptor (Wohltmann and Narahara, 1967), and trypsin does not rapidly modify either insulin or its receptor when they are bound together even before internalization (Suzuki and Kono, unpublished data). As shown in Fig. 4, when dinitrophenol is added to cells after insulin, the effect of the hormone on phosphodiesterase is rapidly reversed and is rendered almost undetectable in approximately 10 minutes (Kono *et al.*, 1977a). Although the data are not presented, similar results are also obtained when dicumarol, KCN, or sodium azide is substituted for dinitrophenol. As mentioned earlier, none of these agents has any significantly injurious effects on the basal phosphodiesterase activity (Kono *et al.*, 1977a; Vega *et al.*,

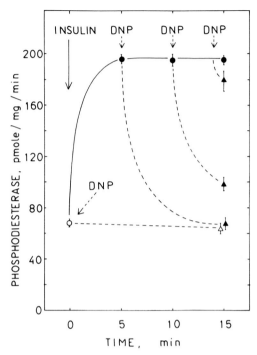

FIG. 4.   Effects of 2,4-dinitrophenol on the insulin-stimulated cAMP phosphodiesterase activity in adipocytes. When dinitrophenol was added to cells after insulin, the effect of the hormone on phosphodiesterase is rapidly reversed. The phosphodiesterase activity was determined in Fraction P-2 (Kono *et al.*, 1977a).

1980). Therefore, we concluded that the insulin effect on phosphodiesterase is reversed in the absence of ATP or metabolic energy (Kono *et al.*, 1977a; Vega *et al.*, 1980). In other words, ATP, which is required for the reversal of insulin effect on Type A enzymes, is apparently involved not in the reversal but in the development of the hormone effect on phosphodiesterase. This statement might sound paradoxical; however, it was shown by Benjamin and Singer (1974), Avruch *et al.* (1976), Forn and Greengard (1976), and others (as reviewed by Denton *et al.*, 1981) that insulin stimulates incorporation of ^{32}P into certain peptides in liver and fat cells and, at the same time, inhibits incorporation of the same label into other peptides in the same cell preparation. Therefore, it can be postulated that insulin stimulates dephosphorylation of Type A enzymes while facilitating phosphorylation of either phosphodiesterase itself or a certain unknown substance that is involved in the activation of this enzyme. This problem will be considered later in detail (see Section IV).

We next examined the effects of ATP deficiency on the insulin-stimulated glucose transport activity. The results of our short-term experiments (which we did first) indicated that dinitrophenol "significantly" lowers the transport activity in 10 minutes although the level of the decline is considerably less than that expected from the phosphodiesterase experiment (Kono *et al.*, 1977a). However, the results of our long-term experiments revealed that the effect of insulin on glucose transport is "largely" preserved for at least 1 hour in the presence of dinitrophenol (Kono *et al.*, 1977b). Therefore, in the experiment presented in Fig. 5, we took insulin-treated fat cells, mixed them with KCN, washed them to remove excess insulin either in the presence or absence of KCN, and suspended them in fresh buffer with or without KCN. The data show that the effect of insulin is largely preserved for at least 1 hour in the presence of KCN while it gradually declines in the absence of the agent. The rate of this decline is significantly accelerated by the addition of pyruvate which probably sup-

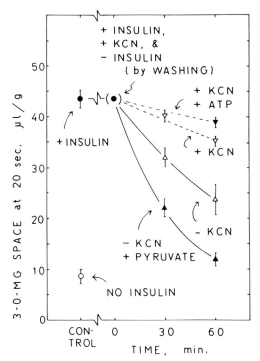

FIG. 5.   Effects of KCN on the insulin-stimulated glucose transport activity in fat cells. The cells were first stimulated with insulin, mixed with KCN, washed, and then incubated for 1 hour with insulin-free buffer containing the indicated agents. The insulin effect was largely preserved in the presence of KCN while gradually declined in the absence of the agent; the rate of this decline was stimulated by pyruvate (Vega *et al.*, 1980).

plies metabolic energy. The above effect of KCN (Fig. 5) is mimicked by dinitrophenol, dicumarol, or sodium azide (Kono *et al.*, 1977b; Vega *et al.*, 1980). Based on these observations, we concluded that either ATP or metabolic energy is involved not only in the development of the insulin effect (as described earlier) but also in the reversal of the effect on glucose transport (Kono *et al.*, 1977b; Vega *et al.*, (1980). The latter part of this conclusion was confirmed by the independent work of Ciaraldi and Olefsky (1981), Laursen *et al.* (1981), and Häring *et al.* (1981). The problem of how ATP or metabolic energy might be involved both in the activation and deactivation of the glucose transport activity is considered in Section III.

III. Mechanism of Insulin Action on Glucose Transport

The transport of glucose across the plasma membrane is the first step of its intracellular metabolism. In addition, this is the first step that was identified by Levine and Goldstein (1955) to be the site of insulin action on glucose metabolism. Levine and Goldstein (1955) used dogs in their experiments. Dogs and other whole animals are still used in insulin studies; however, the general trend in this field has been to employ simpler and simpler systems. Thus, Kipnis and Cori (1957) introduced the intact rat diaphragm preparation that is highly responsive to insulin. Kono and Colowick (1961) showed that the precision of the experiment can be considerably increased by using a pair of intact hemidiaphgrams. Morgan *et al.* (1961) employed perfused rat hearts and established that the insulin-sensitive glucose transport is a carrier-mediated passive diffusion. Winegrad and Renold (1958) found that glucose transport in rat epididymal adipose tissue is highly insulin sensitive, and Rodbell (1964) was successful in preparing highly hormone-sensitive isolated adipocytes by digesting rat epididymal adipose tissue with crude bacterial collagenase. Using isolated adipocytes, Vinten *et al.* (1976) concluded that insulin increases the V_{max} value of sugar transport without changing its K_m value.

As for the possible mechanism of insulin action on glucose transport, the dephosphorylation hypothesis of Randle and Smith (1958) mentioned in Section II was most popular in the 1960s and 1970s. A number of other theories that have been proposed include oxidation hypothesis, peroxidation hypothesis, cAMP theory, cGMP theory, Ca^{2+} ion hypothesis, insulin protease hypothesis, etc., as extensively reviewed previously (Pilkis and Park, 1974; Czech, 1977, 1980); however, none of these theories appears to be entirely satisfactory. More recently, Amatruda and Finch (1979) and Pilch *et al.* (1980) suggested that insulin might stimulate glucose transport by increasing the fluidity of the plasma membrane. One of the bases of their suggestion is the observation made by Czech (1976), Vega and Kono (1979), Whitesell and Gliemann (1979), and Amatruda and Finch (1979) that glucose transport activities in the basal and plus insulin forms of fat cells apparently have different temperature coefficients. I shall discuss this problem later in this section. Wardzala *et al.* (1978), on the other hand, reported that insulin increases the glucose-inhibitable cytochalasin B-binding activity in the plasma membrane of adipocytes. Since cytochalasin B is a potent competitive inhibitor of glucose transport, they interpreted their data as indicating that insulin increases the number of the active transport carriers. It was not clear at this point, however, whether the hormone induces translocation of additional transport carriers from elsewhere to the plasma membrane or simply facilitates the unmasking of the inactive form of the transport carriers that are already present in the membrane.

When we were studying the internalization of fat cell-bound insulin, we observed that ^{125}I-labeled iodoinsulin is translocated from the plasma membrane-rich fraction to the "light" microsomal fraction which is separable from the former by sucrose density gradient centrifugation (see Section V). In addition, we found that there are several similarities between the characteristics of internalization of cell-bound insulin and those of the hormone action on glucose transport. For example, (1) both reactions are largely completed in approximately 5–10 minutes at 37°C when the hormone concentration is 1 nM (Kono *et al.*, 1977a; Vega and Kono, 1979), (2) both reactions are very slow at 15°C (Kono *et al.*, 1977a), and (3) both reactions appear to require ATP or metabolic energy not only for their forward processes (Kono *et al.*, 1977a) but also for the reverse processes (Kono *et al.*, 1977b; Suzuki and Kono, 1979; Vega *et al.*, 1980). Therefore, we postulated as a working hypothesis that internalization of the insulin–receptor complex might be accompanied by cointernalization of the glucose–transporter complex.

We decided to test the above working hypothesis by measuring the glucose transport activity in a cell-free system after reconstitution of the solubilized transport activity into egg lecithin. The basic methods of reconstitution had already been worked out by Kasahara and Hinkle (1976, 1977) for the glucose transport activity from erythrocytes, by Crane *et al.* (1976) and Fairclough *et al.* (1979) for that from intestine, and by Shanahan and Czech (1977) for that from adipocytes. The method adapted for our work is illustrated in Fig. 6. We solubilized the glucose transport activity from adipocytes with sodium cholate, separated macromolecules by gel filtration, and incorporated the macromolecules including the transporter protein into egg lecithin liposomes by sonication, freezing, thawing, and a second sonication. The details of this method have been pub-

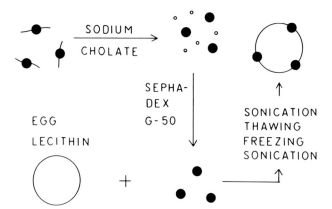

FIG. 6.   The outline of the method of reconstitution of the glucose transport activity from adipocytes. The glucose transport activity associated with membrane structures was solubilized with sodium cholate, separated from small molecules by gel filtration, and incorporated into egg lecithin liposomes by sonication, freezing, thawing, and a second sonication (Kono, unpublished).

lished (Robinson *et al.*, 1982). The efficiency of reconstitution by our current method is approximately 25–30% (Kono *et al.*, 1982).

The glucose transport activity in reconstituted liposomes was determined by two methods. In the first method, we incubated liposomes with D-[³H]glucose either in the presence or absence of cytochalasin B and calculated the carrier-mediated glucose transport activity on the assumption that the latter is completely and specifically inhibited by cytochalasin B (Suzuki and Kono, 1980; Kono *et al.*, 1982). In the second method, we incubated liposomes with a mixture of D-[³H]glucose and L-[¹⁴C]glucose and calculated the results on the assumption that only D-glucose is taken up by the mediated mechanism (Kono *et al.*, 1981, 1982). The results obtained by the two methods are indistinguishable from each other (Kono *et al.*, 1981). In either method, we collected the incubated liposomes on a piece of Millipore filter (GSWP), and measured the radioactivity on the filter by the liquid scintillation counting method.

Figure 7 shows the distribution of the glucose transport activity in subcellular fractions of adipocytes that are separated by a linear sucrose density gradient centrifugation. The data indicate that two distinct peaks of glucose transport activity are found in both basal (Fig. 7A) and plus insulin (Fig. 7B) forms of the preparation. The position of the small peak (Peak A) coincides with a peak of 5′-nucleotidase (a marker enzyme of the plasma membrane), and that of the larger peak (Peak B) coincides with a peak of UDPgalactose : N-acetylglucosamine galactosyltransferase (a marker enzyme of the Golgi apparatus). The data in this figure further show that insulin apparently increases the height of Peak A while decreasing the height of Peak B (Suzuki and Kono, 1980).

The above observation suggested to us for the first time that, contrary to our initial working hypothesis (see above), the function of insulin might be to translocate glucose transport activity from the Golgi-rich fraction to the plasma membrane-rich fraction. In order to convince ourselves, we repeated the above experiment 16 times (8 times with insulin and 8 times

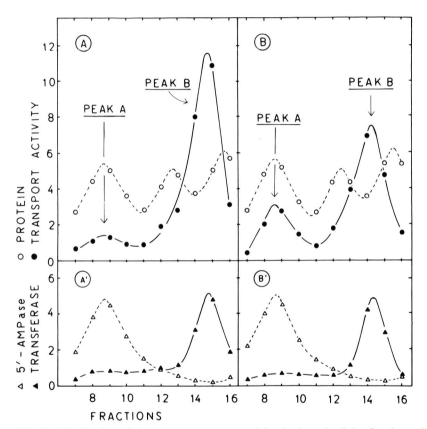

FIG. 7. Distribution of the glucose transport activity in the subcellular fractions of adipocytes separated by sucrose density gradient centrifugation. Two peaks of glucose transport activity, determined by the reconstitution method (see Fig. 6), were found both in the basal preparation (Panel A) and in the plus insulin preparation (Panel B). The location of Peak A coincided with that of the marker enzyme of the plasma membrane, while the position of Peak B coincided with that of the Golgi marker. The height of Peak A was higher in (B) than in (A), while the height of Peak B was lower in (B) than in (A). This suggests that insulin (added to cells) causes translocation of the glucose transport activity from the Golgi-rich fraction to the plasma membrane-rich fraction (Suzuki and Kono, 1980).

without the hormone) and found that the effects of the hormone observed on Peaks A and B are both highly significant ($p < 0.01$) (Suzuki and Kono, 1980). During this study we also found that insulin does not significantly alter the activity of UDPgalactose:N-acetylglucosamine galactosyltransferase (the Golgi marker).

In the next series of experiments, we prepared the plasma membrane-rich and Golgi-rich fractions of the basal and plus insulin forms of fat cells from a pooled cell suspension. Then, we divided each subcellular fraction into several aliquots, individually reconstituted the transport activity in each aliquot, and determined the glucose transport activity at two separate time points in each reconstituted preparation. The purpose of this rather tedious operation was to monitor the reproducibility of the reconstitution process and the transport assay. As shown in Fig. 8, results of the experiment carried out by this protocol clearly indicate that insulin (added to cells) increases the glucose transport activity in the plasma membrane-rich fraction (Fig. 8A) while decreasing the activity in the Golgi-rich fraction (Fig. 8B). The standard errors shown in this figure represent those involved in the reconstitution process and the transport assay (Kono *et al.*, 1981). Using the same experimental protocol, we

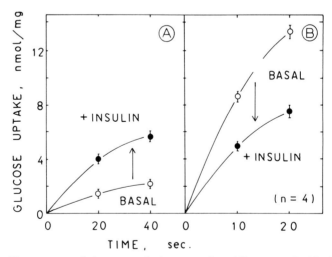

FIG. 8. Time courses of glucose uptake by reconstituted liposomes. In (A), liposomes reconstituted with glucose transport activity from the plasma membrane-rich fraction of insulin-treated fat cells took up glucose faster than the control. In (B), liposomes reconstituted with glucose transport activity from the Golgi-rich fraction of insulin-treated cells took up glucose slower than the control. All the experiments shown in this figure were performed with aliquots of a pooled cell preparation. The number of observations indicates the number of aliquots reconstituted and assayed separately (Kono *et al.*, 1981).

TABLE III

Effects of Insulin (Added to Cells) on the Glucose Transport Activity in the Plasma Membrane-Rich and Golgi-Rich Fractions[a]

	Glucose transport activity	
	nmol/min/mg	nmol/min/fraction
Plasma membrane-rich fraction		
No insulin	4.2 ± 0.2	0.9
+ Insulin	26.4 ± 1.0	6.0
Insulin effect	×6.3	+5.1
Golgi-rich fraction		
No insulin	80.6 ± 3.4	16.6
+ Insulin	46.6 ± 3.0	9.9
Insulin effect	×0.58	−6.7

[a] The transport activity was determined in the reconstituted system (Kono *et al.*, 1982).

found (1) that both the development and reversal of insulin effects on the glucose transport activity in the two subcellular fractions are blocked by 1 mM 2,4-dinitrophenol or 2 mM KCN, and (2) that they are not significantly inhibited by 0.1 mM puromycin or 1 mM cycloheximide (which are both inhibitors of protein synthesis) (Kono *et al.*, 1981). Based on these observations, we proposed as a working hypothesis (1) that insulin induces translocation of the glucose transport mechanism from the Golgi-rich fraction to the plasma membrane-rich fraction, (2) that this reaction is reversible, and (3) that the glucose transport activity is recycled between the two subcellular fractions by an energy-dependent and protein synthesis-independent process (Suzuki and Kono, 1980; Kono *et al.*, 1981).

In the early phase of our reconstitution studies, the insulin effect observed in the plasma membrane-rich fraction was only approximately 2.0- to 2.5-fold (V_{+ins}/V_{basal}). Later, this value was increased to approximately 6.3-fold when care was taken to minimize contamination of the plasma membrane-rich fraction by the Golgi-rich fraction (Table III, Kono *et al.*, 1982). The data in Table III further show that the insulin-dependent increase in the transport activity in the plasma membrane-rich fraction accounts for approximately 75% of the activity decreased in the Golgi-rich fraction. This suggests that the recovery of the plasma membrane-rich fraction is slightly less than that of the Golgi-rich fraction; however, exact figures have been unavailable since galactosyltransferase is not absolutely a specific marker of the Golgi apparatus in fat cells (Kono *et al.*, 1982).

   In agreement with the translocation hypothesis, the glucose transport activity associated with the plasma membrane-rich and the Golgi-rich fractions is concomitantly affected both by the addition of insulin to cells (Fig. 9) and by the subsequent elimination of the hormone from the system (data not shown) (Kono *et al.*, 1982). Several agents that are known to have insulin-like effects (hydrogen peroxide, sodium vanadate, trypsin, and *p*-chloromercuriphenyl sulfonate) not only increase the glucose transport activity in the plasma membrane-rich fraction but also decrease the activity in the Golgi-rich fraction (Kono *et al.*, 1982). Furthermore, so far as tested, the glucose transport activities associated with the two subcellular fractions exhibit identical responses to pH, heat, heavy metals, and various metabolic inhibitors (Kono *et al.*, unpublished data).

   As mentioned earlier, the apparent temperature coefficients of the glucose transport activity in the basal and plus insulin forms of fat cells are different. However, it was recently learned in our laboratory that this difference is caused, not by insulin, but by an insulin-like effect of low temperature (Ezaki and Kono, 1982). When the development of this insulin-like effect is blocked with 2,4-dinitrophenol, the temperature coeffi-

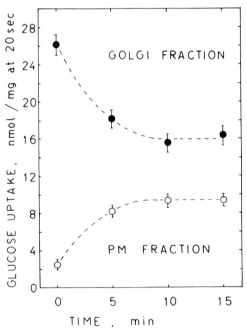

FIG. 9.   Time courses of insulin effects on the glucose transport activity in the plasma membrane-rich and Golgi-rich fractions of fat cells (Kono *et al.*, 1982).

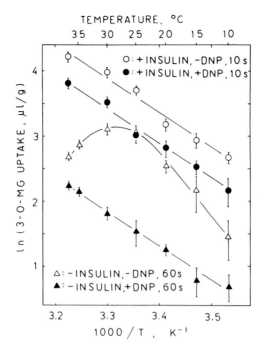

FIG. 10. Arrhenius plots of the glucose transport activity in intact fat cells. The rate of uptake of 3-O-methyl-D-glucose was determined at different temperatures in the presence or absence of insulin either in the presence or absence of 2,4-dinitrophenol. The plot of the basal transport activity (which was normally curvilinear) was rendered straight and parallel to the plot of the plus insulin activity when the insulin-like effect of low temperature was blocked with dinitrophenol (Ezaki and Kono, 1982).

cients of the glucose transport activity associated with the basal and plus insulin forms of adipocytes are rendered identical (Fig. 10). Therefore, we proposed as an additional working hypothesis that insulin promotes translocation of the glucose transport activity without changing its physicochemical properties, including the activation energy for glucose transport (Ezaki and Kono, 1982). The latter part of this proposal is in agreement with the negative data published by Ludvigsen and Jarett (1980).

All of the observations mentioned above are consistent with the view (1) that translocation of the glucose transport activity from the Golgi-rich fraction to the plasma membrane-rich fraction is the major, if not the only, mechanism of insulin action on glucose transport in fat cells, and (2) that the glucose transport activity is recycled between the plasma membrane-rich and the Golgi-rich fractions by an energy-dependent and protein synthesis-independent process (Suzuki and Kono, 1980; Kono et al., 1981, 1982).

The morphological nature of the vesicles associated with the "reserve" glucose transport activity and recovered in the Golgi-rich fraction is yet to be ascertained. Since insulin has no effect on the activity of galacto-syltransferase (a Golgi marker), we tentatively assume that the above vesicles with the "reserve" transport activity are distinct from the Golgi vesicles; however, our attempts to separate the two activities by differential and density gradient centrifugations have been unsuccessful. The mechanism of the proposed translocation of the transport mechanism is also unknown. However, we tentatively postulate that the translocation is mediated by endocytotic and exocytotic reactions, as schematically illustrated in Fig. 11. This suggestion is based on the observation that the stimulation of glucose transport by the apparent translocation is (1) energy dependent, (2) protein synthesis independent, and (3) very slow at 15°C. As noted earlier, these characteristics are similar to those of the internalization of cell-bound insulin which is generally thought to be caused by endocytosis (see Section V). The concept of recycling of a membrane-bound protein by endocytotic and exocytotic reactions is not new; it was previously discussed by Palade (1975).

Significantly, the translocation hypothesis, or the recruitment theory, of insulin action was not only proposed from our laboratory but also

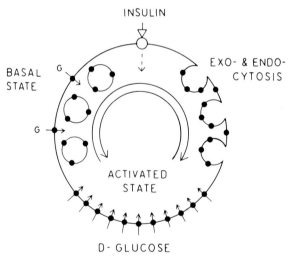

FIG. 11. Schematic diagram of the translocation hypothesis of insulin action on glucose transport. It is suggested (1) that insulin induces translocation of the glucose transport mechanism from an unidentified intracellular pool to the plasma membrane, (2) that the reaction is reversible, and (3) that the translocation is mediated by exocytotic and endocytotic reactions which are energy dependent and protein synthesis independent (Kono, unpublished).

independently advanced by Cushman and Wardzala (1980). These investigators measured the glucose-inhibitable cytochalasin B-binding activity which, as mentioned earlier, presumably shows the number of glucose transport carriers. They found that insulin (added to cells) not only increases the cytochalasin B-binding activity in the plasma membrane fraction as reported earlier (Wardzala et al., 1978), but also decreases the activity in the microsome fraction. Apparently, their microsome fraction contained the aforementioned Golgi-rich fraction. In fact, in a subsequent publication from the same laboratory, Karnieli et al. (1981) localized the intracellular pool of the transport carriers in the low-density microsome fraction, which exactly corresponds to our Golgi-rich fraction. Therefore, the two sets of data obtained in different laboratories by different methods appear to collaborate rather nicely in support of the translocation hypothesis. It may be added at this point that while our data show the level of the functional transport activity, their data indicate the number of the active (not masked) transport carriers.

The time courses of development and reversal of insulin effects on the cytochalasin B-binding activity observed by Karnieli et al. (1981) are similar to those shown above in Fig. 9, which we obtained after their experiment. However, they concluded that the apparent translocation of the cytochalasin B-binding activity occurs slightly ahead of the stimulation of the glucose transport activity. Based on this conclusion, they suggested that insulin not only translocates the glucose transport carriers, but also converts the latter from an inactive form to an active form. This interesting suggestion is yet to be confirmed by additional experimentation, however.

Wheeler et al. (1982) and Lienhard et al. (1982) reported that the glucose transporter protein from rat adipocytes appears to cross-react with the antibody against the counterpart from human erythrocytes. They both found, in agreement with the translocation hypothesis, that insulin (added to cells) increases the immunoreactivity of the band of glucose transporter ($M = 45,000$) electrophoretically separated from the plasma membrane fraction of adipocytes. Wardzala and Jeanrenaud (1981) reported that insulin alters the glucose-inhibitable cytochalasin B-binding activity in rat diaphragm in a manner consistent with the translocation hypothesis. Gorga and Lienhard (1982) reconstituted the adipocyte glucose transporter in small liposomes, and they obtained data which are also in agreement with the translocation theory. In contrast, Carter-Su and Czech (1980) reported that insulin (added to fat cells) increases the glucose transport activity in the plasma membrane fraction without changing the activity in the microsome fraction. The cause of this discrepancy between their data and those of others is not immediately clear.

IV. Mechanism of Insulin Action on cAMP Phosphodiesterase

Historically, Butcher *et al.* (1966) reported that insulin decreases the cAMP concentration in fat cells when the cAMP level is greatly elevated by a joint action of a catecholamine and a methylxanthine. Under these conditions, however, the antilipolytic effect of insulin (which is secondary to the decrease in the cAMP level) is not seen. Later, by improving the sensitivity and precision of the cAMP assay, Khoo *et al.* (1973) and we (Kono and Barham, 1973) were able to observe that insulin decreases both the cAMP concentration and lipolysis under physiological conditions, i.e., in the absence of methylxanthine. During this study, we further noted that insulin significantly lowers the basal level of cAMP in the absence of any lipolytic agent; this observation was in agreement with the subsequent finding that insulin stimulates cAMP phosphodiesterase in the absence of any lipolytic agent.

Since cAMP is formed by adenylate cyclase and decomposed by phosphodiesterase, the site of action of insulin in this system must be on either one, or both, of these enzymes. After considerable initial confusion, one of the observations made by Loten and Sneyd (1970) was confirmed by Manganiello and Vaughan (1973) and Zinman and Hollenberg (1974), and it was empirically established that insulin increases the V_{max} value of low-K_m phosphodiesterase without changing the K_m value. In addition, Manganiello and Vaughan (1973) discovered that hormone-sensitive phosphodiesterase is associated with a certain subcellular structure, and Zinman and Hollenberg (1974) found (1) that phosphodiesterase in adipocytes is stimulated not only by insulin but also by catecholamines and (2) that the actions of both hormones are blocked with oligomycin. Although these observations made by Zinman and Hollenberg (1974) might appear paradoxical, it was also reported by Pawlson *et al.* (1974) that the enzyme in adipocytes is stimulated by adrenocorticotropin as well, and by Loten *et al.* (1978) that the hepatocyte enzyme is stimulated not only by insulin but also by glucagon. Therefore, there seems to be little doubt that phosphodiesterase in liver and fat cells is stimulated not only by insulin but also by the so-called lipolytic agents that are known to increase the cellular level of cAMP. A possible explanation for this observation is provided later in this section.

Although the results of our cAMP assay mentioned above was consistent with the view that insulin stimulates phosphodiesterase in fat cells, we were unable to demonstrate it at the time. Later, by comparing our methods with the successful protocol of Manganiello and Vaughan (1973), we found that the effect of insulin on phosphodiesterase is rapidly abolished if insulin-treated cells are homogenized in the presence of EDTA or other metal chelating agents. Interestingly, these agents have no effect at all when added to the system a few minutes after homogenization (Kono et al., 1975). Apparently, the plus insulin form of phosphodiesterase is very unstable unless it is stabilized by air oxidation of certain sulfhydryl groups. As is well documented, air oxidation of sulfhydryl groups is catalyzed by a trace quantity of heavy metals (Kono et al., 1975).

Using a homogenization buffer free of EDTA, we found that insulin (added to cells) increases the phosphodiesterase activity (determined in a crude microsomal fraction designated as Fraction P-2) approximately 2.5- to 3.0-fold when the hormone concentration is 1–3 nM (Fig. 12, Kono et al., 1975). This observation is highly reproducible, especially when the homogenization buffer is adjusted to pH 7.0 (instead of 7.4) with 10 mM Na-2[tris(hydroxymethyl)amino]ethanesulfonic acid (TES) (Vega et al., 1980). We also found that most of the hormone-sensitive phosphodiesterase in fat cells is associate with the endoplasmic reticulum rather than the plasma membrane (Fig. 13) (Kono et al., 1975). This observation promoted us to examine whether insulin enters into fat cells and directly interacts with the enzyme, as discussed later in Section V.

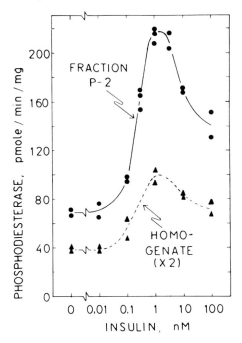

FIG. 12. Effect of insulin on cAMP phosphodiesterase in adipocytes. Insulin added to cells stimulated phosphodiesterase activity, which was determined either in the cell homogenate or in Fraction P-2 (a crude microsomal fraction) (Kono et al., 1975).

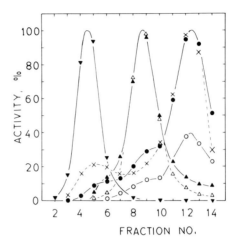

FIG. 13.   Distribution of phosphodiesterase activity in subcellular fractions of adipocytes separated by sucrose density gradient centrifugation. Most of the enzyme activity [either in the basal (○) or plus insulin (●) form] was associated with the endoplasmic reticulum detected from its NADH dehydrogenase activity (×). The above peaks were clearly separated from those of cytochrome c reductase of mitochondria (▼) and those of 5′-nucleotidase (▲) and adenylate cyclase (△) of the plasma membrane (Kono et al., 1975).

Unlike the glucose transport activity discussed in Section III, phosphodiesterase is apparently stimulated not by translocation but by activation of the inactive form of the enzyme. This view is supported by the observations that (1) no apparent storage site for this enzyme has been found in subcellular fractions of fat cells including those separated by sucrose density gradient centrifugation (see Fig. 13 above) (Kono et al., 1975), (2) insulin stimulates this enzyme fairly rapidly at 15°C, whereas the hormone-dependent stimulation of glucose transport (or the endocytotic and exocytotic reactions in general) is very slow at 15°C (Kono et al., 1977a), and (3) the fully active catalytic domain of phosphodiesterase is solubilized not only from the plus insulin form, but also from the basal form of Fraction P-2 (Loten et al., 1980; Makino et al., 1980), as described below.

As reviewed previously (Francis and Kono, 1982), phosphodiesterase from several cell types is known to be activated by a mild proteolysis. Loten et al. (1980) found that the insulin-sensitive enzyme from liver and fat cells is also stimulated by proteolysis and, at the same time, solubilized. They postulated that this enzyme (1) has the catalytic and regulatory domains, (2) is bound to the cellular structure at the regulatory domain, (3) shows only a limited catalytic activity in the basal state because of the inhibitory effect of the regulatory domain, and (4) exhibits full activity when the catalytic domain is freed from the inhibitory effect of

the regulatory domain by either physical separation (e.g., due to proteolysis) or by a certain conformational change (e.g., induced by a hormone).
The solubilization of the catalytic domain of phosphodiesterase is also
observed (1) when the liver enzyme (in a crude microsomal fraction) is
exposed to a hypotonic solution in which lysosomes may be disrupted
(Loten *et al.*, 1980), (2) when the adipocyte enzyme is incubated overnight at 4°C with 1 m*M* dithiothreitol which probably activates a cathep-
sin-like proteinase in the microsomal fraction (Makino and Kono, 1980),
or (3) when the adipocyte enzyme is kept overnight at 4°C in the presence
of certain batches of sucrose at 0.25 *M* (Kono, unpublished observation).
We assume that proteolysis is involved in these three reactions because
they are all blocked by proteolytic inhibitors, such as benzamidine (in the
first reaction, Loten *et al.*, 1980), leupeptin, or pepstatin (in the latter two
cases, Makino *et al.*, 1982; Kono, unpublished data).

As shown in Fig. 14, the catalytic domain of phosphodiesterase gives a
single, almost symmetrical peak by gel filtration with Sepharose 4B. The
shape and position of the peaks in the eluates are almost identical regardless of whether the catalytic domain is solubilized from the basal or plus
insulin forms of Fraction P-2, or whether it is solubilized by treatment of
Fraction P-2 with dithiothreitol or with trypsin (Makino *et al.*, 1980). The

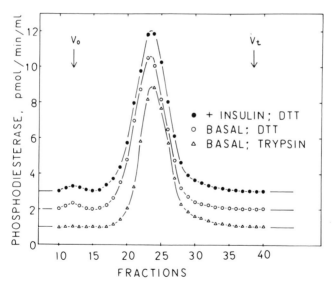

FIG. 14.   Gel filtration of the catalytic domain of phosphodiesterase. Three preparations
of the catalytic domain of phosphodiesterase activity solubilized from the basal and plus
insulin forms of Fraction P-2 with dithiothreitol (DDT; 1 m*M*, 4°C overnight) or with trypsin
(10 μg/ml, 0°C, 10 minutes) gave almost identical peaks by gel filtration with Sepharose 4B
(Makino *et al.*, 1980).

Stokes radius of the solubilized catalytic domain estimated from the gel filtration data (Fig. 14) is approximately 53 Å (Makino *et al.*, 1980), which is considerably less than that of the holoenzyme (87 Å) solubilized with detergent (Makino and Kono, 1980).

As mentioned earlier, phosphodiesterase in liver and adipocytes is stimulated by both insulin and lipolytic agents. The action of the latter agents is probably mediated by cAMP as first suggested by Zinman and Hollenberg (1974), and this may be the mechanism by which cells destroy "excess" cAMP. As is well documented, when cells are exposed to a lipolytic hormone, their cAMP concentration is increased rapidly during the first 5–10 minutes and then decreased (e.g., see Pawlson *et al.*, 1974). Pawlson *et al.* (1974) and Loten *et al.* (1978) suggested that the mechanisms involved in the activation of phosphodiesterase by insulin and lipolytic agents are different. However, the data obtained in our laboratory are apparently in disagreement with this view. Thus, (1) the maximum effects of insulin and lipolytic agents are not additive (Makino and Kono, 1980); (2) the patterns of distribution of the insulin-stimulated and isoproterenol-stimulated enzyme activities in the subcellular fractions of adipocytes are identical (Makino and Kono, 1980); (3) the responses of the activated enzyme to pH, temperature, and SH-blocking agents are identical regardless of whether the enzyme is stimulated by insulin or lipolytic agents (Makino and Kono, 1980); (4) the insulin-stimulated and isoproterenol-stimulated enzyme activities (after detergent solubilization) form identical single peaks by gel filtration, and their Stokes radii are both 94 Å while that of the control enzyme is 87 Å (Makino and Kono, 1980); and (5) the insulin-dependent stimulation of the enzyme apparently requires either ATP or metabolic energy (Kono *et al.*, 1977a) as discussed earlier (see Section II) while the stimulation of the enzyme by lipolytic agents appears to involve the cAMP-dependent phosphorylation (Zinman and Hollenberg, 1974). In fact, the only difference we have noticed between the actions of insulin and lipolytic agents on phosphodiesterase is that the former agent activates the enzyme to a greater extent than the latter.

Based on the aforementioned observations, we proposed as a working hypothesis that (1) Fraction P-2 of fat cells contains only one species of hormone-sensitive phosphodiesterase, (2) when stimulated by either insulin or lipolytic agents, this enzyme assumes an activated form which is identical regardless of which stimulants are used, and (3) the common mechanism involved in the stimulation by insulin and lipolytic agents is probably phosphorylation (Makino and Kono, 1980). In this connection, Marchmont and Houslay (1981) reported that liver phosphodiesterase is stimulated by ATP-dependent phosphorylation in a cell-free system. However, we have been unable to obtain any similar results with the adipocyte enzyme (Makino and Kono, 1981). Therefore, we tentatively assume that the site of phosphorylation may not be in phosphodiesterase itself, but in an unknown factor that is involved in the hormone-dependent stimulation of phosphodiesterase. Our tentative model of the activation mechanism is schematically illustrated in Fig. 15. In this figure, we further suggest that a certain substance is attached to the hormone-stimulated enzyme. This suggestion is based on our observation that the Stokes radius of the hormone-stimulated enzyme is larger than that of the control (94 vs 87 Å) (Makino and Kono, 1980). Recently, it was further observed in our laboratory that the sedimentation coefficient of the insulin-stimulated enzyme is larger than that of the control (Francis and Kono, unpublished data). Since hormone-sensitive phosphodiesterase is not activated by calmodulin, it is highly unlikely that the above substance is calmodulin (Makino and Kono, 1980), although the substance could be a calmodulin-like protein activator.

In apparent disagreement with our observation, Lovell-Smith *et al.* (1977) and Weber and Appleman (1982) reported that phosphodiesterase from adipocytes can be separated into two or four enzymes. Although the exact cause of this disagreement is not clear, we suggest that these data should be interpreted with caution since phosphodiesterase is readily

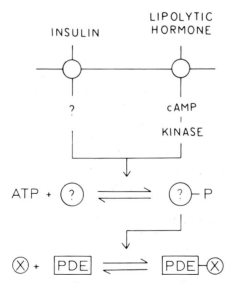

FIG. 15. A hypothetical model of phosphodiesterase stimulation by insulin or lypolytic hormones. It is suggested that both insulin and lipolytic hormones first stimulate phosphorylation of an unknown factor, which then stimulates phosphodiesterase by a certain mechanism that enlarges the enzyme (Kono, unpublished).

cleaved by proteolysis (Loten *et al.*, 1980; Makino *et al.*, 1982), and the enzyme is either activated or deactivated by salt treatment, oxidation, or reduction (Makino *et al.*, 1980). More recently, Parker *et al.* (1982) reported that phosphodiesterase is activated in a cell-free system by the insulin mediator substance for Type A enzymes. In addition, Macaulay *et al.* (1982) suggested that the mediator substance might not be a peptide, but a phospholipid. How these new observations fit into the general scheme of insulin action is yet to be ascertained.

V. Early Phase of Insulin Action

A. HOW MANY TYPES OF INSULIN RECEPTORS?

Since insulin exhibits several different types of metabolic activities, I would like to start this section by discussing whether cells are equipped with a single type or multiple types of insulin receptors on their surface. One experimental piece of evidence which indicates that the insulin receptors are localized on the cell surface is our old observation that when fat cells are exposed to a proteolytic enzyme (which does not enter the cells), the cells are deprived not only of their physiological responsiveness to insulin (Kono, 1969a,b), but also of their ability to bind [^{125}I]iodoinsulin (Kono and Barham, 1971b). During this study, we noticed that the glucose transport activity in fat cells is stimulated maximally when only less than 5% of the total insulin receptors are occupied by the hormone, and that only less than 10% of the total receptors would ever be occupied by the hormone under physiological conditions as the apparent K_d value (dissociation constant) of the insulin receptor complex is approximately 5–7 nM (Kono and Barham, 1971b; Kono and Crofford, 1972) while the maximum concentration of this hormone in the normal peripheral blood is approximately 1 nM (150 μunits/ml). This does not mean, however, that more than 90% of the total insulin receptors are in excess because we also found in our trypsin experiment that cells are rendered less sensitive to the hormone when they are deprived of the so-called spare receptors. Thus, by treating cells with trypsin followed by fresh buffer for a partial recovery, we obtained fat cell preparations that have less than normal B_{max} values (the maximum insulin binding capacities = the total numbers of the insulin receptors). As shown in Fig. 16, the glucose oxidation in each of these cell preparations (Preparations II and III) is stimulated by insulin almost normally (i.e., as in Preparation I) if the hormone concentration is increased so that a certain fixed quantity of insulin is associated with the cell (approximately 1.5 μunits/100 mg cells)

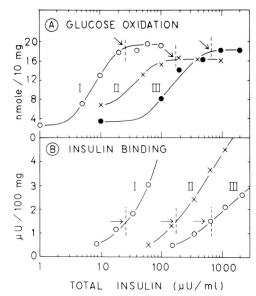

FIG. 16.   Effects of the number of insulin receptors on the cellular response to insulin. Aliquots of a pooled adipocyte preparation were exposed to trypsin (1 mg/ml) for 0 seconds (I), 15 seconds (II), or 15 minutes (III), and then allowed to recover partially. All of these three cell preparations responded to the hormone in full (A) when cells in each preparation were bound with a fixed amount of insulin (approximately 1.5 μunits/100 mg cells), regardless of the shape of the insulin-binding curve (B) (Kono and Barham, 1971b).

(Kono and Barham, 1971a,b). We interpret these data as indicating (see Fig. 17) that (1) a metabolic activity (e.g., glucose oxidation) is stimulated maximally when a certain quantity of insulin is bound to fat cells, (2) the physiological concentration of insulin is so low that only a certain fraction of the total cellular receptors is bound by the hormone as dictated by the law of mass action, and (3) therefore, fat cells must be equipped with seemingly excess insulin receptors to attract the necessary number of the hormone molecules (Kono and Barham, 1971b). As shown in Fig. 16 and schematically illustrated in Fig. 17, the apparent hormone sensitivity of this system decreases when the number of seemingly excess receptors (i.e., the B_{max} value) is reduced (Kono and Barham, 1971b; Kono and Crofford, 1972). In other words, our data (Kono and Barham, 1971b) suggest that most, if not all, of the insulin receptors in fat cells are fully active and identical hormone receptors. In agreement with these observations discussed above, El-Allawy and Gliemann (1972) reported that adipocytes that have been treated with trypsin under very mild conditions respond to the hormone in full provided that the insulin concentration is increased to an extremely high level.

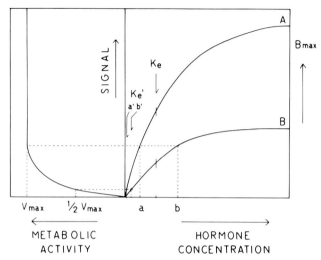

FIG. 17. A suggested function of the so-called "spare" receptors. It is proposed that cells are equipped with a large number of the same species of insulin receptors so that they can attract a certain number of the hormone molecules as dictated by the law of mass action. In this system, the apparent insulin sensitivity of the metabolic activity decreases if the total number of the receptors (B_{max}) is reduced without changing the K_m values (Kono and Crofford, 1972).

In the early days of insulin-binding studies, the dissociation constant of the hormone-receptor complex (K_d value) was reported to be 60–70 pM by Cuatrecasas (1971), 0.5 and 5 nM by Hammond *et al.* (1972), 3 nM by Gammeltoft and Gliemann (1973), 5 nM by Kono and Crofford (1972), and 7 nM by Kono and Barham (1971b). However, it was later proposed by DeMeyts *et al.* (1973) that there is only one species of insulin receptors, and that the binding of the hormone with the receptor is negatively cooperative. This proposal is based on their observation that the rate of replacement of cell-bound [^{125}I]iodoinsulin by the unlabeled hormone is increased when the concentration of the latter is elevated. More recently, however, it was pointed out by Gammeltoft *et al.* (1978) that all the previous experiments on this subject were carried out at low temperatures, and that if the experiment is carried out at 37°C, no negative cooperativity is detectable. According to their data at 37°C, hepatocytes are equipped with a single type of insulin receptors with a fixed K_d value of 0.52 nM.

To summarize, our hypothesis on the possible role of the so-called "spare" receptors (Kono and Barham, 1971b), the negative cooperative theory of DeMeyts *et al.* (1973), and the fixed K_d concept of Gammeltoft *et al.* (1978) all suggest (though they may not exactly prove) that cells are equipped with a large number of a single type of insulin receptors.

B. INTERNALIZATION OF CELL-BOUND INSULIN

As the first solid experimental evidence for the internalization of insulin, Terris and Steiner (1976) discovered that ^{125}I activity appears in bile when rat liver is perfused with [^{125}I]iodoinsulin. Carpenter and Cohen (1976) observed that the degradation of epidermal growth factor by fibroblasts is inhibited by lysosomotropic inhibitors, such as chloroquine. Marshall and Olefsky (1979) and Posner *et al.* (1982) reported that internalized iodoinsulin accumulates in fat and liver cells that are poisoned with chloroquine. Schlessinger *et al.* (1978) visualized internalization of rhodamine-labeled insulin using a special microscope. In addition, several investigators detected ^{125}I activity of internalized iodoinsulin by electron microscopic autoradiography. However, the results of these morphological studies are somewhat controversial. Thus, (1) Gorden *et al.* (1978) and Carpentier *et al.* (1978) reported that the internalized hormone is apparently taken up by lysosomes that are located near the cell surface, (2) Goldfine *et al.* (1978) suggested that internalized insulin is associated with the endoplasmic reticulum and nuclear membrane, and (3) Bergeron *et al.* (1978, 1979) and Posner *et al.* (1978) noted that the internalized hormone is first taken up by secretory elements of the Golgi apparatus as well as by lysosome-like vacuoles and then degraded in lysosomes (see Posner *et al.*, 1981, for review).

As mentioned earlier (see Section IV) our initial interest in this subject was to examine whether insulin directly interacts with the hormone-sensitive phosphodiesterase which is mostly associated with the endoplasmic reticulum in fat cells (Kono *et al.*, 1975). To test this possibility, we exposed adipocytes to [^{125}I]iodoinsulin and fractionated the subcellular components by sucrose density gradient centrifugation. As shown in Fig. 18B, we found two peaks of radioactivity. The location of the larger peak (Peak 1) coincided with the peak of 5′-nucleotide and that of norepinephrine-sensitive adenylate cyclase (both are markers of the plasma membrane). From these and other experimental evidences, we concluded that Peak 1 represents iodoinsulin associated with the hormone receptor on the cell surface (Kono *et al.*, 1975). On the other hand, the position of the smaller peak (Peak 2) was on the right hand side (i.e., on the lower density side) of the peak of phosphodiesterase (PDE) and that of NADH dehydrogenase (not shown in Fig. 18) and on the left-hand side of a peak of *N*-acetylglucosaminidase (a marker enzyme of lysosomes) (Kono *et*

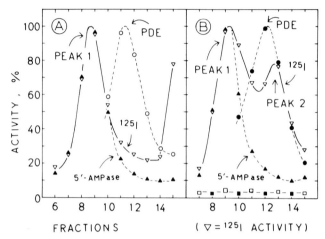

FIG. 18. Separation of internalized [^{125}I]iodoinsulin from the hormone associated with the surface receptor. Iodoinsulin labeled with ^{125}I was added to the fat cell suspension either at the time of homogenization (A) or 5 minutes prior to homogenization (B). Subsequently, the homogenates were subjected to sucrose density gradient centrifugation. Peak 1 corresponded to the hormone associated with the surface receptor, while Peak 2 represented the internalized hormone (Kono *et al.*, 1975).

al., 1975, 1977a). Later, we further found that Peak 2 is on the left-hand side of the peak of the "reserve" glucose transporter and that of UDPgalactose:*N*-acetylglucosamine galactosyltransferase (a Golgi marker) (Suzuki and Kono, 1980).

Since the location of Peak 2 in sucrose gradient did not agree with any of the peaks of the marker enzymes tested, we studied the characteristics of this peak and concluded that it represents [^{125}I]iodoinsulin which is internalized by the cell and is associated with certain vesicles (Suzuki and Kono, 1979). The reasons are (1) Peak 2 is not found when [^{125}I]iodoinsulin is added to cells at the time of homogenization (Fig. 18A); (2) Peak 2 is formed by the hormone first associated with the surface receptor (i.e., Peak 1) (Suzuki and Kono, 1979); (3) the radioactive material solubilized from Peak 2 is mostly intact insulin which is precipitable with anti-insulin serum (Kono *et al.*, 1977a); (4) either ATP or metabolic energy is required for the accumulation of iodoinsulin in Peak 2 (Kono *et al.*, 1977a); (5) ATP or metabolic energy is also needed for dissociation of the hormone from Peak 2 in intact fat cells (Suzuki and Kono, 1979); (6) a part of iodoinsulin in Peak 2 is degraded in lysosomes by a reaction which is inhibitable by several lysosomotropic agents (see below) (Suzuki and Kono, 1979); and (7) a majority of the rest of the hormone in Peak 2 is recycled back into the incubation medium as the intact hormone (Suzuki and Kono, 1979).

In the presence of lysosomotropic inhibitors, such as chloroquine, dibucaine, or tetracaine, undigested [^{125}I]iodoinsulin is accumulated in the cell (Suzuki and Kono, 1979); this finding is in agreement with the independent observation made by Marshall and Olefsky (1979) and by Posner *et al.* (1982). If such poisoned cells are homogenized and subjected to sucrose density gradient centrifugation, a large peak of ^{125}I activity (Peak 3, not shown) appears on the left-hand side of Peak 1 (Suzuki and Kono, 1979). As is well documented, when the activity of a certain lysosomal enzyme is blocked or lost (e.g., by genetic diseases), the substrate of the enzyme accumulates in lysosomes (Neufeld *et al.*, 1975). Therefore, we assume that the above accumulation of iodoinsulin occurs in lysosomes. However, the position of Peak 3 is entirely different from the major peaks of the lysosomal activity, suggesting that only a specific type of lysosomes is involved in this reaction (Suzuki and Kono, 1979).

Naturally, it would be desirable to compare our biochemical data with electron microscopic observations. Unfortunately, I was told that adipocytes are difficult to study by electron microscopy. In fact, most of the morphological studies on internalization of hormones have been carried out with either fibroblasts or hepatocytes. On the other hand, according to our experience, the subcellular structures of adipocytes can be separated much more easily and clearly than those of muscle or liver cells, if the fractionation is done by linear sucrose density gradient centrifugation (either 15.0–45.0 or 15.0–32.5% in w/w) for 40 minutes at 35,000 rpm ($\omega^2 t$ = 2.81 × 10^{10}) in a Beckman SW 41 rotor (Kono *et al.*, 1975, 1977a, 1982; Suzuki and Kono, 1980; Makino *et al.*, 1980).

Our best estimation of the relative activities of the pathways involved in the insulin metabolism in fat cells is presented in Fig. 19. The basis of this

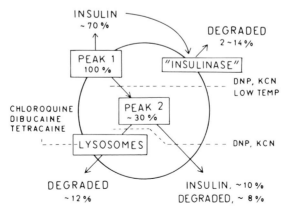

FIG. 19.   Metabolism of insulin that was first bound to the receptor on the surface of fat cells (Kono, unpublished).

estimation is our observations (1) that approximately 12% of [^{125}I]iodoin-
sulin associated with the surface receptor (i.e., the Peak 1 activity) is
degraded by the lysosomal pathway; (2) that approximately 40% of the
internalized hormone (i.e., the Peak 2 activity) is degraded in lysosomes
while at least approximately 35% is translocated back into the incubation
buffer as intact insulin; and (3) 2–14% of the cell-bound hormone is degraded by a nonlysosomal mechanism, presumably after dissociation
from cells, by the so-called "insulinase" on the cell surface; the rate of
this degradation is proportional to the cell concentration (Suzuki and
Kono, 1979).

C. SIGNAL GENERATION

In order to regulate various enzyme activities as shown earlier in Fig.
1, insulin probably generates an intracellular signal, or signals, at a certain
step, or steps, in its metabolic pathways presented in Fig. 19. As mentioned earlier (Sections II and IV), several investigators have already
reported that a certain substance appears to mediate Type A insulin
actions (Larner et al., 1979; Jarett and Seals, 1979; Seals and Czech, 1981;
Parker et al., 1982; Macaulay et al., 1982). In addition, Parker et al. (1982)
and Macaulay et al. (1982) noted that the same factor appears to mediate
the actions of insulin on both Type A and Type B enzymes.

While we have no information of our own on the nature of the intracellular signal of insulin, I would like to discuss the possible sites of the
signal generation. As shown in Table IV, the effects of insulin on phosphodiesterase and glucose transport are not significantly affected by the
indicated concentrations of chloroquine, dibucaine, or tetracaine which
are strong enough to inhibit the lysosomal activity (Suzuki and Kono,
1979). Therefore, we concluded that the lysosomal degradation of insulin
or its receptor is not involved in the actions of insulin on Type B and Type

TABLE IV

*Absence of Any Significant Effects of Lysosomotropic Agents on the Actions of
Insulin on Glucose Transport and Phosphodiesterase[a]*

Inhibitor	Concentration (mM)	3-O-Me-D-glucose uptake (μl/g cells at 20 seconds)		Phosphodiesterase (pmol/min/mg)	
None		9 ± 1	43 ± 5	80 ± 9	196 ± 3
Chloroquine	0.1	8 ± 3	41 ± 7	85 ± 11	173 ± 7
Dibucaine	1.0	6 ± 2	37 ± 5	74 ± 3	195 ± 8
Tetracaine	1.0	9 ± 3	38 ± 2	86 ± 6	186 ± 3

[a] Suzuki and Kono (1979).

C reactions (Suzuki and Kono, 1979). We further feel that it is unlikely that the internalization of insulin or its receptor is involved in the hormone-dependent stimulation of phosphodiesterase (Type B), because insulin rapidly stimulates phosphodiesterase at 15°C while the rate of the internalization is very slow at the same temperature (Kono *et al.*, 1977a). On the other hand, available data fail to prove or disprove the possibility that the proposed endocytotic internalization of the insulin–receptor complex is somehow coupled with the exocytotic translocation of the "reserve" glucose transport activity. We have already discussed the similarities between the characteristics of the two processes (Section III). In addition, we feel that the energy-dependent recycling of the insulin–receptor complex between the plasma membrane and the intracellular site (see Fig. 19) may have a certain physiological significance. It should be noted, however, that hydrogen peroxide can induce the apparent translocation of the glucose transport activity in trypsin-treated fat cells that are insensitive to insulin (Kono *et al.*, 1982). This indicates that internalization of the intact insulin receptor or insulin itself is not essential for the apparent translocation of the glucose transport activity. Furthermore, the peak locations of internalized insulin (Peak 2) and that of the "reserve" glucose transport activity (Peak B) in the sucrose density gradient fractions are different (Suzuki and Kono, 1979; Ezaki and Kono, unpublished data).

VI. SUMMARY

It is proposed that insulin regulates enzyme activities involved in energy metabolism by three distinct mechanisms. In Type A, insulin regulates the activities of glycogen synthase, phosphorylase, pyruvate dehydrogenase, etc., apparently by either stimulating dephosphorylation or inhibiting phosphorylation of the enzyme proteins. This type of insulin effects is reversed by lipolytic hormones such as catecholamines or glucagon. In Type B, insulin stimulates cAMP phosphodiesterase by a process which appears to involve phosphorylation of an unknown factor; the Stokes radius of the enzyme is increased by this process. This type of insulin effect is mimicked by lipolytic hormones. In Type C, insulin stimulates the cellular glucose transport activity by promoting the apparent translocation of the glucose transport activity from the Golgi-rich fraction to the plasma membrane-rich fraction. In this type of insulin effect, metabolic energy is apparently required for both forward and reverse reactions. Lipolytic hormones neither mimic nor antagonize this type of insulin effect in fat cells.

A part of cell-bound insulin is internalized, some of the internalized hormone is degraded in lysosomes, but the rest is apparently recycled back into the extracellular buffer. No lysosomal degradation appears to be involved in the actions of insulin Types B and C.

ACKNOWLEDGMENTS

Our original work cited above was carried out in collaboration, in chronological order, with Frances W. Barham, Dr. Oscar B. Crofford, Janine A. Sarver, Frances W. Robinson, Dr. Felix V. Vega, Dr. Richard H. Pointer, Dr. Perla M. de Buschiazzo, Dr. Sara J. Shumway, Dr. Kristen Raines, Dr. Kazuo Suzuki, Rosa J. Key, Jan E. Jordan, Dr. Hideichi Makino, Lynn E. Dansey, Dr. Sharron H. Francis, Teresa L. Blevins, Dr. Yukiko Tokumitsu, Dr. Osamu Ezaki, Tina M. Pate, Melinda M. Smith, Dr. Tomoyuki Watanabe, and Dr. Masakazu Ueda, to whom I am most grateful. I am also grateful to Dr. Sidney P. Colowick and Dr. Charles R. Park for their continuous encouragement and helpful discussions and to Dr. Sharron H. Francis for reading this manuscript. I am also thankful to those medical students who participated in this work during summer vacations and to Mrs. Patsy Barrett who helped us in typing this and many of our original manuscripts. Our original work was supported by the United States Public Health Service Grants R01 AM 06725, P01 AM 07462, 1P17 AM 17026, and R01 AM 19925 from NIH, as well as by Grant 80-R-340 from the Juvenile Diabetes Foundation.

REFERENCES

Amatruda, J. M., and Finch, E. D. (1979). *J. Biol. Chem.* **254**, 2619–2625.
Avruch, J., Leone, G. R., and Martin, D. B. (1976). *J. Biol. Chem.* **251**, 1511–1515.
Benjamin, W. B., and Singer, I. (1974). Biochim. Biophys. Acta **351**, 28–41.
Bergeron, J. J. M., Posner, B. I., Josefsberg, Z., and Sikstrom, R. (1978). *J. Biol. Chem.* **253**, 4058–4066.
Bergeron, J. J. M., Sikstrom, R., Hand, A. R., and Posner, B. I. (1979). *J. Cell Biol.* **80**, 427–443.
Butcher, R. W., Sneyd, J. G. T., Park, C. R., and Sutherland, E. W., Jr. (1966). *J. Biol. Chem.* **241**, 1652–1653.
Carpenter, G., and Cohen, S. (1976). *J. Cell Biol.* **71**, 159–171.
Carpentier, J.-L., Gorden, P., Amherdt, M., Van Obberghen, E., Kahn, C. R., and Orci, L. (1978). *J. Clin. Invest.* **61**, 1057–1070.
Carter-Su, C., and Czech, M. P. (1980). *J. Biol. Chem.* **255**, 10382–10386.
Chandramouli, V., Milligan, M., and Carter, J. R., Jr. (1977). *Biochemistry* **16**, 1151–1158.
Ciaraldi, T. P., and Olefsky, J. M. (1981). *Arch. Biochem. Biophys.* **208**, 502–507.
Claus, T. H., El-Maghrabi, M. R., and Pilkis, S. J. (1979). *J. Biol. Chem.* **254**, 7855–7864.
Crane, R. K., Malathi, P., and Preiser, H. (1976). *FEBS Lett.* **67**, 214–216.
Cuatrecasas, P. (1971). *Proc. Natl. Acad. Sci. U.S.A.* **68**, 1264–1268.
Cushman, S. W., and Wardzala, L. J. (1980). *J. Biol. Chem.* **255**, 4758–4762.
Czech, M. P. (1976). *Mol. Cell. Biochem.* **11**, 51–63.
Czech, M. P. (1977). *Annu. Rev. Biochem.* **46**, 359–384.
Czech, M. P. (1980). *Diabetes* **29**, 399–409.
DeMeyts, P., Roth, J., Neville, D. M., Jr., Gavin, J. R., III., and Lesniak, M. A. (1973). *Biochem. Biophys. Res. Commun.* **55**, 154–161.
Denton, R. M., Brownsey, R. W., and Belsham, G. J. (1981). *Diabetologia* **21**, 347–362.
El-Allawy, R. M. M., and Gliemann, J. (1972). *Biochim. Biophys. Acta* **273**, 97–109.
Ezaki, O., and Kono, T. (1982). *J. Biol. Chem.* **257**, 14306–14310.

Fairclough, P., Malathi, P., Preiser, H., and Crane, R. K. (1979). *Biochim. Biophys. Acta* **553**, 295–306.

Forn, J., and Greengard, P. (1976). *Arch. Biochem. Biophys.* **176**, 721–733.

Francis, S. H., and Kono, T. (1982). *Mol. Cell. Biochem,* **42**, 109–116.

Fritz, I. B. (1972). *In* "Insulin Action" (I. B. Fritz, ed.), pp. 571–602. Academic Press, New York.

Gammeltoft, S., and Gliemann, J. (1973). *Biochim. Biophys. Acta* **320**, 16–32.

Gammeltoft, S., Kristensen, L. Ø., and Sestoft, L. (1978). *J. Biol. Chem.* **253**, 8406–8413.

Gliemann, J., Gammeltoft, S., and Vinten, J. (1975). *J. Biol. Chem.* **250**, 3368–3374.

Goldfine, I. D., Jones, A. L., Hradek, G. T., Wong, K. Y., and Mooney, J. S. (1978). *Science* **202**, 760–763.

Gorden, P., Carpentier, J.-L., Freychet, P., LeCam, A., and Orci, L. (1978). *Science* **200**, 782–784.

Gorga, J. C., and Lienhard, G. E. (1982). *Fed. Proc. Fed. Am. Soc. Exp. Biol.* **41**, 627.

Greengard, P. (1978). *Science* **199**, 146–152.

Hammond, J. M., Jarett, L., Mariz, I. K., and Daughaday, W. H. (1972). *Biochem. Biophys. Res. Commun.* **49**, 1122–1128.

Häring, H. U., Biermann, E., and Kemmler, W. (1981). *Am. J. Physiol.* **240**, E556-E565.

Jarett, L., and Seals, J. R. (1979). *Science* **206**, 1407–1408.

Karnieli, E., Zarnowski, M. J., Hissin, P. J., Simpson, I. A., Salans, L. B., and Cushman, S. W. (1981). *J. Biol. Chem.* **256**, 4772–4777.

Kasahara, M., and Hinkle, P. C. (1976). *Proc. Natl. Acad. Sci. U.S.A.* **73**, 396–400.

Kasahara, M., and Hinkle, P. C. (1977). *J. Biol. Chem.* **252**, 7384–7390.

Khoo, J. C., Steinberg, D., Thompson, B., and Mayer, S. E. (1973). *J. Biol. Chem.* **248**, 3823–3830.

Kipnis, D. M., and Cori, C. F. (1957). *J. Biol. Chem.* **224**, 681–693.

Kono, T., (1969a). *J. Biol. Chem.* **244**, 1772–1778.

Kono, T. (1969b). *J. Biol. Chem.* **244**, 5777–5784.

Kono, T., and Barham, F. W. (1971a). *J. Biol. Chem.* **246**, 6204–6209.

Kono, T., and Barham, F. W. (1971b). *J. Biol. Chem.* **246**, 6210–6216.

Kono, T., and Barham, F. W. (1973). *J. Biol. Chem.* **248**, 7417–7426.

Kono, T., and Colowick, S. P. (1961). *Arch. Biochem. Biophys.* **93**, 514–519.

Kono, T., and Crofford, O. B. (1972). *In* "The Role of Membranes in Metabolic Regulation" (M. A. Mehlman and R. W. Hanson, eds.), pp. 237–247. Academic Press, New York.

Kono, T., Robinson, F. W., and Sarver, J. A. (1975). *J. Biol. Chem.* **250**, 7826–7835.

Kono, T., Robinson, F. W., Sarver, J. A., Vega, F. V., and Pointer, R. H. (1977a). *J. Biol. Chem.* **252**, 2226–2233.

Kono, T., Vega, F. V., Raines, K. B., and Shumway, S. J. (1977b). *Fed. Proc. Fed. Am. Soc. Exp. Biol.* **36**, 341.

Kono, T., Suzuki, K., Dansey, L. E., Robinson, F. W., and Blevins, T. L. (1981). *J. Biol. Chem.* **256**, 6400–6407.

Kono, T., Robinson, F. W., Blevins, T. L., and Ezaki, O. (1982). *J. Biol. Chem.* **257**, 10942–10947.

Korbl, G. P., Sloan, I. G., and Gould, M. K. (1977). *Biochim. Biophys. Acta* **465**, 93–109.

Krebs, E. G., and Beavo, J. A. (1979). *Annu. Rev. Biochem.* **48**, 923–959.

Larner, J., Galasko, G., Cheng, K., DePaoli-Roach, A. A., Huang, L., Daggy, P., and Kellogg, J. (1979). *Science* **206**, 1408–1410.

Laursen, A. L., Foley, J. E., Foley, R., and Gliemann, J. (1981). *Biochim. Biophys. Acta* **673**, 132–136.

Levine, R., and Goldstein, M. S. (1955). *Recent Prog. Horm. Res.* **11**, 343–380.

Lienhard, G. E., Kim, H. H., Ransome, K. J., and Gorga, J. C. (1982). *Biochem. Biophys. Res. Commun.* **105**, 1150–1156.

Loten, E. G., and Sneyd, J. G. T. (1970). *Biochem. J.* **120**, 187–193.

Loten, E. G., Assimacopoulos-Jeannet, F. D., Exton, J. H., and Park, C. R. (1978). *J. Biol. Chem.* **253**, 746–757.

Loten, E. G., Francis, S. H., and Corbin, J. D. (1980). *J. Biol. Chem.* **255**, 7838–7844.

Lovell-Smith, C. J., Manganiello, V. C., and Vaughan, M. (1977). *Biochim. Biophys. Acta* **497**, 447–458.

Ludvigsen, C., and Jarett, L. (1980). *Diabetes* **29**, 373–378.

Macaulay, S. L., Kiechle, F. L., and Jarett, L. (1982). *Fed. Proc. Fed. Am. Soc. Exp. Biol.* **41**, 1082.

Makino, H., and Kono, T. (1980). *J. Biol. Chem.* **255**, 7850–7854.

Makino, H., and Kono, T. (1981). *Biomed. Res.* **2**, 52–56.

Makino, H., de Buschiazzo, P. M., Pointer, R. H., Jordan, J. E., and Kono, T. (1980). *J. Biol. Chem.* **255**, 7845–7849.

Makino, H., Kanatsuka, A., Osegawa, M., and Kumagai, A. (1982). *Biochim. Biophys. Acta* **704**, 31–36.

Manganiello, V., and Vaughan, M. (1973). *J. Biol. Chem.* **248**, 7164–7170.

Marchmont, R. J., and Houslay, M. D. (1981). *Biochem. J.* **195**, 653–660.

Marshall, S., and Olefsky, J. M. (1979). *J. Biol. Chem.* **254**, 10153–10160.

Morgan, H. E., Henderson, M. J., Regen, D. M., and Park, C. R. (1961). *J. Biol. Chem.* **236**, 253–261.

Neufeld, E. F., Lim, T. W., and Shapiro, L. J. (1975). *Annu. Rev. Biochem.* **44**, 357–376.

Palade, G. (1975). *Science* **189**, 347–358.

Park, C. R., Morgan, H. E., Henderson, M. J., Regen, D. M., Cadenas, E., and Post, R. L. (1961). *Recent Prog. Horm. Res.* **17**, 493–538.

Parker, J. C., Kiechle, F. L., and Jarett, L. (1982). *Arch. Biochem. Biophys.* **215**, 339–344.

Pawlson, L. G., Lovell-Smith, C. J., Manganiello, V. C., and Vaughan, M. (1974). *Proc. Natl. Acad. Sci. U.S.A.* **71**, 1639–1642.

Pilch, P. F., Thompson, P. A., and Czech, M. P. (1980). *Proc. Natl. Acad. Sci. U.S.A.* **77**, 915–918.

Pilkis, S. J., and Park, C. R. (1974). *Annu. Rev. Pharmacol.* **14**, 365–388.

Popp, D. A., Kiechle, F. L., Kotagal, N., and Jarett, L. (1980). *J. Biol. Chem.* **255**, 7540–7543.

Posner, B. I., Josefsberg, Z., and Bergeron, J. J. M. (1978). *J. Biol. Chem.* **253**, 4067–4073.

Posner, B. I., Bergeron, J. J. M., Josefsberg, Z., Khan, M. N., Khan, R. J., Patel, B. A., Sikstrom, R. A., and Verma, A. K. (1981). *Recent Prog. Horm. Res.* **37**, 539–582.

Posner, B. I., Patel, B. A., Khan, M. N., and Bergeron, J. J. M. (1982). *J. Biol. Chem.* **257**, 5789–5799.

Randle, P. J., and Smith, G. H. (1958). *Biochem. J.* **70**, 490–500, 501–506.

Reeves, J. B. (1975). *J. Biol. Chem.* **250**, 9413–9420.

Robinson, F. W., Blevins, T. L., Suzuki, K., and Kono, T. (1982). *Anal. Biochem.* **122**, 10–19.

Rodbell, M. (1964). *J. Biol. Chem.* **239**, 375–380.

Schlessinger, J., Shechter, Y., Willingham, M. C., and Pastan, I. (1978). *Proc. Natl. Acad. Sci. U.S.A.* **75**, 2659–2663.

Seals, J. R., and Czech, M. P. (1981). *J. Biol. Chem.* **256**, 2894–2899.

Shanahan, M. F., and Czech, M. P. (1977). *J. Biol. Chem.* **252**, 8341–8343.

Suzuki, K., and Kono, T. (1979). *J. Biol. Chem.* **254**, 9786–9794.

Suzuki, K., and Kono, T. (1980). *Proc. Natl. Acad. Sci. U.S.A.* **77**, 2542–2545.

Terris, S., and Steiner, D. F. (1976). *J. Clin. Invest.* **57**, 885–896.

Vega, F. V., and Kono, T. (1979). *Arch. Biochem. Biophys.* **192**, 120–127.

Vega, F. V., Key, R. J., Jordan, J. E., and Kono, T. (1980). *Arch. Biochem. Biophys.* **203**, 167–173.

Vinten, J., Gliemann, J., and Østerlind, K. (1976). *J. Biol. Chem.* **251**, 794–800..

Wardzala, L. J., and Jeanrenaud, B. (1981). *J. Biol. Chem.* **256**, 7090–7093.

Wardzala, L. J., Cushman, S. W., and Salans, L. B. (1978). *J. Biol. Chem.* **253**, 8002–8005.

Weber, H., and Appleman, M. M. (1982). *J. Biol. Chem.* **257**, 5339–5341.

Wheeler, T. J., Simpson, I. A., Sogin, D. C., Hinkle, P. C., and Cushman, S. W. (1982). *Biochem. Biophys. Res. Commun.* **105**, 89–95.

Whitesell, R. R., and Gliemann, J. (1979). *J. Biol. Chem.* **254**, 5276–5283.

Winegrad, A. I., and Renold, A. E. (1958). *J. Biol. Chem.* **233**, 267–272.

Wohltmann, H. J., and Narahara, H. T. (1967). *Biochim. Biophys. Acta* **135**, 173–175.

Yu, K. T., and Gould, M. K. (1978). *J. Am. Physiol.* **234**, E407-E416.

Zinman, B., and Hollenberg, C. H. (1974). *J. Biol. Chem.* **249**, 2182–2187.

DISCUSSION

U. Zor: First of all, I'd like to thank you, Dr. Kono for the beautiful and revolutionary study that you did. In regard to the glucose transport you did not suggest any mechanism which explains how insulin induces translocation of the glucose transporter system from the endoplasmic reticulum to the plasma membrane. What do you think about the possibilities that the cytoskeletal elements, microfilaments, or intermediate filaments are involved in these kinds of translocation?

T. Kono: I don't have any data to show how insulin induces translocation. We studied possible involvement of microfilaments and microtubules by adding cytochalasin B, colchicine, and vinblastine, the agents that are said to inhibit endocytosis in some cell types. These agents did not inhibit the insulin-dependent activation of glucose transport. However, these agents did not inhibit the internalization of the insulin–receptor complex either. The latter reaction is well established to be caused by endocytosis. So I'm not sure whether these agents inhibit endo- and exocytosis in fat cells. Therefore, I think that these negative data on glucose transport do not necessarily mean that endo- and exocytosis are not involved in the insulin action.

R. Levin: Thank you very much for the clear exposition of your ideas in relation to insulin action. The area that comes closest to my own interests is the novel view of how insulin enhances transport of glucose. I must say that it was surprising to read your paper and that of Cushman, as to how insulin increases the V_{max} of transport not by increasing the performance of each transporter molecule but by raising the number of transporters in the membrane. That was a most surprising finding. The translocation of transporters was found independently and by entirely different techniques in your laboratory and by the Cushman group. I'm somewhat unclear in relation to the role of ATP. The contention is that ATP is necessary both for the translocation of the transporter in either direction. What about glucose transport itself? Does the movement of the transporter molecule with the sugar on it require ATP? As you pointed out, in the presence of KCN the rate of transport is maintained. Your explanation is simply that the transporters which were in the cell and are now at the membrane can't go back. Therefore transport is enhanced in the absence of ATP. What about the translocation of glucose? Wouldn't that be disturbed by the lack of ATP? I can see why the transporters don't go back inside the cell but why shouldn't it stop glucose transport altogether? Is no energy necessary for the movement of the transporter with glucose to get through the membrane?

T. Kono: According to my interpretation, the glucose transport mechanism in the insulin-stimulated adipocytes remains in the plasma membrane unless energy is supplied. Since metabolic energy is not required for glucose transport itself, glucose molecules may go into the cell as long as the transport mechanism is present. I think that the transport action is going on independently even when the translocation is blocked by the loss of ATP.

R. Levine: The transport of glucose is over a much shorter distance within the membrane than the translocation. This does not require ATP while the translocation does?

T. Kono: Well, some kind of movement is required for transport: either the translocator molecule turns around or the transport channel opens and closes. ATP is not required, however, for glucose transport itself.

E. Rall: It just seems to me that the intracellular concentration of glucose is so low that all that a "transporter" does is to transport or open a door for a downhill movement. Hence no energy is required because you're just permitting movement down a concentrator gradient. Is that correct?

T. Kono: Yes

G. B. Cutler: Do you have any thoughts about the antagonism by glucocorticoids of insulin-mediated glucose transport in certain tissues?

T. Kono: I have no thoughts at all.

G. B. Cutler: Do glucocorticoids affect the translocation of the glucose transport system?

T. Kono: The effects of glucocorticoids are so difficult to comprehend that I have never tested its effects myself.

J. Larner: Let me ask, do you visualize that the translocation process is going on normally at a certain rate and is influenced by insulin in these agents or do you think that insulin turns it on?

T. Kono: That's a difficult question to answer, and I don't have the answer to that question. However, I do know that the insulin receptor is internalized only when it is bound with insulin. The system is different from the system for internalization of lipoprotein. The latter system is always recycling. Now, your question is whether glucose transporter is always turning around or not. I don't know how to study that point by experiment. In theory, however, it is possible to postulate that the transporter is always recycling between the two subcellular sites. In my presentation, I said that the insulin initiates translocation of the transporter from the Golgi-rich fraction to the plasma membrane-rich fraction. However, the system may always be recycling, and there may be some sort of equilibrium between the numbers of the transport mechanism in the two subcellular fractions. If that is the case, the function of insulin or its mimickers is to shift the equilibrium.

A. L. Goodman: Do you have any evidence for coupling of the translocation of the insulin receptor with either hexokinase or glucokinase activity?

T. Kono: Glucokinase or hexokinase is stimulated by insulin. However, this is a long-term effect, presumably caused by modulation of protein synthesis. It is not an acute form of insulin effect that I am discussing.

J. Larner: If I may ask another question. You mentioned that in the Stokes radius the activated phosphodiesterase was larger than the control. What is the order of magnitude of the difference in these?

T. Kono: In terms of molecular weight, if I assume that the enzyme is spherical, the increase is about 10,000.

J. Larner: So that would rule out any kind of a dimerization mechanism? Have you been able to solubilize the intact phosphodiesterase out of the endoplasmic reticulum?

T. Kono: Yes. That's how we measured the Stokes radius. We can solubilize the enzyme with a mixture of Lubrol-WX and Zwittergent 3-14.

J. Larner: And this is not proteolytically cleaved?

T. Kono: No. The stokes radius of the catalytic domain obtained by proteolysis is 54 Å while that of the holoenzyme solubilized with detergent is 87 Å in the basal form.

M. Saffran: In muscle there is a system that can pull lots of things around within the cell. It's the myocin. It needs ATP. It can be visualized as transporting things to the surface quite easily. Is there a similar system in your fat cell?

T. Kono: I do not know. However, the endocytosis of the insulin–receptor complex does occur in fat cells. In addition, we do not know whether the glucose transport mechanism is translocated a long distance from the Golgi region of the cell to the plasma membrane. Although the intracellular transport activity is recovered in the Golgi-rich fraction, I have no idea where it is in the cell. The vesicles with the "reserve" transporter might exist just below the plasma membrane, and all it requires might be the opening and closing of a hole. In other words, there may not be a long travel of the vesicles in the cell. I am very anxious to study these morphological changes. If there are electron microscopists in this audience who would like to study these problems, I would be most happy to send samples.

Hormone-Induced Morphogenesis and Growth: Role of Mesenchymal–Epithelial Interactions

GERALD R. CUNHA,* LELAND W. K. CHUNG,† JOHN M. SHANNON,‡ OSAMU TAGUCHI,§ AND HIROHIKO FUJII**

*Anatomy Department, University of California, San Francisco, California; †Pharmacology/School of Pharmacy, University of Colorado, Boulder, Colorado; ‡Department of Oncology, University of Colorado, Denver, Colorado; §Laboratory of Experimental Pathology, Aichi Cancer Center Research Institute, Chikusa-Ku, Nagoya, Japan; and **Anatomy Department, Kumamoto University Medical School, Honjo, Kumamoto City, Japan

I. Introduction

The mechanism of steroid hormone action is thought to involve specific high-affinity receptor proteins. The hormone enters the cell, binds to the cytoplasmic receptor, which after activation translocates to the nucleus. The hormone-receptor complex in turn binds to nuclear acceptor sites on the chromatin. This activates a variety of metabolic processes, one of the most important being the stimulation of mRNA synthesis and the ultimate production of new proteins (Clark and Peck, 1979; Mainwaring, 1977). How induction of macromolecular synthesis is in turn linked to stimulation of epithelial growth and the production of complex epithelial morphologies is largely unknown. We are convinced that the morphogenetic effects of hormones are linked to a requisite interaction of epithelium with stromal cells. Consequently, an appreciation of the mechanism of hormone-induced morphogenesis is ultimately dependent upon understanding the biological properties and molecular biology of individual cell types that constitute developing hormone target organs. For this reason biochemical studies are generally not relevant in a direct sense to this question because analysis of any measurable activity in homogenates of target organs rarely can be correlated with the individual activities of the many biologically distinct cell types that constitute a given hormone target organ. For example, the uterus is composed of three basic cell types: epithelium, endometrial stroma, and myometrium, which contribute, respectively, 5–10, 30–35, and 60% of the total mass of the uterus (McCormack and Glasser, 1980; Martin *et al.*, 1973; Kirkland *et al.*, 1979). This in itself

559

is an oversimplification because the epithelium is in turn divisible into glandular and luminal epithelia, which are quite different both morphologically and functionally (Ferenczy and Richart, 1974; Wynn, 1977). Similarly, morphological and autoradiographic evidence suggests that cells of the endometrial stroma are not homogeneous but may contain several biologically distinct cellular subpopulations (Prasad *et al.*, 1976; Glasser, 1981). Myometrium appears to be fairly homogeneous, but does contain fibroblastic cells that lie between smooth muscle layers. Finally, every hormone target organ contains blood and lymph vessels as well as perivascular cells and wandering leukocytes that in the case of the uterus may constitute a significant proportion of the stromal cell population during certain phases of the estrous cycle (Tchernitchin *et al.*, 1974). In fact, in response to exogenous estrogen, the influx of immigrating eosinophils into the uterus is so great that almost all of the peroxidase activity of the uterus is contributed by these cells (King *et al.*, 1981). Cellular heterogeneity within hormone target organs, which has been largely overlooked in the past, must now be seriously considered because mounting evidence now suggests that many hormone responses within epithelial cells may not be elicited directly in these target cells, but instead may be elicited by putative growth factors or inductors elaborated in neighboring stromal cells in response to hormonal stimulation.

II. Technical Considerations

Since data from steroid autoradiographic analysis of hormone target organs provide crucial evidence for our hypothesis, recent developments in steroid autoradiography will be described that provide validation for this type of analysis of hormone receptors. In the past, steroid autoradiography has been performed on tissues taken from animals that were injected with tritiated steroids. By this *in vivo* method, it was unclear whether silver grain localization represented the parent steroid or its metabolites because of the possibility of hepatic or peripheral metabolism of the parent steroid. In biochemical studies peripheral and hepatic metabolism could be eliminated, and furthermore target organ metabolism could be assessed if desired. Recently, *in vitro* methods of steroid autoradiography (Shannon *et al.*, 1982) have been developed that also eliminate peripheral and hepatic metabolism so that this problem is no greater for autoradiographic than for biochemical methods. Moreover, because of the relatively high constant level of ^{3}H-labeled steroid that can be maintained in the incubation mixture, the radiolabeled parent steroid should at all times exceed the concentration of any of its metabolites. This means that silver grain localization in autoradiograms processed by *in vitro* methods can be interpreted with confidence as indicating the true distribution of the parent steroid.

Despite this former problem of metabolism, it is noteworthy that on the whole autoradiographic studies have correlated precisely with biochemical results; that is, biochemical demonstration of hormone receptors in target organ homogenates could usually be correlated with the autoradiographic demonstration of nuclear binding sites for that hormone in individual cells of the target organ. Steroid specificity of nuclear binding has been assessed autoradiographically by appropriate competition experiments, and the histotypic distribution of nuclear binding in turn correlated with biologic response in the cells under examination. Thus, results from autoradiographic studies fulfilled three important criteria of hormone receptors: target organ specificity, hormone specificity, and correlation with biologic response. Two other diagnostic features of hormone receptors, finite binding capacity and high affinity, initially were not assessed autoradiographically. Recently, Holderegger *et al.* (1981) demonstrated that if rats are injected with increasing amounts of [³H]estradiol the intensity of nuclear labeling increased and finally plateaued. Injection of higher levels of [³H]estradiol did not further increase the intensity of nuclear labeling (silver grains/nucleus). Even though these studies cannot be construed as a true saturation analysis because neither the steroid nor receptor was in free solution, the results appear to be a clear manifestation of saturability. More recently, we have performed a "saturation" analysis of nuclear estradiol binding in vaginal stromal cells incubated *in vitro*. Utilizing estradiol concentrations ranging from 0.025 to 40 n*M* alone and in combination with a 600-fold excess of unlabeled diethylstilbestrol, specific nuclear binding could be computed as a function of estradiol concentration (Cunha *et al.*, 1983a). The results depicted in Fig. 1a demonstrate finite binding capacity which reaches one-half saturation at an [³H]estradiol concentration of 0.35 n*M*. This compares favorably to parallel biochemical analysis of saturation which yielded a one-half saturation at 1.5 n*M* (Fig. 1b). Both of these values are in the range reported in the literature for the estrogen receptor (Clark and Peck, 1979). Thus, through recent developments in steroid autoradiography it is now possible to satisfy all of the criteria established by Clark and Peck (1979) for hormone receptors; steroid specificity, organ specificity, correlation with biologic response, finite binding capacity, and high affinity. Precise cellular localization of hormone receptors afforded by autoradiographic analysis when coupled to morphological, histochemical, or immunocytochemical studies

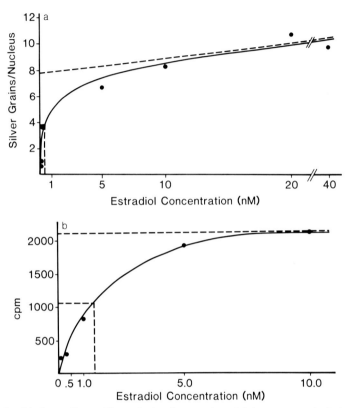

FIG. 1. (a) Autoradiographic analysis of saturation. Adult mouse vaginal tissue was incubated for 1.5 hours in serum-free medium containing 0.025 to 40.0 nM of [^{3}H]estradiol alone or in combination with a 600-fold excess of diethylstilbestrol (DES). Following washing by continuous perfusion for 3 hours at room temperature to remove unbound steroid, specimens were frozen in liquid propane, sectioned at 4 μm, and processed autoradiographically. By assessing nuclear grain counts in stromal cells of specimens incubated with estradiol alone or in combination with radioinert DES, nuclear labeling was analyzed as a function of steroid concentration. As can be seen, nuclear estrogen binding is saturable reaching one-half saturation at 0.35 nM. Each point is derived from analysis of 400–500 cells (see Cunha *et al.*, 1983a). (b) Biochemical analysis of estrogen binding. Parallel biochemical analysis of estrogen binding was assessed in nuclear extracts of adult mouse vaginas by standard methods (see Cunha *et al.*, 1983a, for technical details). Estrogen binding exhibits finite capacity with a one-half saturation at 1.5 nM.

makes feasible the correlation of hormonal response at the cellular level with the expression (or nonexpression) of hormone receptors even in minute embryonic hormone target organs. This approach has been particularly useful for studying nuclear hormone binding sites in developing hormone target organs.

III. Role of Mesenchyme in Hormonal Response of Epithelial Cells in Developing Hormone Target Organs

The genital tract of embryonic and neonatal rodents is sensitive to exogenous estrogen, which elicits a multitude of effects that are expressed within the epithelium of the uterus, cervix, vagina, prostate, and seminal vesicle (Takasugi, 1976; McLachlan *et al.*, 1980; Chung *et al.*, 1981). According to the prevalent view of hormone action, one would expect that the expression of estrogenic effects within developing urogenital epithelia to be correlated with the presence of estrogen receptors within these cells. However, autoradiographic analysis of the developing urogenital sinus and Müllerian ducts of embryonic mice indicates that nuclear [^{3}H]diethylstilbestrol binding sites are restricted to the mesenchymal cells of these embryonic rudiments, the epithelium being devoid of nuclear estrogen binding sites (Stumpf *et al.*, 1980). Similarly in the neonatal mouse, nuclear estrogen receptors are observed only in the mesenchymal cells (Fig. 2) of the vagina, cervix, and uterus. The onset of estrogen receptor activity in the epithelia of these organs occurs between days 10 and 20 postpartum (Cunha *et al.*, 1982a; Taguchi and Cunha, 1983). Injection of diethylstilbestrol (5 μg/day) during days 1 to 4 postpartum elicits by day 5 marked epithelial proliferation and cornification of the lower (sinus) vaginal epithelium without eliciting the expression of estrogen receptors within the epithelium (Fig. 3). By contrast, the underlying mesenchymal cells express intense nuclear labeling with [^{3}H]estradiol (Cunha *et al.*, 1982b). These findings raise the possibility that estrogen may elicit certain effects (growth and differentiation) within epithelial cells via indirect mechanisms in which the actual epithelial effect may be elicited by growth factors produced by estrogen receptor-positive mesenchymal cells (Fig. 4).

Before pursuing this idea further, it is important to consider whether the epithelium of the neonatal female mouse genital tract is truly deficient in nuclear estrogen receptors? Although this question is to some extent unanswerable, it should be recognized that the pattern and intensity of labeling within urogenital epithelia of the female neonatal mouse are indistinguishable from the background labeling of true nontarget tissues even after a 12 month autoradiographic exposure. It should be noted that through use of such long exposures autoradiographic techniques are much more sensitive than standard scintillation counting methods used in biochemical analysis of steroid receptors. We, therefore, conclude that estrogenic effects may be elicited in epithelial cells whose ability to bind estrogen appears to be below the level of detection of the most sensitive methodology available. The basis of estrogenic response in these epithe-

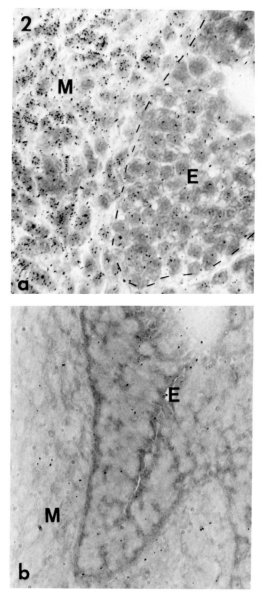

FIG. 2.   Autoradiograms of [³H]estradiol localization in the 1-day-old vaginal fornix (a and b) and 3-day-old uterus (c and d) of neonatal mice. Note that in both the vagina (a) and uterus (c) nuclear estrogen binding sites are present in the mesenchymal cells (M) but labeling in the epithelium (E) is essentially at background and without preferential nuclear uptake. Utilization of a 600-fold excess of radioinert estradiol in combination with the [³H]estradiol completely abolishes the nuclear labeling (b and d). ×500. (From Cunha *et al.*, 1982b.)

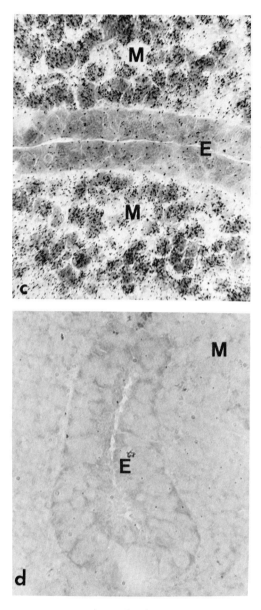

FIG. 2c–d.

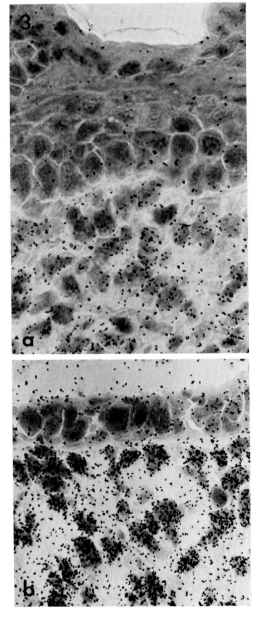

FIG. 3. Autoradiographic analysis of [³H]estradiol localization in neonatal mouse vagina. New born mice (<36 hours old) were injected daily for 4 days with 5 μg of DES or oil
vehicle. Twenty-four hours after the last injection, the mice were sacrificed, and the vagina
processed for autoradiographic localization of [³H]estradiol (see Cunha *et al.*, 1982b). Note

MORPHOGENESIS

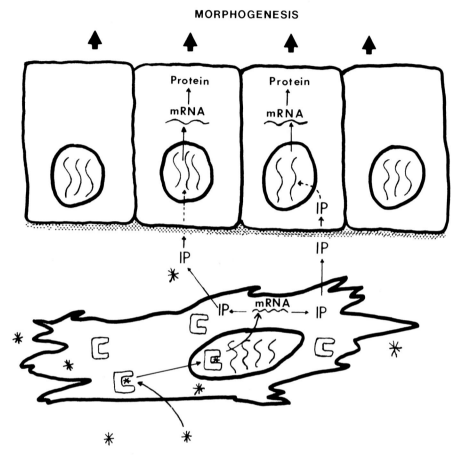

FIG. 4. A proposed mechanism of hormone action for morphogenetic processes in which nuclear hormone activity is present in the mesenchyme only. Sex steroids elicit synthesis of putative inductor molecules (IP) via classical hormone receptor mechanisms (open C, receptor; asterisk, hormone). Complex hormonal effects (morphogenesis and growth) are in turn elicited within epithelial cells by these inductor molecules. The mode of action of such hypothetical inductors is at present purely speculative, but may be similar to those proposed for growth factors, peptide hormones, or growth inhibitors. (From Cunha *et al.*, 1982b.)

that the vaginal epithelium of DES-treated mice (a) is cornified and hyperplastic as compared with the oil-injected control(b). In both specimens nuclear estrogen binding is prominent in mesenchymal cells, whereas within the epithelium no such activity is detectable. Instead the distribution of silver grains over the epithelium is random and without preferential nuclear uptake. ×800. (From Cunha *et al.*, 1982b.)

lial cells is presumed to be the receptor-positive mesenchymal cells with which they are associated. This observation does not negate the hormone receptor theory, but merely emphasizes that "hormonal" effects may not require the presence of hormone receptors within the responding epithelial cell providing they are associated with hormonally sensitive mesenchymal cells. The most compelling evidence for this idea is derived from analysis of androgen-dependent morphogenesis.

The first indication that androgens may elicit their effects upon epithelial morphogenesis via the mediation of mesenchymal cells came from studies in which urogenital epithelia from the embryonic seminal vesicle or urogenital sinus were grown in association with either urogenital mesenchyme or with nontarget integumental mesenchyme (Cunha, 1970, 1972a–c). Growth of these tissue recombinants in male hosts (and, thus, exposure to physiological levels of androgens) resulted in androgen-dependent prostatic or seminal vesicle morphogenesis only when these epithelia were associated with urogenital mesenchyme. By contrast, urogenital morphogenesis was abortive when these epithelia were grown under identical conditions but in association with integumental mesenchyme. Although these data have many possible interpretations, continued analysis verified the initial suggestion that the androgenic effects upon epithelial development were mediated via the mesenchyme. This point is emphasized by tissue recombination studies between Tfm and wild-type tissues.

The testicular feminization (Tfm) mutation, by virtue of either a complete absence, reduction, or an abnormality in the androgen receptor, renders target organs insensitive to androgens (Ohno, 1977, 1979; Wilson *et al.*, 1981). In Tfm mice the level of androgen receptor activity is exceedingly low or undetectable (Attardi and Ohno, 1974; Wieland and Fox, 1979). Due to impairment of androgen receptor function, these mice are totally feminized. Consequently, the urogenital sinus develops into vagina instead of forming prostate, while mammary epithelial development proceeds in males instead of being totally inhibited by androgens secreted by the fetal testes (Ohno, 1979). Analysis of development in tissue recombinants prepared with wild-type and Tfm urogenital sinuses or mammary glands demonstrates the importance of mesenchyme as the target and mediator of androgenic effects upon epithelium.

In the developing mammary gland, testosterone-induced epithelial regression occurs only when wild-type mesenchyme is present regardless of the genotype of the epithelium (Tfm or wild-type). When Tfm mesenchyme is utilized epithelial regression cannot be elicited by testosterone whether the epithelium is derived from either Tfm or wild-type mice (Fig. 5) (Kratochwil and Schwartz, 1976; Drews and Drews, 1977). Analysis of

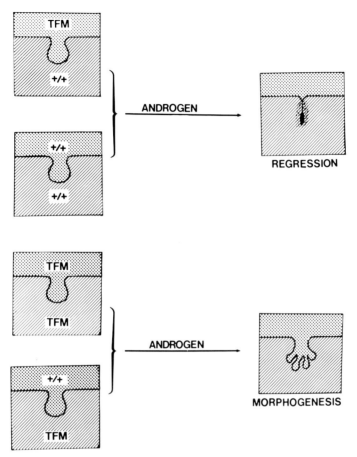

FIG. 5. Summary of Kratochwil and Schwartz's (1976) analysis of androgen-induced mammary epithelial regression in Tfm × wild-type tissue recombinants. The positive androgenic effect induced by testosterone (epithelial regression) occurs in those recombinants prepared with wild-type mesenchyme and either wild-type or Tfm epithelium. By contrast, these epithelia fail to regress when grown in association with Tfm mesenchyme. (From Cunha *et al.*, 1980a.)

prostatic epithelial development in Tfm × wild-type recombinants yields identical results. Androgen-dependent prostatic development occurs in tissue recombinants prepared with wild-type mesenchyme (Fig. 6), but never occurs when Tfm mesenchyme is utilized (Cunha and Lung, 1978; Lasnitzki and Mizuno, 1980). Furthermore, analysis of prostatic induction in recombinants composed of wild-type urogenital sinus mesenchyme and Tfm bladder epithelium (UGM + Tfm BLE recombinants) indicates that the entire morphogenetic process, which is absolutely dependent

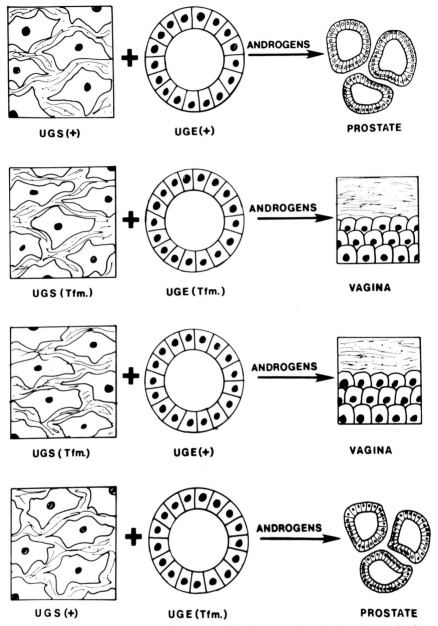

FIG. 6.   Summary of Tfm × wild-type recombination experiments of prostatic induction in urogenital sinuses. Androgen-induced prostatic morphogenesis occurs in all recombinants prepared with wild-type mesenchyme (UGS + plus UGE + or UGS + plus UGE Tfm). Conversely, vaginal epithelial development occurs when Tfm mesenchyme is used. (From Cunha *et al.*, 1980a.)

upon androgens, occurs in the Tfm epithelium that continues to remain androgen receptor deficient (Fig. 7). Thus, the following phenomena, all of which are absolutely dependent upon androgen, occur in Tfm androgen receptor-deficient epithelium: (1) generation of an elaborately arborized glandular network from the undifferentiated Tfm epithelium, (2) expression of marked epithelial growth which accompanies this morphogenetic process, and (3) expression of secretory cytodifferentiation in the Tfm epithelium. Autoradiographic analysis of [³H]thymidine uptake demonstrates that the labeling index is high in the induced prostatic acini of UGM + Tfm BLE recombinants grown in intact male hosts, whereas in the absence of androgen (castrated hosts), epithelial labeling is greatly reduced (Fig. 8). These studies indicate that it is the mesenchyme which is the actual target and mediator of androgenic effects upon the epithelium and suggest that certain hormonal effects within the epithelium may be mediated indirectly via androgen receptor-positive mesenchymal cells that in turn influence epithelial morphogenesis, growth, and cytodifferentiation via putative growth factors, morphogens, or inductors yet to be defined.

These conclusions receive additional support from autoradiographic analysis of the developing prostate and mammary gland of wild-type mice. The Tfm × wild-type recombination studies emphasize the need for an androgen-sensitive (wild-type) mesenchyme and indicate that androgenic sensitivity of the epithelium is unimportant. Autoradiographic analysis of [³H]DHT labeling in the developing prostate and mammary gland of wild-type mouse embryos demonstrates intense nuclear labeling in the mesenchyme (Fig. 9) and a total absence of such activity within the epithelium (Cunha *et al.*, 1981a; Shannon *et al.*, 1981; Shannon and Cunha, 1983; Heuberger *et al.*, 1982). In the developing prostate the epithelium remains deficient in nuclear androgen receptors until about 4 to 6 days postnatal at which time the solid epithelial cords begin to canalize and undergo secretory cytodifferentiation. Thus, the expression of nuclear androgen receptor activity within the epithelium of the developing prostate appears to correlate with the initiation of secretory activity. However, in the developing wild-type prostate, early epithelial aborization (glandular morphogenesis) and epithelial growth associated with this morphogenetic process occur within an epithelium in which androgen receptor activity is undetectable, thus corroborating the Tfm × wild-type recombination experiments.

This body of evidence suggests that the histotypic complexity of hormone target organs is of importance in understanding complex morphogenetic effects of hormones. Although the basic theory of hormone-receptor action can be related to hormonal induction of macromolecular synthesis,

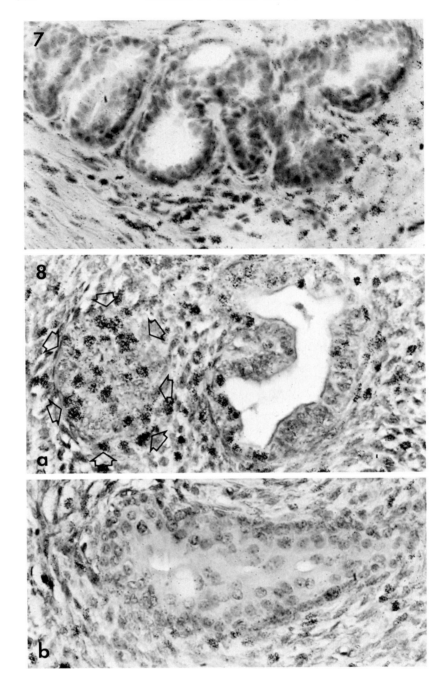

it may not be directly applicable to more complex hormonal effects involving morphogenesis and cellular differentiation. Certainly there is ample evidence that hormones, following interaction with their respective receptors, stimulate RNA and protein synthesis, and ultimately secretion of specific products. Secretory products produced by epithelial cells may be essential for reproductive processes. The secretory products of mesenchymal or stromal cells, substances that remain ill-defined to this day, may in fact be the growth factors, morphogens, or inductors which elicit hormonal effects within epithelium (Fig. 4). If this is true, then one would predict that it should not be possible to elicit growth in primary cultures of urogenital epithelial cells by addition of steroidal sex hormones. With few exceptions this in fact has been the general experience of investigators in this field (see Sonnenschein and Soto, 1980a,b). Moreover, Sirbasku (1980) has demonstrated that growth in estrogen responsive target epithelial cells can be enhanced *in vitro* by nonsteroidal, macromolecular growth factors called estromedins. Our studies point to the mesenchymal or stromal cell as a crucial regulatory factor of hormonal response in epithelium. The biological and molecular dynamics of cells of the stroma present exciting challenges for the future.

IV. Regulation of Epithelial Growth, Morphogenesis, Cytodifferentiation, and Function by Mesenchymal Cells

A. REGULATION OF EPITHELIAL GROWTH

For any accessory sexual organ a typical size and weight can be determined which is the characteristic mature size of that organ. For many organs the epithelial parenchyma constitutes the bulk of the total organ. This is particularly true for the rodent prostate in which epithelial mass

---

FIG. 7.   Autoradiographic analysis of [³H]dihydrotestosterone localization in tissue recombinants composed of wild-type UGM and Tfm bladder epithelium. The prostatic acini induced in Tfm bladder epithelium are completely devoid of androgen receptors whereas this activity is prominently displayed in the surrounding wild-type mesenchymal cells ×400. (Shannon and Cunha, in preparation.)

FIG. 8.   Autoradiograms of [³H]thymidine incorporation in tissue recombinants composed of wild-type UGM and Tfm bladder epithelium. (a) Recombinants grown in intact male hosts undergo prostatic morphogenesis. The induced epithelium of these recombinants exhibits marked labeling. Note the fully canalized acinus and solid epithelial bud (arrows) which are heavily labeled. (b) Same type of recombinant grown in a castrated host. Under these conditions prostatic morphogenesis does not occur, and the epithelium is totally devoid of label. ×400.

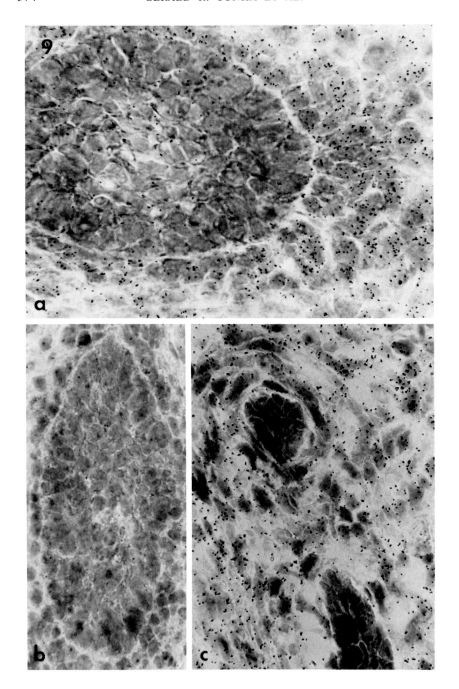

constitutes 82% of the total (de Klerk *et al.*, 1976). Prostatic epithelial growth proceeds rapidly in the pre-adult, and upon sexual maturation full adult size is attained, and further growth ceases (except under pathological conditions). Since the epithelium constitutes most of the prostate, regulation of epithelial growth (which is defective during prostatic tumorigenesis) is a particularly important biological question. To discern whether regulation of epithelial growth is intrinsic or extrinsic to the epithelium, tissue recombinants were prepared with embryonic urogenital sinuses in which the ratio of epithelium and mesenchyme was varied. Designating as $1\times$ the total amount of epithelium and mesenchyme obtainable from a 16-day old embryonic urogenital sinus, tissue recombinants were prepared in which the amount of mesenchyme was held constant at $1\times$ and the epithelium varied from $1\times$ to $0.01\times$. Such variations had no effect upon the amount (wet weight and DNA content) of prostatic acinar tissue that developed following 1 month of growth in male hosts (Fig. 10). By contrast, when the epithelium was held constant at $1\times$ and the amount of mesenchyme varied from $0.1\times$ to $2\times$, the amount of prostatic acinar tissue that developed increased as the mesenchymal mass was increased (Chung and Cunha, 1983). Thus, epithelial growth and, therefore, absolute prostatic size appear to be regulated by mesenchymal tissue. Similarly, mammary epithelial growth and morphogenesis appear to be regulated by mammary stroma (the fat pad) (Daniel and De Ome, 1965). The inability to obtain a convincing growth response to trophic hormones in primary epithelial cell cultures of the prostate, mammary gland, vagina, cervix, or uterus is, therefore, not surprising since this activity may be regulated primarily by other cell types.

B. MESENCHYMAL REGULATION OF EPITHELIAL MORPHOGENESIS, CYTODIFFERENTIATION, AND FUNCTION IN THE FEMALE GENITAL TRACT

Most of the female genital tract develops from the Müllerian ducts which form the uterine tubes, uterus, cervix, and upper portion of the vagina (Taguchi *et al.*, 1982; O'Rahilly, 1977). The lower vagina is derived

---

FIG. 9.   Autoradiographs of [³H]dihydrotestosterone (DHT) localization in 14-day-old embryonic mammary glands (a and b) and prostate (c) from 6-day-old postnatal mice. In (a) nuclear labeling (androgen receptor activity) is distinct in the mammary mesenchyme but is absent over epithelial nuclei. In (b), coadministration of radioinert DHT completely abolishes nuclear labeling in the embryonic mammary gland. In (c), a section of 6-day-old neonatal mouse prostate, the developing epithelial cords are still solid (without lumen). In these areas nuclear labeling is prominent in mesenchymal cells and absent in the epithelium, despite the fact that considerable androgen-induced glandular aborization has occurred.

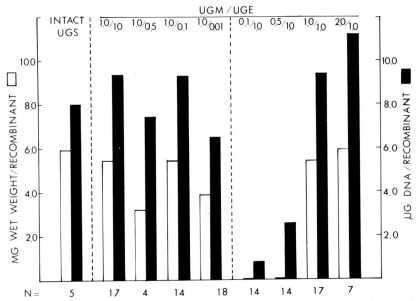

FIG. 10. The effect of varying the ratio of epithelium to mesenchyme in homotypic recombinants prepared with mouse urogenital sinuses. In these experiments, urogenital sinus recombinants were prepared in which the amounts of epithelium and mesenchyme were varied from 0.01× to 2×. Prostatic acinar growth (wet weight and DNA content) was measured at the end of a 1-month growth period (intact adult male hosts). Data represent the average wet weights and DNA contents from 4 to 18 recombinants/group (*N* = number of recombinants).

from the endodermal urogenital sinus (Cunha, 1975; Ulfelder and Robboy, 1976). Epithelium of the embryonic Müllerian ducts initially exhibits no regional differences in cytodifferentiation whatsoever, but later differentiates regionally into the epithelial parenchyma of the uterine tube, uterus, cervix, and vagina, whose morphology, cytodifferentiation, and function are vastly different in adulthood. These differences in epithelial differentiation are elicited by the mesenchyme which induces and specifies epithelial differentiation in an organ-specific manner (Cunha, 1976a,b). For instance, growth of uterine epithelium in combination with vaginal or cervical mesenchyme from neonatal mice elicits differentiation of a stratified squamous vaginal or cervical epithelium from the originally simple columnar uterine epithelium (Cunha, 1976a). Similarly, the normally stratified squamous epithelium of the neonatal mouse vagina is induced to undergo uterine differentiation when grown in association with uterine mesenchyme (Fig. 11). Evidence suggests that this mesenchyme-induced change in epithelial morphology and cytodifferentiation is cou-

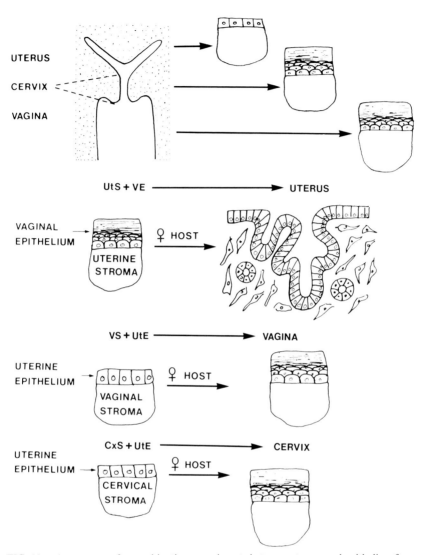

FIG. 11. A summary of recombination experiments between stroma and epithelium from uterus, cervix, and vagina of neonatal mice. In the upper portion of the figure the morphological organization of the epithelium is depicted in these regions: uterus has a simple columnar epithelium, whereas vaginal and cervical epithelia are stratified squamous. Epithelial morphogenesis and cytodifferentiation is induced and specified by the mesenchyme as depicted in the lower half of the figure. (From Cunha and Fujii, 1981.)

pled to functional (biochemical) changes as well. For instance, tissue recombinations of uterine epithelium and either vaginal or cervical mesenchyme undergo development of a stratified vaginal or cervical epithelium which cycles during the estrous cycle in concert with the host's vaginal and cervical epithelium. Consequently, alternating layers of cornified and mucified cells are sloughed and accumulate in the lumen of these tissue recombinants. Thus, as the host progresses through several estrous cycles, alternating epithelial layers accumulate that provide a morphological record of the number of estrous cycles the host traversed while the graft was in place (Fig. 12). More importantly, the alternating sequence of epithelial mucification and cornification induced and expressed in an epithelium that was originally a uterine epithelium is a distinctive functional hallmark of vaginal or cervical epithelial differentiation. This putative change in epithelial function is supported by analysis of protein synthesis in these tissue recombinants.

For any given organ a spectrum of unique proteins defines the biosynthetic and functional attributes characteristic of that organ. Organ-specific

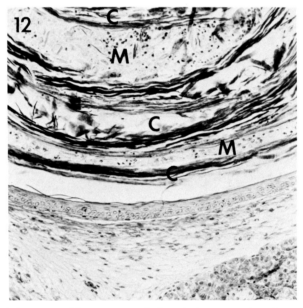

FIG. 12.   A tissue recombinant composed of cervical stroma and uterine epithelium from 5-day-old mice. Note that the epithelium has been induced to express a stratified squamous differentiation. During the 5 weeks of growth in a cycling female host, alternating layers of mucified (M) and cornified (C) cells have sloughed into the graft lumen. ×320. (From Cunha and Fujii, 1981.)

protein synthetic "fingerprints" can be readily demonstrated by separation of proteins in two dimensions by electrophoresis in polyacrylamide gels. By this method proteins labeled with [^{35}S]methionine were analyzed in the following tissue recombinants: uterine stroma and uterine epithelium (US + UE), vaginal stroma and vaginal epithelium (VS + VE), uterine stroma and vaginal epithelium (US + VE), and vaginal stroma and uterine epithelium (VS + UE). In addition, each one of the following tissues was analyzed separately (US, VS, UE, and VE). Gels of US + UE and VS + VE showed distinct differences that reflected differences in the proteins synthesized by control specimens of uterus and vagina. Furthermore, analysis of gels of the separated organ components (VS, VE, US, and UE) indicated that most of the protein spots in the tissue recombinants were accounted for by synthetic activity of the epithelium; that is, the stroma did not contribute substantially to the overall pattern of protein synthetic activity under the experimental conditions utilized (see Cunha *et al.*, 1983b). Analysis of gels of US + VE and VS + UE indicated that the gel pattern followed precisely the mode of epithelial morphological induction. For example, recombinants that expressed uterine differentiation (US + VE) exhibited a protein synthetic "fingerprint" that resembled that of uterus. Similarly, vaginal induction from uterine epithelium (VS + UE) was associated with protein synthetic activity indicative of vagina. Therefore, morphological inductions in which epithelial cytodifferentiation is altered (columnar-glandular to squamous, or squamous to columnar-glandular) appear to be coupled to altered functional (biochemical) activity.

Simple morphological analysis indicates that the developmental processes involved in morphogenesis of the female genital tract are similar in most vertebrate species. Similarities in the basic morphogenetic sequence appear to be based in turn upon the conservation during evolution of the same developmental signals which mediate these morphogenetic epithelial–mesenchymal interactions. For this reason, morphogenetic interactions between mesenchyme and epithelium can occur across species lines. For instance, mouse vaginal stroma will support differentiation of human vaginal epithelium including the continued expression of epithelial estrogen receptors (Cunha and Fujii, 1981; Cunha, unpublished). Similarly uterine epithelial differentiation proceeds normally in recombinants prepared with uterine epithelium and mesenchyme derived from neonatal rabbits and mice (mouse US + rabbit UE or rabbit US + mouse UE) (Cunha, unpublished). Furthermore, human fetal vaginal stroma can elicit squamous differentiation from neonatal mouse uterine epithelium (Cunha and Taguchi, unpublished). Thus, the physicochemical signals that mediate mesenchymal–epithelial interactions (messages that are permissive for expression of the developmental fate of an epithelium, or messages that can reprogram epithelial differentiation) appear to have been highly conserved during evolution of mammals and, therefore, are common to many vertebrate species.

C. MESENCHYMAL REGULATION OF EPITHELIAL MORPHOGENESIS, CYTODIFFERENTIATION, AND FUNCTION IN THE MALE GENITAL TRACT

The male genital tract develops from two embryonic anlage: the Wolffian duct and urogenital sinus. The Wolffian duct, whose epithelium is mesodermal in origin, gives rise to the epididymis, ductus deferens, seminal vesicle, and ejaculatory ducts. The urogenital sinus whose epithelium is endodermal in origin gives rise to the prostate, bulbourethral glands, urethra, and periurethral glands, and contributes substantially to the urinary bladder (Cunha, 1983). Since normally the mesodermal epithelium of the seminal vesicle does not have within its developmental repertoire the ability to form prostate (which is endodermal in origin), recombinants prepared with urogenital sinus mesenchyme (a prostatic inductor) and seminal vesicle epithelium (UGM + SVE) undergo development characteristic of seminal vesicle (Fig. 13). Mesenchyme of the urogenital sinus (UGM) is, thus, able to support, but not reprogram the developmental fate of epithelium of the seminal vesicle (SVE). Similarly, mesenchyme of the seminal vesicle (SVM) permits the normal expression of prostatic differentiation in epithelium of the urogenital sinus (UGE), but does not elicit seminal vesicle development from UGE (Fig. 13) (Cunha, 1972a). We have proposed that expression of normal prostatic and seminal vesicle development in heterotypic urogenital recombinants (UGM + SVE and SVM + UGE) is afforded by the fact that both types of mesenchyme possess androgen receptors and both are glandular inductors. Developmental response in heterotypic tissue recombinants, that is, whether the epithelium continues its normal developmental program or is reprogrammed into another developmental pathway, appears to be related not only to mesenchymal induction, but also to epithelial competence (responsiveness), which may be correspondingly restricted by the germ cell layer from which the epithelium is derived. Thus, epithelia of mesodermal origin may only be able to differentiate into mesodermal derivatives, whereas endodermal epithelia may only be able to form endodermal derivatives. This concept receives support from analysis of tissue recombinants composed of bladder epithelium (BLE) and mesenchyme from either urogenital sinus (UGM) or seminal vesicle (SVM). Epithelium of the urinary bladder (BLE) is endodermal in origin and is responsive to glan-

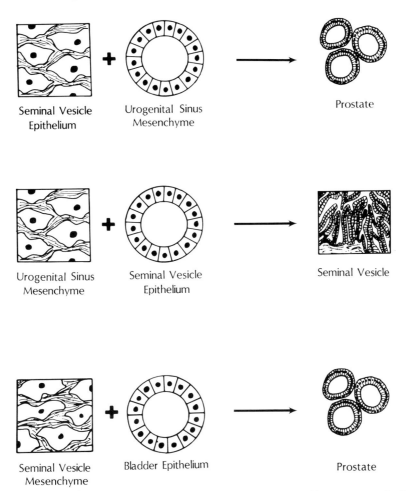

Seminal Vesicle
Epithelium

Urogenital Sinus
Mesenchyme

Prostate

Urogenital Sinus
Mesenchyme

Seminal Vesicle
Epithelium

Seminal Vesicle

Seminal Vesicle
Mesenchyme

Bladder Epithelium

Prostate

FIG. 13. Developmental response of heterotypic tissue recombinants prepared with epithelium and mesenchyme derived from embryonic urogenital sinus, bladder, and seminal vesicle. Recombinants of urogenital sinus mesenchyme and seminal vesicle epithelium differentiate as seminal vesicle, while recombinants composed of seminal vesicle mesenchyme and urogenital sinus epithelium differentiate as prostate. Therefore, in these permissive inductions the heterotypic mesenchyme promotes expression of the normal developmental fate of the epithelium. By contrast, in recombinants composed of seminal vesicle mesenchyme (SVM) and bladder epithelium, the SVM reprograms epithelial differentiation by eliciting glandular morphogenesis, but the type of gland formed is prostate, not seminal vesicle.

dular inductions. Prostatic development is elicited in recombinants of UGM + BLE (Figs. 13 and 14) (Cunha and Lung, 1978; Cunha et al., 1980b). In combination with SVM, bladder epithelium also forms prostatic acini instead of forming seminal vesicle (Fig. 13) (Cunha, unpublished). Our explanation for this unusual developmental response is based upon the endodermal origin of BLE. Endodermal BLE may not be capable of expressing differentiation unique to the mesodermal layer, i.e., the formation of seminal vesicle. Instead BLE responds to this glandular inductor (SVM) by forming prostate, which is within the developmental repertoire of this endodermal epithelium. It is further noteworthy that in the developing rodent SVM supports the development of both seminal vesicle and coagulating gland, a lobe of the prostate. Thus, SVM supports development of both seminal vesicle and prostatic morphology, and in recombinants of SVM + BLE, the type of response (prostatic development) appears to be specified by virtue of the developmental history and developmental repertoire of the epithelium, as well as the general glandular inductive capability of the mesenchyme.

D. PROSTATIC INDUCTION: A MODEL FOR INSTRUCTIVE INDUCTIONS

An instructive induction is one in which the mesenchyme reprograms the developmental fate of the epithelium. For example, mesenchyme of the urogenital sinus (UGM), when associated with epithelium of the urinary bladder (BLE), elicits prostatic morphogenesis from the BLE provided the tissue recombinant is grown under androgenic conditions, i.e., in a male host (Fig. 14). Surprisingly, prostatic differentiation can be induced whether the bladder epithelium is derived from either fetal or adult rodents (Cunha and Lung, 1978; Cunha et al., 1980a, 1983d). Providing that wild-type mesenchyme is utilized, prostatic morphogenesis can even be elicited from Tfm BLE (Fig. 15) (Cunha and Chung, 1981). Furthermore, prostatic induction in UGM + BLE recombinants occurs across species lines as demonstrated in experiments utilizing mouse, rat, rabbit, and human tissues (Cunha et al., 1983c). Therefore, the mechanism of prostatic development is also highly conserved in different mammalian species including man (Table I).

Prostatic induction from bladder epithelium exhibits the hormonal requirements known to be necessary for normal prostatic morphogenesis. Therefore, UGM + BLE recombinants grown in castrated or DES-treated hosts fail to exhibit prostatic development. In castrated hosts, the BLE maintains its normal urothelial morphology, whereas in hosts treated with DES, an abnormal hyperplastic urothelium develops. Admin-

TABLE I

Prostatic Differentiation in Chimeric Glands Prepared with Mouse, Rat, Rabbit, and Human Tissues[a]

Tissue recombinants		Developmental response
Mesenchyme	Epithelium	
Rat UGM	Mouse UGE	Prostate (14/14)
Mouse UGM	Rat UGE	Prostate (4/4)
Rat UGM	Rabbit UGE	Glands (6/6)
Rabbit UGM	Rat UGE	Prostate (4/4)
Mouse UGM	Rabbit UGE	Glands (3/3)
Rabbit UGM	Mouse UGE	Prostate (10/10)
Rat UGM	Mouse embryonic BLE	Prostate (15/15)
Mouse UGM	Rabbit embryonic BLE	Glands (3/3)
Mouse UGM	Rat embryonic BLE	Prostate (7/7)
Mouse UGM	Rat adult BLE	Prostate (4/4)
Rat UGM	Mouse adult BLE	Prostate (20/20)
Mouse UGM	Human fetal BLE	Glands (38/38)

[a] From Cunha *et al.* (1983c).

istration of cyproterone acetate (20 mg pellet) to intact hosts bearing UGM + BLE recombinants results in partial suppression of prostatic development (Cunha, unpublished). Thus, prostatic induction in UGM + BLE recombinants is androgen dependent and, therefore, is impaired by androgen deprivation whether accomplished by physical or chemical means.

Utilizing the favorable conditions afforded by grafting developing tissue recombinants to highly vascularized graft sites (renal capsule), glandular morphogenesis proceeds rapidly, considerable growth occurs, and induced epithelial cells undergo secretory cytodifferentiation (Cunha *et al.*, 1980a, 1981a,b, 1983d). In 2 to 4 weeks of growth, histological and fine structural features unique to bladder epithelium (the stratified urothelial morphology, the asymmetric cell membrane, and the fusiform vesicles) disappear as prostatic acini develop that are lined by a simple columnar epithelium. Morphological analysis of the time-course of prostatic development from BLE demonstrates that solid epithelial downgrowths proliferate from the basal cells of the BLE (Cunha *et al.*, 1983d). These solid epithelial cords (which resemble prostatic buds that appear *in situ* during normal prostatic development) elongate, arborize, and secondarily develop lumina lined by a simple columnar secretory epithelium (Cunha *et al.*, 1980a,b, 1983d). This process precisely mimics that observed *in situ* in the developing rodent in both a morphological and a temporal sense.

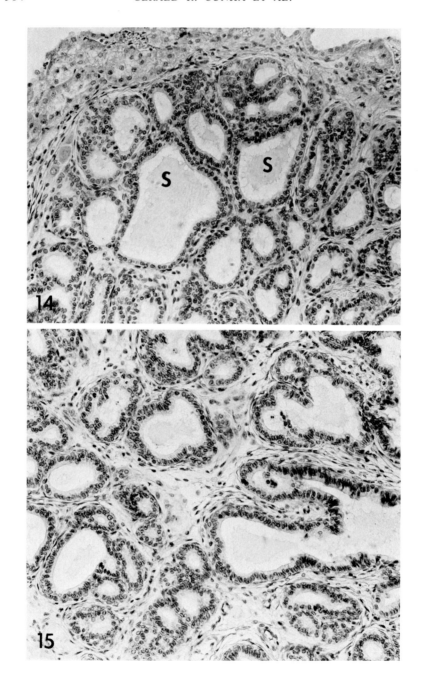

TABLE II

Histochemical Analysis of Prostate, Bladder, and Tissue Recombinants Prepared with Urogenital Sinus Mesenchyme (UGM) and Epithelium from Urinary Bladder (BLE) of Embryonic Mice[a]

| Specimen | Epithelial morphology | Histochemical characteristics of epithelia | | |
		Alcian Blue	Nonspecific esterase	Alkaline phosphatase
Adult prostate	Glandular	+	+	–
Adult urinary bladder	Transitional	–	– or ±	+
UGM + BLE	Glandular	+	+	–

[a] From Cunha and Lung (1980).

The induced acinar epithelium exhibits fine structural features associated with prostatic acinar cells such as basally situated nuclei and rough endoplasmic reticulum, supranuclear Golgi zones, and apically located secretory granules (Cunha *et al.*, 1980a, 1981a, 1983d). Secretory material is frequently observed in the acinar lumina (Fig. 14).

Morphological evidence of secretory activity raises the possibility that this alteration in urothelial (BLE) morphology and cytodifferentiation may be coupled to altered functional activity. Indeed, this appears to be the case. Histochemical analysis demonstrates a loss of markers associated with the bladder phenotype and a concomitant acquisition of markers indicative of the prostatic phenotype (Cunha and Lung, 1980; Cunha *et al.*, 1980a, 1983d) (Table II). Furthermore, the androgen receptor-negative BLE is induced to express nuclear dihydrotestosterone binding sites (Fig. 16) whether the BLE is derived from either embryonic or adult mice (Cunha *et al.*, 1980c; Neubauer *et al.*, 1983; Taguchi and Cunha, 1983). Biochemical analysis of androgen binding in UGM + BLE recombinants demonstrates many features indicative of androgen receptor activity: organ specificity, high affinity (K_d = 0.3 nM), saturability, correlation with biologic response, and presence in cytosol and nucleus (Neubauer *et al.*,

FIG. 14. A tissue recombinant prepared with 16-day-old embryonic mouse urogenital sinus mesenchyme and adult bladder epithelium. Prostatic development has occurred following 4 weeks of growth in a male host. Note secretion (S) within acinar lumina. ×320.

FIG. 15. A recombinant prepared with wild-type urogenital sinus mesenchyme from a 16-day-old embryonic mouse and bladder epithelium from an adult Tfm mouse. Following 4 weeks of growth in a male host, prostatic morphogenesis has occurred. ×320. (From Cunha *et al.*, 1980a.)

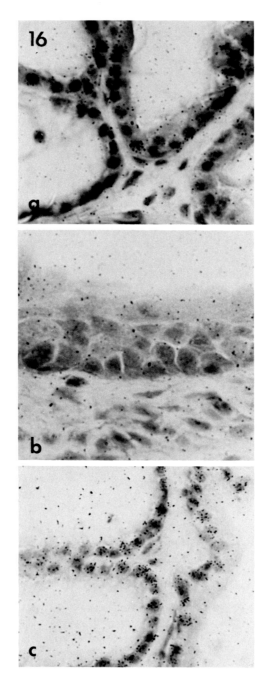

1983). Protein synthetic activity in UGM + BLE recombinants analyzed by two-dimensional gel electrophoresis exhibits an overall synthetic "fingerprint" which closely resembles that of prostate and which is markedly different from that of urinary bladder (Cunha and Chung, 1981; Neubauer *et al.*, 1983). DNA synthesis in UGM + BLE recombinants as well as secretory cytodifferentiation are both inducible by androgens, and this stimulatory effect of androgens on these parameters is antagonized by coadministration of the antiandrogen, cyproterone acetate (Cunha and Chung, 1981). Finally, the induced prostatic epithelium in UGM + BLE recombinants expresses prostate-specific antigens as demonstrated by immunoperoxidase techniques (Cunha and Fujii, 1981; Cunha *et al.*, 1983c; Taguchi and Cunha, 1983). From this body of data, it is evident that urogenital sinus mesenchyme elicits the expression of a true prostatic phenotype from either embryonic or adult bladder epithelium. This degree of developmental plasticity of an adult epithelium has important implications in abnormal developmental processes that involve both the bladder and the prostate (see below).

V. Stromal–Parenchymal Interactions in Adulthood

Organs of the male and female genital tracts and the mammary gland exhibit marked morphological and functional change during reproductive cycles. As hormonal stimulation wanes, secretory processes cease, and epithelial architecture is eliminated to a greater or lesser degree. During this process overall organ size and weight decreases significantly. At later periods, as titers of trophic hormones rise, epithelial growth and morphogenesis resume, and new parenchymal elements form and become functional as the organ is restored to its maximal size. Evidence indicates that these true morphogenetic processes are accomplished by developmental mechanisms identical to those operative during the initial development of the organ. For instance, embryonic development of the mammary gland is induced by mammary mesenchyme which elicits a specific pattern of ductal outgrowth and secretory cytodifferentiation in fetal mammary epithelium (Kratochwil, 1969; Sakakura *et al.*, 1976). In adulthood, mam-

---

FIG. 16.   Autoradiograms of [^{3}H]DHT in (a) prostate, (b) bladder, and (c) tissue recombinant prepared with 16-day-old embryonic mouse urogenital sinus mesenchyme and bladder epithelium (see Cunha *et al.*, 1980c, for technical details). Prostatic epithelium (a) exhibits its characteristic nuclear localization of label indicative of androgen receptor activity (×500), whereas bladder epithelium (b), a nontarget tissue, exhibits a random distribution of silver grains (×800). Note that in the tissue recombinant (c), the induced bladder epithelium exhibits nuclear labeling indicative of androgen receptor activity (×500).

mary stroma (the fat pad) can elicit mammary morphogenesis from either adult or embryonic mammary epithelium (Daniel and De Ome, 1965; Sakakura *et al.*, 1979a,b). Similarly, morphogenetically quiescent epithelium of the adult mammary gland, when associated with embryonic mammary mesenchyme, is induced to form new ductal architecture (Sakakura *et al.*, 1979b). Thus, mammary epithelium and stroma (mesenchyme) from both the embryo and adult are fundamentally similar in terms of their development properties. Similarly, evidence indicates that adult prostatic epithelium, which in the steady state of an intact male is quiescent in both a proliferative and a morphogenetic sense, can be induced by embryonic urogenital sinus mesenchyme to rapidly grow in 1 month from a starting population of a few hundred prostatic epithelial cells contained in a single prostatic acinus to a mass of prostatic tissue whose wet weight is 30 to 70

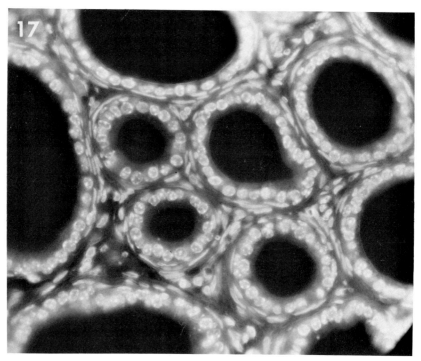

FIG. 17. A recombinant prepared with 18-day-old embryonic rat UGM and a single acinus from adult mouse dorso-lateral prostate. During 1 month of growth in an athymic male nude mouse, the limited number of epithelial cells in the adult mouse prostatic acinus proliferated and formed hundreds of prostatic acini. Utilizing the Hoechst dye 33258, which permits discrimination of mouse versus rat cells (Cunha and Vanderslice, 1982) (mouse cells contain bright intranuclear fluorescent spots), it is apparent that adult prostatic epithelium can interact morphogenetically with UGM (×320).

mg and contains several hundred fully differentiated prostatic acini (Fig. 17) (Cunha, unpublished observations). Indirect evidence further indicates that adult prostatic stroma is able to induce prostatic morphogenesis from epithelium of both the embryonic urogenital sinus and urinary bladder (Cunha, unpublished). In females, vaginal stroma from either neonatal or adult mice can induce neonatal uterine epithelium to express vaginal differentiation (Cunha, 1976a,b). Furthermore, both vaginal and bladder epithelium from adult mice can be induced by urogenital sinus mesenchyme to form prostate (Cunha *et al.,* 1980a, 1981b). Therefore, it is evident that the term embryonic induction should not be applied to epithelial–mesenchymal interactions, which instead are phenomena initiated in the embryo and perpetuated throughout the reproductive life of the animal. In adulthood these interactions appear to be involved in maintaining epithelial differentiation and in mediating morphogenetic events during reproductive cycles. It comes as no surprise, therefore, that epithelial–stromal interactions also are involved in abnormal epithelial differentiation including carcinogenesis.

VI. Mesenchymal–Epithelial Interactions in Abnormal Epithelial Differentiation

Epithelial neoplasms frequently progress through several abnormal states before overt invasive behavior is expressed. This is particularly true for cervical and endometrial carcinogenesis in which a progression of epithelial atypias has been described (Langley, 1976; Sherman and Brown, 1979). Mice injected perinatally with exogenous estrogen develop a spectrum of vaginal abnormalities, some structural and others functional, which ultimately progress to the development of vaginal carcinomas (Takasugi, 1976, 1979; McLachlan *et al.,* 1980; Mori and Takasugi, 1981). One abnormal antecedent condition is ovary-independent persistent vaginal hyperplasia and cornification (Takasagi, 1976). In this condition mice injected with estrogen during the perinatal period continue to express a hyperplastic, cornified vaginal epithelium in adulthood even following combined endocrine ablations that reduce if not totally eliminate systemic estrogens (ovariectomy, adrenalectomy, and hypophysectomy). Induction of this abnormal vaginal epithelial condition requires the maintenance of epithelial–mesenchymal interactions during the time of exposure to the estrogen (Cunha *et al.,* 1977). Once induced, the continued expression of ovary-independent persistent hyperplasia is maintained in adulthood by an interaction between the abnormal epithelium and mesenchyme (Cunha *et al.,* 1977). Furthermore, prostatic enlargement, benign prostatic hyperplasia, which results in part from the neoformation of new ductal-acinar architecture, is thought to result from reactivation of embryonic inductive properties in prostatic stroma of aged human males (McNeal, 1978).

The carcinogenic process is also regulated to some degree by epithelial–stromal interactions. One current view of neoplasia is that it may be an abnormal (and potentially reversible) form of differentiation (Pierce *et al.*, 1978; Mintz, 1978). This view, based until recently upon analysis of biological phenomena, now receives support from molecular studies suggesting that transforming genes activated in neoplasms may be related to the expression of normal differentiation by neoplastic cells (Cooper, 1982). If the relationship between neoplasia and differentiation is correct, then for each neoplasm an appropriate "embryonic" inductor should exist that may regulate the neoplasm. Support for this concept exists for embryonal carcinoma cells (EC), which mimic cells of the embryonic inner cell mass, and may be regulated by introduction of EC cells into the blastocyst (Pierce *et al.*, 1978; Mintz, 1978). Since carcinomas are derived from epithelial cells, the appropriate *mesenchymal* environment should have some regulatory influence upon the induction, progression, and continued maintenance of carcinomas. Indeed, considerable evidence for this concept already exists for bladder (Hodges *et al.*, 1977; Fujii *et al.*, 1982), mammary (DeCosse *et al.*, 1973, 1975; Sakakura *et al.*, 1979c, 1981), skin (Cooper and Pinkus, 1977; MacKenzie *et al.*, 1979), prostatic (L. W. K. Chung, personal communication), and salivary tumors (Dawe *et al.*, 1976). To illustrate this point, we have recently demonstrated that epithelial cells from nonglandular transitional cell carcinomas (bladder tumors) can be induced to express a glandular (adenocarcinomatous) phenotype when associated with urogenital sinus mesenchyme (a prostatic inductor) and grown in male hosts (Fig. 18) (Fujii *et al.*, 1982). This experiment is, of course, based upon our earlier success in inducing normal adult bladder epithelium to express prostatic differentiation (Cunha *et al.*, 1980a,b; 1983d). In these studies morphological change of the normal bladder epithelium was coupled to expression of prostatic function. We, therefore, conclude that expression of the adenocarcinomatous phenotype by cells that originally were derived from a nonglandular transitional cell carcinoma, also implies a marked change in biological properties. Consequently, it is appropriate to determine whether the induced adenocarcinomas are in fact prostatic in nature.

In conclusion, epithelial morphogenesis (the generation of new epithelial form) is a process expressed in all organ systems possessing an epithelial parenchyma. In all secretory organs examined, both those whose development is dependent and independent of hormones, the generation of new architecture from undifferentiated epithelium requires an interac-

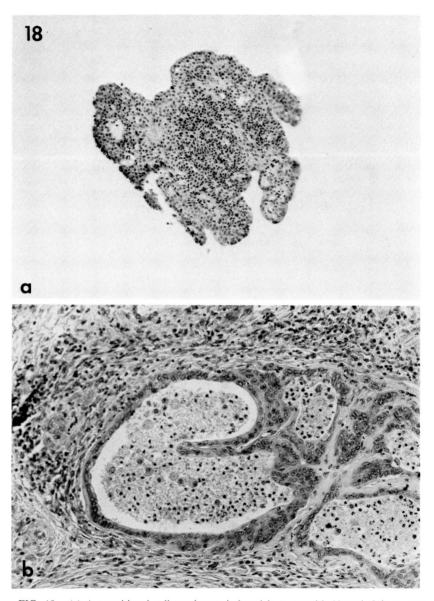

FIG. 18. (a) A transitional cell carcinoma induced in a rat with *N*-methylnitrosourea (MNU). This tumor of the urinary bladder is organized as a nonglandular papillomatous growth. ×100. (b) A heterotypic recombinant of 17-day-old embryonic rat urogenital sinus mesenchyme and epithelium from an MNU-induced tumor as depicted in (a). Following 1 month of growth in an intact male host, the epithelium has formed adenocarcinomatous structures. ×400. (From Fujii *et al.*, 1982.)

tion with mesenchymal cells or with mesenchymal cell products (Grobstein, 1967; Kratochwil, 1972; Wolff, 1968; Cunha, 1976b; Kollar, 1972; Rutter and Pictet, 1976). Epithelial growth is invariably an important component of the morphogenetic process, which is regulated by mesenchyme. Therefore, it is not surprising that urogenital mesenchyme induces specific epithelial morphogenesis, growth, and function within the genital tract and that the hormonal sensitivity of these morphogenetic processes resides in the mesenchyme, which invariably contains nuclear hormone receptors. Since morphogenetic processes are cyclic in adult genital tracts of many species, developmental properties (mesenchymal induction and epithelial competence) are expressed in adulthood and, for this reason, appear to play a regulatory role in abnormal epithelial differentiation including carcinogenesis.

ACKNOWLEDGMENTS

The authors gratefully acknowledge the expert assistance of Beth Meloy, Marnie Sekkingstad, Ken D. Vanderslice, Kathleen McCormick, Caroline Montoya, Virginia Miller, and Betty Aguilar in performing the experiments and to Alana Schilling and her assistants in typing the manuscript. We also wish to thank Dr. Robert M. Bigsby for critically reading the manuscript.

This was supported in part by NIH Grants HD12166, HD17491, AM25266, CA27418, and AMCA 16570, American Cancer Society Grant PDT-139, and March of Dimes Grant 1-670.

REFERENCES

Attardi, B., and Ohno, S. (1974). *Cell* **2**, 205.
Chung, L. W. K., and Cunha, G. R. (1982). *Prostate* (submitted).
Chung, L. W. K., Anderson, N. G., Neubauer, B. L., Cunha, G. R., Thompson, T. C., and Rocco, A. K. (1981). *In* "The Prostate Cell: Structure and Function" (G. R. Murphy, A. A. Sandberg, and J. P. Karr, eds.), Part A, p. 177. Liss, New York.
Clark, J. H., and Peck, E. J. (1979). *Monogr. Endocrinol.* **14.**
Cooper, G. M. (1982). *Science* **218**, 801.
Cooper, M., and Pinkus, H. (1977). *Cancer Res.* **37**, 2544.
Cunha, G. R. (1970). *Anat. Rec.* **166**, 295 (Abstr.).
Cunha, G. R. (1972a). *Anat. Rec.* **172**, 179.
Cunha, G. R. (1972b). *Anat. Rec.* **172**, 529.
Cunha, G. R. (1972c). *Anat. Rec.* **173**, 105.
Cunha, G. R. (1975). *Am. J. Anat.* **143**, 387.
Cunha, G. R. (1976a). *J. Exp. Zool.* **196**, 361.
Cunha, G. R. (1976b). *Int. Rev. Cytol.* **47**, 137.
Cunha, G. R. (1983). *In* "Urologic Endocrinology" (J. Rajfer, ed.). Saunders, Philadelphia, Pennsylvania, in Press.
Cunha, G. R., and Chung, L. W. K. (1981). *J. Steroid Biochem.* **14**, 1317.
Cunha, G. R., and Fujii, H. (1981). *In* "Developmental Effects of Diethylstilbestrol (DES) in Pregnancy" (A. L. Herbst and H. A. Bern, eds.), p. 179. Thieme-Stratton, New York.

Cunha, G. R., and Lung, B. (1978). *J. Exp. Zool.* **205**, 181.

Cunha, G. R., and Lung, B. (1980). *In* "Accessory Glands of the Male Reproductive Tract" (E. Spring-Mills and E. S. E. Hafez, eds.), p. 39. North-Holland Publ., Amsterdam.

Cunha, G. R., and Vanderslice, K. D. (1982). *Stain Technol.* (submitted).

Cunha, G. R., Lung, B., and Kato, K. (1977). *Dev. Biol.* **56**, 51.

Cunha, G. R., Chung, L. W. K., Shannon, J. M., and Reese, B. A. (1980a). *Biol. Reprod.* **22**, 19.

Cunha, G. R., Lung, B., and Reese, B. (1980b). *Invest. Urol.* **17**, 302.

Cunha, G. R., Reese, B. A., and Sekkingstad, M. (1980c). *Endocrinology* **107**, 1767.

Cunha, G. R., Shannon, J. M., Neubauer, B. L., Sawyer, L. M., Fujii, H., Taguchi, O., and Chung, L. W. K. (1981a). *Hum. Genet.* **56**, 68.

Cunha, G. R., Fujii, H., Neubauer, B. L., Shannon, J. M., and Reese, B. A. (1981b). *In* "Pediatric Andrology" (S. J. Kogan and E. S. E. Hafez, eds.), p. 21. Nijhoff, The Hague.

Cunha, G. R., Shannon, J. M., Vanderslice, K. D., Sekkingstad, M., and Robboy, S. J. (1982a). *J. Steroid Biochem.* **17**, 281.

Cunha, G. R., Shannon, J. M., Taguchi, O., Fujii, H., and Chung, L. W. K. (1982b). *J. Anim. Sci.* **55** (Suppl. II), 14.

Cunha, G. R., Shannon, J. M., Vanderslice, K. D., and McCormick, K. (1983a). *Endocrinology* (submitted).

Cunha, G. R., Shannon, J. M., Taguchi, O., Fujii, H., and Meloy, B. A. (1983b). *In* "Epithelial-Mesenchymal Interactions in Development" (R. H. Sawyer and J. F. Fallon, eds.), p. 51. Praeger, New York.

Cunha, G. R., Sekkingstad, M., and Meloy, B. A. (1983c). *Differentiation* (in press).

Cunha, G. R., Fujii, H., Neubauer, B. L., Shannon, J. M., Sawyer, L. M., and Reese, B. A. (1983d). *J. Cell Biol.* (in press).

Daniel, C. W., and De Ome, K. B. (1965). *Science* **149**, 634.

Dawe, C. J., Morgan, W. D., Williams, J. E., and Summerous, J. P. (1976). *Prog. Differ. Res.* p. 305.

DeCosse, J. J., Gossens, C. L., and Kuzma, J. F. (1973). *Science* **181**, 1057.

DeCosse, J. J., Gossens, C. L., Kuzma, J. R., and Unsworth, B. R. (1975). *J. Natl. Cancer Inst.* **54**, 913.

de Klerk, D. P., Heston, W. D. W., and Coffey, D. S. (1976). *In* "Benign Prostatic Hyperplasia" (J. T. Grayhack, J. D. Wilson, and M. J. Scherbenske, eds.), p. 43. U.S. Govt. Printing Office, Washington, D.C.

Drews, U., and Drews, U. (1977). *Cell* **10**, 401.

Ferenczy, A., and Richart, R. M. (1974). "Female Reproductive System: Dynamics of Scan and Transmission Electron Microscopy." Wiley, New York.

Fujii, H., Cunha, G. R., and Norman, J. T. (1982). *Invest. Urol.* **128**, 858.

Glasser, S. R. (1981). *In* "Blastocyst-Endometrial Relationships" (F. Leroy, C. A. Finn, A. Psychoyos, and P. O. Hubinot, eds.), p. 102. Karger, Basel.

Grobstein, C. (1967). *Natl. Cancer Inst. Monogr.* **26**, 279.

Heuberger, B., Fitzka, I., Wasner, G., and Kratochwil, K. (1982). *Proc. Natl. Acad. Sci. U.S.A.* **79**, 2957.

Hodges, G. M., Hicks, R. M., and Spacey, G. D. (1977). *Cancer Res.* **37**, 3720.

Holderegger, C., Keefer, D. A., Babler, W., and Langman, J. (1981). *Biol. Reprod.* **25**, 719.

Kirkland, J. L., LaPointe, L., Justin, E., and Stancel, G. M. (1979). *Biol. Reprod.* **21**, 269.

King, W. J., Allen, T. C., and DeSombre, E. R. (1981). *Biol. Reprod.* **25**, 859.

Kollar, E. J. (1972). *Am. Zool.* **12**, 125.

Kratochwil, K. (1969). *Dev. Biol.* **20**, 46.

Kratochwil, K. (1972). *In* "Tissue Interactions in Carcinogenesis" (D. Tarin, ed.), p. 1. Academic Press, New York.

Kratochwil, K., and Schwartz, P. (1976). *Proc. Natl. Acad. Sci. U.S.A.* **73,** 4041.

Langley, F. A. (1976). *In* "The Cervix" (J. A. Jordan and A. Singer, eds.), p. 345. Saunders, Philadelphia, Pennsylvania.

Lasnitzki, I., and Mizuno, T. (1980). *J. Endocrinol.* **85,** 423.

McCormack, S. A., and Glasser, S. R. (1980). *Endocrinology* **106,** 1634.

MacKenzie, J. C., Dabelsteen, E., and Roed-Petersen, B. (1979). *Scand. J. Dent. Res.* **87,** 234.

McLachlan, J. A., Newbold, R. R., and Bullock, B. L. (1980). *Cancer Res.* **40,** 3988.

McNeal, J. E. (1978). *Invest. Urol.* **15,** 340.

Mainwaring, W. I. P. (1977). "The Mechanism of Action of Androgens." Springer-Verlag, Berlin and New York.

Martin, L., Finn, C. A., and Trinder, G. (1973). *J. Endocrinol.* **56,** 133.

Mintz, B. (1978). *In* "Cell Differentiation and Neoplasia" (G. F. Saunders, ed.), p. 27. Raven, New York.

Mori, T., and Takasugi, N. (1981). *In* "Hormone Related Tumors" (H. Nagasawa and K. Abe, eds.), p. 227. Japan Scientific Press, Tokyo.

Neubauer, B. L., Chung, L. W. K., McCormick, K., Shannon, J. M., and Cunha, G. R. (1983). *J. Cell Biol.* (in press).

Ohno, S. (1977). *J. Steroid Biochem.* **8,** 585.

Ohno, S. (1979). "Major Sex Determining Genes." Springer-Verlag, Berlin and New York.

O'Rahilly, R. (1977). *In* "Morphogenesis and Malformation of the Genital System" (R. J. Blandau and D. Bergsma, eds.), p. 123. Liss, New York.

Pierce, G. B., Shikes, R., and Fink, L. M. (1978). "Cancer: A Problem of Developmental Biology." Prentice-Hall, New York.

Prasad, M. R. N., Sar, M., and Stumpf, W. E. (1976). *J. Exp. Zool.* **197,** 71.

Rutter, W. J., and Pictet, R. L. (1976). *Ciba Found. Symp. Ser.* **40,** 259.

Sakakura, T., Nishizuka, Y., and Dawe, C. J. (1976). *Science* **194,** 1439.

Sakakura, T., Sakagami, Y., and Nishizuka, Y. (1979a). *Dev. Biol.* **71,** 201.

Sakakura, T., Nishizuka, Y., and Dawe, C. J. (1979b). *J. Natl. Cancer Inst.* **63,** 733.

Sakakura, T., Sakagami, Y., and Nishizuka, Y. (1979c). *Gann* **70,** 459.

Sakakura, T., Sakagami, Y., and Nishizuka, Y. (1981). *J. Natl. Cancer Inst.* **66,** 953.

Shannon, J. M., and Cunha, G. R. (1983). *Prostate* (in press).

Shannon, J. M., and Cunha, G. R., and Vanderslice, K. D. (1981). *Anat. Rec.* **199,** 232A.

Shannon, J. M., and Cunha, G. R., Taguchi, O., Vanderslice, K. D., and Gould, S. F. (1982). *J. Histochem. Cytochem.* **30,** 1059.

Sherman, A. I., and Brown, S. (1979). *Am. J. Obstet. Gynecol.* **135,** 947.

Sirbasku, D. A. (1980). *In* "Control Mechanisms in Animal Cells" (L. Jimenez de Asua, ed.), p. 293. Raven, New York.

Sonnenschein, C., and Soto, A. M. (1980a). *In* "Estrogens in the Environment" (J. A. McLachlan, ed.), p. 169. Elsevier, Amsterdam.

Sonnenschein, C., and Soto, A. M. (1980b). *J. Natl. Cancer Inst.* **64,** 211.

Stumpf, W. E., Narbaitz, R., and Sar, M. (1980). *J. Steroid Biochem.* **12,** 55.

Taguchi, O., and Cunha, G. R. (1983). In preparation.

Taguchi, O., Cunha, G. R., and Robboy, S. J. (1983). *Int. J. Res. Pregnancy.* (in press).

Takasugi, N. (1976). *Int. Rev. Cytol.* **44,** 193.

Takasugi, N. (1979). *In* "Perinatal Carcinogenesis" (J. M. Rice, ed.), p. 57. U.S. Govt. Printing Office, Washington, D.C.

Tchernitchin, A., Roorijck, J., Tchernitchin, X., Vandenhende, J., and Galand, P. (1974). *Nature* (*London*) **248**, 142.

Ulfelder, H., and Robboy, S. J. (1976). *Am. J. Obstet. Gynecol.* **126**, 769.

Wieland, S. J., and Fox, T. O. (1979). *Cell* **17**, 781.

Wilson, J. D., Griffin, J. E., Leshin, M., and George, F. W. (1981). *Hum. Genet.* **58**, 78.

Wolff, E. (1968). *Current Top. Dev. Biol.* **3**, 65.

Wynn, R. M. (1977). *In* "Biology of the Uterus" (R. M. Wynn, ed.), p. 341. Plenum, New York.

DISCUSSION

J. M. Hutson: The epithelial action that you described, does it require cell to cell contact between the mesenchyme and the epithelium; can you separate tissues—and if you can separate them, how can you have them separated and still get the induction by the mesenchyme?

G. R. Cunha: We're not sure on that point. From observations on the developing genital tract reported in the literature as well as those from our own experiments, it is clear that an intact basement membrane is present between these two tissues. Breaks or gaps in the basement membrane or areas of direct cell contact between epithelium and mesenchyme have not been found. From these observations it would appear that direct cell contact is not necessary for these inductive interactions. The maximum distances over which these interactions can occur have not yet been investigated.

J. E. Rall: A persuasive and lucid presentation. I have two questions: There is some concern that perhaps some genes are turned off more or less permanently in adult animals. I won't bother to go through the things which make you suspect that this might be true. You have a system in which you could see a whole battery of putative changes in gene activity. Have you looked, for example, at the combinations of mesenchyme with say bladder epithelia of young rats, mice, adult and aged? Can you elicit prostatic inductions in bladder epithelium, irrespective of age of the epithelium? If so, this would mean that the genetic mechanisms are still capable of being turned on no matter what the age of the animal.

G. R. Cunha: We've utilized bladder epithelium from animals whose age ranged from the embryonic up to old adults. The developmental plasticity of bladder epithelium is virtually identical throughout the entire age span of the urothelium. The one point that perhaps can be made here is that there does indeed seem to be restrictions in development plasticity based upon germ layer of origin of the epithelium. For example, it is not possible to elicit prostatic morphogenesis from epithelium of the seminal vesicle (which is mesodermal in its origin). This apparent developmental restriction, however, may be artificial. When we become a little more clever it may be possible to get around this restriction in developmental potential.

J. E. Rall: So there may be some sort of general restriction which is not age-dependent at all, but tissue dependent. The second question is whether you have been able to grow any of these things in tissue culture so that you can make an extract of mesenchyme to see if a diffusible factor may be involved in mediating these cell–cell interactions?

G. R. Cunha: This can be done. We have utilized the *in vivo* approach simply because developmental end points are expressed to a maximum degree in an *in vivo* site. In the case of the *in vitro* studies, the morphogenetic response or the response in terms of differentiation is very weak, almost on the borderline of negativity. For example, Dr. Lasnitzki in England has performed many of these same experiments *in vitro* with mixed success. The important thing to note is that when she grows the urogenital sinus of the rat to an age equivalent of 1 to 2 days postnatal only 3 or 4 prostatic buds form *in vitro*. During that same time in the intact animal approximately 50 to 100 prostatic buds are generated. Thus, the response *in vitro* is very, very feeble and consequently false negatives are possible by that approach. Another point to be made is that future studies on possible diffusible factors will require biochemical or morphological markers of early (fetal) prostatic morphogenesis to be used as end points indicating that an induction has in fact occurred. All of the markers that I presented to you today are adult markers that are not applicable to the first few days of this inductive process. We are now looking for suitable markers that will ultimately be the keys required to perform the types of *in vitro* experiments that you have suggested.

C. S. Nicoll: I'd like to ask if you have any information on what induces the androgen receptors in the prostatic epithelium at the time it begins to secrete?

G. R. Cunha: As I indicated, association of urogenital sinus mesenchyme with bladder epithelium, which is initially androgen receptor deficient, results in the reprogramming of the urothelium to form prostatic epithelium. One aspect of this induction is the expression of androgen receptors within the urothelium. We presume that during the normal development of the prostate the same is also true. Our evidence indicates that the entire developmental program expressed in the epithelium is induced and specified by mesenchyme. One important component of this in the prostate is the expression of the androgen receptor within the epithelium.

C. S. Nicoll: Why does it take until the secretory activity is initiated to see the appearance of the androgen receptors in the epithelium?

G. R. Cunha: Our feeling based upon the Tfm-wild type recombinations is that the early phases of development involving morphogenesis and growth in the epithelium are not mediated directly within those epithelial cells by androgens per se, but instead indirectly perhaps through nonsteroidal growth factors elaborated by the mesenchyme.

C. S. Nicoll: It might be interesting to look for possible prolactin effects because there are reports that prolactin will increase androgen uptake in the prostatic tissue in several species.

G. R. Cunha: Yes that would be very interesting.

P. K. Donahoe: You've demonstrated to us a speaking of the mesenchyme to the epithelium probably through the extracellular matrix and the basement membrane components. What is the importance of the reverse, i.e., the epithelial cells speaking to the mesenchyme, and is that important in the later induction of androgen receptors in the epithelium? Another question is to consider the loss of androgen receptors in the stroma as an underlying theme in the genesis or expression of epidermoid carcinomas. Such a possibility would be analogous to your Tfm-wild type recombination experiments in which in recombinants using wild-type mesenchyme proliferation and glandular morphogenesis occur, whereas when Tfm mesenchyme is used vaginal (epidermoid) differentiation occurs. Could it be that loss of the androgen receptor in the stroma of a developing carcinoma could lead to the expression of an epidermoid-type of carcinoma?

G. R. Cunha: With respect to your first question concerning the possibility that the epithelium communicates reciprocally with the mesenchyme, most developmental biologists believe in reciprocity of these interactions, but when you get right down to it, there are very few data demonstrating that the epithelium in fact feedsback signals upon the mesenchyme. Most of the information deals with the opposite as was the case in my presentation. We have some preliminary data that epithelium can indeed feedback upon the mesenchyme. In these studies prostatic epithelium, which is already androgen-receptor positive and has gone through its morphogenetic program and expressed androgen receptors, was combined with the very young bladder mesenchyme. Our preliminary data suggest that androgen receptors are elicited in the bladder mesenchyme. This effect is epithelial to mesenchymal and is an example of the type of phenomenon that you have described. With respect to your second question dealing with possible changes in the mesenchyme and the relation to the differentiation and progression of epithelial atypias, I am in agreement with your suggestion. I think perhaps an example of just that sort of phenomenon may occur in situations where carcinoma cells metastasize and then find themselves in a different stromal or mesenchymal bed. At that point in time the metastatic cells may then express a very different morphological and perhaps biological phenotype from that of the primary tumor because of the different stromal matrix. Yes, I would agree that this may be an important aspect in the progression of epithelial atypia, that is, the tumor progressing as the result of a primary change in the stromal environment (loss of receptors) which in turn has important biological consequences for the epithelium.

A. Segaloff: You are aware that the testis does not make DHT. The prostate uses DHT, but it makes it for itself from testosterone. It does not come to it from the outside. Are we perhaps missing the fact that the earliest androgen receptor is for testosterone and what it acquires is the ability to either see or first make and then see DHT?

G. R. Cunha: Yes, this is altogether possible; we really have not addressed that question directly. In adult human prostates the evidence suggests that the 5α-reductase is found in the stroma only; however, that evidence is rather weak. In embryonic rats, DHT is produced by both the epithelium and the mesenchyme, but the epithelium makes about 10 times as much DHT as the mesenchyme. It may be that the epithelium is primarily responsible for producing DHT which in turn is utilized by the mesenchymal cells which possess the androgen receptors.

A. Segaloff: Of course it is easy to use testosterone and block the reduction and find out which one ends up where.

G. R. Cunha: There are now inhibitors of 5α-reductase which might be very useful.

B. Little: I am having a little difficulty between fetal development and the adult stage. Also, are the mesenchymal cell and stromal cell synonymous? Let me give you two kinds of examples. If the Müllerian duct system, early on, is of mesenchymal origin, then there are different types of epithelia (squamous, endometrium, etc.) presumably evolving from the same mesenchyme. The first question is, therefore, what organizes the mesenchyme to give that complex and varied representation? The second question is related, which arises from the diethylstilbestrol stimulated abnormalities of the genital tract (Müllerian duct) in offspring of mothers treated with the drug. How does the drug influence the fetal mesenchyme? There is also one other rather speculative observation, that uterine cancer of the endometrium has changed from being commonly a simple cellular adenocarcinoma of the endometrium to a combined adeno and squamous mixed malignant cell cancer with a poorer prognosis. I have always wondered whether there was something epidemiological in the use of chronic combined steroid usage as in "the pill," for example, that has promoted the change to mixed cancers in these older women. Therefore, I would like to ask you to comment on the pharmacologic influence, to which you have already alluded, in the androgen development, not only in the fetal development, but also in adult differentiation of epithelium.

G. R. Cunha: Your first question relates to what determines what a given area of mesenchyme in the female genital tract will induce. Will it induce uterus or the vagina? How is that program established initially in the mesenchyme? That is completely unknown, not only in the developing genital tract, but in all other systems that have been studied. So that question I can't answer. The second question relates to epithelial differentiation in abnormal processes such as in the progression of uterine tumors and in lesions induced by diethylstilbestrol (DES). Our evidence suggests that morphological (and therefore, biological) phenotype of the epithelium, whether normal or abnormal, is regulated to a greater or lesser extent by mesenchymal or stromal tissue. Thus, squamous or glandular (adenosis) epithelial atypias observed in uterine tumors or in DES-induced anomalies may in fact be related to alterations in stromal activities. In the case of DES-induced anomalies, steroid autoradiographic (Cunha *et al.*, 1982) as well as tissue recombination experiments demonstrate that the mesenchyme is an important estrogen target and functions prominently in the induction, expression, and possibly also the progression of epithelial atypias such as estrogen-independent vaginal cornification (Cunha *et al.*, 1977).

B. M. Dobyns: I was intrigued by your next to last picture of the proliferation changes in bladder epithelium treated with the chemical carcinogen. If I am not mistaken, so far as I know, these papillary growths in the bladder occur unilaterally, they occur in the ureter of the same side of multicentric origin. I wonder if the primitive urogenital ridge in some individuals might have on that side some bearing on the unilaterality of the proliferative change in the wall of the bladder?

G. R. Cunha: We really have not looked at that. The changes that I described were changes elicited by a chemical carcinogen; they appear randomly throughout the entire bladder; therefore, the laterality that you have described does not occur in the experimental model used. This may be very different than the spontaneous lesions that appear in the human population.

H. Shima: Do you think that androgen-dependent release of the substance from mesenchymal tissue is involved in forming the three-dimensional extracellular matrix of the prostate in your tissue recombination experiments. Do you have any idea how to approach that?

G. R. Cunha: Collagens, fibronectin, glycosaminoglycans, substances known to be produced by cells of the stromal compartment, are known to be of immense importance in morphogenetic processes. Our perception is that the extracellular matrix produced by mesenchymal and epithelial cells is involved in prostatic induction and morphogenesis, and that the synthesis and secretion of these substances are probably regulated by androgens and other hormones. Experimental analysis of this question will have to utilize histochemical, immunocytochemical and autoradiographic methods that preserve histotypic architecture.

R. Edgren: Have you looked at nontarget tissue mesenchyme either for receptors or for inductive potential?

G. R. Cunha: Nontarget mesenchyme such as from the integument, the bladder, intestine, cornea, and skeletal musculature are generally devoid of estrogen or androgen receptor activity.

P. K. Donahoe: One quick question and comment in reference to Dr. Shima's comment. I think the three-dimensional construct requires the basement membrane and the extracellular matrix, so some way your mediator (androgen-dependent mediator) must speak to the extracellular matrix and from there a three-dimensional construct will occur.

G. R. Cunha: Right, I would agree with that.

M. New: One brief question. Have you taken mesenchyme from carcinomatous tissue and made a recombinant with normal epithelium and have you gotten carcinomatous changes in the epithelium?

G. R. Cunha: I have not done that personally. There are investigators who have and the end result has not been the formation of carcinoma, but some investigators have been able to elicit certain epithelial atypias which they interpret as preneoplastic change.

Leydig Cell Structure and Steroidogenic Function

L. L. Ewing and B. Zirkin

Division of Reproductive Biology, Department of Population Dynamics, Johns Hopkins School of Hygiene and Public Health, Baltimore, Maryland

I. Introduction

Testosterone concentration in peripheral blood of males including the human changes dramatically during the life cycle (Ewing *et al.*, 1980a). Figure 1 shows that a peak of testosterone occurs in the blood of the human fetus between 12 and 18 weeks of gestation. Another testosterone peak occurs at approximately 2 months of age in the neonate. Testosterone reaches a maximum concentration during the second or third decade of life, plateaus, and declines thereafter. Additionally, annual and daily rhythms (insets A and B, Fig. 1) in testosterone concentration occur. Superimposed on these rhythms are irregular fluctuations in testosterone concentration in peripheral blood (inset C, Fig. 1).

In those species which have been studied thoroughly (Ewing *et al.*, 1980b), the major epochs in testosterone production represent an orderly sequence of temporal signals which cause first, the differentiation and development of the fetal reproductive tract; second, the neonatal organization "marking" of androgen-dependent target tissues assuring their appropriate response later in puberty and adulthood; third, the masculinization of the male at puberty; and fourth, the activation of growth and function of androgen-dependent organs in the adult.

The temporal changes in the development and function of the male reproductive tract described above reflect the production of a single testicular product, testosterone. At least 25 steroidogenic reactions occur in mammalian testes including oxido reduction, group transfer, hydrolytic cleavage of C–C bonds, isomerization, and cleavage of C–C bonds by elimination leaving double bonds (Ewing and Brown, 1977). Under normal circumstances, all combinations of these steroidogenic reactions never occur simultaneously in the testis.

Order is achieved from this potentially chaotic situation because the bulk of testosterone biosynthesizing enzymes is located in the Leydig cell, because these enzymes are sequestered in cytoplasmic organelle

599

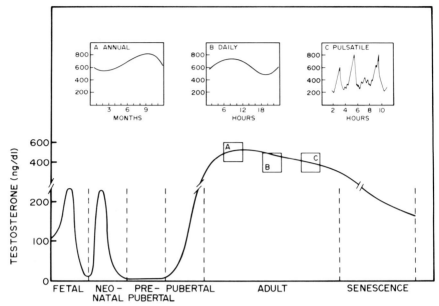

FIG. 1. Concentration of testosterone in peripheral blood of the human male at different times in the life cycle. The peak of testosterone in the peripheral blood of the fetus occurs between 12 and 18 weeks of gestation (lower left corner; gestational age not shown). The peak of testosterone in the peripheral blood of the neonate occurs at approximately 2 months of age. Testosterone declines to low levels during the prepubertal period. The pubertal increase in testosterone concentration in peripheral blood of the human male occurs between 12 and 17 years of age. Testosterone concentration in the adult reaches its maximum during the second or third decade of life and then declines slowly through the fifth decade. Testosterone concentration in peripheral blood of the human male declines dramatically during senescence. Inset A shows the annual rhythm in testosterone concentration in peripheral blood of the adult human male. The peak and nadir occur in the fall and spring, respectively. Inset B shows the daily rhythm in testosterone concentration in peripheral blood of the adult human male. The peak and nadir occur in the morning and evening, respectively. Inset C shows the frequent and irregular fluctuations in testosterone concentration in peripheral blood of the human male. (From Ewing *et al.*, 1980b, by courtesy of the editor, Vol. 22, *International Review of Physiology.*)

membranes, and because some of these spatially isolated reactions are controlled by luteinizing hormone (LH).

In this article the spatial organization of the testosterone biosynthesizing apparatus in the testis will be reviewed. The simple but elegant control gained by separating enzymes inter- and intracellularly will be stressed. The rationale will be developed which led to the hypothesis that Leydig cell steroidogenic activity was closely correlated with structure. Next the advances in stereology and *in vitro* perfusion techniques which facilitated the study of Leydig cell structure and function will be discussed. Then results will be presented which show that Leydig cell steroidogenic activity is correlated closely with structure, particularly with the surface area of smooth endoplasmic reticulum (SER). Finally, the effect of LH on the number and volume of Leydig cells, and on the surface area of Leydig cell cytoplasmic organelle membranes will be described. These results will show that one of the most striking trophic effects of LH on the Leydig cell is to control the biogenesis and/or turnover of the SER.

II. Leydig Cell Structure: A Review

Leydig cells occupy 2–37% of testicular volume depending on the species (Christensen, 1975). There are approximately 25×10^6 and 700×10^6 Leydig cells in rat (Mori and Christensen, 1980) and human (Kaler and Neaves, 1978) testes, respectively. Leydig cells are recognized readily at the light microscopic level in that they are characterized by a round cytoplasmic profile which stains with periodic acid–Schiff (Kaler and Neaves, 1978). At the electron microscopic level Leydig cells are characterized generally by a round or ovoid nucleus, prominant mitochondria, abundant smooth endoplasmic reticulum, scattered patches of rough endoplasmic reticulum, and lipid droplets (Christensen, 1975).

A. INTERCELLULAR ORGANIZATION

Testosterone is derived almost exclusively from Leydig cells (Cooke *et al.,* 1972; Hall, 1979). Therefore, one form of regulation of testosterone production is to control Leydig cell division, growth, differentiation, and/ or death. Apparently, this regulatory strategy is used commonly because fetal development and pubertal masculinization are associated with the appearance of morphologically recognizable, steroidogenically active Leydig cells (see review by Ewing *et al.,* 1980a). The decline in testosterone concentration in the peripheral blood of the senescent human male may be due to the loss of steroidogenically active Leydig cells (Kaler and Neaves, 1978; Harbitz, 1973).

B. INTRACELLULAR ORGANIZATION

The intracellular distribution of Leydig cell steroidogenic enzymes has been studied extensively [refer to several reviews (Cooke *et al.,* 1972; Ewing and Brown, 1977; Hall, 1979; Ewing *et al.,* 1980a) for a complete discussion of this topic]. A simplified illustration of the steroidogenic machinery required to convert acetate to testosterone is presented in Fig.

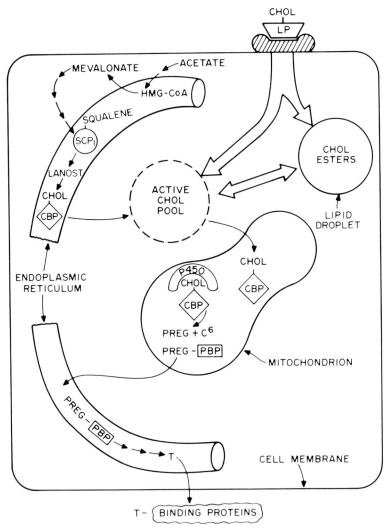

FIG. 2. The spatial organization of the testosterone biosynthetic apparatus in a Leydig cell. Cholesterol (CHOL) in the metabolically active pool is derived from *de novo* synthesis, cholesterol esters in lipid droplets, or blood plasma. Cholesterol probably is transported from the blood plasma into the Leydig cell by high or low density lipoprotein LP, which may bind to Leydig cell membrane receptors. With the exception of HMG–CoA reductase, which resides in the endoplasmic reticulum, most early reactions in cholesterol biosynthesis take place in the cytoplasm of the cell. Squalene is the first water-insoluble intermediate in cholesterol biosynthesis. Note that squalene carrier protein (SCP) is required for the conversion of squalene to lanosterol (LANOST). Other sterol carrier proteins, including cholesterol binding protein (CBP) also may exist. CBP probably transports cholesterol into the

2. Cholesterol in the metabolically active pool can be derived from any of three sources: by *de novo* biosynthesis from acetate, from cholesterol esters stored in lipid droplets, and from the blood plasma via a cholesterol–lipoprotein–cell membrane receptor system which probably is similar to that described for cultured human fibroblasts (Brown and Goldstein, 1976).

Figure 2 shows that cholesterol from the metabolically active pool may be transported into the mitochondria where the cholesterol side chain cleavage enzyme converts it to pregnenolone. Pregnenolone must then be transported into the smooth endoplasmic reticulum (SER) where it is converted into testosterone. Testosterone probably then diffuses across the cell membrane and is trapped in the extracellular fluid and blood plasma by steroid binding macromolecules. It is apparent that most of the important steps in testosterone biosynthesis are sequestered in membranes of Leydig cell cytoplasmic organelles.

Such a highly ordered spatial arrangement of steroid-synthesizing enzymes has important regulatory consequences. First, sequestering steroidogenic enzymes in membranes in all likelihood facilitates the interaction of hydrophobic sterol or steroid molecules with reactants such as oxygen or hydrogen dissolved in the aqueous milieu of the Leydig cell cytoplasm (Ewing *et al.*, 1980a). Second, a membrane bound multienzyme sequence such as that required to convert pregnenolone to testosterone may exist in a highly ordered state to reduce substrate diffusion time, thus preventing leakage of biosynthetic intermediates from the enzyme–membrane complex (Chubb and Ewing, 1979a; Becker *et al.*, 1980). Third, separation of competing steroidogenic reactions in space limits the potential products produced by the testis. Fourth, control points are established when a substrate is separated in space from the enzyme which is required to catalyze its conversion into product (Ewing *et al.*, 1980b). An example of this latter control mechanism follows. The acute stimulation of testosterone production by LH results from the accumulation of a labile cholesterol binding protein which facilitates either the transport of cholesterol into the mitochondria and/or its binding to the

---

mitochondrion, where it may facilitate cholesterol binding to the P-450 component of the cholesterol side-chain cleavage enzyme. Pregnenolone (PREG) and isocaproaldehyde (C^6) are produced by cholesterol side-chain cleavage. Pregnenolone may bind to pregnenolone binding protein (PBP), which theoretically would aid in its transport into or within the endoplasmic reticulum. The secretion of testosterone from the Leydig cell may be facilitated by the presence of binding proteins such as albumin, androgen binding protein, and testosterone–estradiol binding globulin outside the Leydig cell membrane. (From Ewing *et al.*, 1980b, by courtesy of the editor, Vol. 22, *International Review of Physiology*.)

P450 moiety of the cholesterol side-chain cleavage enzyme (Mendelson *et al.*, 1975; Cooke *et al.*, 1975, 1977, 1979; Jansen *et al.*, 1978). Fifth, alteration in the amount or chemical characteristics of Leydig cell cytoplasmic organelle membranes might influence profoundly the activity of the steroidogenic enzymes sequestered therein (Bussman *et al.*, 1976; Hall, 1979).

Taken together, these ideas suggest strongly that organizing testosterone biosynthesizing enzymes into spatially separated cytoplasmic organelle membranes in specialized testicular steroid-producing cells provides an important structural basis for the regulation of testosterone biosynthesis. This led to the hypothesis that Leydig cell structure is tightly coupled to steroidogenic function.

III. Leydig Cell Structure–Function: Techniques

The testes are amenable to a structure–function analysis because the testosterone biosynthesizing enzymes reside either in mitochondria or SER membranes of the Leydig cell. However, the completion of a structure–function study required the adaptation of techniques which allowed the quantitative measurement of cell structure and the determination of testosterone biosynthesis in a physiologically relevant system.

A. STEREOLOGY

Stereological procedures allow the quantification of three-dimensional structures by extrapolation from measurements of two-dimensional cross sections at both the light and electron microscopic levels (Bolender, 1978; Weibel, 1979; Mori and Christensen, 1980). Bolender (1982) has discussed the application of this technique to the testis. The stereological model in Fig. 3 shows that for stereological analysis, the testis was divided into morphologically defined components. We focused our attention on the Leydig cells within the testicular interstitium. Proper application of stereological techniques at the level of the light microscope allows the quantification of the proportion of the testis constituted by Leydig cells, and the number, volume, and mass of Leydig cells in the testis. Similarly, application of stereological techniques to electron micrographs allows estimation of the proportion of Leydig cell cytoplasm constituted by subcellular organelles and determination of their membrane volume and/or surface areas. Such measurements have been accomplished for testes of several species to date (Harbitz, 1973; Kaler and Neaves, 1978; Ewing *et al.*, 1979a; Zirkin *et al.*, 1980; Mori *et al.*, 1980).

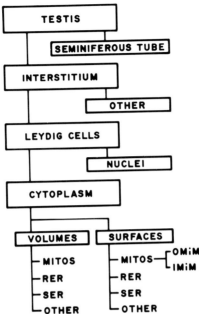

FIG. 3. Stereological model for the mammalian testis. The testis was divided into seminiferous tubule (tube) and interstitium components. The Leydig cells were divided into nuclei and cytoplasm. The cytoplasm of Leydig cells was then subdivided into spaces (volumes) and membranes.

B. *IN VITRO* TESTICULAR PERFUSION

In vitro testicular perfusion was chosen to measure Leydig cell steroidogenic activity because the three-dimensional architecture of the testis is maintained, because substrates, cofactors, oxygen, and products are delivered to and from the Leydig cell as *in situ,* because steroidogenic activity mimics closely that which occurs *in situ,* and because testosterone secretion by *in vitro* perfused testes reflects testosterone biosynthesis. Evidence for these statements is presented below.

Numerous published reports suggest that androgen secretion by *in vitro* perfused testes mimic closely *in situ* testicular steroidogenic function. First, rabbit testes perfused *in vitro* synthesize testosterone from acetate and cholesterol (Ewing and Eik-Nes, 1966). Second, LH stimulates testosterone secretion by *in vitro* perfused rabbit (Ewing, 1975) and rat (unpublished results) testes in a dose-dependent fashion. Third, adult rabbit testes perfused *in vitro* with a physiological concentration of LH secrete testosterone, dihydrotestosterone (DHT), 5α-androstan-3α,17β-diol (3αDIOL), and 5α-androstan-3β,17β-diol (3βDIOL) in amounts identical to that secreted by rabbit testes *in situ* (Ewing *et al.*, 1975). Fourth, androgen secretion by perfused testes from sexually maturing rabbits correlates closely with pubertal changes in rabbits (Chubb *et al.*, 1978). For example, the steep pubertal increase in androgen secretion by *in vitro* perfused rabbit testes coincided with the onset of spermatogenesis, and growth of the accessory sex organs (Chubb *et al.*, 1978). Also the T/DHT + 3αDIOL + 3βDIOL (5α reduced androgens) in spermatic venous effluent from perfused rabbit testes remained unchanged during puberty as did the ratio of these androgens in peripheral blood. This unchanging T/5α reduced androgen was in contrast to *in vitro* perfused pubertal rat testes which secreted predominantly 3αDIOL (Chubb and Ewing, 1981). Fifth, testosterone secretion by *in vitro* perfused testes from rabbits decreased with advanced age concomitant with decreased spermatogenesis (Ewing *et al.*, 1972).

Several lines of evidence support strongly the idea that testosterone secretion by *in vitro* perfused testes reflects testosterone biosynthesis. First, radioactive acetate and cholesterol (Ewing and Eik-Nes, 1966) and pregnenolone (Ewing *et al.*, 1980a) are incorporated rapidly into testosterone secreted by *in vitro* perfused testes. Second, testosterone storage in the testis is low (Chubb and Ewing, 1979b) and testosterone secretion is correlated closely with testicular testosterone content (Eik-Nes, 1975). Third, infusion of inhibitors of specific steroidogenic enzymes into the spermatic artery of perfused testes caused a dramatic decrease in both testosterone content and secretion, accompanied by a quantitative increase in the secretion of the steroid substrate(s) for the inhibited enzyme (Chubb and Ewing, 1979b). Finally, secretory vesicles have not been observed in Leydig cells (Christensen, 1975).

IV. Leydig Cell Structure and Function

Numerous investigators have attempted to relate specific differences in testicular Leydig cell number, volume, or ultrastructure with testicular steroidogenic activity under conditions where testosterone production changed naturally as during the breeding season (Neaves, 1973), puberty (Knorr *et al.*, 1970; Pahnke *et al.*, 1975), and aging (Pirke *et al.*, 1978) or experimentally (Dym and Raj, 1977; Gondos *et al.*, 1980; Nussdorfer *et al.*, 1980). The general conclusion of these studies was that Leydig cell volume and/or number changed in concert with testosterone concentration in peripheral blood. The above studies showed generally that striking changes in SER and lipid droplets accompanied changes in testicular steroidogenic activity. The interpretation of the results of these studies was hampered either because the Leydig cell morphology was assessed qualitatively rather than quantitatively or because testicular steroidogenic function was assessed indirectly. These difficulties were overcome in the two experiments described below in which stereological procedures were used to quantify morphological characteristics and Leydig cell testosterone producing capacity was measured directly in perfused testes.

V. Testosterone Secretion by *in Vitro* Perfused Testes of Five Species: Correlation with Leydig Cell Mass

Previously it was shown that rat and rabbit testes perfused *in vitro* secreted different amounts of testosterone (Chubb and Ewing, 1979a). This observation prompted the comparison of testosterone secretion and Leydig cell mass in testes of five species. Rat, rabbit, guinea pig, dog, and hamster testes were compared because *in vitro* perfused testes from these five species secreted widely divergent amounts of testosterone.

Details of the experimental protocols used in this comparative experiment are described elsewhere (Ewing *et al.,* 1979c). Suffice it to say that all testes were perfused with an artificial medium which contained saturating concentrations of ovine LH, that all testes were perfused at a medium flow rate of 10 ml/g testis/hour, and that all testes were perfused at 34.5°C. Treatment differences in this and in all subsequent experiments were ascertained, by analysis of variance and Duncan's Multiple Range Test and considered significant if $p < 0.05$.

The results in the top panel of Fig. 4 show that testosterone secretion, expressed as μg T/testis/hour varied significantly between species. Dividing the total testosterone secretion by testicular weight failed to remove the significant between species variation (middle panel, Fig. 4). Correcting the testosterone secretion by the mass of Leydig cells in testes of each species still left significant between species variation (lower panel, Fig. 4) in testosterone secretion, now expressed as μg T/g Leydig cell/hour. Surprisingly, guinea pig Leydig cells secreted 20 times more testosterone than hamster Leydig cells.

What is different about Leydig cells among these five species? Testosterone secretion among the rodents was highest in the guinea pig, intermediate in the rat, and lowest in the hamster (lower panel, Fig. 4). Review of the literature regarding Leydig cell ultrastructure revealed that this order was identical to the qualitative assessments of the abundance of smooth endoplasmic reticulum (SER) in the Leydig cells of these three species (Christensen, 1965; Christensen and Gillim, 1969; Wing and Lin, 1977). The electron micrographs in Fig. 5 show the striking difference in the amount of SER in guinea pig (upper panel, Fig. 5) and hamster (lower panel, Fig. 5) Leydig cells. Therefore, it was hypothesized that a high

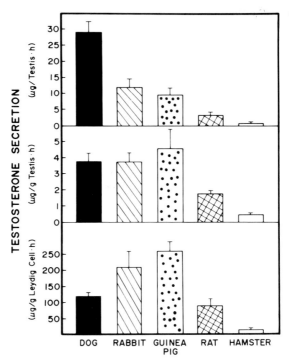

FIG. 4. Testosterone secretion by dog, rabbit, guinea pig, rat, and hamster testes perfused *in vitro* with artificial medium containing 100 ng/ml NIH-LH-S$_{19}$, ovine. Upper panel depicts testosterone secretion per testis. Middle panel expresses the testosterone secretion per gram testis. Bottom panel illustrates the testosterone secretion per gram of Leydig cell. The T above each bar denotes SEM ($N = 6$). (From Ewing *et al.*, 1979c, by courtesy of the editor of *Endocrinology*.)

correlation existed between testosterone secretion/g Leydig cell/hour and the proportion of Leydig cell cytoplasm occupied by SER in the five species studied.

VI. Testosterone Secretion by *in Vitro* Perfused Testes of Five Species: Correlation with Leydig Cell Ultrastructure

In this experiment testosterone secretion by perfused testes of the five species was compared with the proportion (volume density) of Leydig cell cytoplasm occupied by SER, rough endoplasmic reticulum (RER), and mitochondria. Details of this experiment are described elsewhere (Zirkin *et al.*, 1980).

The results in Fig. 6 show testosterone secretion and the proportion (volume density, %) of Leydig cell cytoplasm constituted by mitochon-

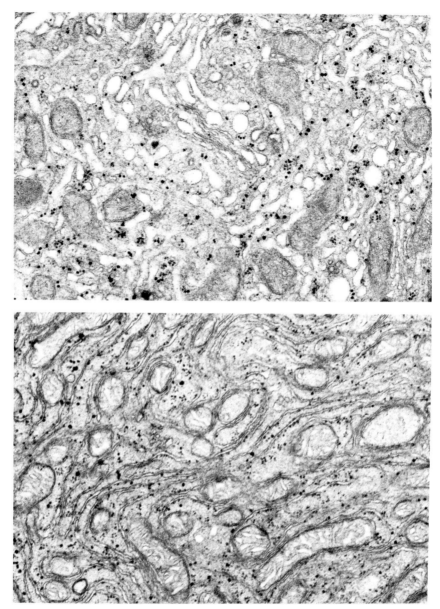

FIG. 5. Representative electron micrographs of guinea pig (upper panel) and hamster (lower panel) Leydig cell cytoplasm. Strikingly greater amounts of smooth endoplasmic reticulum are apparent in the cytoplasm of guinea pig Leydig cells. ×35,750.

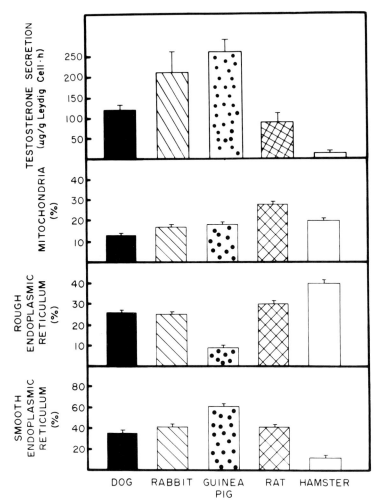

FIG. 6. Testosterone secretion by *in vitro* perfused testes, and volume densities (%) of mitochondria, rough endoplasmic reticulum, and smooth endoplasmic reticulum in Leydig cell cytoplasm of dog, rabbit, guinea pig, rat, and hamster tests. The T above each bar denotes SEM. $N = 5$ for each species. (Redrawn from Zirkin *et al.*, 1980.)

dria, RER, and SER. Clearly, only the proportion of SER in Leydig cell cytoplasm reflects testosterone secretion. The results in Fig. 7 show a significant, linear, and positive correlation ($r = 0.99$) between testosterone secretion and the volume density of SER among the five species studied. In contrast, positive correlations were not found between testosterone secretion and the volume density of the other Leydig cell cytoplasmic organelles. Instead, testosterone secretion was significantly, linearly, and negatively correlated ($r = 0.99$) with the volume density of RER among the five species studied. The interpretation of the RER results is unclear at present. Perhaps a precursor–product relationship exists between rough and smooth endoplasmic reticulum. Taken together, the results of these two experiments suggest that testicular testosterone production is not determined solely by the mass of Leydig cells in a testis. Instead, important differences existed in the testosterone biosynthetic capacity of Leydig cells. In the five species studied to date, an extremely high correlation existed between the testosterone biosynthetic capacity of Leydig cells and the proportion of cytoplasm occupied by SER. While interesting, these were correlative data which required experimental corroboration. Consequently, an experimental treatment was sought that would inhibit reversibly Leydig cell testosterone biosynthesizing capacity.

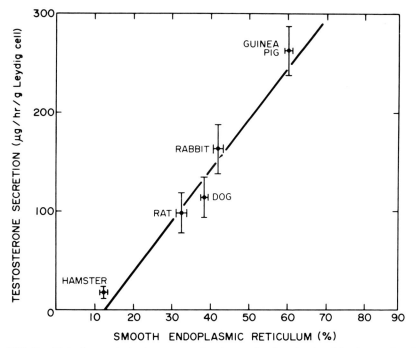

FIG. 7.   Plot of mean testosterone secretion by maximally stimulated *in vitro* perfused testes of the hamster, rat, dog, rabbit, and guinea pig against the mean volume density (%) of smooth endoplasmic reticulum in Leydig cell cytoplasm of contralateral testes. A linear, positive correlation ($r = 0.99$) is seen. Each point represents the mean of five animals. The bars about each point represent the SEM. (From Zirkin *et al.*, 1980, by courtesy of the editor of *Endocrinology*.)

VII. Effect of Testosterone–Estradiol Polydimethylsiloxane Subcutaneous Implants on Testosterone Secretion by Rat Testes Perfused *in Vitro*

Testosterone–estradiol (T-E) polydimethylsiloxane (PDS; Silastic) sub-cutaneous implants have been used to inhibit reversibly LH production, Leydig cell steroidogenesis, and spermatogenesis in rats (Ewing *et al.,* 1977). The results in Fig. 8 show that *in vitro* perfused testes from rats treated for 5 days with testosterone–estradiol PDS implants secreted significantly less testosterone than testes from control rats when both were stimulated maximally with luteinizing hormone (LH). This failure of testes from T-E PDS implanted rats to respond to LH *in vitro* suggested that some change had occurred in Leydig cells which was not readily overcome during the course of the perfusion experiment.

We were particularly interested to learn if the SER was affected by treatment with the T-E PDS implants. The results in Fig. 9 show that infusion of substrate amounts of pregnenolone into the spermatic artery of *in vitro* perfused testes from control rats resulted in testosterone secretion equivalent to that obtained when testes were stimulated with LH (Fig. 8). By contrast, *in vitro* perfused testes from rats treated with T-E PDS implants failed to convert significant amounts of pregnenolone to testos-

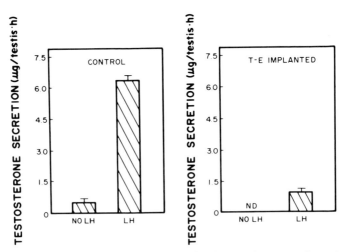

FIG. 8.   Testosterone secretion by *in vitro* perfused testes from control rats (left panel) and rats treated for 5 days with testosterone–estradiol (T-E) polydimethylsiloxane (PDS; Silastic) implants designed to inhibit luteinizing hormone (LH) production (right panel). Testes were perfused with artificial medium without LH (no LH) or containing 100 ng/ml of NIH-LH-S$_{21}$, ovine (LH). Each bar represents the mean of five rats. The T above each bar represents the SEM.

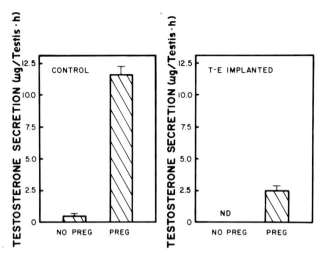

FIG. 9. Testosterone secretion by *in vitro* perfused testes from control rats (left panel) and rats treated for 5 days with testosterone–estradiol (T-E) polydimethylsiloxane (PDS; Silastic) implants designed to inhibit luteinizing hormone (LH) production (right panel). Testes were perfused with artificial medium devoid of LH, either without pregnenolone (NO PREG) or with 6 μg pregnenolone per ml of medium (PREG). Each bar represents the mean of five rats. The T above each bar represents the SEM.

terone (Fig. 9). Based on earlier results (Chubb and Ewing, 1979b), these data were interpreted to mean that the T-E treatment resulted in the inhibition of one or more of the SER enzymes involved in the conversion of pregnenolone to testosterone. Thus it seemed likely that the T-E PDS implants caused a lesion in Leydig cell SER which might be detected with the electron microscope.

VIII. Inhibition and Recovery of Testosterone Secretion in Rats Are Associated with Changes in Leydig Cell Structure

In the next two experiments, Leydig cell structure was compared with testosterone secretion under conditions in which testicular steroidogenesis was first inhibited, and then inhibited and allowed to recover. It was hypothesized that experimental inhibition of testosterone secretion would be reflected in quantitative changes in Leydig cell morphology at the light and electron microscopic level and that recovery of testosterone secretory capacity following removal of the inhibitory treatment would be coupled tightly to changes in Leydig cell morphology. The experimental protocols of these two experiments were described earlier (Zirkin *et al.*, 1982). The stereological procedures used to quantify Leydig cell numbers per testis, average Leydig cell volume, and surface area of SER, RER, inner mitochondrial membrane (IMiM), and outer mitochondrial membrane (OMiM) per Leydig cell have been desribed elsewhere (Ewing *et al.*, 1983).

1. Testosterone secretion and Leydig cell structure in rats following implantation of T-E PDS capsules.

The results in Fig. 10 show testosterone secretion, testis volume, number of Leydig cells, and the average Leydig cell volume in rats implanted with T-E PDS capsules for 0, 1, 2, and 9 days. Testosterone secretion (top panel, Fig. 10) declined rapidly and significantly; each day was different. There was no significant difference in testis volume (Fig. 10). Stereological analysis at the light microscopic level showed that the number of Leydig cells per testis, and the average Leydig cell volume also did not change. Thus dramatic reductions in testosterone biosynthetic capacity

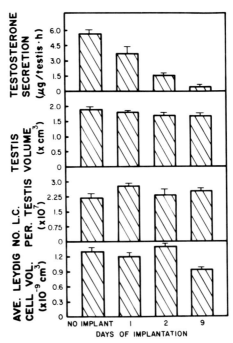

FIG. 10.   Testosterone secretion by *in vitro* perfused testes, and testis volume, number of Leydig cells (L.C.) per testis, and average Leydig cell volume of rats implanted with testosterone–estradiol polydimethylsiloxane capsules for 0 (no implant), 1, 2, and 9 days. Each bar represents the mean of four rats. The T above each bar represents SEM. (Redrawn from Zirkin *et al.*, 1982.)

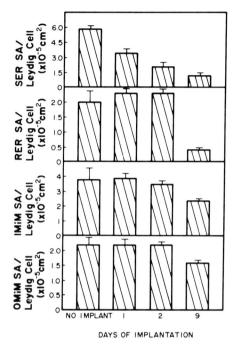

DAYS OF IMPLANTATION

FIG. 11. Surface area (SA) of smooth endoplasmic reticulum (SER), rough endoplasmic reticulum (RER), inner mitochondrial membrane (IMiM), and outer mitochondrial membrane (OMiM) per Leydig cell of rats implanted with testosterone–estradiol polydimetliylsiloxane capsules for 0 (no implant), 1, 2, and 9 days. Each bar represents the mean of four rats. The T above each bar represents SEM. (Redrawn from Zirkin *et al.*, 1982.)

occurred without any measurable changes in the light microscopic morphology of Leydig cells.

The results in Fig. 11 show the surface area of SER, RER, IMiM, and OMiM per Leydig cell in rats implanted with T-E PDS capsules for 0, 1, 2, and 9 days. The surface area of SER per Leydig cell declined rapidly and significantly. Control rats (no implant) contained significantly more SER per average Leydig cell than rats treated with PDS implants for 1, 2, and 9 days. SER surface area was similar for 1 and 2 days, and 2 and 9 days, but was significantly different between 1 and 9 days.

The surface area of RER per Leydig cell (Fig. 11) was significantly reduced only after 9 days of treatment. There was no significant difference in surface area of IMiM and OMiM during the 9 day treatment with T-E PDS implants (Fig. 11). Taken together the results in Figs. 10 and 11 show that implantation of T-E PDS capsules for 9 days caused a striking diminution of Leydig cell testosterone biosynthetic capacity without altering either Leydig cell numbers in the testis or the volume of the average Leydig cell. The surface area of SER was rapidly and specifically depleted coincidentally with the loss of testosterone biosynthetic capacity. Thus the T-E PDS treatment altered dramatically the biogenesis and or turnover of SER.

2. Testosterone secretion and Leydig cell structure in rats following removal of T-E PDS implants.

Rats were implanted with T-E PDS capsules for 2 weeks to inhibit testosterone biosynthesizing capacity. Then the implants were removed and testosterone secretion and Leydig cell structure analyzed at 0, 1, 4, and 12 days after implant removal. The results were compared to controls (no implant). The results in Fig. 12 show that testosterone secretion, the number of Leydig cells per testis, and the volume of an average Leydig cell were significantly reduced after 2 weeks (0 days) of T-E PDS treat-

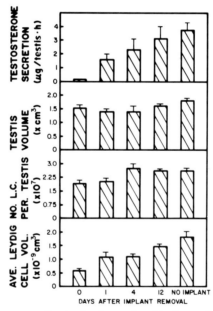

FIG. 12.   Testosterone secretion by *in vitro* perfused testes, and testis volume, number of Leydig cells (L.C.) per testis, and average Leydig cell volume of rats implanted with testosterone-estradiol polydimethylsiloxane capsules for 2 weeks and then allowed to recover from treatment for 0, 1, 4, and 12 days after implant removal. Intact controls are designated NO IMPLANT. Each bar represents the mean of 5 rats. The T above each bar represents SEM. (Redrawn from Zirkin *et al.*, 1982.)

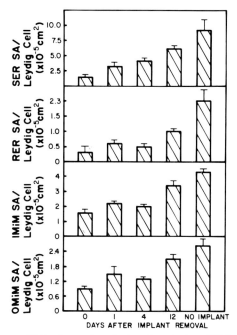

FIG. 13.   Surface area (SA) of smooth endoplasmic reticulum (SER), rough endoplasmic reticulum (RER), inner mitochondrial membrane (IMiM) and outer mitochondrial membrane (OMiM) per Leydig cell of rats implanted with testosterone–estradiol polydimethylsiloxane capsules for 2 weeks and then allowed to recover from treatment for 0, 1, 4 and 12 days after implant removal. Intact controls are designated NO IMPLANT. Each bar represents the mean of five rats. The T above each bar represents SEM. (Redrawn from Zirkin *et al.*, 1982.)

ment as compared to control (no implant) rats. These results show clearly that Leydig cells atrophy if treated long enough with the steroid filled implants probably as a result of the withdrawal of LH (Ewing and Robaire, 1978; Ewing *et al.*, 1979b; Dykman *et al.*, 1981).

The results of the electron microscopic stereological analysis of Leydig cell SER, RER, IMiM, and OMiM are shown in Fig. 13. The surface area of those Leydig cell cytoplasmic membranes measured were significantly reduced after 2 weeks (0 days) of T-E PDS capsule implantation as compared to control (no implant) rats. The surface area of SER recovered more rapidly than the other Leydig cell cytoplasmic organelle membranes because the surface area of SER was significantly higher at 4 than at 0 days, whereas the surface areas of the other membranes were significantly higher than 0 days only after 12 days of recovery. RER and SER membrane replacement was not completed by 12 days, however; the surface areas of these two membranes still were significantly lower than control (no implant).

The results of this experiment show clearly that Leydig cells atrophy, if treated long enough with the T-E PDS implants. With the exception of RER and SER the structure and function of Leydig cells were restored completely 12 days after removal of the T-E PDS implants.

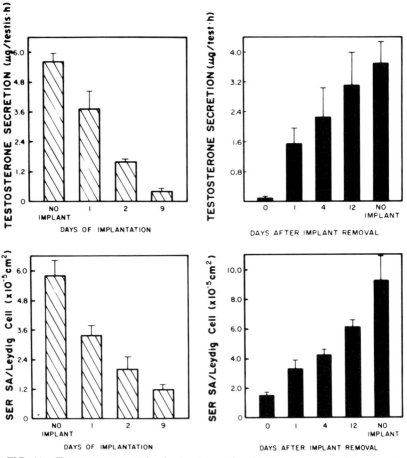

FIG. 14.   Testosterone secretion by *in vitro* perfused testes (upper panels) and surface area (SA) of smooth endoplasmic reticulum (SER) (lower panels) of (1) rats implanted with testosterone capsules for 0, 1, 2, and 9 days (left panels; cross hatched bars) or (2) of rats implanted for 2 weeks and then allowed to recover from treatment for 0, 1, 4, and 12 days after implant removal (right panels; solid bars). In both treatment groups, the intact controls are designated NO IMPLANT. Each bar represents the mean of four or five rats (see description for Figs. 10, 11, 12, and 13). The T above each bar represents SEM.

The most striking results from these two experiments were the close associations between testosterone biosynthetic capacity and the surface area of SER per Leydig cell as summarized in Fig. 14. These latter results were consistent with those from the comparative experiment described above which showed that the differences in testosterone secretion by testes of five species were related closely to the proportion of Leydig cell cytoplasm occupied by SER.

Taken together, the results of the comparative and T-E PDS implant experiments demonstrated the first quantitative, positive correlation between Leydig cell ultrastructure and steroidogenic function. Obviously, the regulation of SER biogenesis and/or turnover plays an important part in determining whether a Leydig cell is steroidogenically active. The T-E PDS implants most likely influence Leydig cell structure and steroidogenic activity indirectly via an effect on LH production (Ewing and Robaire, 1978; Ewing et al., 1979b; Dykman et al., 1981). This brings us to a discussion of the trophic effects of LH on Leydig cell structure and function.

IX. Trophic Effects of LH on Leydig Cell Structure and Function

The control of Leydig cell steroidogenesis has been reviewed extensively (Rommerts et al., 1974; Catt and Dufau, 1976; Dufau and Catt, 1978; Dufau et al., 1978; Hall, 1979; Ewing et al., 1980a). Attention has been focused largely on the acute and positive stimulation of Leydig cell steroidogenesis involving the LH receptor, adenyl cyclase, protein phosphorylation cascade of events which culminate in increased conversion of cholesterol to pregnenolone. Relatively, little attention has been given to the trophic (slow) effects of LH on Leydig cell growth and differentiation. However, the literature abounds with qualitative descriptions demonstrating that Leydig cell ultrastructure generally and SER specifically is altered after hypophysectomy or gonadotropin injection (DeKretser, 1967; Merkow et al., 1968; Aoki, 1970; Neaves, 1973; Chemes et al., 1976; Dym and Raj, 1977; Morat, 1977; Gondos et al., 1980).

A striking example of the effect of hypophysectomy on Leydig cell structure is shown in Fig. 15. These low-power electron micrographs taken at the same magnification show clearly the atrophy of the Leydig cell 2 weeks after hypophysectomy in the rat (lower panel, Fig. 15) compared to controls (upper panel, Fig. 15).

A series of experiments follow which test the hypothesis that LH administered simultaneously with T-E PDS implants or immediately upon hypophysectomy will maintain the number, volume, ultrastructure, and testosterone biosynthetic capacity of Leydig cells.

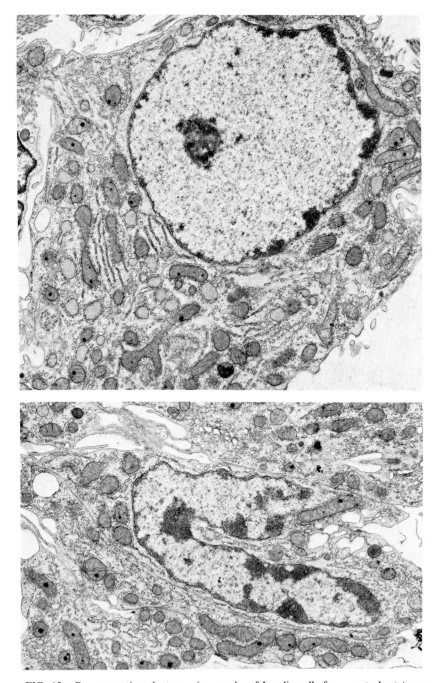

FIG. 15. Representative electron micrographs of Leydig cells from control rat (upper panel) and rat hypophysectomized for 2 weeks (lower panel) taken at the same magnification. Atrophy of Leydig cells following hypophysectomy is apparent. ×13,475.

X. Effect of LH Dose *in Situ* on Testosterone Secretion by *in Vitro* Perfused Testes Obtained from Rats Treated Simultaneously with T-E PDS Implants

The objective of this experiment was to identify the dose of LH *in situ* required to maintain the testosterone biosynthesizing capacity of *in vitro* perfused testes obtained from rats treated with T-E PDS implants. The experimental protocol, and stereological and perfusion methods have been described elsewhere (Ewing *et al.*, 1983). Briefly, the rats were implanted with T-E PDS capsules known to inhibit LH but not FSH production (Robaire *et al.*, 1979). Rats simultaneously received Alzet miniosmotic pumps programmed to deliver various doses of LH. Rats were killed 5 days later, testes perfused *in vitro,* and testosterone secretion measured.

The results in Fig. 16 show that there was a significant, linear, and positive correlation ($r = 0.99$) for LH dose *in situ* and testosterone secretion *in vitro* between 1.5 and 12 μg LH/day. There was no significant difference in testosterone secretion by testes from rats treated simultaneously with T-E implants plus 12, 24, or 36 μg LH/day. The results of

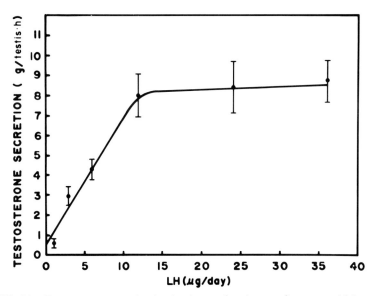

FIG. 16. Testosterone secretion by *in vitro* perfused testes from rats which received testosterone–estradiol polydimethylsiloxane implants simultaneously with 0, 1.5, 3, 6, 12, 24, and 36 μg ovine LH/day *in situ* for 5 days. Each point represents the mean of four testes. The vertical bars represent the SEM. (From Ewing *et al.*, 1983, by courtesy of the editor of *Endocrinology*.)

this experiment demonstrate (1) that the LH maintenance *in situ* of testosterone biosynthesizing capacity was dose responsive, (2) that an LH treatment of 12 μg/day maintained the testosterone secreting capacity of testes at levels similar to testes from control rats, and (3) that downregulation of testosterone secreting capacity did not occur in T-E-implanted rats treated simultaneously with 24 and 36 μg LH/day. In subsequent experiments in this article, LH was administered *in situ* at 12 μg/day.

XI. The Effect of LH *in Situ* on Leydig Cell Structure and Testosterone Secretion in Rats Treated with T-E PDS Implants for 5 Days

The objective of this experiment was to determine whether LH administered simultaneously with the T-E PDS implants would maintain not only Leydig cell steroidogenic function but also structure. The experimental protocol and stereological and perfusion methods have been described elsewhere (Ewing *et al.*, 1983). Briefly, the rats were implanted with T-E PDS capsules and Alzet miniosmotic pumps programmed to release buffer or 12 μg LH/day. The rats were killed 5 days later and one testis was perfusion fixed. Please note that in this and subsequent experiments the tissue was postfixed with unbuffered 2% osmium tetroxide and 1.5% ferrocyanide to facilitate visualization of membranous structures at the electron microscopic level. Contralateral testes were perfused *in vitro* and testosterone secretion was measured.

The results in Fig. 17 show that the T-E PDS implant treatment for 5 days significantly reduced the testosterone secretion by *in vitro* perfused testes. As expected, the simultaneous treatment of T-E-implanted rats with 12 μg LH/day maintained testosterone secretion at control levels. Implantation of T-E capsules for 5 days did not alter significantly testis volume or the number of Leydig cells in a testis (Fig. 17). However, as expected, the average Leydig cell volume was diminished significantly (bottom panel, Fig. 17). Treatment of T-E-implanted rats simultaneously with 12 μg LH/day for 5 days maintained the average Leydig cell volume, and increased significantly the number of Leydig cells per testis when compared to intact controls.

The results in Fig. 18 show that the T-E PDS implant treatment for 5 days significantly reduced the surface area of SER per Leydig cell from control values. The surface areas of RER, IMiM, and OMiM also were reduced (Fig. 18); however, of these, only the reduction of RER was significant. Importantly, simultaneous treatment of T-E-implanted rats

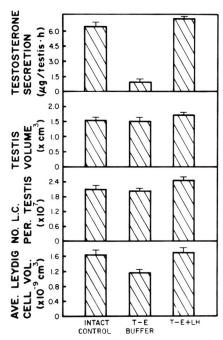

FIG. 17. Testosterone secretion by *in vitro* perfused testes, and testis volume, number of Leydig cells (L.C.) per testis, and average Leydig cell volume of intact control rats, and of rats implanted with testosterone–estradio (T-E) polydimethylsiloxane capsules for 5 days. The T-E-treated rats simultaneously received an Alza miniosmotic pump which released either buffer (T-E BUFFER) or 12 μg luteinizing hormone/day (T-E + LH). Each bar represents the mean of seven rats. The T above each bar represents the SEM. (Redrawn from Ewing *et al.*, 1983.)

with 12 μg LH/day maintained the surface area of all membranous structures in Leydig cell cytoplasm (Fig. 18) of Leydig cells.

The atrophy of Leydig cells, caused by the T-E PDS implants, was characterized by a reduction in Leydig cell volume and SER. These results were similar to those obtained by Dym and Raj (1977) when LH antiserum was injected into rats. The increased Leydig cell number per testis in T-E-implanted rats treated simultaneously with LH compared to intact control rats (Fig. 17) was similar to results by Christensen and Peacock (1980) who showed that hCG caused both hyperplasia and hypertrophy of Leydig cells in rats. Thus, LH maintains quantitatively not only steroidogenic function but also the volume and the ultrastructure of Leydig cells. Clearly, one of the most striking ultrastructural effects of LH is to maintain the integrity of the membranes of the SER which

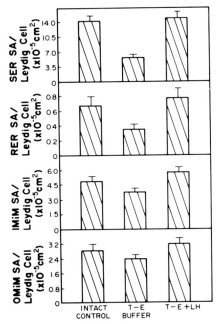

FIG. 18. Surface area (SA) of smooth endoplasmic reticulum (SER), rough endoplasmic reticulum (RER), inner mitochondrial membrane (IMiM), and outer mitochondrial membrane (OMiM) per Leydig cell of intact control rats, and of rats implanted with testosterone–estradiol (T-E) polydimethylsiloxane capsules for 5 days. The T-E-treated rats simultaneously received an Alza miniosmotic pump which released either buffer (T-E BUFFER) or 12 μg ovine luteinizing hormone/day (T-E + LH). Each bar represents the mean of seven rats. The T above each bar represents the SEM. (Redrawn from Ewing *et al.*, 1983.)

contain the enzymes responsible for the conversion of pregnenolone to testosterone.

XII. The Effect of FSH, PRL, TSH, and GH *in Situ* on Leydig Cell Structure and Testosterone Secretion in Rats Treated with T-E PDS Implants for 5 Days

The objective of this experiment was to determine whether polypeptide hormones other than LH administered simultaneously with the T-E PDS implants would maintain Leydig cell structure and function. The experimental protocol and stereological and perfusion methods were the same as those used for the LH experiment described above. Briefly, the rats were implanted with T-E PDS capsules and Alzet miniosmotic pumps programmed to release buffer or 12 μg of each polypeptide hormone per day. The rats were killed 5 days later and one testis perfusion fixed. The contralateral testis was perfused *in vitro* and testosterone secretion was measured.

The results in the top panel of Fig. 19 show that the reduction in testosterone secretion caused by T-E treatment for 5 days was not prevented by FSH, Prl, TSH, or GH. Similarly, the average Leydig cell volume, which was significantly reduced by the T-E implants, was not maintained by FSH, Prl, TSH, or GH (Fig. 19). Lastly, the significant reductions in the surface area of SER and RER per average Leydig cell caused by the T-E implants were not prevented by simultaneous *in situ* treatment with FSH, Prl, TSH, or GH (Fig. 20).

Taken together the results of these last two experiments are consistent with the idea that LH but not FSH, Prl, TSH, and GH maintains the number, growth, ultrastructure, and differentiated steroidogenic function

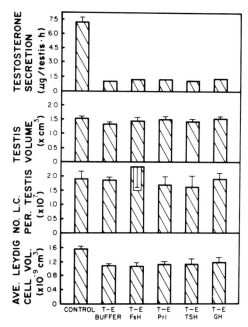

FIG. 19.   Testosterone secretion by *in vitro* perfused testes, and testis volume, number of Leydig cells (L.C.) per testis, and average Leydig cell volume of intact control rats and of rats implanted with testosterone–estradiol polydimethylsiloxane capsules for 5 days. The T-E-treated rats simultaneously received an Alza miniosmotic pump which released buffer (T-E BUFFER), or ovine follicle stimulating hormone-14 (T-E FSH), ovine prolactin-15 (T-E Prl), ovine thyroid stimulating hormone-9 (T-E TSH), or ovine growth hormone-S11 (T-E GH). Each polypeptide hormone was administered at 12 μg/day. Each bar represents the mean of three rats. The T above each bar represents the SEM. (Redrawn from Ewing *et al.*, 1983.)

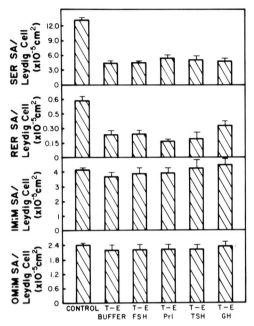

FIG. 20. Surface area (SA) of smooth endoplasmic reticulum (SER), rough endoplasmic reticulum (RER), inner mitochondrial membrane (IMiM), and outer mitochondrial membrane (OmiM) per Leydig cell of intact control rats, and of rats implanted with testosterone–estradiol (T-E) polydimethylsiloxane capsules for 5 days. The T-E-treated rats simultaneously received an Alza miniosmotic pump which released buffer (T-E BUFFER) or ovine follicle stimulating hormone-14 (T-E FSH), ovine prolactin-15 (T-E Prl), ovine thyroid stimulating hormone-9 (T-E TSH), or ovine growth hormone-S11 (T-E GH). Each polypeptide hormone was administered at 12 μg/day. Each bar represents the mean of three rats. The T above each bar represents the SEM. (Redrawn from Ewing *et al.*, 1983.)

of Leydig cells. It seemed possible, however, that these results are peculiar to T-E-implanted rats and that similar results would not be forthcoming if the rats were hypophysectomized.

XIII. The Effect of LH and LH Plus T-E PDS Implants *in Situ* on Leydig Cell Structure and Function in Hypophysectomized Rats

The objective of this experiment was twofold. The first objective was to show that LH *in situ* would maintain Leydig cell structure and function in hypophysectomized rats as in T-E-implanted rats. The second objective was to show that testosterone and estradiol from the PDS implants did not directly inhibit the Leydig cell steroidogenic apparatus. Twelve rats were divided into four groups of three rats each including (1) intact controls, (2) hypophysectomized, (3) hypophysectomized rats treated with 12 μg LH/ day, and (4) hypophysectomized rats treated simultaneously with T-E PDS implants and 12 μg LH/day. T-E PDS capsules and Alzet miniosmotic pumps containing either buffer or LH were implanted into the rats at the time of hypophysectomy. The rats were killed 5 days later; one testis from each rat was perfusion fixed for stereological analysis and the other was perfused *in vitro* for assessment of testosterone-producing capacity. The perfusion and stereological procedures have been described in detail (Ewing *et al.,* 1983).

The results in the top panel of Fig. 21 show that hypophysectomy for 5 days significantly reduced the capacity of *in vitro* perfused testes to secrete testosterone. However, the simultaneous treatment of hypophysectomized rats with LH or with T-E PDS implants plus LH maintained

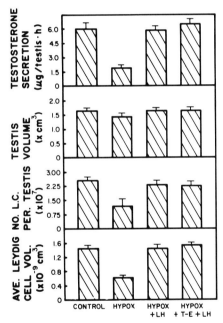

FIG. 21. Testosterone secretion by *in vitro* perfused testes, and testis volume, number of Leydig cells (L.C.) per testis, and average Leydig cell volume of intact control rats and of rats hypophysectomized for 5 days. One group of hypophysectomized rats (HYPOX) received no further treatment. The remaining hypophysectomized rats each received an Alza miniosmotic pump which released 12 μg/day ovine luteinizing hormone-S22. One group received only LH (HPOX + LH), the other received both testosterone–estradiol polydimethylsiloxane capsules and LH (HPOX + T-E + LH). Each bar represents the mean of three rats. The T above each bar represents the SEM.

testosterone secreting capacity at control levels. Although hypophysectomy for 5 days did not alter testicular volume, it did reduce significantly
the number of Leydig cells and the average Leydig cell volume (Fig. 21).
Importantly, treatment of hypophysectomized or hypophysectomized
plus T-E-implanted rats with 12 μg LH/day for 5 days maintained the
number and volume of Leydig cells at control levels.

The results in Fig. 22 show that hypophysectomy for 5 days significantly reduced the surface area of the membranes of all the Leydig cell
cytoplasmic organelles measured in this experiment. Treatment of hypophysectomized or hypophysectomized plus T-E-implanted rats with 12
μg LH/day for 5 days maintained these Leydig cell cytoplasmic ultrastructural elements (Fig. 22).

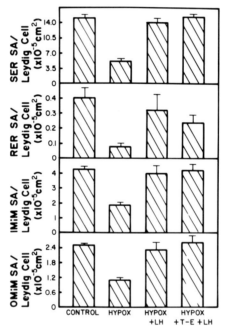

FIG. 22.   Surface area (SA) of smooth endoplasmic reticulum (SER), rough endoplasmic
reticulum (RER), inner mitochondrial membrane (IMiM), and outer mitochondrial membrane (OMiM) per Leydig cell of intact control rats and of rats hypophysectomized for 5
days. One group of hypophysectomized rats (HYPOX) received no further treatment. The
remaining hypophysectomized rats each received an Alza miniosomotic pump which released 12 μg/day ovine luteinizing hormone-S22. One group received only LH (HYPOX +
LH), the other received both testosterone–estradiol polydimethylsiloxane capsules and LH
(HPOX + T-E + LH). Each bar represents the mean of three rats. The T above each bar
represents the SEM.

Apparently, hypophysectomy for 5 days caused more Leydig cell death, greater atrophy, and ultrastructural damage (Figs. 21 and 22) then did the T-E implant treatment (Figs. 17 and 18).

This difference might occur if additional hormones were required to maintain Leydig cell structure and differentiated function. Alternatively, hypophysectomy might cause some nonspecific deleterious effect on testicular function. Several lines of evidence support the latter explanation. First, LH (Figs. 17 and 18) but not FSH, Prl, TSH, or GH (Figs. 19 and 20) overcomes the effects of T-E PDS implants on Leydig cell structure and function. Second, treatment of hypophysectomized rats with 12 μg each of LH plus FSH plus Prl did not increase testosterone secretion (8.5 ± 0.8 μg/testis/hour) significantly above that seen in control testes (7.0 ± 0.8 μg/testis/hour). Third, T-E PDS-implanted rats were more robust, continued to gain weight, and withstood better the rigors of anesthesia and surgery than hypophysectomized rats. Fourth, unpublished results from our laboratory showed that blood flow to the testes and numerous other organs was diminished by hypophysectomy but not by T-E PDS implants.

Several lines of evidence support the idea that T-E PDS implants mimic the effect of hypophysectomy on testosterone production by diminishing LH production rather than by some direct effect of T-E on the testis. First, it is well established that the physiological doses of testosterone and estradiol used in this study inhibit LH but not FSH production in male rats (Robaire *et al.*, 1979). Second, infusion of testosterone (Darney and Ewing, 1981) or estradiol (unpublished results), at concentrations found in the peripheral blood of T-E PDS-implanted rats, directly into the artery of *in vitro* perfused testes is without effect on testosterone secretion. Third, as shown in the present study, the capacity of testes from hypophysectomized rats or from rats implanted with T-E PDS capsules for 5 days to secrete testosterone was maintained at control levels with LH (Figs. 17 and 21) but not with other polypeptide hormones (Fig. 19). Fourth, this maintenance of testosterone-producing capacity by LH in the T-E PDS-implanted rats was dose responsive (Fig. 16). Fifth, testosterone secretion by Testes from hypophysectomized rats treated for 5 days with both T-E PDS implants and LH was identical to testosterone secretion by testes from control and intact rats treated simultaneously with T-E PDS implants and LH (Fig. 21).

Taken together, the results of the last three experiments support the idea that Leydig cell growth and differentiated function is maintained by LH. One of the most striking trophic effects of LH on the Leydig cell is the control of SER biogenesis and/or turnover.

XIV. Summary

The major epochs in the development and function of the male reproductive tract depend on the timely production of testosterone by Leydig cells. Important regulatory consequences accrue from the organization of the testosterone biosynthesizing enzymes into spatially separated membrane compartments in specialized steroid-producing cells. This highly ordered spatial organization of the testicular testosterone synthesizing apparatus provides the structural basis for the regulation of testosterone biosynthesis and led to the hypothesis that Leydig cell structure was coupled tightly to steroidogenic function. The surface area of smooth endoplasmic reticulum was the most obvious structural correlate of Leydig cell steroidogenic function. LH, but not FSH, Prl, TSH, or GH, prevented Leydig cell atrophy and loss of steroidogenic function in hypophysectomized rats. The most striking ultrastructural change resulting from LH withdrawal was a rapid loss of SER. These results demonstrate that one of the trophic effects of LH is to regulate the biogenesis and/or turnover of SER in the Leydig cell.

ACKNOWLEDGMENTS

The authors wish to express their sincere gratitude to Mrs. Jeanne Whitaker for her expert help in preparing this manuscript.

The research described in this paper was funded in part by NIH Research Grant HD-07204, AM 19300, and Population Center Grant HD-06268.

REFERENCES

Aoki, A. (1970). *Protoplasma* **71**, 209–225.
Becker, S., Chubb, C., and Ewing, L. (1980). *Am. J. Physiol.* **239**, R184–R195.
Bolender, R. P. (1978). *Int. Rev. Cytol.* **55**, 247–289.
Bolender, R. P. (1982). *Ann. N.Y. Acad. Sci.* **383**, 1–16.
Brown, M. S., and Goldstein, J. L. (1976). *Science* **191**, 150–154.
Buesmann, L., Huseby, R. A., and Samuels, L. T. (1976). *Mol. Cell. Endocrinol.* **6**, 91–104.
Catt, K. J., and Dufau, M. L. (1976). *Biol. Reprod.* **14**, 1–15.
Chemes, H. E., Rivarola, M. A., and Bergada, C. (1976). *J. Reprod. Fertil.* **46**, 279–282.
Christensen, A. K. (1965). *J. Cell Biol.* **26**, 911–935.
Christensen, A. K. (1975). *Handb. Physiol. Endocrinol.* **5**, 57–94.
Christensen, A. K., and Gillim, S. W. (1969). *In* "The Gonads" (K. W. McKerns, ed.), pp. 415–487. Appleton, New York.
Christensen, A. K., and Peacock, K. C. (1980). *Biol. Reprod.* **22**, 383–391.
Chubb, C., and Ewing, L. L. (1979a). *Am. J. Physiol.* **237**, E231–E238.
Chubb, C., and Ewing, L. L. (1979b). *Am. J. Physiol.* **237**, E239–E246.
Chubb, C., and Ewing, L. L. (1981). *Endocrinology* **109**, 1999–2003.
Chubb, C., Ewing, L. L., Irby, D. C., and Desjardins, C. (1978). *Biol. Reprod.* **18**, 212–218.
Cooke, B. A., DeJong, F. H., van der Molen, H. J., and Rommerts, F. F. G. (1972). *Nature (London) New Biol.* **237**, 255–256.

Cooke, B. A., Janszen, F. H. A., Clotscher, W. F., and van der Molen, H. J. (1975). *Biochem. J.* **150,** 413–418.

Cooke, B. A., Lindh, M. L., and Janszen, F. H. A. (1977). *Biochem. J.* **168,** 43–48.

Cooke, B. A., Janszen, F. H. A., van Driel, M. J. A., and van der Molen, H. J. (1979). *Mol. Cell. Endocrinol.* **14,** 181–189.

Darney, K. J., Jr., and Ewing, L. (1981). *Endocrinology* **109,** 993–995.

DeKretser, D. M. (1967). *Z. Zellforsch.* **83,** 344–358.

Dufau, M. L., and Catt, K. J. (1978). *Vitam. Horm.* **36,** 461–592.

Dufau, M. L., Hsueh, A. J., Cigorraga, S., Bankal, A. J., and Catt, K. J. (1978). *Int. J. Androl. Suppl.* **2,** 193–239.

Dykman, D. D., Cochran, R., Wise, P. M., Barraclough, C. A., Dubin, N. H., and Ewing, L. L. (1981). *Biol. Reprod.* **25,** 235–243.

Dym, M., and Raj, H. G. M. (1977). *Biol. Reprod.* **17,** 676–696.

Eik-Nes, K. B. (1975). *Handb. Physiol. Endocrinol.* **5,** 95–115.

Ewing, L.L. (1975). *In* "Hormonal Regulation of Spermatogenesis" (F. S. French, V. Hansson, E. M. Ritzen, and S. N. Nayfeh, eds.), pp. 145–164. Plenum, New York.

Ewing, L. L. (1983). *In* "Male Infertility" (L. I. Lipshultz and S. Howards, eds.). Churchill, London, in press.

Ewing, L. L., and Brown, B. L. (1977). *In* "The Testis" (A. D. Johnson and W. R. Gomes, eds.), Ch. 7, pp. 239–287. Academic Press, New York.

Ewing, L. L., and Eik-Nes, K. B. (1966). *Can. J. Biochem.* **44,** 1327–1344.

Ewing, L. L., and Robaire, B. (1978). *Annu. Rev. Pharmacol. Toxicol.* **18,** 167–187.

Ewing, L. L., Johnson, B. H., Desjardins, C., and Clegg, R. F. (1972). *Proc. Soc. Exp. Biol. Med.* **140,** 907–910.

Ewing, L., Brown, B., Irby, D. C., and Jardine, I. (1975). *Endocrinology* **96,** 610–617.

Ewing, L. L., Desjardins, C., Irby, D. C., and Robaire, B. (1977). *Nature (London)* **269,** 409–411.

Ewing, L. L., Adams, R. J., and Cochran, R. (1979a). *In* "Animal Models for Research on Contraception and Fertility" (N. J. Alexander, ed.), pp. 326–343. Harper, New York.

Ewing, L. L., Gorski, R. A., Sbordone, R. J., Tyler, J. V., Desjardins, C., and Robaire, B. (1979b). *Biol. Reprod.* **21,** 765–772.

Ewing, L. L., Zirkin, B. R., Cochran, R. C., Kromann, N., Peters, C., and Ruiz-Bravo, N. (1979c). *Endocrinology* **105,** 1135–1142.

Ewing, L. L., Cochran, R. C., Zirkin, B., and Chubb, C. E. (1980a). *In* "Testicular Development, Structure and Function" (A. Steinberger and E. Steinberger, eds.), pp. 117–127. Raven, New York.

Ewing, L. L., Davis, J. C., and Zirkin, B. R. (1980b). *Int. Rev. Physiol.* **22,** 41–115.

Ewing, L. L., Wing, T.-Y., Cochran, R. C., Kromann, N., and Zirkin, B. R. (1983). *Endocrinology* **112,** 1763–1769.

Gondos, B., Rao, A., and Ramachandran, J. (1980). *J. Endocrinol.* **87,** 265–270.

Hall, P. F. (1979). *In* "Endocrinology" (L. J. DeGroot, G. F. Cahill, Jr., W. D. Odell, L. Martin, J. T. Potts, Jr., D. H. Nelson, E. Steinberger, and A. I. Winegrad, eds.), p. 1511. Grune & Stratton, New York.

Harbitz, T. B. (1973). *Acta Pathol. Microbiol. Scand. (A)* **81,** 301–314.

Janszen, F. H. A., Cook, B. A., van Driel, M. J. A., and van der Molen, H. J. (1978). *Biochem. J.* **172,** 147–153.

Kaler, L. W., and Neaves, W. B. (1978). *Anat. Rec.* **192,** 513–518.

Knorr, D. W., Vanha-Perttula, T., and Lipsett, M. B. (1970). *Endocrinology* **86,** 1298–1304.

Mendelson, C., Dufau, M., and Catt, K. (1975). *Biochim. Biophys. Acta* **411,** 222–230.

Merkow, L., Acevedo, H. F., Slotkin, M., and Caits, B. J. (1968). *Am. J. Pathol.* **53,** 47–61.

Morat, M. (1977)., *Arch. Anat. Microsc.* **66,** 119–142.

Mori, H., and Christensen, A. K. (1980). *J. Cell Biol.* **84,** 340–354.

Mori, H., Shimizu, D., Takeda, A., Takioka, Y., and Fukunishi, R. (1980). *J. Electron Microsc.* **29,** 8–21.

Neaves, W. B. (1973). *Biol. Reprod.* **8,** 451–466.

Nussdorfer, G. G., Robba, C., Mazzocchi, G., and Rebuffat, P. (1980). *Int. J. Androl.* **3,** 319–332.

Pahnke, V. G., Leidenberger, F. A., and Kunzig, H. J. (1975). *Acta Endocrinol.* **79,** 610–618.

Pirke, K. M., Vogt, H. J., and Geiss, M. (1978). *Acta Endocrinol.* **89,** 393–403.

Robaire, B., Ewing, L. L., Irby, D. C., and Desjardins, C. (1979). *Biol. Reprod.* **21,** 455–463.

Rommerts, F. F. G., Cooke, B. A., and van der Molen, H. J. (1974). *J. Steroid Biochem.* **5,** 279–285.

Weibel, E. R. (1979). "Stereologic Methods." Academic Press, New York.

Wing, T.-Y. and Lin, H.-S. (1977). *Cell Tissue Res.* **183,** 385–393.

Zirkin, B. R., Ewing, L. L., Kromann, N., and Cochran, R. C. (1980). *Endocrinology* **107,** 1867–1874.

Zirkin, B. R., Dykman, D. D., Kromann, N., Cochran, R. C., and Ewing, L. L. (1982). *Ann. N.Y. Acad. Sci.* **383,** 17–28.

DISCUSSION

N. B. Schwartz: Since you are interested in the contraceptive implications what effect do your implants have on spermatogenesis?

L. L. Ewing: With the Silastic implants?

N. B. Schwartz: Does testosterone plus estrogen have a differential effect on LH versus FSH and on spermatogenesis via FSH?

L. L. Ewing: With regard to spermatogenesis?

N. B. Schwartz: Yes.

L. L. Ewing: We found a decrease in the production of LH within 2 days but no significant change in spermatid production for several weeks. The inhibition occurs at myosis and it takes a long time to rid the testes of the more mature spermatids by maturation depletion.

N. B. Schwartz: It seems to me that this would be a very good model to do the work that Steinberger did and find out whether FSH is necessary for spermatogenesis.

L. L. Ewing: At the doses of testosterone and estradiol used in our experiments LH but not FSH is inhibited.

C. S. Nicoll: I believe it was the hamster which you said had the abundant rough endoplastic reticulum. Do you see any evidence that the hamster Leydig cell can secrete any protein? Does it package anything for export by exocytosis?

L. L. Ewing: That is a very good question and we just have not had time to follow up.

C. S. Nicoll: My second question is where does the smooth ER come from?

L. L. Ewing: I am not an expert in this area. Perhaps someone could help us with that.

G. B. Cutler: LH is secreted in a pulsatile fashion and yet most people who have looked at humans for pulses of testosterone corresponding to them do not see testosterone pulses. This is in contrast, for example, to the marked pulsatility of cortisol which requires a similar number of biosynthetic steps. Also, I believe that there are some other species where there is a marked pulsatility of testosterone. Do you have any idea why Leydig cells from some species release testosterone in a pulsatile fashion while others do not seem to?

L. L. Ewing: I am not sure I understand the question but in many species, there is a very high correlation between the pulse of LH and the pulse of testosterone.

G. B. Cutler: Several years ago Bob Vigersky and Lynn Loriaux showed that if you slow down the rate of LH pulses in humans using a synthetic androgen, that one is then able to see rather nice pulses of testosterone, with a delay between the LH and testosterone pulses. It suggests that perhaps there is a longer time delay for testosterone production than for cortisol production, although there are five biosynthetic steps in each case. If one looks at the pulses in other species it appears that perhaps that time delay is not present in all species, such as in the sheep. I wondered if you had any thoughts about what might account for a time delay between the LH and the testosterone pulse?

L. L. Ewing: Claude Desjardins has looked into that in the chronically catheterized rat. We have shown in the *in vitro* perfusion system that testosterone itself inhibits testosterone biosynthesis. So there may be a local product inhibition. In fact, we have localized that inhibition to some step in the conversion of pregnenolone to testosterone. I believe that it is possible that at the testicular level, you can override the effects of LH on the Leydig cell. If this were the case, the Leydig cells might be refractive to LH for some period of time.

S. L. Cohen: In the late 1930s Ruth Deanasly did some interesting experiments where she implanted the testes into the abdominal cavity and found that the animals tended to become emasculated and feminized and this presumably is due to a stimulation of aromatase activity by higher temperature. Is this estrogen formed by the Leydig cell or by the Sertoli cell?

L. L. Ewing: The evidence suggests that in the rat prior to puberty a fair amount of estradiol is derived from Sertoli cells. In the adult rat, however, most of the estradiol is produced by the Leydig cell.

S. L. Cohen: Do you know whether the estradiol production of testes implanted into the abdominal cavity or wrapped in wool, I think she did that as well, is increased?

L. L. Ewing: There is a fair amount of evidence that experimental cryptorchidism reduces the testosterone production by Leydig cells. If you leave them in the abdominal cavity for a long enough period of time you see striking changes in the ultrastructure of Leydig cell and they are not as efficient in producing testosterone compared to Leydig cells in testes in the scrotum.

S. L. Cohen: Well, I wondered would that be due to a conversion of the testosterone to estradiol?

L. L. Ewing: It is unlikely because the conversion rate of testosterone to estradiol in rat testes is a very small amount compared to the total testosterone production.

R. A. Huseby: I was wondering in your perfusion experiments if you had ever perfused an estrogen such as estradiol since it has been reported that estrogen administration *in vivo* suppresses all three enzymes converting progesterone to testosterone?

L. L. Ewing: We have infused estradiol into the spermatic artery of rat testes at fairly high concentrations and observed no effect on testosterone biosynthesis.

R. A. Huseby: You did infuse the estrogen right into the artery? Does this mean that the rat is considerably different than the mouse?

L. L. Ewing: Yes, except that a lot of the data that says there is a direct effect of estradiol on Leydig cell steroidogenesis has been done in the rat.

R. A. Huseby: The initial information that Leo Samuels and I presented (*Recent Prog. Horm. Res.* **17**, 1, 1961) was obtained in mice where there was a very striking depression of enzyme activities in hypophysectomized mice in the presence of constant LH administration.

S. Plymate: You mentioned that in your T-implanted rats that you did give prolactin—was that in concert with LH or was it alone. The importance of this point is that prolactin has been reported to be necessary for testosterone production in the male rat; however, you report no increase in the smooth endoplasmic reticulum.

L. L. Ewing: We've done it both ways—we've added prolactin by itself at the same concentration as we gave LH and we've added prolactin in addition to FSH and LH.

S. Plymate: And did you see increased testosterone secretion?

L. L. Ewing: No.

F. C. Bartter: In your beautiful diagram of the functions of the cell, do you visualize a limiting step in the entrance of cholesterol into the mitochondria, and do you picture LH as serving the same function of admitting cholesterol to the mitochondrion as is served by ACTH in the zona fasciculata and by angiotensin in the zona glomerulosa of the adrenal cortex?

L. L. Ewing: The evidence is much better in the adrenal than it is in the Leydig cell. However there is some evidence in the Leydig cell which suggests that LH facilitates the transport of cholesterol into the inner mitochondrial membrane and/or facilitates the binding of cholesterol to the cholesterol side chain cleavage enzyme.

F. C. Bartter: And the dynamics of it is not understood?

L. L. Ewing: Not that I know of.

W. F. Crowley: Very nice presentation. Just in follow-up to one of Dr. Cutler's questions about the pulsatile release of testosterone in some species correlating well with LH and in others not so well. We've reported two men in whom an abnormality of LH release has been documented such that rather than the usual 12 or 13 LH pulses per day, they have 6 to 8/24 and very similar to the data produced by Vigersky and Loriaux where they administered a synthetic androgen to slow down the LH pulses by a hypothalamic feedback mechanism, we could also see the emergence of a better correlation of LH pulses followed by T pulses. This especially occurs when these men had an LH interpulse interval that was sufficiently wide enough to permit you to see the clearcut emergence of testosterone "wells"—not really pulses but tides in the rhythm which are normally not present. Furthermore, if you give them clomiphene to increase their LH pulse frequency, the testosterone pulses disappear and the testosterone levels rise, so I suspect that it is the LH pulse frequency being slow enough to allow the emergence of T pulses. Exactly why there is a better correlation of LH and T pulses in some species like the rhesus and not so clear in man, I don't know. However, my other question follows from this observation. In most of the species that have been examined carefully in this manner, LH has to be delivered in an episodic fashion to restore gonadal function to normal and in all of the implantation experiments you performed, LH was delivered via a continuous delivery system. Have you tried to administer LH in an episodic fashion and, if so, do you see any differences in either the testosterone secretion or more interestingly in the morphogenesis of the Leydig cell between the continuous versus the intermittent LH delivery systems?

L. L. Ewing: Very important question and I didn't go into details. In our initial studies, we attached PE 60 to the Alza pump and we programmed it with boluses of oil and borate buffer which contained the LH. We delivered a total of 12 μg of LH/day in half hour pulses every 2 hours subcutaneously. Subsequently, we have delivered the same amount of LH/24 hours in a nonpulsatile mode. It maintains the testosterone synthesizing capacity and the structure of the cells very well.

J. C. Penhos: You presented in one of the figures three sizes of silastic capsules. Does this mean different relations between estrogen and testosterone or was it the same relation and different amounts? Is your isolated testicle perfusion an open or a closed system?

L. L. Ewing: Yes, in all of these studies we administered a 2.5-cm capsule of testosterone and a 0.3-cm capsule of estradiol. That is we gave two separate capsules. Our perfusion system is an open system.

M. I. New: You know that in the newborn human male there is a surge in serum concentration of testosterone. It can be as high as that of adult man and then there is a fall. Have you had an opportunity to study that?

L. L. Ewing: No, I have not. I have reviewed the literature very carefully in that regard and I have found that testosterone concentration in the peripheral blood increases at about 2 months of age in the neonate. I have never found any description of Leydig cell morphology at this stage of neonatal development.

INDEX